Technical Calculus with Analytic Geometry

ALLYN J. WASHINGTON

Department of Mathematics · Dutchess Community College
Poughkeepsie, New York

CUMMINGS PUBLISHING COMPANY

Menlo Park, California

Other books by the author

Introduction to Technical Mathematics

Essentials of Basic Mathematics

Basic Technical Mathematics, Second Edition

Basic Technical Mathematics with Calculus,
Second Edition

Sixth printing—August 1971
First three printings by Addison-Wesley Publishing Company, Inc.

DEFGHIJKL75432

Cummings Publishing Company
2727 Sand Hill Road
Menlo Park, California 94025

Preface

This book is intended primarily for students taking technical programs at two-year colleges and institutes. The emphasis in this text is on elementary topics in calculus and certain selected topics from the more advanced areas. These have been selected due to their application in the technologies, with an emphasis on electrical and mechanical technologies. The topics are developed in a nonrigorous and intuitive manner, with stress being placed on the interpretation and applications of the material presented.

It is assumed that students using this text will have had courses covering the basic topics of algebra and trigonometry. However, several sections on algebra and trigonometry are included for review and reference purposes. These are the topics essential for proper development and understanding of the calculus.

The general topics covered in the text are basic analytic geometry, differentiation and integration of algebraic and elementary transcendental functions, an introduction to partial derivatives and double integrals, expansion of functions in series, and differential equations.

The analytic geometry is developed primarily for use in the calculus, although numerous direct applications of curves such as the conic sections are discussed. A chapter on polar coordinates is included to demonstrate the use of different coordinate systems. Also, empirical curve fitting is included to show how a curve may be fitted to data. In the chapter dealing with partial derivatives and double integrals, a section is devoted to solid analytic geometry. In addition to these specific topics from analytic geometry, graphical techniques and interpretations are included throughout the text. The graphs of the trigonometric, inverse trigonometric, exponential, and logarithmic functions as well as methods of graphical differentiation and integration are discussed.

The calculus will give the student a mathematical understanding of many topics which arise in his other courses. Numerous applications from all fields of technology are included to show the wide application of calculus. Among these are many definitions of physical quantities, the relations among distance, velocity and acceleration, areas and volumes, centroids and moments of inertia.

The chapter on partial derivatives and double integrals is included in order to introduce these topics in curricula for which they may be deemed necessary. Their applications are shown for such fields as electronics, thermodynamics, and mechanics.

The chapter on expansion of functions in series will give an understanding of the development of numerical tables and some of the other uses of this method of expressing functions. Also, the section on Fourier series is appropriate for curricula in electrical technology.

Differential equations provide one of the richest areas of mathematics for applications in technical areas, especially electrical and mechanical technologies. Here a mathematical basis can be established for many concepts and formulas which previously the student has had to accept without basis. For this reason considerable space is devoted to differential equations.

Laplace transforms are introduced to show the methods and terminology for electrical and mechanical technology students. Numerical methods of solving differential equations are appropriate for use with modern computers, although methods are developed such that direct use of a computer is not required. Introduction of such topics will make the technician more effective in modern industry.

Most instructors will probably find that not all of the material included in the text is necessary for their particular programs. Many of the topics included, especially in the later portions of the text, may be omitted without loss of continuity. The choice of topics used will depend upon the needs of each program.

One of the basic features of the text is the use of more than 430 worked examples. These examples are used advantageously to introduce certain points as well as to clarify and illustrate the points made in the text. The author has found that these worked examples are very beneficial to the student.

There are over 2100 exercises. The answers to nearly all the odd-numbered exercises, including answers to graphical problems, are given at the back of the book. Also, a set of miscellaneous exercises is included after each chapter. These may be used either for additional problems or for review assignments.

The author wishes to acknowledge the help and suggestions given him by those who reviewed the manuscript. In particular I wish to thank Harry Boyd, James Parent, and Samuel Plotkin, members of the faculty of Dutchess Community College, for their many suggestions. Also, the suggestions of F. Raymond Hardy of Lowell Technical Institute and Harvey V. Smith Jr. of Southern Technical Institute are greatly appreciated. I also wish to express my gratitude to the many others for their valuable assistance.

I am especially indebted to my publisher's staff for their valuable assistance throughout the preparation of this text. The many comments by users of the author's earlier texts are also appreciated. Finally, special mention is due my wife, who helped in many phases of the preparation of the text.

Poughkeepsie, New York   A.J.W.
November 1965

Table of Contents

v

**Chapter 15   Other Methods of Solving Differential
              Equations**

1 Plane analytic geometry

deals with relationship between geometry & algebra.

Difference between Dif & Intg Calculus

Differential Calc will find rate of change while integral calc will find the function if rate of change is known.

1-1 Introduction

Analytic geometry deals with the relationship between algebra & Geometry.

The problems which can be solved by the methods of algebra and trigonometry are numerous. There are, however, a great many problems which arise in the various fields of technology which require for their solution methods beyond those available from algebra and trigonometry. The use of these traditional topics remains of definite importance, but it is necessary to develop additional methods of analyzing and solving problems.

One very important type of problem which arises involves the rate of change of one quantity with respect to another. Examples of rates of change are velocity (the rate of change of distance with respect to time), the rate of change of the length of a metal rod with respect to temperature, the rate of change of light intensity with respect to the distance from the source, the rate of change of electric current with respect to time, and many other similar physical situations. The methods of *differential calculus*, which we shall start developing in Chapter 2, will enable us to solve problems involving these quantities.

Another principal type of problem which calculus allows us to solve is that of finding a function when its rate of change is known. This is *integral calculus*, a study of which starts in Chapter 4. One of the principal applications comes from electricity, where current is the time rate of change of electric charge. Although apparently unrelated, integral calculus also leads to the solution of a great many other problems, which include plane areas, volumes, and the physical concepts of work and pressure.

Before starting a study of the calculus, we will first develop some of the basic concepts of *analytic geometry*. This branch of mathematics deals with the relationship between algebra and geometry. The definitions and methods developed here, along with certain basic curves and their characteristics will enable us to more readily develop the calculus. Also, many technical applications of analytic geometry itself are illustrated.

1

Integral Calculus will also find plane areas, volumes, work & pressure

a, b, c constants.
u, v, w, x, y, z variables

1-2 Rectangular coordinates

From algebra we recall that a *variable* is a quantity which may take on admissible values during a given discussion. A *constant* is a quantity which remains fixed during the discussion. Generally letters toward the end of the alphabet are used to denote variables, and letters near the beginning of the alphabet denote constants.

One of the most valuable ways of representing an equation in two variables is by means of a graph of the equation. By using graphs we are able to obtain a "picture" of the equation, and this picture enables us to learn a great deal about the equation.

To achieve this graphical representation we use the fact that we may represent numbers by points on a line. Since two variables are involved, it is necessary to use a line for each. This is done most conveniently by placing the lines perpendicular to each other.

Thus we place one line horizontally and label it the *x-axis*. The other line we place vertically and label it the *y-axis*. The point of intersection is called the *origin* and is designated by 0. This is called the *rectangular coordinate system*.

Starting from the origin, equal intervals are marked off along each of the axes, and the *integers* (the numbers 1, 2, 3, . . . which represent whole quantities) are placed at these positions. The *positive* integers are placed on the *x*-axis to the right of the origin, and the *negative* integers are placed to the left. On the *y*-axis, the positive integers are placed above the origin and the negative integers are placed below. The four parts into which the plane is divided are called quadrants. (See Fig. 1-1.)

The points between the integers represent either the *rational* numbers (numbers which are represented by dividing one integer by another) or the *irrational*

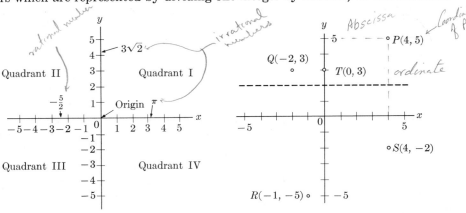

FIGURE 1-1   FIGURE 1-2

different type of numbers

numbers (those numbers which cannot be represented by dividing one integer by another; π and $\sqrt{2}$ are such numbers). In this way all *real* numbers, which include the rational numbers (the integers are rational) and irrational numbers, may be represented as points on the axes. We shall use real numbers throughout this text unless otherwise noted. We will occasionally refer to and use *imaginary* numbers, which is the name given to square roots of negative numbers.

→ types of numbers – Rational, Irrational, real, imaginary / IMAGINARY

Example A. The number 7 is an integer, rational (since $7 = \frac{7}{1}$), and real (the real numbers include all the rational numbers); 3π is irrational and real; $\sqrt{5}$ is irrational and real; $\frac{1}{8}$ is rational and real; $7\sqrt{-1}$ is imaginary; $\frac{6}{3}$ is rational and real (it is an integer when we use the symbol "2" to represent it); $\pi/6$ is irrational and real; $\sqrt{-3}/2$ is imaginary.

A point P in the plane is designated by the pair of numbers (x, y). The x-value, called the *abscissa* is the perpendicular distance of P from the y-axis. The y-value, called the *ordinate,* is the perpendicular distance of P from the x-axis. The values x and y together, written as (x, y) are the *coordinates* of P.

→ Points in any quadrant – around origin

Q-I   Q-II   Q-III   Q-IV

Example B. The positions of points $P(4, 5)$, $Q(-2, 3)$, $R(-1, -5)$, $S(4, -2)$ and $T(0, 3)$ are shown in Fig. 1–2. Note that this representation allows for *one point for any pair of values* (x, y).

→ a line on a graph.   → in Q I & Q II

Example C. Where are all the points whose ordinates are 2? All such points are two units above the x-axis; thus the answer can be stated as "on a line 2 units above the x-axis." Note the dashed line in Fig. 1–2.

→ is always positive regardless of Quadrant

The number of units that a given number on either axis is from the origin is called the *absolute value* of that number. The absolute value of any number, except zero, is considered to be positive, and is designated by $| \ |$ placed around the number.

→ absolute values

Example D. The absolute value of 6, $|6|$, equals 6. Also $|-7| = 7$, $|-\pi| = \pi$, $|\frac{7}{5}| = \frac{7}{5}$, $|-\sqrt{2}| = \sqrt{2}$.

On the x-axis, if a first number is to the right of a second number, the first number is said to be *greater than* the second. If the first number is to the left of the second, it is *less than* the second. On the y-axis, if one number is above a second, the first number is greater than the second. "Greater than" is designated by $>$, and "less than" is designated by $<$. These are called signs of inequality.

→ $>$ or $<$

Example E.

$6 > 3$, $8 > -1$, $5 < 9$, $0 > -4$, $-2 > -4$, $-1 < 0$.

$|3|$ $|9|$ $|4|$ $|4|$ $|2|$ $|1|$

Exercises

1. Designate the following numbers as integers, rational, irrational, real, or imaginary (more than one designation may be correct):
   (a) $\frac{5}{4}$ (b) $-\pi$ (c) $\sqrt{-4}$ (d) $6\sqrt{-1}$ (e) 3 (f) $6 + \sqrt{2}$ (g) $\sqrt{7}/3$ (h) $\frac{7}{3}$

2. Find the absolute values of the following numbers:
   (a) $|3|$ (b) $|\frac{7}{2}|$ (c) $|-4|$ (d) $|-(\pi/18)|$ (e) $|x|$ (if $x < 0$)

3. Insert the correct inequality signs ($>$ or $<$) between the following pairs of numbers: (a) $6 < 8$ (b) $7 > -5$ (c) $\pi > -1$ (d) $-4 < -3$
   (e) $-\sqrt{2} > -9$ (f) $0.2 < 0.6$

4. Plot the points $A(2, 7)$, $B(-1, -2)$, and $C(-4, 2)$.

5. Plot the points $A(3, \frac{1}{2})$, $B(-6, 0)$, and $C(-\frac{5}{2}, -5)$.

6. Plot the points $A(1, 3)$, $B(-1, -1)$, and $C(6, 13)$. Join these points by straight-line segments. What conclusion do you draw?

7. Where are all the points whose abscissas are 1?

8. Where are all the points whose ordinates are -3?

9. What is the abscissa of all points on the y-axis?

10. What is the ordinate of all points on the x-axis?

11. Where are all the points for which $x > 0$?

12. Locate all points (x, y) for which $x > 0$ and $y < 0$.

13. Locate all points (x, y) for which $x < 0$ and $y > 1$.

14. Locate all points for which $|x| < 1$.

15. In which quadrants is the ratio y/x positive?

16. Three vertices of a rectangle are $(5, 2)$, $(-1, 2)$, and $(-1, 4)$. What are the coordinates of the fourth vertex?

17. Two vertices of an equilateral triangle are $(7, 1)$ and $(2, 1)$. What is the abscissa of the third vertex?

18. After 2 sec, the current in a certain circuit is less than 3 amp. Using t to represent time and i to represent current, this statement may be written as "for $t > 2$, $i < 3$." Using the x-axis for values of t and the y-axis for values of i, shade in the region for the above statement (assume $i > 0$).

19. Less than three feet from a light source the intensity of illumination is greater than 8 lumens. Using x for the distance and y for the illumination, shade in the appropriate region.

1–3 The graph of an equation

   The graph of an equation is the set of all points whose coordinates (x, y) satisfy the equation relating x and y. In order to find sets of coordinates for the purpose of constructing the graph, we assume certain values of one of the variables, usually x, and then determine the values of the other variable by use of the equation.

Since there is no limit to the possible number of points which can be chosen, we normally select a few values of x, obtain the corresponding values of y, and plot these points. The points are then connected by a *smooth* curve (not short straight lines from one point to the next), and are normally connected from left to right.

Example A. Graph the equation $y = 3x - 5$.

If we let $x = 0$ we find that $y = -5$. Choosing another value of x, 1 for example, we find that $y = -2$. Continuing to choose a few other values of x, we tabulate these results. (In the table it is best if it is tabulated with increasing values of x.) Finally we join the points (Fig. 1–3).

x	y
-1	-8
0	-5
1	-2
2	1
3	4
4	7

FIGURE 1–3

x	y
-2	-6
-1	-2
0	0
1	0
2	-2
3	-6

FIGURE 1–4

There are some special points with regard to certain curves which should be noted. Each of the next three examples illustrates and explains a particular point to be considered when plotting the graph of an equation.

Example B. Graph the equation $y = x - x^2$.

In plotting the points shown in the table we note that $y = 0$ for both $x = 0$ and $x = 1$. Since most common curves are smooth, any irregularities or sudden changes in the graph should be rechecked. Since there is a question as to what happens between $x = 0$ and $x = 1$, we try $x = \frac{1}{2}$ and find that $y = \frac{1}{4}$. Using this point completes the information necessary to draw a reasonable graph for the equation. (See Fig. 1–4.)

Example C. Graph the equation $y = 2x^2 - 4$.

We first tabulate the values as shown. In constructing the table we note that the same value of y appears for both $+3$ and -3. Also the same value of y appears for $+2$ and for -2, and again for $+1$ and for -1. Since $(-x)^2 = x^2$

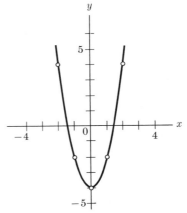

x	y
-3	14
-2	4
-1	-2
0	-4
1	-2
2	4
3	14

FIGURE 1–5

and $(+x)^2 = x^2$ we can understand why this happens. The graph of this equation (see Fig. 1–5) is seen to be *symmetrical* to the y-axis. This can be thought of as meaning that the right half of the curve is the reflection of the left half, and conversely. As in this case, *any time* $-x$ *can replace* x *in an equation without changing the equation, its graph will be symmetrical to the y-axis.* In the same way, *if* $-y$ *can replace* y *in an equation without changing the equation, its graph is symmetrical to the x-axis.* Many of the curves to be discussed in the coming sections will demonstrate the property of symmetry.

Example D. Graph the equation $y = 1 + (1/x)$.

In finding points on this graph (see Fig. 1–6) we note that y is not defined if we try $x = 0$, since *division by zero is not defined.* Although x cannot *equal* zero, it can take on any value near zero. Thus, by choosing values of x between -1 and $+1$ we obtain the points necessary to determine the shape of the graph.

x	y
-4	3/4
-3	2/3
-2	1/2
-1	0
$-1/2$	-1
$-1/3$	-2
1/3	4
1/2	3
1	2
2	3/2
3	4/3
4	5/4

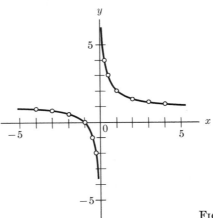

FIGURE 1–6

In examining the possible values of x more closely, we note that as the values of x get closer and closer to zero the values of y become numerically larger and larger. That is, as x approaches zero, y becomes numerically unbounded. In this case we say that $x = 0$ (the y-axis) is an *asymptote* of the curve. More generally, an asymptote is a line which the graph of an equation approaches. In trigonometry asymptotes are found for the graph of $y = \tan x$. This curve approaches the values $x = \pi/2$, $x = 3\pi/2, \ldots$, but the curve is not defined for these values. Asymptotes will be seen to be of importance when we discuss the hyperbola.

Graphs and graphical methods will be used throughout this text. It will be seen that a great deal of information can be learned about an equation by analyzing its graph. Also, graphs can often demonstrate a given property more clearly than can other descriptions. The following example illustrates an application of graphing an equation along with conclusions that can easily be seen from the graph.

Example E. The power of a certain voltage source in terms of the load resistance is given by

$$P = \frac{100R}{(0.5 + R)^2},$$

where P is measured in watts and R in ohms. Plot the graph, using the y-direction for power and the x-direction for resistance.

Since a negative value for resistance has no physical significance, we need plot P for positive values of R only. The following table of values is obtained.

R	0	0.25	0.50	1.0	2.0	3.0	4.0	5.0	10.0
P	0.0	44.4	50.0	44.4	32.0	24.5	19.8	16.5	9.1

The values 0.25 and 0.50 are used for R when it is found that P is less for $R = 2$ than for $R = 1$. In this way a smoother, more useful curve is obtained. (See Fig. 1-7.)

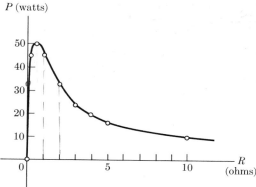

FIGURE 1-7

From the graph we see that P changes quite rapidly for small values of R with a peak value of about 50 watts when $R = 0.50$ ohms (actually this is exact for this equation). Also, as R becomes larger, P becomes smaller, but much less rapidly. This shows some of the conclusions that can be drawn from a graph.

Exercises

In Exercises 1 through 15, graph the equations.

1. $y = 2x - 4$

2. $y = \frac{1}{2}x - 2$

3. $y = x^2$

4. $y = 3 - x^2$

5. $y = x^2 + 2x$

6. $y = x^2 - 3x + 1$

7. $y = 3x - x^3$

8. $y = x^4 - 4x^2$

9. $y = x + \dfrac{1}{x}$

10. $y = \dfrac{1}{x^2}$

11. $y = \sqrt{4 - x}$

12. $y = \dfrac{1}{x + 2}$

13. $y = \dfrac{1}{x^2 + 1}$

14. $y = \pm\sqrt{25 - x^2}$

15. $y = \pm\sqrt{x^2 - 25}$

16. What can you say with regard to the symmetry of the graph of the equation of (a) Exercise 8, (b) Exercise 10, (c) Exercise 15?

17. Do the graphs of the equations of the following exercises have asymptotes? (a) Exercise 7, (b) Exercise 10, (c) Exercise 12.

In Exercises 18 through 25, graph the given equations. When you are asked to plot a first variable A in terms of a second variable B, plot A as the ordinate and B as the abscissa.

18. The surface area of a cube is given by $A = 6e^2$, where e is the side of the cube. Plot A in terms of e.

19. The velocity (in ft/sec) of an object under the influence of gravity is given by $v = v_0 - at$. Plot v in terms of t(sec) if $v_0 = 100$ and $a = 32$ ft/sec^2.

20. If a group of resistors are connected in series, the total resistance R_T is the sum of the individual resistances. If a variable resistor R is connected in series with resistors of 3 and 2 ohms, plot the graph of R_T in terms of the resistor R.

21. The intensity (in lumens) of a certain source of light in terms of the distance (in cm) from the source is given by $I = 400/r^2$. Plot I in terms of r.

22. The heat capacity (in cal/gm) of an organic liquid is related to the temperature (in °C) by the equation $c_p = 0.555 + 0.00113T$ for the temperature range of -40°C to 120°C. Graphically show that this equation does not satisfy experimental data above 120°C. Plot the graph of the equation and the following data points.

c_p	0.725	0.770	0.800
T	140	160	200

23. The energy in an electric field around an inductor is given by $E = \frac{1}{2}LI^2$, where I is the current in the inductor and L is the inductance. Plot E in terms of I (a) if $L = 1$ unit, (b) if $L = 0.1$ unit, and (c) if the E-axis is marked off in units of L.

24. The deflection y of a beam at a horizontal distance x from one end is given by $y = -k(x^4 - 30x^2 + 1000x)$, where k is a constant. Plot the deflection (in terms of k) in terms of x (in feet) if there are 10 ft between the end supports of the beam.

25. If two capacitors are connected in series, the capacitance of the combination is given by

$$C_T = \frac{C_1 C_2}{C_1 + C_2} \, .$$

Plot C_T in terms of C_1 if $C_2 = 500 \times 10^{-6}$ farad. Use the range of 100×10^{-6} to 1000×10^{-6} farad for C_1.

1–4 Some basic definitions

In Section 1–1 it was noted that analytic geometry deals with the relationship between algebra and geometry. In the sections which follow we will see that proper recognition of certain important equations will lead immediately to the graph of that equation. In this section we will develop certain basic concepts which are needed to establish the proper relationships between equation and curve.

The first of these concepts involves the distance between any two points in the coordinate plane. If these two points lie on a line parallel to one of the axes, for instance the x-axis, the absolute value of the distance between them is the difference of the abscissas of these points. This is due to the fact that the abscissa of any point represents the distance from the y-axis to that point, and this distance may be either positive or negative, depending upon the location of the point. Thus the distance between the points is the difference of these distances from the y-axis. Also, if two points are on a line parallel to the y-axis, the distance between them is the difference between the ordinates of the points. (See Fig. 1–8.)

If two points are on a line which is not parallel to either of the axes (Fig. 1–9), we must use the Pythagorean theorem to find the distance between them. By making a right triangle with the line segment joining the two points as the hypotenuse, and line segments parallel to the axes as the legs, we have the formula which gives the distance between any two points in the plane. This

FIGURE 1–8   FIGURE 1–9

formula, called the *distance formula*, is

$$d = \sqrt{(x_2 - x_1)^2 + (y_2 - y_1)^2}. \tag{1-1}$$

Example A. The distance between $(2, -3)$ and $(2, 6)$ is 9 units. The line joining these points is parallel to the y-axis, and thus we need to find the difference between the y-coordinates. In a similar manner the distance between $(-1, 5)$ and $(-4, 5)$ is 3 units.

Example B. The distance between $(3, -1)$ and $(-2, -5)$ is given by

$$d = \sqrt{[(-2) - 3]^2 + [(-5) - (-1)]^2}$$
$$= \sqrt{(-5)^2 + (-4)^2} = \sqrt{25 + 16} = \sqrt{41}.$$

It makes no difference which point is chosen as (x_1, y_1) and which is chosen as (x_2, y_2), since the difference in the x-coordinates (and y-coordinates) is squared. We also obtain $\sqrt{41}$ if we set up the distance as

$$d = \sqrt{[3 - (-2)]^2 + [(-1) - (-5)]^2}.$$

Another important quantity which is defined for a line is its *slope*. The slope gives a measure of the direction of a line, and is defined as the vertical distance from one point to another on the same straight line, divided by the horizontal distance from the first point to the second. Thus, using the letter m to represent slope, we have

$$m = \frac{y_2 - y_1}{x_2 - x_1}. \tag{1-2}$$

Example C. The slope of the line joining $(3, -5)$ and $(-2, -6)$ is

$$m = \frac{-6 - (-5)}{-2 - 3} = \frac{-6 + 5}{-5} = \frac{1}{5}.$$

(See Fig. 1–10.) Again we may interpret either of the points as (x_1, y_1) and the other as (x_2, y_2). We can also obtain the slope of this same line from

$$m = \frac{-5 - (-6)}{3 - (-2)} = \frac{1}{5}.$$

FIGURE 1–10

We might note that the larger the numerical value of the slope of a line, the more nearly vertical is the line. Also, a line rising to the right will have a positive slope, and a line falling to the right will have a negative slope.

$$m = \frac{-10-9}{4-3} = \frac{-19}{1} = -19$$

x_1 y_1 x_2 y_2

Example D. The line joining $(3, 9)$ and $(4, -10)$ has a slope of -19. This line falls sharply to the right.

(3) From the definition of slope, we may conclude that the slope of a line parallel to the y-axis cannot be defined (this is due to the fact that the x-coordinates of any two points on the line would be the same, a fact which would then necessitate division by zero). This, however, does not prove to be of any trouble.

If a given line is extended indefinitely in either direction, it must cross the x-axis at some point unless it is parallel to the x-axis. The angle measured from the x-axis in a positive direction to the line is called the *inclination* of the line. The inclination of a line parallel to the x-axis is defined to be zero. An alternative definition of slope, in terms of the inclination, is

$$m = \tan \alpha, \qquad 0 \le \alpha < 180°, \qquad (1\text{–}3)$$

where α is the inclination. This can be seen from the fact that the slope can be defined in terms of any two points on the line. Thus, if we choose as one of these points that point where the line crosses the x-axis and any other point, we see from the definition of the tangent of an angle that Eq. (1–3) is in agreement with Eq. (1–2). (See Fig. 1–11.)

Example E. The slope of a line with an inclination of $45°$ is 1. The slope of a line having an inclination of $120°$ is $-\sqrt{3}$.

FIGURE 1–11   FIGURE 1–12

$\alpha_1 + 90 = \alpha_2$

$90° = \alpha_2 - \alpha_1$

$90° - 120° = -\alpha_1$

$-30° = -\alpha_1$

$\therefore 30° = \alpha_1$

Any two parallel lines crossing the x-axis will have the same inclination. Therefore, the slopes of parallel lines are equal. This can be stated as

$$m_1 = m_2, \qquad \text{for } \| \text{ lines.} \qquad (1\text{–}4)$$

If two lines are perpendicular, this means that there must be $90°$ between their inclinations (Fig. 1–12). The relation between their inclinations is

$$\alpha_2 = \alpha_1 + 90°, \qquad = 60 + 90 = 150°$$

which can be written as

$$90° - \alpha_2 = -\alpha_1. \qquad 90 - 150 = -60°$$

$\therefore \alpha = 30$

distance (d), slope (m),

Taking the tangent of each of the angles in this last relation, we have

$$\tan (90° - \alpha_2) = \tan (-\alpha_1)$$

or

$$\frac{1}{\tan \alpha_2} = \cot \alpha_2 = -\tan \alpha_1,$$

since a function of the complement of an angle is equal to the cofunction of that angle, and since $\tan (-\alpha) = -\tan \alpha$. But $\cot \alpha_2 = 1/\tan \alpha_2$, which means $1/\tan \alpha_2 = -\tan \alpha_1$. Using the inclination definition of slope, we may write, as the relation between slopes of perpendicular lines,

$$m_2 = -\frac{1}{m_1} \quad \text{or} \quad m_1 m_2 = -1, \quad \text{for} \perp \text{lines.} \qquad (1\text{–}5)$$

Example F. Lines with slopes of 2 and $-\frac{1}{2}$ would be perpendicular. Lines joining $(3, -5)$ and $(2, -7)$, and $(4, -6)$ and $(2, -5)$ are such lines.

Using the formulas for distance and slope, we can show certain basic geometric relations. The following examples illustrate the use of the formulas, and thus show the use of algebra in solving problems which are basically geometric. This illustrates the methods of analytic geometry.

Example G. Show that line segments joining $A(-5, 3)$, $B(6, 0)$, and $C(5, 5)$ form a right triangle.

If these points are vertices of a right triangle, the slopes of two of the sides must be negative reciprocals. This would show perpendicularity (Fig. 1–13). Thus we find the slopes of the three lines to be

$$m_{AB} = \frac{3 - 0}{-5 - 6} = -\frac{3}{11},$$

$$m_{AC} = \frac{3 - 5}{-5 - 5} = \frac{1}{5},$$

$$m_{BC} = \frac{0 - 5}{6 - 5} = -5.$$

FIGURE 1–13

We see that the slopes of AC and BC are negative reciprocals, which means that $AC \perp BC$. From this we can conclude that the triangle is a right triangle.

Example H. Find the area of the triangle in Example G.

Since the right angle is at C, the legs of the triangle are AC and BC. The area is one-half the product of the lengths of the legs of a right triangle. Therefore

$$\text{Area} = \frac{1}{2} \sqrt{(-5 - 5)^2 + (3 - 5)^2} \sqrt{(6 - 5)^2 + (0 - 5)^2}$$

$$= \frac{1}{2} \sqrt{104} \sqrt{26} = \frac{1}{2} \sqrt{(8 \cdot 13)(2 \cdot 13)} = 26.$$

Exercises

In Exercises 1 through 6, find the distances between the given pairs of points.

1. (3, 8) and (−1, −2) $2\sqrt{29}$
2. (−1, 3) and (−8, −4)
3. (4, −5) and (4, −8) 3 Slope undefined
4. (−3, 7) and (2, 10)
5. (−1, 0) and (5, −7)
6. (15, −1) and (−11, 1)

In Exercises 7 through 12, find the slopes of the lines joining the points in Exercises 1 through 6.

13. Show that lines joining (6, −1) and (4, 3), and (−5, 2) and (−7, 6) are parallel.
14. Show that lines joining (−3, 9) and (4, 4), and (9, −1) and (4, −8) are perpendicular.
15. If points (6, −1), (3, k), and (−3, −7) are all on the same line, what must be the value of k?
16. If the points in Exercise 15 are to be vertices of a right triangle, with right angle at (3, k), what must be the value of k?
17. What is the inclination of a line with slope of 0.3640? $20°$
18. What is the inclination of a line with slope of −1.428?
19. Show that the points (2, 3), (4, 9), and (−2, 7) are the vertices of an isosceles triangle.
20. Show that (−1, 3), (3, 5), and (5, 1) are the vertices of a right triangle.
21. Find the area of the triangle in Exercise 20.
22. Show that the points (3, 2), (7, 3), (−1, −3), and (3, −2) are the vertices of a parallelogram.
23. Show that the points (−5, 6), (0, 8), (−3, 1), and (2, 3) are the vertices of a square.

1–5 The straight line

Using the definition of slope, we can derive the equation which always represents a straight line. This is another basic method of analytic geometry. That is, equations of a particular form can be shown to represent a particular type of curve. When we recognize the form of the equation, we know the kind of curve it represents. This can be of great assistance in sketching the graph.

A straight line can be defined as a "curve" with constant slope. By this we mean that for any two different points chosen on a given line, if the slope is calculated, the same value is always found. Thus, if we consider one point (x_1, y_1) on a line to be fixed (Fig. 1–14), and another point $P(x, y)$ which can *represent* any other point on the line, we have

$$m = \frac{y - y_1}{x - x_1},$$

FIGURE 1–14

which can be written as

$$y - y_1 = m(x - x_1). \quad \text{point slope form} \quad (1\text{--}6)$$

FIXED POINT *a FIXED POINT* *point slope form*

Equation (1–6) is known as the *point-slope form* of the equation of a straight line. It is useful when we know the slope of a line and some point through which the line passes. Direct substitution can then give us the equation of the line. Such information is often available about a given line.

slope is a point on the line *FIXED POINT* $x_1 \, y_1$

Example A. Find the equation of the line which passes through $(-4, 1)$ with a slope of -2.

By using Eq. (1–6), we find that

$$y - 1 = (-2)(x + 4), = -2x - 8$$

$y_1 \quad m \quad x_1$

$\therefore y + 8 - 1 + 2x = 0$

which can be simplified to

$$y + 2x + 7 = 0.$$

Example B. Find the equation of the line through $(2, -1)$ and $(6, 2)$.

We first find the slope of the line through these points:

$x_1 \, y_1 \quad x \, y$

$$m = \frac{2 + 1}{6 - 2} = \frac{3}{4}.$$

using 6, 2

$y - 2 = \frac{3}{4}(x - 6)$

$4(y - 2) = 3(x - 6)$

Then, by using either of the two known points and Eq. (1–6), we can find the equation of the line:

$4y - 8 = 3x - 18$

$$y + 1 = \tfrac{3}{4}(x - 2) \quad \therefore 4(y+1) = 3(x-2)$$

$= 4y - 3x + 10 = 0$

or

$$4y + 4 = 3x - 6$$

or

$$4y - 3x + 10 = 0.$$

Equation (1–6) can be used except for a line parallel to the y-axis. Such a line has an undefined slope. However, it does have the property that all points have the same x-coordinate, regardless of the y-coordinate. We represent a line parallel to the y-axis as

$$x = a. \quad \text{represents a line parallel to y axis} \quad (1\text{--}7)$$

constant

A line parallel to the x-axis has a slope of 0. From Eq. (1–6), we can find its equation to be $y = y_1$. To keep the same form as Eq. (1–7), we normally write this as

$$y = b. \quad \text{represents a line parallel to x axis} \quad (1\text{--}8)$$

constant

Example C. The line $x = 2$ is a line parallel to the y-axis and two units to the right of it.

Example D. The line $y = -4$ is a line parallel to the x-axis and 4 units below it.

If we choose the special point $(0, b)$, which is the y-intercept of the line, as the point to use in Eq. (1–6), we have

$$y - b = m(x - 0)$$

or

$$y = mx + b. \qquad (1–9)$$

Equation (1–9) is known as the *slope-intercept* form of the equation of a straight line. Its usefulness lies in the fact that once we find the equation of a line and then write it in slope-intercept form, we know that the slope of the line is the coefficient of the x-term, and that it crosses the y-axis with the coordinate indicated by the constant term.

Example E. Find the slope of the line $2y + 4x - 5 = 0$.

We write this equation in slope-intercept form:

$$2y = -4x + 5 \qquad \text{or} \qquad y = -2x + \tfrac{5}{2}.$$

Thus the coefficient of x in this form is -2, which means that the slope is -2.

From Eqs. (1–6) and (1–9), and from the examples of this section, we see that the equation of the straight line has certain characteristics: namely, that we have a term in y, a term in x, and a constant term, if we simplify as much as possible. This form is represented by the equation

$$Ax + By + C = 0, \qquad (1–10)$$

which is known as the *general form* of the equation of the straight line.

Example F. What are the intercepts of the line $3x - 4y - 12 = 0$?

The intercepts of a curve are those points where it crosses each of the axes. At the point where any curve crosses the x-axis, the y-coordinate must be 0. Thus, by letting $y = 0$ in the above equation, we solve for x, and obtain $x = 4$. Hence one intercept is $(4, 0)$. By letting $x = 0$, we find the other intercept as $(0, -3)$.

In many physical situations a linear relationship exists between variables. A few examples of situations where such relationships exist are between (1) the amount a spring stretches and the force applied, (2) the change in electrical resistance and the change in temperature, (3) the force applied to an object and the resulting acceleration, and (4) the pressure at a certain point within a liquid and the depth of the point. The following example illustrates the use of a straight line in dealing with an applied problem.

Example G. Under the condition of constant acceleration, the velocity of an object varies linearly with the time. If after 1 sec a certain object has a velocity of 40 ft/sec, and 3 sec later it has a velocity of 55 ft/sec, find the equation relating the velocity and time, and graph this equation. From the graph determine the initial velocity (the velocity when $t = 0$) and the velocity after 6 sec.

If we treat the velocity v in the same way as y, and the time t in the same way as x, the slope of the straight line is

$$m = \frac{(v_2 - v_1)}{(t_2 - t_1)}$$

Using the information given in the problem, we have

$$m = \frac{55 - 40}{4 - 1} = 5.$$

Then, using the point-slope form of the equation of a straight line, we have

$$v - 40 = 5(t - 1), \qquad \text{or} \qquad v = 5t + 35,$$

which is the required equation. (See Fig. 1–15.) For purposes of graphing the line, the given values are sufficient. Of course, there is no need to include negative values of t, since these have no physical meaning. From the graph we see that the line crosses the v-axis at 35. This means that the initial velocity is 35 ft/sec. Also, when $t = 6$ we see that

$$v = 65 \text{ ft/sec.}$$

Exercises

In Exercises 1 through 11, find the equation of each of the lines with the given properties.

1. Passes through $(-3, 8)$ with a slope of 4.
2. Passes through $(-2, -5)$ and $(4, 2)$.
3. Passes through $(1, 3)$ and has an inclination of $45°$.
4. Passes through $(6, -3)$ and is parallel to the x-axis.
5. Passes through $(-4, -2)$ and is perpendicular to the x-axis.
6. Has a y-intercept of -2 and an inclination of $120°$.
7. Has an x-intercept of 4 and a y-intercept of -6.
8. Is perpendicular to a line with slope of 3 and passes through $(1, -2)$.
9. Is perpendicular to the line joining $(4, 2)$ and $(3, -5)$ and passes through $(4, 2)$.
10. Is parallel to the line $2y - 6x - 5 = 0$, and passes through $(-4, -5)$.

11. Is parallel to the y-axis and is 3 units to the left of it.

12. Draw the line whose equation is $4x - y = 7$.

13. Draw the line whose equation is $2x - 3y - 6 = 0$.

14. Find the slope and both intercepts of the line $6x - 4y - 2 = 0$.

15. Reduce the equation of the line $5x - 2y + 5 = 0$ to slope-intercept form.

16. What must be the value of k if the lines $4x - ky = 6$ and $6x + 3y + 2 = 0$ are to be parallel?

17. What must k equal in Exercise 16, if the given lines are to be perpendicular?

18. Find the equation of the line with a slope of -3 which also passes through the intersection of the lines $5x - y = 6$ and $x + y = 12$.

19. Show that the lines $6x - 3y - 5 = 0$ and $x + 2y - 4 = 0$ are perpendicular.

20. Show that the altitudes of the triangle with vertices $(2, -4)$, $(3, -1)$ and $(-2, 5)$ meet at a single point.

21. Within certain limits, the amount which a spring stretches varies linearly with the amount of force applied. If a spring whose natural length is 15 in. stretches 2 in. when 3 lb of force are applied, find the equation relating the length of the spring and the applied force.

22. The electric resistance of a certain resistor increases by 0.005 ohm for every increase of 1°C. Given that its resistance is 2.000 ohms at 0°C, find the equation relating the resistance and temperature. From the equation find the resistance when the temperature is 50°C.

23. The amount of heat required to raise the temperature of water varies linearly with the increase in temperature. However, a certain quantity of heat is required to change ice (at 0°C) into water without a change in temperature. An experiment is performed with 10 gm of ice at 0°C. It is found that it requires 1000 cal to change it into water at 20°C. Another 300 cal is required to warm the water to 50°C. How many calories were required to melt the ice at 0°C into water at 0°C?

24. The pressure at a point below the surface of a body of water varies linearly with the depth of the water. If the pressure at a depth of 1000 cm is 1.99×10^6 dynes/cm² and the pressure at a depth of 3000 cm is 3.95×10^6 dynes/cm², what is the pressure at the surface? (This is the atmospheric pressure due to the air above the water.)

25. Sometimes it is desirable to treat a nonlinear function as a linear function. For example, if $y = 2 + 3x^2$, this can be plotted as a straight line by plotting y versus x^2. A table of values for this graph is

x	0	1	2	3	4	5
x^2	0	1	4	9	16	25
y	2	5	14	29	50	77

and the graph appears in Fig. 1–16. Using this method, sketch the func-

FIGURE 1–16

(Handwritten margin notes: $\frac{20}{10}$ $\frac{2}{1}$, $C = 10a$, $C = 10(1/E)$)

tion $C = 10/E$ as a linear function. That is, plot C versus $1/E$. This is the equation between the voltage across a capacitor and the capacitance, assuming the charge on the capacitor is constant.

26. Another method of treating a nonlinear function as a linear one is by means of logarithms. Since distances corresponding to $\log y$ and $\log x$ are plotted automatically if the graph is logarithmic in the respective directions, many nonlinear functions are linear when plotted on this paper. A function of the form $y = ax^n$ is straight when plotted on logarithmic paper, since $\log y = \log a + n \log x$ is in the form of a straight line. The variables are $\log y$ and $\log x$; the slope can be found from $(\log y - \log a)/\log x = n$, and the intercept is a. (To get the slope from the graph, it is necessary to measure vertical and horizontal distances between two points. The $\log y$ intercept is found where $\log x = 0$; this occurs when $x = 1$.) Plot $y = 3x^4$ on logarithmic paper to verify this analysis.

27. A function of the form $y = a(b^x)$ is a straight line on semilogarithmic paper, since $\log y = \log a + x \log b$ is in the form of a straight line. The variables are $\log y$ and x, the slope is $\log b$, and the intercept is a. [To get the slope from the graph, we must calculate $(\log y - \log a)/x$ for some set of values x and y. The intercept is read directly off the graph where $x = 0$.] Plot $y = 3(2^x)$ on semilogarithmic paper to verify this analysis.

28. If experimental data is plotted on logarithmic paper, and the points lie on a straight line, it is possible to determine the function (see Exercise 26). The following data comes from an experiment to determine the functional relation between the tension in a string and the velocity of a wave in the string. From the graph on logarithmic paper, determine v as a function of T.

v (cm/sec)	1600	3200	4530	5540	6400
T (10^4 dynes)	1.00	4.00	8.00	12.0	16.0

29. If experimental data are plotted on semilogarithmic paper, and the points lie on a straight line, it is possible to determine the function (see Exercise 27). The following data come from an experiment designed to determine the relationship between the voltage across an inductor and the time, after the switch is opened. Determine v as a function of t.

v (volts)	40	15	5.6	2.2	0.8
t (10^{-2} sec)	0	2	4	6	8

1–6 The circle

We have found that we can obtain a general equation which represents a straight line by considering a fixed point on the line and then a general point $P(x, y)$ which can represent any other point on the same line. Mathematically we can state this as "the line is the *locus* of a point $P(x, y)$ which *moves* along the line." That is, the point $P(x, y)$ can be considered as a variable point which moves along the line.

In this way we can define a number of important curves. The circle is defined as the locus of a point $P(x, y)$ which moves so that it is always equidistant from a fixed point. This fixed distance we call the radius, and the fixed point is called the center of the circle. Thus, using this definition, calling the fixed point (h, k) and the radius r, we have

$$\sqrt{(x - h)^2 + (y - k)^2} = r = distance \; formula$$

VARIABLE *FIXED*

or, by squaring both sides, we have

$$(x - h)^2 + (y - k)^2 = r^2. \qquad (1\text{-}11)$$

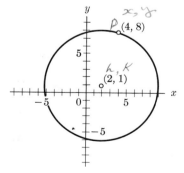

FIGURE 1–17

Variable point- which is equidistant fr fixed point

fixed point

Equation (1–11) is called the *standard equation* of a circle with center at (h, k) and radius r (Fig. 1–17).

If the center of the circle is at the origin, which means that the coordinates of the center are $(0, 0)$, the equation of the circle becomes

$$x^2 + y^2 = r^2. \qquad (1\text{-}12)$$

A basic characteristic of this circle, its symmetry to both coordinate axes, can be shown since x and y can each be replaced by its negative without changing the equation (see Section 1–3). That is, $(-x)^2 + y^2 = r^2$, $x^2 + (-y)^2 = r^2$, and $x^2 + y^2 = r^2$ are the same.

Example A. Find the equation of the circle with center at the origin and with radius of 6.

Substitution into Eq. (1–12) with $r = 6$ gives us

$$x^2 + y^2 = 36.$$

Example B. Find the equation of the circle with center at $(2, 1)$ and which passes through $(4, 8)$.

In Eq. (1–11), we can determine the equation if we can find h, k, and r for this circle. From the given information, $h = 2$ and $k = 1$. To find r, we use the fact that *all points on the circle must satisfy the equation of the circle.* The point $(4, 8)$ must satisfy Eq. (1–11), with $h = 2$ and $k = 1$. Thus $(4 - 2)^2 + (8 - 1)^2 = r^2$. From this relation we find $r^2 = 53$. The equation of the circle (Fig. 1–18) is

$$(x - 2)^2 + (y - 1)^2 = 53.$$

FIGURE 1–18

If we multiply out each of the terms in Eq. (1–11), we may combine the resulting terms to obtain the following result:

$$x^2 - 2hx + h^2 + y^2 - 2ky + k^2 = r^2,$$

$$x^2 + y^2 - 2hx - 2ky + (h^2 + k^2 - r^2) = 0. \qquad (1\text{–}13)$$

Since each of $h, k,$ and r is constant for any given circle, the coefficients of x and y and the term within parentheses in Eq. (1–13) are constants. Equation (1–13) can then be written as

$$x^2 + y^2 + Dx + Ey + F = 0. \qquad (1\text{–}14)$$

Equation (1–14) is called the *general equation* of the circle. It tells us that any equation which can be written in that form will represent a circle.

Example C. Find the center and radius of the circle

$$x^2 + y^2 - 6x + 8y - 24 = 0.$$

We can find this information if we can write the given equation in standard form. To do so, we must complete the square in the x-terms, and also in the y-terms. This is done by first writing the equation in the form

$$(x^2 - 6x \qquad) + (y^2 + 8y \qquad) = 24.$$

To complete the square of the x-terms, we take half of 6, which is 3, square it and add the result, 9, to each side. In the same way, we complete the square of the y-terms by adding 16 to each side of the equation, which gives

$$(x^2 - 6x + 9) + (y^2 + 8y + 16) = 24 + 9 + 16,$$

or

$$(x - 3)^2 + (y + 4)^2 = 49.$$

FIGURE 1–19

Thus the center is $(3, -4)$, and the radius is 7 (see Fig. 1–19). The value of k is found to be -4, by considering the y-term as $[y - (-4)]^2$.

Example D. The equation $3x^2 + 3y^2 + 6x - 20 = 0$ can be seen to represent a circle by writing it in general form. This is done by dividing through by 3. In this way we have

$$x^2 + y^2 + 2x - \tfrac{20}{3} = 0.$$

$$\left(x^2 + 2x + 1\right) + y^2 = \tfrac{20}{3} + 1$$

$$(x + 1)^2 + (y - 0)^2 = \tfrac{23}{3} \qquad r = \sqrt{\tfrac{23}{3}}$$

Center at $-1, 0$

Exercises

In Exercises 1 through 9, find the equation of each of the given circles.

1. Center at $(0, 0)$, radius 3   2. Center at $(0, 2)$, radius 2
3. Center at $(2, 2)$, radius 4   4. Center at $(-3, -5)$, radius 8
5. Center at $(2, 1)$, passes through $(4, -1)$
6. Center at $(-3, 5)$, tangent to the x-axis
7. Center on the line $5x = 2y$, radius of 5, tangent to the x-axis
8. The points $(3, 8)$ and $(-3, 0)$ are the ends of a diameter.
9. Tangent to both axes, radius 4, in the second quadrant

Find the center and radius of each of the circles in Exercises 10 through 14. Sketch each circle.

10. $x^2 + y^2 - 25 = 0$ 11. $x^2 + y^2 - 2x - 8 = 0$
12. $x^2 + y^2 - 4x - 6y - 12 = 0$ 13. $x^2 + y^2 + 8x - 10y - 8 = 0$
14. $2x^2 + 2y^2 - 4x - 8y - 1 = 0$
15. Determine where the circle $x^2 - 6x + y^2 - 7 = 0$ crosses the x-axis.
16. Find the points of intersection of the circle $x^2 + y^2 - x - 3y = 0$ and the line $y = x - 1$.
17. Find the locus of a point $P(x, y)$ which moves so that its distance from $(2, 4)$ is twice its distance from $(0, 0)$. Describe the locus.
18. Find the equation of the locus of a point $P(x, y)$ which moves so that the line joining it and $(2, 0)$ is always perpendicular to the line joining it and $(-2, 0)$. Describe the locus.
19. If an electrically charged particle enters a magnetic field of flux density B with a velocity v at right angles to the field, the path of the particle is a circle. The radius of the path is given by $R = mv/Bq$, where m is the mass of the particle and q is its charge. If a proton ($m = 1.67 \times 10^{-27}$ kg, $q = 1.60 \times 10^{-19}$ coul) enters a magnetic field of flux density 1.5 webers/m^2 with a velocity of 10^8 m/sec, find the equation of the path of the proton. (The fact that a charged particle travels in a circular path in a magnetic field is an important basis for the construction of a cyclotron.)
20. If the relationship of impedance Z with resistance R, capacitive reactance X_C, and inductive reactance X_L in an electric circuit is

$$Z = \sqrt{(X_L - X_C)^2 + R^2},$$

sketch the graph of resistance versus inductive reactance for a constant (magnitude) impedance and capacitive reactance.
21. A cylindrical oil tank, 4 ft in diameter, is on its side. A circular hole, with center 18 in. below the center of the end of the tank, has been drilled in the end of the tank. If the radius of the hole is 3 in., what is the equation of the circle of the end of the tank and the equation of the circle of the hole? Use the center of the end of the tank as the origin.

Vertex is midway between Directrix & Focus
Directrix, focus-Point $P(x, y)$,
axis is through Focus & Perpendicular to directrix.

1–7 The parabola

Another important curve is the parabola. In this section we shall find the form of the equation of the parabola, and see that this is a familiar form.

The parabola is defined as the locus of a point $P(x, y)$ which moves so that it is always equidistant from a given line and a given point. The given line is called the *directrix*, and the given point is called the *focus*. The line through the focus which is perpendicular to the directrix is called the *axis* of the parabola. The point midway between the directrix and focus is the *vertex* of the parabola. Using the definition, we shall find the equation of the parabola for which the focus is the point $(p, 0)$ and the directrix is the line $x = -p$. By choosing the focus and directrix in this manner, we shall be able to find a general representation of the equation of a parabola with its vertex at the origin.

According to the definition of the parabola, the distance from a point $P(x, y)$ on the parabola to the focus $(p, 0)$ must equal the distance from $P(x, y)$ to the directrix $x = -p$. The distance from P to the focus can be found by use of the distance formula. The distance from P to the directrix is the perpendicular distance, and this can be found as the distance between two points on a line parallel to the x-axis. These distances are indicated in Fig. 1–20. Thus we have

$$d_1 = \sqrt{(x - p)^2 + (y - 0)^2} = x + p. \; = d$$

Squaring both sides of this equation, we have

$$(x - p)^2 + y^2 = (x + p)^2$$

vertex is equaldistance from Focus & directrix

or

$$x^2 - 2px + p^2 + y^2 = x^2 + 2px + p^2.$$

Simplifying, we obtain

$$y^2 = 4px. \tag{1–15}$$

coeficient of x (P), at p, the parabola is $4p$ wide

Equation (1–15) is called the *standard form* of the equation of a parabola with its axis along the x-axis and the vertex at the origin. Its symmetry to the x-axis can be proven since $(-y)^2 = 4px$ is the same as $y^2 = 4px$.

Example A. Find the coordinates of the focus, the equation of the directrix, and sketch the graph of the parabola $y^2 = 12x$. $= 4 \times 3x$, $P = 3$ hence focus $(3,0)$

From the form of the equation, we know that the vertex is at the origin (Fig. 1–21). The coefficient of 12 tells us that the focus is $(3, 0)$, since $p = \frac{12}{4}$ [note that the coefficient of x in Eq. (1–15) is $4p$]. Also, this means that the directrix is the line $x = -3$.

FIGURE 1–20

ELEMENTS OF PARABOLA : DIRECTRIX
FOCUS
AXIS
VERTEX

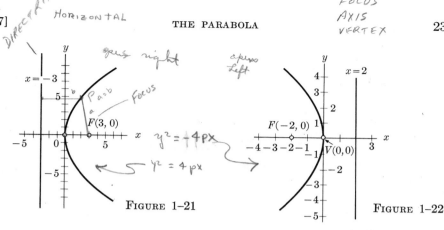

FIGURE 1–21   FIGURE 1–22

Example B. If the focus is to the left of the origin, with the directrix an equal distance to the right, the coefficient of the x-term will be negative. This tells us that the parabola opens to the left, rather than to the right, as is the case when the focus is to the right of the origin. For example, the parabola $y^2 = -8x$ has its vertex at the origin, its focus at $(-2, 0)$, and the line $x = 2$ as its directrix. This is consistent with Eq. (1–15), in that $4p = -8$, or $p = -2$. The parabola opens to the left as shown in Fig. 1–22.

If we chose the focus as the point $(0, p)$ and the directrix as the line $y = -p$, we would find that the resulting equation is

$$x^2 = 4py. \qquad (1\text{–}16)$$

This is the standard form of the equation of a parabola with the y-axis as its axis and the vertex at the origin. Its symmetry to the y-axis can be proven since $(-x)^2 = 4py$ is the same as $x^2 = 4py$. We note that the difference between this equation and Eq. (1–15) is that x is squared and y appears to the first power in Eq. (1–16), rather than the reverse, as in Eq. (1–15).

Example C. The parabola $x^2 = 4y$ has its vertex at the origin, focus at the point $(0, 1)$ and its directrix the line $y = -1$. The graph is shown in Fig. 1–23, and we see that in this case the parabola opens up.

FIGURE 1–23   FIGURE 1–24

Example D. The parabola $x^2 = -6y$ has its vertex at the origin, its focus at the point $(0, -\frac{3}{2})$, and its directrix the line $y = \frac{3}{2}$. This parabola opens down, as Fig. 1–24 shows.

handwritten: $y^2 = 4px$ $x^2 = 4py$

Equations (1–15) and (1–16) give us the general form of the equation of a parabola with its vertex at the origin and its focus on one of the coordinate axes. The following example illustrates the use of the definition of the parabola to find the equation of a parabola which has its vertex at a point other than at the origin.

Example E. Using the definition of the parabola, determine the equation of the parabola with its focus at $(2, 3)$ and its directrix the line $y = -1$.

Choosing a general point $P(x, y)$ on the parabola (Fig. 1–25), and equating the distances from this point to $(2, 3)$ and to the line $y = -1$, we have

$$d = \sqrt{(x-2)^2 + (y-3)^2} = y + 1.$$

Squaring both sides of this equation and simplifying, we have

$$(x-2)^2 + (y-3)^2 = (y+1)^2,$$
$$x^2 - 4x + 4 + y^2 - 6y + 9 = y^2 + 2y + 1,$$

or

$$8y = 12 - 4x + x^2.$$

FIGURE 1–25

When we see it in this form, we note that this type of equation appeared previously in Section 1–3, when the graph of an equation was discussed. The x-term and the constant (12 in this case) are characteristic of a parabola which does not have its vertex at the origin if the directrix is parallel to the x-axis.

Thus we can conclude that a parabola is characterized by the presence of the square of either (but not both) x or y, and a first-power term in the other. In this way we can recognize a parabola by inspecting the equation.

Exercises

In Exercises 1 through 9, find the coordinates of the focus and the equation of the directrix of each of the given parabolas. Sketch each curve.

1. $y^2 = 4x$ 2. $y^2 = -4x$ 3. $x^2 = -4y$

4. $y^2 = 16x$ 5. $y^2 = -16x$ 6. $x^2 = 2y$

7. $x^2 = -7y$ 8. $x^2 = 14y$ 9. $y = x^2$

In Exercises 10 through 14, find the equations of the parabolas satisfying the given conditions.

10. Focus $(3, 0)$, directrix $x = -3$ 11. Focus $(-2, 0)$, directrix $x = 2$

12. Focus $(0, 4)$, vertex $(0, 0)$ 13. Vertex $(0, 0)$, directrix $y = -1$

14. Vertex at the origin, axis along the y-axis, passes through $(-1, 8)$.

In Exercises 15 through 18, by use of the definition of the parabola, find the equation of the parabolas satisfying the given conditions. Sketch each curve.

15. Focus $(6, 1)$, directrix $x = 0$ 16. Focus $(1, -4)$, directrix $y = 2$

17. Focus $(1, 1)$, vertex $(1, 3)$ 18. Vertex $(-2, -4)$, directrix $x = 3$

19. In calculus it can be shown that a light ray emanating from the focus of a parabola will be reflected off parallel to the axis of the parabola. Suppose that a light ray from the focus of the parabola $y^2 = 8x$ strikes the parabola at the point $(2, 4)$. What is the equation of the reflected light ray?

20. The rate of development of heat H (measured in watts) in a resistor R (resistance measured in ohms) of an electric circuit is given by $H = Ri^2$, where i is the current (measured in amperes) in the resistor. Sketch the graph of H versus i, if $R = 6$ ohms.

21. The period T (measured in seconds) of the oscillation for resonance in an electric circuit is given by $T = 2\pi\sqrt{LC}$, where L is the inductance (in henrys) and C is the capacitance (in farads). Sketch the graph of the period versus capacitance for a constant inductance of 1 henry. Assume values of C from 10^{-6} farad to 250×10^{-6} farad, for this is a common range of values.

22. Under certain conditions, a cable which hangs between two supports can be closely approximated as being parabolic. Assuming that this cable hangs in the shape of a parabola, find its equation if a point 10 ft horizontally from its lowest point is 1 ft above its lowest point. Choose the lowest point as the origin of the coordinate system.

23. The vertical position of a projectile is given by the equation $y = -16t^2$, and its horizontal position is given by $x = 60t$. By eliminating t between the equations, show that the path of the projectile is a parabola. Sketch the path of this parabola.

24. Under certain circumstances, the maximum power P in an electric circuit varies as the square of the voltage of the source E_0 and inversely as the internal resistance R_i of the source. If 10 watts is the maximum power for a source of 2 volts and internal resistance of 0.1 ohms, sketch the graph of P vs. E_0 if R_i remains constant.

1-8 The ellipse

The next important curve we shall discuss is the ellipse. The ellipse is defined as the locus of a point $P(x, y)$, which moves so that the sum of its distances from two fixed points is constant. These two fixed points are called the *foci* of the ellipse. Letting this fixed sum equal $2a$ and the foci be the points $(c, 0)$ and $(-c, 0)$, we have (see Fig. 1-26) from the definition of the ellipse,

$$\sqrt{(x - c)^2 + y^2} + \sqrt{(x + c)^2 + y^2} = 2a.$$

major axis — vertices — a, −a
Foci — c, −c
minor axis — b, −b

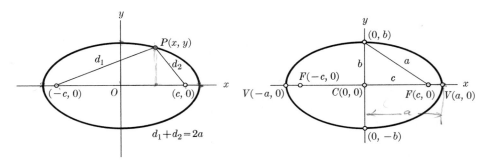

FIGURE 1–26   FIGURE 1–27

We remove one of the radicals to the right side, and then square each side. Thus we have the following steps:

$$\sqrt{(x+c)^2 + y^2} = 2a - \sqrt{(x-c)^2 + y^2},$$

$$(x+c)^2 + y^2 = 4a^2 - 4a\sqrt{(x-c)^2 + y^2} + (\sqrt{(x-c)^2 + y^2})^2,$$

$$x^2 + 2cx + c^2 + y^2 = 4a^2 - 4a\sqrt{(x-c)^2 + y^2} + x^2 - 2cx + c^2 + y^2,$$

$$4a\sqrt{(x-c)^2 + y^2} = 4a^2 - 4cx,$$

$$a\sqrt{(x-c)^2 + y^2} = a^2 - cx,$$

$$a^2(x^2 - 2cx + c^2 + y^2) = a^4 - 2a^2cx + c^2x^2,$$

$$(a^2 - c^2)x^2 + a^2y^2 = a^2(a^2 - c^2).$$

At this point we define (and the usefulness of this definition will be shown presently) $a^2 - c^2 = b^2$. This substitution gives us

$$b^2x^2 + a^2y^2 = a^2b^2.$$

Dividing through by a^2b^2, we have

$$\frac{x^2}{a^2} + \frac{y^2}{b^2} = 1. \tag{1–17}$$

If we let $y = 0$, we find that the x-intercepts are $(-a, 0)$ and $(a, 0)$. We see that the distance $2a$, originally chosen as the sum of the distances in the derivation of Eq. (1–17), is the distance between the x-intercepts. These two points are known as the *vertices* of the ellipse, and the line between them is known as the *major axis* of the ellipse. Thus, a is called the semi-major axis.

If we now let $x = 0$, we find the y-intercepts to be $(0, -b)$ and $(0, b)$. The line joining these two intercepts is called the *minor axis* of the ellipse (Fig. 1–27) which means b is called the semi-minor axis. The point $(0, b)$ is on the ellipse, and is also equidistant from $(-c, 0)$ and $(c, 0)$. Since the sum of the distances from these points to $(0, b)$ equals $2a$, the distance from $(c, 0)$ to $(0, b)$ must be a. Thus we have a right triangle formed by line segments of lengths a, b, and c, with a as the hypotenuse. From this we have the relation

$$a^2 = b^2 + c^2 \tag{1–18}$$

between the distances a, b, and c. This equation also shows us why b was defined as it was in the derivation.

Equation (1–17) is called the *standard equation* of the ellipse with its major axis along the x-axis and its center at the origin.

If we choose points on the y-axis as the foci, the standard equation of the ellipse, with its center at the origin and its major axis along the y-axis, is

$$\frac{y^2}{a^2} + \frac{x^2}{b^2} = 1. \tag{1–19}$$

In this case the vertices are $(0, a)$ and $(0, -a)$, and the foci are $(0, c)$ and $(0, -c)$.

The symmetry of the ellipses given by Eqs. (1–17) and (1–19) to each of the axes can be proven since each of x and y can be replaced by its negative in these equations without changing the equations.

Example A. The ellipse $x^2/25 + y^2/9 = 1$ has vertices at $(5, 0)$ and $(-5, 0)$. Its minor axis extends from $(0, 3)$ to $(0, -3)$, as we see in Fig. 1–28. This information is directly obtainable from this form of the equation, since the 25 tells us that $a^2 = 25$, or $a = 5$. In the same way we have $b = 3$. Since we know both a^2 and b^2, we can find c^2 from the relation $c^2 = a^2 - b^2$. Thus $c^2 = 16$, or $c = 4$. This in turn tells us that the foci of this ellipse are at $(4, 0)$ and $(-4, 0)$.

Example B. The ellipse $x^2/4 + y^2/9 = 1$ has vertices at $(0, 3)$ and $(0, -3)$. The minor axis extends from $(2, 0)$ to $(-2, 0)$. This we can find directly from the equation, since $a^2 = 9$ and $b^2 = 4$. One might ask how we chose $a^2 = 9$ in this example and $a^2 = 25$ in the preceding example. Since $a^2 = b^2 + c^2$, a is always larger than b. Thus we can tell which axis (x or y) the major axis is along by seeing which number (in the denominator) is larger, when the equation is written in standard form. The larger one stands for a^2. In this example, the foci are $(0, \sqrt{5})$ and $(0, -\sqrt{5})$. (See Fig. 1–29.)

Example C. Find the coordinates of the vertices, ends of the minor axis, and the foci of the ellipse $4x^2 + 16y^2 = 64$.

This equation must be put in standard form first, which we do by dividing through by 64. When this is done, we obtain

$$\frac{x^2}{16} + \frac{y^2}{4} = 1.$$

FIGURE 1–28

FIGURE 1–30

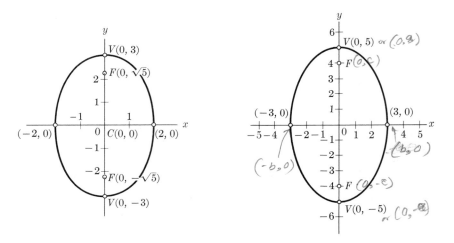

FIGURE 1–29

FIGURE 1–31

Thus $a = 4, b = 2$, and $c = 2\sqrt{3}$. The vertices are at $(4, 0)$ and $(-4, 0)$. The ends of the minor axis are $(0, 2)$ and $(0, -2)$ and the foci are $(2\sqrt{3}, 0)$ and $(-2\sqrt{3}, 0)$. See Fig. 1–30.

Example D. Find the equation of the ellipse for which the center is at the origin, the major axis is along the y-axis, the minor axis is 6 units long, and there are 8 units between foci.

Directly we know that $2b = 6$, or $b = 3$. Also $2c = 8$, or $c = 4$. Thus we find that $a = 5$ (Fig. 1–31). Since the major axis is along the y-axis, we have the equation

$$\frac{y^2}{25} + \frac{x^2}{9} = 1.$$

Equations (1–17) and (1–19) give us the standard form of the equation of an ellipse with its center at the origin and its foci on one of the coordinate axes. The following example illustrates the use of the definition of the ellipse to find the equation of an ellipse with its center at a point other than the origin.

Example E. Using the definition, find the equation of the ellipse with foci at (1, 3) and (9, 3), with a major axis of 10. Using the same method as in the derivation of Eq. (1–17), we have the following steps. (Remember, the sum of distances in the definition equals the length of the major axis.)

2a = 10

$$\sqrt{(x-1)^2 + (y-3)^2} + \sqrt{(x-9)^2 + (y-3)^2} = 10,$$

$$\sqrt{(x-1)^2 + (y-3)^2} = 10 - \sqrt{(x-9)^2 + (y-3)^2},$$

$$(x-1)^2 + (y-3)^2 = 100 - 20\sqrt{(x-9)^2 + (y-3)^2}$$
$$+ (\sqrt{(x-9)^2 + (y-3)^2})^2,$$

$$x^2 - 2x + 1 + y^2 - 6y + 9 = 100 - 20\sqrt{(x-9)^2 + (y-3)^2}$$
$$+ x^2 - 18x + 81 + y^2 - 6y + 9,$$

$$20\sqrt{(x-9)^2 + (y-3)^2} = 180 - 16x, \quad \div 4$$

$$5\sqrt{(x-9)^2 + (y-3)^2} = (45 - 4x,)$$

$$25(x^2 - 18x + 81 + y^2 - 6y + 9) = 2025 - 360x + 16x^2, \quad squared.$$

$$25x^2 - 450x + 2250 + 25y^2 - 150y = 2025 - 360x + 16x^2,$$

$$9x^2 - 90x + 25y^2 - 150y + 225 = 0.$$

The additional x- and y-terms are characteristic of the equation of an ellipse whose center is not at the origin. See Fig. 1–32.

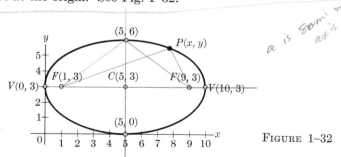

a is semi major axis

FIGURE 1–32

We can conclude that the equation of an ellipse is characterized by the presence of both an x^2- and a y^2-term, having different coefficients (in value but not in sign). The difference between the equation of an ellipse and that of a circle is that the coefficients of the squared terms in the equation of the circle are the same, whereas those of the ellipse differ.

Exercises

In Exercises 1 through 9, find the coordinates of the vertices and foci of the given ellipses. Sketch each curve.

1. $\dfrac{x^2}{4} + \dfrac{y^2}{1} = 1$ 2. $\dfrac{x^2}{100} + \dfrac{y^2}{64} = 1$ 3. $\dfrac{x^2}{25} + \dfrac{y^2}{36} = 1$

4. $4x^2 + 9y^2 = 36$ 5. $x^2 + 36y^2 = 144$ 6. $49x^2 + 4y^2 = 196$

7. $8x^2 + y^2 = 16$ 8. $9x^2 + 4y^2 = 9$ 9. $2x^2 + 3y^2 = 6$

In Exercises 10 through 15, find the equation of each of the ellipses satisfying the given conditions. (Each has its center at the origin.)

10. Vertex $(15, 0)$, focus $(9, 0)$ 11. Minor axis 8, vertex $(0, -5)$

12. Focus $(2, 0)$, major axis 6   13. Semi-minor axis 2, focus $(3, 0)$

14. Vertex $(8, 0)$, passes through $(2, 3)$ 15. Passes through $(2, 2)$ and $(1, 4)$

16. By use of the definition, find the equation of the ellipse with foci at $(-2, 1)$ and $(4, 1)$, and a major axis of 10.

17. By use of the definition, find the equation of the ellipse with vertices at $(1, 5)$ and $(1, -1)$, and foci at $(1, 4)$ and $(1, 0)$.

18. Find the points of intersection of the ellipses

$$25x^2 + 4y^2 = 100 \quad \text{and} \quad 4x^2 + 9y^2 = 36.$$

19. The arch of a bridge across a stream is in the form of half an ellipse above the water level. If the span of the arch at water level is 100 ft and the maximum height of the arch above water level is 30 ft, what is the equation of the arch? Choose the origin of the coordinate system at the most convenient point.

20. An elliptical gear (Fig. 1–33) which rotates about its center is kept continually in mesh with a circular gear which is free to move horizontally. If the equation of the ellipse of the gear (with the origin of the coordinate system at its center) in its present position is $3x^2 + 7y^2 = 20$, how far does the center of the circular gear move in going from one extreme position to the other? (Assume the units are inches.)

FIGURE 1–33

21. An artificial satellite of the earth has a minimum altitude of 500 mi and a maximum altitude of 2000 mi. If the path of the satellite about the earth is an ellipse with the center of the earth at one focus, what is the equation of its path? (Assume the radius of the earth is 4000 mi.)

22. An electric current is caused to flow in a loop of wire rotating in a magnetic field. In a study of this phenomenon, a piece of wire is cut into two pieces, one of which is bent into a circle and the other into a square. If the sum of areas of the circle and square is always π units, find the relation between the radius r of the circle and the side x of the square. Sketch the graph of r vs. x.

[handwritten notes at top: foci $(c,0)$ & $(-c,0)$ / Vertices $(a,0)$ & $(-a,0)$ / Transverse axis $2a$ / Conjugate axis $2b$]

1–9 The hyperbola

The final curve we shall discuss in detail is the hyperbola. The hyperbola is defined as the locus of a point $P(x, y)$ which moves so that the difference of the distances from two fixed points is a constant. These fixed points are the *foci* of the hyperbola. Assuming that the foci of the hyperbola are the points $(c, 0)$ and $(-c, 0)$ (see Fig. 1–34) and that the constant difference is $2a$, we have

$$\sqrt{(x + c)^2 + y^2} - \sqrt{(x - c)^2 + y^2} = 2a.$$

Following the same procedure as in the preceding section, we find the equation of this hyperbola to be

[handwritten: Horizontal]
$$\frac{x^2}{a^2} - \frac{y^2}{b^2} = 1. \tag{1–20}$$

[handwritten: Hyperbola]

[handwritten: Hyperbola $Ax^2 (-) By^2 + Cx + Dy + E = 0$]

FIGURE 1–34

[figure annotations: c, d_1, $P(x, y)$, d_2 b, $(-c, 0)$, O, a, $(c, 0)$, $d_1 - d_2 = 2a$, center at origin]

When we derive this equation, we have a definition of the relation between a, b, and c which is different from that for the ellipse. This relation is

$$c^2 = a^2 + b^2. \tag{1–21}$$

An analysis of Eq. (1–20) will reveal the significance of a and b. First, by letting $y = 0$, we find that the x-intercepts are $(a, 0)$ and $(-a, 0)$, just as they are for the ellipse. These points are called the *vertices* of the hyperbola. By letting $x = 0$, we find that we have imaginary solutions for y, which means that there are no points on the curve which correspond to a value of $x = 0$.

In order to find the significance of b, we shall solve Eq. (1–20) for y in a particular form. First we have

$$\frac{y^2}{b^2} = \frac{x^2}{a^2} - 1 = \frac{x^2}{a^2} - \frac{a^2 x^2}{a^2 x^2} = \frac{x^2}{a^2}\left(1 - \frac{a^2}{x^2}\right).$$

Multiplying through by b^2 and then taking the square root of each side, we have

$$y^2 = \frac{b^2 x^2}{a^2}\left(1 - \frac{a^2}{x^2}\right),$$

$$y = \pm \frac{bx}{a}\sqrt{(1 - a^2/x^2)}. \tag{1–22}$$

We note that if large values of x are assumed in Eq. (1–22), the quantity under the radical becomes approximately 1. In fact, the larger x becomes, the nearer 1 this expression becomes, since the x^2 in the denominator of a^2/x^2 makes this term nearly zero. Thus, for large values of x, Eq. (1–22) is approximately

$$y = \pm \frac{bx}{a}. \tag{1–23}$$

Equation (1–23) can be seen to represent the equations for two straight lines, each of which passes through the origin. One has a slope of b/a and the other a slope of $-b/a$. These lines are the *asymptotes* of the hyperbola. The concept of an asymptote was introduced in Section 1–3. The fact that the hyperbola *approaches* the asymptote as x becomes large without bound (*approaches* infinity) is designated by

$$y \rightarrow \frac{bx}{a} \quad \text{as} \quad x \rightarrow \infty.$$

It is emphasized here that the symbol for infinity, ∞, should not be thought of as a number, but should be thought of as a process of numbers becoming large without bound.

Since straight lines are easily sketched, the easiest way to sketch a hyperbola is to draw its asymptotes, and then to draw the hyperbola so that it comes closer and closer to these lines as x becomes larger numerically. To draw in the asymptotes, the usual procedure is to first draw a small rectangle, $2a$ by $2b$, with the origin in the center. Then straight lines are drawn through opposite vertices. These lines are the asymptotes (see Fig. 1–35). Thus we see that the significance of the value of b lies in the slope of the asymptotes of the hyperbola.

Equation (1–20) is called the *standard equation* of the hyperbola with its center at the origin. It has a *transverse axis* of length $2a$ along the x-axis and a *conjugate axis* of length $2b$ along the y-axis. This means that a represents the length of the semi-transverse axis, and b represents the length of the semi-conjugate axis. The relation between a, b, and c is given in Eq. (1–21).

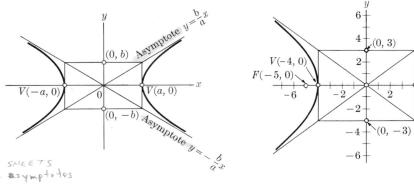

FIGURE 1–35   FIGURE 1–36

If the <u>transverse axis</u> is along the y-axis and the <u>conjugate axis</u> is along the x-axis, the equation of a hyperbola with its center at the origin is

$$\frac{y^2}{a^2} - \frac{x^2}{b^2} = 1. \qquad\qquad (1\text{–}24)$$

(handwritten: vertical)

(handwritten to the right: $\frac{(y-1)^2}{a^2} - \frac{(x-1)^2}{b^2} = 1$)

The symmetry of the hyperbola given by Eqs. (1–20) and (1–24) to each of the axes can be proven since each of x and y can be replaced by its negative in these equations without changing the equations.

Example A.   The hyperbola $x^2/16 - y^2/9 = 1$ has vertices at $(4, 0)$ and $(-4, 0)$. Its transverse axis extends from one vertex to the other. Its conjugate axis extends from $(0, 3)$ to $(0, -3)$. Since $c^2 = a^2 + b^2$, we find that $c = 5$, which means that the foci are the points $(5, 0)$ and $(-5, 0)$. Drawing in the rectangle and then the asymptotes (Fig. 1–36), we draw the hyperbola from each vertex toward the asymptotes. Thus the curve is sketched.

Example B.   The hyperbola $y^2/4 - x^2/16 = 1$ has vertices at $(0, 2)$ and $(0, -2)$. Its conjugate axis extends from $(4, 0)$ to $(-4, 0)$. The foci are $(0, 2\sqrt{5})$ and $(0, -2\sqrt{5})$. Since, with 1 on the right side of the equation, the y^2-term is the positive term, this hyperbola is in the form of Eq. (1–24). [Example A illustrates a hyperbola of the type (1–20), since the x^2-term is the positive term.] Since $2a$ extends along the y-axis, we see that the equations of the asymptotes are $y = \pm(a/b)x$. This is not a contradiction of Eq. (1–23), but an extension of it for the case of a hyperbola with its transverse axis along the y-axis. The ratio a/b simply expresses the slope of the asymptote. See Fig. 1–37.

Example C.   Find the coordinates of the vertices and foci of the hyperbola $4x^2 - 9y^2 = 36$.

(handwritten: $= \frac{4x^2}{36} - \frac{9y^2}{36} = \frac{36}{36} : \frac{x^2}{9} - \frac{y^2}{4} = 1$)

FIGURE 1–37   FIGURE 1–38

(handwritten: $c^2 = \pm 13$ ∴ $c = \sqrt{13}$)

First, by dividing through by 36, we can put this equation in standard form. Thus we have

$$\frac{x^2}{9} - \frac{y^2}{4} = 1.$$

The transverse axis is along the x-axis with vertices at $(3, 0)$ and $(-3, 0)$. Also,

$$c^2 = a^2 + b^2 \text{ and } c = \sqrt{13}.$$

This means that the foci are at $(\sqrt{13}, 0)$ and $(-\sqrt{13}, 0)$. See Fig. 1–38.

Example D. Find the equation of the hyperbola with its center at the origin, a vertex at $(3, 0)$, and which passes through $(5, \frac{4}{3})$.

When we know that the hyperbola has its center at the origin and a vertex at $(3, 0)$, we know that the standard form of its equation is given by Eq. (1–20). This also tells us that $a = 3$. By using the fact that the coordinates of the point $(5, \frac{4}{3})$ must satisfy the equation, we are able to find the value of b^2. (See Fig. 1–39.) Substituting, we have

$$\frac{25}{9} - \frac{(16/9)}{b^2} = 1,$$

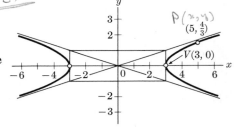

from which we find $b^2 = 1$. Therefore the equation of the hyperbola is

$$\frac{x^2}{9} - \frac{y^2}{1} = 1$$

or

$$x^2 - 9y^2 = 9.$$

FIGURE 1–39

Equations (1–20) and (1–24) give us the standard form of the equation of the hyperbola with its center at the origin and its foci on one of the coordinate axes. There is one other important equation form which represents a hyperbola, and that is

$$xy = c. \tag{1–25}$$

The asymptotes of this hyperbola are the coordinate axes, and the foci are on the line $y = x$, or on the line $y = -x$, if c is negative. The following example illustrates this type of hyperbola.

Example E. Plot the graph of the equation $xy = 4$.

We find the values in the following table, and then plot the appropriate points. Here it is permissible to use a limited number of points, since we know that the equation represents a hyperbola (Fig. 1–40). Thus, using $y = 4/x$, we obtain the values in the table.

x	-8	-4	-1	$-\frac{1}{4}$	$\frac{1}{4}$	1	4	8
y	$-\frac{1}{2}$	-1	-4	-16	16	4	1	$\frac{1}{2}$

We conclude that the equation of a hyperbola is characterized by the presence of both an x^2- and a y^2-term, having different signs, or by the presence of an xy-term with no squared terms.

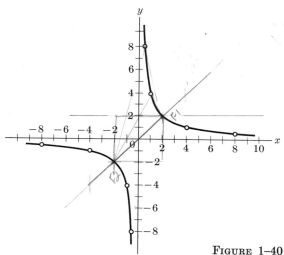

FIGURE 1–40

Exercises

In Exercises 1 through 9, find the coordinates of the vertices and the foci of the given hyperbolas. Sketch each curve.

1. $\dfrac{x^2}{25} - \dfrac{y^2}{144} = 1$ 2. $\dfrac{y^2}{9} - \dfrac{x^2}{1} = 1$ 3. $\dfrac{y^2}{2} - \dfrac{x^2}{2} = 1$

4. $2x^2 - y^2 = 4$ 5. $4x^2 - y^2 + 4 = 0$ 6. $9x^2 - y^2 - 9 = 0$

7. $4x^2 - 9y^2 = 16$ 8. $y^2 - 9x^2 = 25$ 9. $3y^2 - 2x^2 = 6$

In Exercises 10 through 13, find the equation of the hyperbola satisfying each of the given sets of conditions. Each has its center at the origin.

10. Vertex $(3, 0)$, focus $(5, 0)$ 11. Conjugate axis $= 12$, vertex $(0, 10)$

12. Focus $(0, 8)$, transverse axis 4   13. Passes through $(2, 3)$, focus $(2, 0)$

14. Sketch the graph of the hyperbola $xy = 2$.

15. Sketch the graph of the hyperbola $xy = -4$.

16. By use of the definition of the hyperbola, find the equation of the hyperbola with foci at $(1, 2)$ and $(11, 2)$, with a transverse axis of 8.

17. Find the points of intersection of the hyperbola $y^2 - x^2 = 1$ and the ellipse $x^2 + 25y^2 = 25$.

18. Sketch the graph of impedance vs. resistance if the reactance $X_L - X_C$ of a given electric circuit is constant at 60 ohms. (See Exercise 20 of Section 1–6.)

19. One statement of Boyle's law is that the product of the pressure and volume, for constant temperature, remains a constant for a perfect gas. If one set of values for a perfect gas under the condition of constant temperature is that the pressure is 3 atm for a volume of 8 liters, sketch a graph of pressure versus volume.

20. The relationship between the frequency f, wavelength λ, and the velocity v of a wave is given by $v = f\lambda$. The velocity of light is a constant, being 3×10^{10} cm/sec. The visible spectrum ranges in wavelength from about 4×10^{-5} cm (red) to about 7×10^{-5} cm (violet). Sketch a graph of frequency f (in cycles/sec) as a function of wavelength for the visible spectrum.

21. The wavelength of gamma rays varies from about 10^{-8} cm to about 10^{-13} cm, but they have the same velocity as light. On logarithmic paper, plot the graph of frequency versus wavelength for gamma rays. What type of curve results when this type of hyperbola is plotted on logarithmic paper?

22. An electronic instrument located at a point P records the sounds of a rifle shot and the impact of the bullet striking the target at the same instant. Show that P lies on a branch of a hyperbola.

1–10 Translation of axes

Until now, the equations considered for the parabola, the ellipse, and the hyperbola have been restricted to the particular cases in which the vertex of the parabola is at the origin and the center of the ellipse or hyperbola is at the origin. In this section we shall consider the equations of these curves for the cases in which the axis of the curve is parallel to one of the coordinate axes. This is done by *translation of axes*.

We choose a point (h, k) in the xy-coordinate plane and let this point be the origin of another coordinate system, the $x'y'$-coordinate system. The x'-axis is

FIGURE 1–41

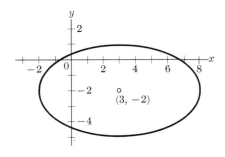

FIGURE 1–42

parallel to the x-axis and the y'-axis is parallel to the y-axis. Every point in the plane now has two sets of coordinates associated with it, (x, y) and (x', y'). From Fig. 1–41 we see that

$$x = x' + h$$

and

$$y = y' + k. \tag{1–26}$$

Equations (1–26) can also be written in the form

$$x' = x - h,$$
$$y' = y - k. \tag{1–27}$$

The following examples illustrate the use of Eqs. (1–27) in the analysis of equations of the parabola, ellipse, and hyperbola.

Example A. Describe the locus of the equation

$$\frac{(x - 3)^2}{25} + \frac{(y + 2)^2}{9} = 1.$$

In this equation, given that $h = 3$ and $k = -2$, we have $x' = x - 3$ and $y' = y + 2$. In terms of x' and y', the equation is

$$\frac{(x')^2}{25} + \frac{(y')^2}{9} = 1.$$

We recognize this equation as that of an ellipse (see Fig. 1–42) with a semi-major axis of 5 and a semi-minor axis of 3. The center of the ellipse is at $(3, -2)$, since this was the choice of h and k to make the equation fit a standard form.

Example B. Find the equation of the parabola with vertex at $(2, 4)$ and focus at $(4, 4)$.

If we let the origin of the $x'y'$-coordinate system be the point $(2, 4)$, the point $(4, 4)$ would be the point $(2, 0)$ in the $x'y'$-system. This means that $p = 2$ and $4p = 8$ (see Fig. 1–43). In the $x'y'$-system, the equation is

$$(y')^2 = 8(x'). \quad = 4 \times 2x'$$

Therefore, since $(2, 4)$ is the origin of the $x'y'$-system, this means that $h = 2$ and $k = 4$.

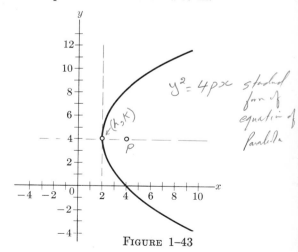

$y^2 = 4px$ standard form of equation of parabola

FIGURE 1–43

Using Eq. (1–27), we have

$$(y-k)^2 = (y')^2 = (y - 4)^2 = 8(x - 2) = 8(x - h) = 8(x')$$

as the equation of the parabola in the xy-coordinate system. If this equation is multiplied out, and like terms are combined, we obtain

$$y^2 - 8x - 8y + 32 = 0.$$

Example C. Find the center of the hyperbola

$$2x^2 - y^2 - 4x - 4y - 4 = 0.$$

In order to analyze this curve, we first complete the square in the x-terms and in the y-terms. This will allow us to properly recognize the choice of h and k.

$$2x^2 - 4x - y^2 - 4y = 4,$$
$$2(x^2 - 2x \quad) - (y^2 + 4y \quad) = 4,$$
$$2(x^2 - 2x + 1) - (y^2 + 4y + 4) = 4 + 2 - 4,$$
$$2(x - 1)^2 - (y + 2)^2 = 2,$$
$$\frac{(x - 1)^2}{1} - \frac{(y + 2)^2}{2} = 1.$$

Thus, if we let $h = 1$ and $k = -2$, the equation in the $x'y'$-system becomes

$$\frac{(x')^2}{1} - \frac{(y')^2}{2} = 1.$$

This means that the center is at $(1, -2)$, since this point corresponds to the origin of the $x'y'$-coordinate system. (See Fig. 1–44.)

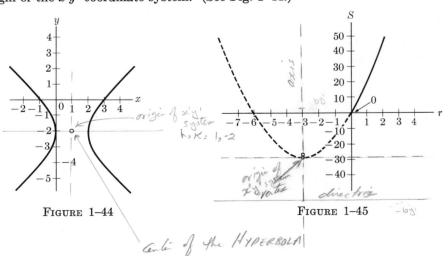

FIGURE 1–44   FIGURE 1–45

Example D. Glass beakers are to be made with a height of 3 in. Express the surface area of the beakers in terms of the radius of the base. Sketch the graph of area vs. radius.

The total surface area of a beaker is the sum of the area of the base and the lateral surface area of the side. In general, this surface area S in terms of the radius r of the base and the height h of the side is

$$S = \pi r^2 + 2\pi rh. \quad (\text{area of circle}) + (\text{circumference} \times \text{height})$$

Since h is constant at 3 in., we have

$$S = \pi r^2 + 6\pi r, \quad \text{equation of parabola } x^2 = 4py$$

which is the desired relationship.

For purposes of sketching the graph of S and r, we now complete the square of the r terms:

$$S = \pi(r^2 + 6r),$$
$$S + 9\pi = \pi(r^2 + 6r + 9),$$
$$\text{or } y = S + 9\pi = \pi(r + 3)^2. \text{ or } \pi(x')^2 = y \quad \text{or } (x')^2 = \frac{y'}{\pi}$$

We note that this equation represents a parabola with vertex at $(-3, -9\pi)$ for its coordinates (r, S). Since $4p = \pi$, $p = \pi/4$ and the focus of this parabola is at $(-3, -35\pi/4)$. Only positive values for S and r have meaning, and therefore the part of the graph for negative r is shown as a dashed curve. (See Fig. 1–45.)

Exercises

In Exercises 1 through 6, describe the locus of each of the given equations. Identify the type of curve and its center (vertex if it is a parabola). Sketch each curve.

1. $(y - 2)^2 = 4(x + 1)$

2. $\dfrac{(x + 4)^2}{4} + \dfrac{(y - 1)^2}{1} = 1$

3. $\dfrac{(x - 1)^2}{4} - \dfrac{(y - 2)^2}{9} = 1$

4. $(y + 5)^2 = -8(x - 2)$

5. $\dfrac{(x + 1)^2}{1} + \dfrac{y^2}{9} = 1$

6. $\dfrac{(y - 4)^2}{16} - \dfrac{(x + 2)^2}{4} = 1$

In Exercises 7 through 9, find the equation of each of the curves described by the given information.

7. Parabola: vertex $(-1, 3)$, $p = 4$, axis parallel to the x-axis

8. Ellipse: center $(-2, 2)$, focus $(-5, 2)$, vertex $(-7, 2)$

9. Hyperbola: center $(1, -4)$, focus $(1, 1)$, transverse axis 8 units long

In Exercises 10 through 12, determine the center (or vertex if the curve is a parabola) of the given curves. Identify and sketch each curve.

10. $x^2 + 2x - 4y - 3 = 0$ 11. $4x^2 + 9y^2 + 24x = 0$

12. $5x^2 - 4y^2 + 20x + 8y = 4$

13. Find the equation of the parabola with focus at $(0, 2)$ and directrix the line $y = 4$.

14. Find the equation of the hyperbola with asymptotes $x - y = -1$ and $x + y = -3$, and vertex $(3, -1)$.

15. Verify each of the following equations as being the standard form as indicated.

Parabola, vertex at (h, k), axis parallel to the x-axis:

$$(y - k)^2 = 4p(x - h).$$

Parabola, vertex at (h, k), axis parallel to the y-axis:

$$(x - h)^2 = 4p(y - k).$$

Ellipse, center at (h, k), major axis parallel to the x-axis:

$$\frac{(x - h)^2}{a^2} + \frac{(y - k)^2}{b^2} = 1.$$

Ellipse, center at (h, k), major axis parallel to the y-axis:

$$\frac{(y - k)^2}{a^2} + \frac{(x - h)^2}{b^2} = 1.$$

Hyperbola, center at (h, k), transverse axis parallel to the x-axis:

$$\frac{(x - h)^2}{a^2} - \frac{(y - k)^2}{b^2} = 1.$$

Hyperbola, center at (h, k), transverse axis parallel to the y-axis:

$$\frac{(y - k)^2}{a^2} - \frac{(x - h)^2}{b^2} = 1.$$

16. The power supplied to a circuit by a battery with a voltage E and an internal resistance r is given by $P = EI - rI^2$, where P is the power (in watts) and I is the current (in amps). Sketch the graph of P vs. I for a 6-volt battery with an internal resistance of 0.3 ohms.

17. A rectangular tract of land is to have a perimeter of 800 ft. Express the area in terms of its width and sketch the graph.

1–11 The second-degree equation

The equations of the circle, parabola, ellipse, and hyperbola have certain properties in common. In this section we shall briefly discuss some of these properties.

Each of these curves can be represented by a second-degree equation of the form

$$Ax^2 + Bxy + Cy^2 + Dx + Ey + F = 0. \qquad (1\text{–}28)$$

The coefficients of the second-degree terms determine the type of curve which results. From the previous sections of this chapter, we have the following results.

Equation (1–28) represents the indicated curve for the given conditions for A, B, and C.

1. If $A = C$, $B = 0$, a circle.
2. If $A \neq C$ (but they have the same sign), $B = 0$, an ellipse.
3. If A and C have different signs, $B = 0$, a hyperbola.
4. If $A = 0$, $C = 0$, $B \neq 0$, a hyperbola.
5. If either $A = 0$ or $C = 0$ (but not both), $B = 0$, a parabola.

(Special cases, such as a single point or no real locus, can also result.)

Another conclusion about Eq. (1–28) is that, if either $D \neq 0$ or $E \neq 0$ (or both), the center (or vertex of a parabola) of the curve is not at the origin. If $B \neq 0$, the axis of the curve has been rotated. We have considered only one such case (the hyperbola $xy = c$) in this chapter.

Example. The equation $3x^2 = 6x - y^2 + 3$ represents an ellipse. Before we analyze the equation, we should put it in the form of Eq. (1–28). For the given equation, this form is

$$3x^2 + y^2 - 6x - 3 = 0.$$

Here we see that $B = 0$ and $A \neq C$. Therefore it is an ellipse. The $-6x$ term indicates that the center of the ellipse is not at the origin.

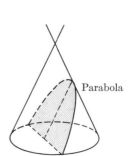

FIGURE 1–46

The circle, parabola, ellipse, and hyperbola are usually referred to as *conic sections*. This is due to the fact that if a plane is passed through a cone, the intersection of the plane and the cone results in one of these curves, depending on the angle the plane has with respect to the axis of the cone. This is indicated in Fig. 1–46.

Exercises

In Exercises 1 through 10, identify each of the equations as representing either a circle, parabola, ellipse, or hyperbola.

1. $x^2 - 2y^2 - 3x - 1 = 0$
2. $2x^2 + 2y^2 - 3x = 0$
3. $2x^2 - x - y = 1$
4. $2x^2 + 4y^2 - y - 2x = 4$
5. $x^2 = y - y^2$
6. $x^2 = y^2 - 1$
7. $x(y + 3x) = x^2 + xy - y^2 + 1$
8. $x(2 - x) = y^2$
9. $2xy + x - 3y = 6$
10. $(y + 1)^2 = x^2 + y^2 - 1$
11. What type of curve would result if impedance is graphed against inductive reactance for constant values of resistance and capacitive reactance for a given alternating current circuit? (See Exercise 20 of Section 1–6.)

Miscellaneous exercises for Chapter 1

In Exercises 1 through 9, find the equation of the indicated curve subject to the given conditions. Sketch each curve.

1. Straight line: passes through $(-1, 5)$ and $(-2, -3)$
2. Circle: center at $(1, -2)$, passes through $(4, -3)$
3. Parabola: focus $(3, 0)$, vertex $(0, 0)$
4. Ellipse: vertex $(10, 0)$, focus $(8, 0)$, center $(0, 0)$
5. Hyperbola: vertex $(0, 13)$, center $(0, 0)$, conjugate axis of 24
6. Parabola: directrix $y = -5$, vertex $(0, 0)$
7. Circle: tangent to the line $x = 3$, center at $(5, 1)$
8. Hyperbola: foci $(0, 10)$ and $(0, -10)$, vertex $(0, 8)$
9. Ellipse: center $(0, 0)$, passes through $(0, 3)$ and $(2, 1)$

In Exercises 10 through 15, find the indicated quantities for each of the given equations. Sketch each curve.

10. $x^2 + y^2 + 6x - 7 = 0$, center and radius
11. $x^2 = -20y$, focus and directrix
12. $16x^2 + y^2 = 16$, vertices and foci
13. $2x^2 - 5y^2 = 8$, vertices and foci
14. $x^2 - 8x - 4y - 16 = 0$, vertex and focus
15. $4x^2 + y^2 - 16x + 2y + 13 = 0$, center

16. In two ways show that the line segments joining $(-3, 11)$, $(2, -1)$, and $(14, 4)$ form a right triangle.

17. Write the equation of the straight line $3x - 5y + 6 = 0$ in slope-intercept form.

18. Find the line through the point $(1, 2)$ and parallel to the line $2x + 4y - 7 = 0$.

19. Find the equation of the line which passes through the vertex of the parabola $y = x^2 + 4x$ and which is perpendicular to the line $2x - 6y = 9$.

20. By means of the definition, find the equation of the parabola with focus at $(3, 1)$ and directrix the line $y = -3$. Find the same equation by the method of translation of axes.

21. In a certain electric circuit, two resistors R_1 and R_2 act as a voltage divider. The relation between them is $\alpha = R_1/(R_1 + R_2)$, where α is a constant less than 1. Sketch the curve of R_1 versus R_2 (both in ohms), if $\alpha = 1/2$.

22. The arch of a small bridge across a stream is parabolic. If, at water level, the span of the arch is 80 ft, and the maximum height of the span above water level is 20 ft, what is the equation of the arch? Choose the most convenient point for the origin of the coordinate system.

23. At very low temperatures certain metals have an electric resistance of zero. This phenomenon is called superconductivity. A magnetic field also effects the superconductivity. A certain level of magnetic field, the threshold field, is related to the temperature T by

$$\frac{H_T}{H_0} = 1 - \left(\frac{T}{T_0}\right)^2,$$

where H_0 and T_0 are specifically defined values of magnetic field and temperature. Sketch H_T/H_0 versus T/T_0.

24. If a source of light is placed at the focus of a parabolic reflector, the reflected rays are parallel. Where is the focus of a parabolic reflector which is 8 in. across and 6 in. deep?

25. Under certain conditions the work W done on a wire by increasing the tension from T_1 to T_2 is given by $W = k(T_2^2 - T_1^2)$, where k is a constant depending on the properties of the wire. If the work is constant for various sets of initial and final tensions, sketch a graph of T_2 versus T_1.

26. A machine part designer wishes to make a model for an elliptical cam by placing two pins in his design board, putting a loop of string over the pins and marking off the outline by keeping the string taut. (Note that he is using the definition of the ellipse.) If the cam is to measure 10 in. by 6 in., how long should the loop of string be and how far apart should the pins be?

27. The vertical position of a projectile is given by the equation $y = 120t - 16t^2$, and its horizontal position is given by $x = 60t$. By eliminating t, determine the path of the projectile. Sketch this path for the length of time it would need to strike the ground, assuming level terrain.

28. In order to study the relationship between velocity and pressure of a stream of water, a pipe is constructed such that its cross section is a hyperbola. If the pipe is 10 ft long, 1 ft in diameter at the narrow point (middle) and 2 ft in diameter at the ends, what is the equation of the cross-section of the pipe? (In physics it is shown that where the velocity of a fluid is greatest, the pressure is the least.)

29. The inside of the top of an arch is a semi-ellipse with a major axis (width) of 26 ft
and a minor axis of 10 ft. The arch is 7 ft thick at all points. Is the outside of the
arch a portion of an ellipse? (*Hint:* Check the equation of the outer "ellipse" 1 ft
to the right of center.)

30. A 60-ft rope passes over a pulley 10 ft above the ground and an object on the
ground is attached at one end. A man holds the other end at a level of 4 ft above
the ground. If the man walks away from the pulley, express the height of the
object above the ground in terms of the distance the man is from directly below
the object. Sketch the graph of distance vs. height.

31. The earth moves about the sun in an elliptical path. If the closest the earth gets
to the sun is 90.5 million miles, and the farthest it gets from the sun is 93.5 million
miles, find the equation of the path of the earth. The sun is at one focus of the
ellipse.

2 The derivative

2-1 Algebraic functions

In Chapter 1 we discussed a number of equations and their associated graphs. In each case discussed, the equation expressed a relationship between the two variables. If the equation is solved for one of the variables, say y, in terms of the other, x, then we say that y is a *function* of x. Here y is called the *dependent variable* and x is called the *independent variable*.

Example A. The equation of a straight line written in slope-intercept form, $y = mx + b$, expresses y, the dependent variable, as a function of x, the independent variable.

Relationships which can be expressed as functions exist between various quantities in all fields of technology. An experiment to determine whether or not a relationship exists between the distance an object falls and the time of fall should indicate (approximately) that $s = 16t^2$, where s is the distance in feet and t is the time in seconds. Electrical measurements of current and voltage with respect to a particular resistor would show that $V = kI$, where V is the voltage, I is the current, and k is a constant.

Example B. The power developed in a certain resistor by a current I is given by $P = 4I^2$. Here P is a function of I. The dependent variable is P, and the independent variable is I.

As we mentioned in Section 1–1 the rate of change of a quantity is of importance in many physical situations. Since relationships between the appropriate quantities can be expressed as functions, and through differential calculus we can determine the rate of change of a function, we find it necessary to review various operations on functions.

We shall now make our definition of a function more explicit. *Whenever a relationship exists between two sets of numbers, this relationship defines a function.* We shall also mean that for each value of the independent variable there is only one value of the dependent variable. In some references this is called a single-valued function.

There are many ways to express functions. Formulas, such as those mentioned above, define functions. Other ways to express functions are by means of tables, charts, and graphs.

For convenience of notation, the phrase "function of x" is written as $f(x)$. This, in turn, is a simplification of the statement that "y is a function of x," in that we may now write it as $y = f(x)$. One of the most important uses of this notation is to designate the value of the function for a particular value of the independent variable. That is, for the expression "the value of the function $f(x)$ when $x = a$" we may write $f(a)$.

Example C. If $y = 6x^3 - 5x$, we may say that y is a function of x, where the function $f(x)$ is $6x^3 - 5x$. We may also write $f(x) = 6x^3 - 5x$. It is common to write functions in this manner, as well as in the form $y = 6x^3 - 5x$. Also, when $x = -2$, we find that $f(x) = -38$, or $f(-2) = -38$.

FIGURE 2–1

The functional notation $f(x)$ is very useful in another respect. This notation emphasizes the significance of a function. The function itself may be looked upon as a set of instructions. These instructions tell us how to obtain the value of the dependent variable for a particular value of the independent variable, even if this is expressed in symbols. For example, the function $f(x) = x^2 - 3x$ tells us to "square the independent variable x, multiply x by 3, and finally subtract the second result from the first." An analogy would be a machine which was made so that when a number x was fed into the machine, it would square the number and then subtact 3 times the value of the number. In diagram form, this can be represented as in Fig. 2–1.

Numerous functions are restricted as to the values of the independent variable which are permissible. Values of the independent variable which would lead to imaginary values for the function or which lead to division by zero are not included in the permissible values. Also, if the function is related to a physical situation, the values may be restricted due to their physical significance.

Example D. If $f(u) = u/(u - 4)$, this function is not defined if $u = 4$, since this would require division by zero. Therefore the values of u are restricted to values other than 4.

Example E. If the formula in Example B is solved for I, we have $I = \sqrt{P}/2$. In this case the current is a function of the power. This could be stated as $g(P) = \sqrt{P}/2$ (symbols other than f may be used to designate functions). Even though P is the independent variable in this case it is restricted to values greater than or equal to zero. Negative values of P would lead to imaginary values of I. Such values would not have significance either mathematically or from the physical point of view.

The functions which are studied in mathematics fall into two general classes. These are *algebraic functions* and *transcendental functions*. In this chapter we will be concerned with the calculus associated with algebraic functions. Transcendental functions, such as the trigonometric functions and the logarithmic function will be taken up in later chapters.

Algebraic functions are numerous, but those which are of concern to us are: (1) *polynomials*, which are of the form

$$P(x) = a_0 x^n + a_1 x^{n-1} + \cdots + a_{n-1} x + a_n, \qquad (2\text{--}1)$$

where the a's are constants and n is an integer; (2) *rational fractions*, which are of the form

$$F(x) = f(x)/g(x), \qquad (2\text{--}2)$$

where $f(x)$ and $g(x)$ are polynomials; and (3) *irrational functions* of the form

$$I(x) = \sqrt[n]{F(x)}, \qquad (2\text{--}3)$$

which is the root of a rational function. Combinations of these functions may also be encountered.

Since we will be dealing with exponents and radicals, we shall now review their basic properties. We list here the basic laws of exponents:

$$a^m \cdot a^n = a^{m+n}, \qquad (2\text{--}4)$$

$$\frac{a^m}{a^n} = a^{m-n}, \quad a \neq 0, \qquad (2\text{--}5)$$

$$(a^m)^n = a^{mn}, \qquad (2\text{--}6)$$

$$(ab)^n = a^n b^n, \quad \left(\frac{a}{b}\right)^n = \frac{a^n}{b^n} \quad \text{if } b \neq 0, \qquad (2\text{--}7)$$

$$a^0 = 1, \qquad (2\text{--}8)$$

$$a^{-n} = \frac{1}{a^n}. \qquad (2\text{--}9)$$

We shall find it convenient to express radicals in the form of fractional exponents. Therefore we list here the relationship between fractional exponents and radicals along with the basic operations with radicals:

$$a^{m/n} = \sqrt[n]{a^m} \quad (m \text{ and } n \text{ integers}), \tag{2-10}$$

$$\sqrt[n]{a^n} = a, \tag{2-11}$$

$$\sqrt[m]{\sqrt[n]{a}} = \sqrt[mn]{a}, \tag{2-12}$$

$$\sqrt[n]{a} \cdot \sqrt[n]{b} = \sqrt[n]{ab}, \tag{2-13}$$

$$\frac{\sqrt[n]{a}}{\sqrt[n]{b}} = \sqrt[n]{\frac{a}{b}}, \quad b \neq 0. \tag{2-14}$$

The following examples illustrate the use of these laws of exponents and radicals with functions.

Example F. For the function $f(x) = 2x^2 - 1$, we have:

(a) $(2x^2 - 1)^2(2x^2 - 1)^5 = (2x^2 - 1)^{2+5} = (2x^2 - 1)^7$,

(b) $[(2x^2 - 1)^3]^4 = (2x^2 - 1)^{3 \cdot 4} = (2x^2 - 1)^{12}$,

(c) $(2x^2 - 1)^{-2} = 1/(2x^2 - 1)^2$,

(d) $(2x^2 - 1)^{2/3} = \sqrt[3]{(2x^2 - 1)^2}$,

(e) $\sqrt[4]{\sqrt{2x^2 - 1}} = \sqrt[4 \cdot 2]{2x^2 - 1} = \sqrt[8]{2x^2 - 1}$.

Example G. Simplify the expression for the function

$$f(x) = \frac{(3x^2 - 1)^{1/3}(2x) - (2x^3)(3x^2 - 1)^{-2/3}}{(3x^2 - 1)^{2/3}}.$$

By multiplying numerator and denominator of this expression by $(3x^2 - 1)^{2/3}$ (this expression is chosen since it clears the fractional exponents in the numerator) and applying the laws of exponents, we proceed with the simplification:

$$f(x) = \frac{(3x^2 - 1)^{1/3}(2x) - (2x^3)(3x^2 - 1)^{-2/3}}{(3x^2 - 1)^{2/3}} \cdot \frac{(3x^2 - 1)^{2/3}}{(3x^2 - 1)^{2/3}}$$

$$= \frac{(3x^2 - 1)^{1/3}(3x^2 - 1)^{2/3}(2x) - (2x^3)(3x^2 - 1)^{-2/3}(3x^2 - 1)^{2/3}}{[(3x^2 - 1)^{2/3}]^2}$$

$$= \frac{(3x^2 - 1)(2x) - (2x^3)(3x^2 - 1)^0}{(3x^2 - 1)^{4/3}}$$

$$= \frac{6x^3 - 2x - 2x^3}{(3x^2 - 1)^{4/3}} = \frac{4x^3 - 2x}{(3x^2 - 1)^{4/3}}.$$

Algebraic simplifications such as this one are found commonly in calculus problems.

Exercises

1. Find the area of a square as a function of its side s.
2. Find the circumference of a circle as a function of its radius.
3. Find the area of a circle as a function of its diameter.
4. Find the volume of a right circular cone of height 8 as a function of the radius of the base.
5. Find the perimeter of a square as a function of its area.
6. A taxi fare is 55¢ plus 10¢ for every 1/5 mile traveled. Express the fare F as a function of the distance s traveled.
7. The distance s, in feet, traveled by a certain object is related to the time t, in seconds, by the equation $16t^2 = 120t - s$. Express s as a function of t.
8. Given $f(x) = x^2 - 9x$, find $f(3)$, $f(-5)$, and $f(4)$.
9. Given $f(x) = 2x^3 - 7x$, find $f(1)$ and $f(\frac{1}{2})$.
10. Given $f(x) = ax^2 - a^2x$, find $f(a)$ and $f(2a)$.
11. Given $g(x) = 6\sqrt{x} - 3$, find $g(9)$ and $g(a^2)$.
12. Given $\phi(x) = 6x - x^2 + 2x^3$, find $\phi(1)$ and $\phi(-a)$.
13. Given $H(t) = t^4 - t + 3$, find $H(0)$ and $H(-2)$.
14. Given $K(s) = 3s^2 - s + 6$, find $K(2s)$ and $K(s - 1)$.
15. Given $T(t) = 5t + 7$, find $T(-t)$ and $T[T(t)]$.
16. Given $X(f) = \dfrac{f + 5}{1 - f}$, find $X(f - 2)$ and $X[X(-f)]$.

In Exercises 17 through 20 use the functions $F(x) = \sqrt{x - 1}$ and $G(x) = x^2 + 4$.

17. Find $F[G(x)]$.   18. Find $[F(x)]^6$.
19. Find $F(x)/G(x)$.   20. Find $\{G[F(x)]\}^2$.

In Exercises 21 through 24 sketch the graph of the given functions. Algebraically each can be shown to be a familiar form. However, be careful to show only the appropriate portion.

21. $f(x) = 6 - 3x$ 22. $f(x) = 4x^2 - 8$
23. $f(x) = \sqrt{9 - x^2}$ 24. $f(x) = \sqrt{x^2 - 9}$

In Exercises 25 through 30 perform the indicated operations and simplify.

25. $(\sqrt{x - 1})(\sqrt{x^2 + x + 1})$ 26. $\dfrac{(4x - 5)^4}{(4x - 5)^{1/2}}$

27. $(2x + 1)^{1/2} + (x + 3)(2x + 1)^{-1/2}$
28. $(3x - 1)^{-2/3}(1 - x) - (3x - 1)^{1/3}$
29. $\dfrac{(x^2 + 1)^{1/2} - x^2(x^2 + 1)^{-1/2}}{x^2 + 1}$

30. $\dfrac{(1 - 2x^2)^{1/4}(2x) + 4x^3(1 - 2x^2)^{-3/4}}{(1 - 2x^2)^{1/2}}$

31. If $Y(y) = (y + 1)/(y - 1)$, are there any restrictions on the values of the independent variable?

32. If $F(y) = \sqrt{y - 1}$, are there any restrictions on the values of the independent variable?

33. If a 500×10^{-6}-farad capacitor is connected in series with another capacitor C, the combined capacitance as a function of C is

$$C_T = \frac{(500 \times 10^{-6})C}{500 \times 10^{-6} + C}.$$

Is there any restriction on the values of C?

34. The distance s, in feet, that a certain object falls as a function of the time t, in seconds, is given by $s = 16t^2$. Are there any restrictions on the values of t?

35. The voltage of a certain thermocouple as a function of the temperature is given by $E = 2.8T + 0.006T^2$. Find the voltage when the temperature is $T + 100$.

36. The electrical resistance of a certain ammeter as a function of the resistance of the coil of the meter is

$$R = \frac{10R_c}{10 + R_c}.$$

Find the function which represents the resistance of the meter if the resistance of the coil is doubled.

37. A piece of wire 60 in. long is cut into two pieces, one of which is bent into a circle and the other into a square. Express the total area of the two figures as a function of the perimeter of the square.

38. A window is in the form of a rectangle surmounted by a semicircle. If the perimeter of the window is 20 ft, express the area of the window as a function of the vertical side of the rectangle.

39. Express the perimeter of a rectangular field in terms of one of its dimensions if the area of the field is A.

40. The power of an electric circuit varies jointly as the resistance and the square of the current. Given that the power is 10 watts when the current is 0.5 amps and the resistance is 40 ohms, express the power as a function of the current for this 40-ohm resistor.

2-2 Limits

Another important concept for the development of differential calculus is that of a *limit.* Reasoning similar to that which is necessary for establishing the meaning of a limit was encountered when we discussed the asymptotes of a hyperbola. Continuing with this reasoning and using terminology developed there, we now establish the meaning of a limit.

In discussing the asymptotes of a hyperbola, we used the symbol $\rightarrow$, which means "approaches." When we say that $x \rightarrow 5$, we mean that x may take on any value as close to 5 as may be desired, but, at the same time, we distinctly mean that x does *not equal* 5. The sequence of numbers

$$6, 5.1, 5.01, 5.001, \ldots$$

approaches 5, although the number 5 itself will never be included, regardless of the number of terms we write.

Another way of writing the above sequence is to let the nth term be denoted by x_n, where $x_n = 5 + 1/10^n$ and n takes on the values 0, 1, 2, ... We can then see that, as n becomes larger, the difference between x_n and 5 approaches zero. That is, $(x_n - 5) \to 0$ as $n \to \infty$.

This leads us to the meaning of a limit of a function. If, instead of letting $x_n = 5 + 1/10^n$, we say that $f(n) = 5 + 1/10^n$, where $n = 0, 1, 2, \ldots$, then $f(n) \to 5$ as $n \to \infty$, which means that the function approaches 5 as n becomes large without bound. In general, the limit of a function $f(x)$ is that value which the function approaches as x approaches a given value a. Remember, in approaching a, x may get as close as arbitrarily desired to a, although it may not equal a. This is written as

$$\lim_{x \to a} f(x) = L, \tag{2-15}$$

where L is the limiting value of the function.

Example A. Given that $f(x) = 3x + 2$, find $\lim_{x \to 2} f(x)$.

We note that as $x \to 2$, $f(x) \to 8$. Thus $L = 8$, or $\lim_{x \to 2} (3x + 2) = 8$. The value 8 is found by considering values of x as they become very close to 2, *but not equal to* 2. If we consider x taking on the successive values 2.1, 2.01, 2.001, ..., $f(x)$ takes on the values 8.3, 8.03, 8.003, ...

Example B. Find

$$\lim_{x \to \infty} \left(3 + \frac{1}{x^2}\right).$$

As x becomes larger and larger, $1/x^2$ becomes smaller and smaller and approaches zero. This means that $f(x) \to 3$ as $x \to \infty$. Thus

$$\lim_{x \to \infty} \left(3 + \frac{1}{x^2}\right) = 3.$$

Example C. Find

$$\lim_{x \to 2} \left(\frac{x^2 - 4}{x - 2}\right).$$

Since

$$\frac{x^2 - 4}{x - 2} = \frac{(x - 2)(x + 2)}{x - 2} = x + 2$$

is valid as long as $x \neq 2$, we find that

$$\lim_{x \to 2} \left(\frac{x^2 - 4}{x - 2}\right) = \lim_{x \to 2} (x + 2) = 4.$$

We do not have to concern ourselves with the fact that this procedure is not valid for $x = 2$, since in taking the limit, we cannot let $x = 2$. It should be noted that this limit cannot be found by letting $x = 2$ in the original function, since division by 0 would be indicated. The direct substitution would result in $0/0$, which in itself is meaningless. However, when such a form is indicated, it is possible that the limit exists (as it does in this case), and the form $0/0$ is called an *indeterminate form*.

Example D. Find

$$\lim_{x \to \infty} \frac{x^2 + 1}{2x^2 + 3}.$$

We note that as $x \to \infty$ both the numerator and denominator become large without bound. However, if we divide numerator and denominator by x^2, the function becomes

$$\frac{1 + 1/x^2}{2 + 3/x^2}$$

we see that $1/x^2$ and $3/x^2$ both approach zero as $x \to \infty$. This means that the numerator approaches 1 and the denominator approaches 2. Thus

$$\lim_{x \to \infty} \frac{x^2 + 1}{2x^2 + 3} = \frac{1}{2}.$$

Example E. Find $\lim_{x \to 0} (x\sqrt{x - 3})$.

We see that $x\sqrt{x - 3} = 0$ if $x = 0$, but this function does not have real values for values of x less than 3. Therefore, since x cannot approach 0, $f(x)$ does not approach 0 and *the limit does not exist*. The point of this example is that we cannot properly find $\lim_{x \to a} f(x)$ by finding $f(a)$, even though they are equal in many cases. We must consider values of x near a, but not equal to a.

The definition and development of limits presented in this section is not mathematically rigorous. However, the concept of the limit is the principal concern.

Exercises

1. Evaluate the function

$$f(x) = \frac{x^3 - x}{x - 1}$$

for the following values of x: 0, 0.90, 0.99, 1.01, 1.10, 2.00.

2. Evaluate the function

$$f(x) = \frac{9 - (x + 3)^2}{x}$$

for the following values of x: -1.00, -0.10, -0.01, 0.01, 0.10 and 1.00.

In Exercises 3 through 14, evaluate the given limits.

3. $\lim\limits_{x \to 3} (x + 4)$ 4. $\lim\limits_{x \to 5} \left(\dfrac{3}{x^2 + 2}\right)$ 5. $\lim\limits_{x \to 2} \dfrac{x^2 - 1}{x + 1}$

6. $\lim\limits_{x \to \infty} \dfrac{6}{1 + 2/x^2}$ 7. $\lim\limits_{x \to -1} \dfrac{x^2 - 1}{x + 1}$ 8. $\lim\limits_{x \to 2} \dfrac{x^2 - 2x}{x - 2}$

9. $\lim\limits_{x \to 3} \dfrac{x^2 - 2x - 3}{3 - x}$ 10. $\lim\limits_{x \to 0} \dfrac{(2 + x)^2 - 4}{x}$ 11. $\lim\limits_{x \to \infty} \dfrac{3x^2 + 5}{x^2 - 2}$

12. $\lim\limits_{x \to \infty} \dfrac{x - 1}{7x + 4}$ 13. $\lim\limits_{x \to \infty} \dfrac{2x - 6}{x^2 - 9}$ 14. $\lim\limits_{x \to 1} (x - 1)\sqrt{x^2 - 4}$

15. The magnetic field B at the center of a loop of wire due to a current i in the wire is given by $B = ki/r$, where r is the radius of the loop and k is a constant. If $k = 6.3 \times 10^{-7}$ w/amp-m and $r = 0.1$ m, find $\lim_{i \to 0.3} B$ in webers (w).

16. The kinetic energy of a moving object is given by KE $= \frac{1}{2}mv^2$, where m is the mass of the object and v is its velocity. Find $\lim_{v \to 60}$ (KE) for a 50-gm object if the velocity is in units of cm/sec. The kinetic energy will be expressed in ergs.

17. A certain object, after being heated, cools at such a rate that its centigrade temperature T decreases 10% each minute. If the object is originally heated to 100°C find $\lim_{t \to 10} T$ and $\lim_{t \to \infty} T$, where t is the time in minutes.

18. Show that

$$\lim_{x \to 0^+} 2^{1/x} \neq \lim_{x \to 0^-} 2^{1/x},$$

where $\lim_{x \to 0^+}$ means to find the limit as x approaches zero through positive values only, and $\lim_{x \to 0^-}$ means to find the limit as x approaches zero through negative values only.

2–3 The slope of a tangent to a curve

Slope has physical significance
Slope = K constant for straight line

Having developed the basic operations with functions and the concept of a limit, we shall now turn our attention to a graphical interpretation of the rate of change of a function. This interpretation, basic to an understanding of the calculus, deals with the slope of a line tangent to the curve of a function.

Consider the points $P(x_1, y_1)$ and $Q(x_2, y_2)$ in Fig. 2–2. From Chapter 1 we know that the slope of the line through these points is given by

$$m = \frac{y_2 - y_1}{x_2 - x_1}.$$

This, however, represents the slope of the line through P and Q, and no other line. If we now allow Q to be a point closer to P, the slope of PQ will more closely approximate the slope of a line drawn tangent to the curve at P (see Fig. 2–3). In fact, the closer Q is to P, the better this approximation becomes. It is not possible to allow Q to coincide with P, for then it would not be possible to define

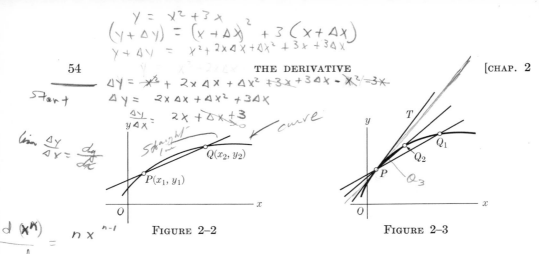

Handwritten annotations around figure:

$y = x^2 + 3x$

$(y + \Delta y) = (x + \Delta x)^2 + 3(x + \Delta x)$

$y + \Delta y = x^2 + 2x\Delta x + \Delta x^2 + 3x + 3\Delta x$

Start

$\lim \dfrac{\Delta y}{\Delta x} = \dfrac{dy}{dx}$

$\Delta y = x^2 + 2x\Delta x + \Delta x^2 + 3x + 3\Delta x - x^2 - 3x$

$\Delta y = 2x\Delta x + \Delta x^2 + 3\Delta x$

$\dfrac{\Delta y}{\Delta x} = 2x + \Delta x + 3$

straight / curve

$Q(x_2, y_2)$

$P(x_1, y_1)$

$\dfrac{d(x^n)}{dx} = n x^{n-1}$

FIGURE 2–2

$\dfrac{d(cx^n)}{dx} = nc x^{n-1}$

$\dfrac{dy}{dx}\Big|_{2/0} = 2x + 3 = (2 \cdot 2) + 3 = 7$

slope = 2

slope = 0

$x = -\dfrac{3}{2}$

FIGURE 2–3

the slope of PQ in terms of two points. The slope of the tangent line, often referred to as the slope of the curve, is the limiting value of the slope of PQ as Q approaches P.

With the proper notation, it is possible to express the coordinates of Q in terms of the coordinates of P. If we define the quantity Δx ("delta" x) by the equation

$$x_2 = x_1 + \Delta x, \tag{2-16}$$

and Δy by the equation

$$y_2 = y_1 + \Delta y, \tag{2-17}$$

the coordinates of Q become $(x_1 + \Delta x, y_1 + \Delta y)$. The quantities Δx and Δy represent the difference in the coordinates of P and Q. They are not to be thought of as "Δ times x," for the symbol Δ, by itself, has no meaning here. The name *increment* is given to the difference of the coordinates of two points, and therefore Δx and Δy are the increments in x and y, respectively.

Using Eqs. (2–16) and (2–17) along with the definition of slope, we can express the slope of PQ as

$$m_{PQ} = \frac{(y_1 + \Delta y) - y_1}{(x_1 + \Delta x) - x_1} = \frac{\Delta y}{\Delta x}. \tag{2-18}$$

By the previous discussion, as Q approaches P, the slope of the tangent line is more nearly approximated by $\Delta y/\Delta x$.

Example A. Find the slope of a line tangent to the curve $y = x^2 + 3x$ at the point $(2, 10)$.

In this example, point P has the coordinates $(2, 10)$. Thus the coordinates of any other point Q can be expressed as $(2 + \Delta x, 10 + \Delta y)$. The slope of PQ then becomes

$$m_{PQ} = \frac{(10 + \Delta y) - 10}{(2 + \Delta x) - 2} = \frac{\Delta y}{\Delta x}.$$

This expression itself does not enable us to find the slope, since values of Δx

and Δy are not known. If, however, we can express Δy in terms of Δx, we might derive more information. Both P and Q are on the curve of the function, which means that the coordinates of each must satisfy the function. Using the co-ordinates of Q, we have

$$(10 + \Delta y) = (2 + \Delta x)^2 + 3(2 + \Delta x) = 4 + 4\,\Delta x + (\Delta x)^2 + 6 + 3\,\Delta x.$$

Subtracting 10 from each side, we have $\Delta y = 7\,\Delta x + (\Delta x)^2$. We then substitute this into the equation for m_{PQ}, which gives us

$$m_{PQ} = \frac{7\,\Delta x + (\Delta x)^2}{\Delta x} = 7 + \Delta x.$$

As P approaches Q, Δx becomes smaller and smaller. The limiting value of Δx is zero. Using this fact, we can see that the slope of the tangent line is

$$m_{\text{tan}} = \lim_{\Delta x \to 0} m_{PQ} = 7.$$

Example B. Find the slope of a line tangent to the curve $y = 4x - x^2$ at the point (x_1, y_1).

The points P and Q are $P(x_1, y_1)$ and $Q(x_1 + \Delta x, y_1 + \Delta y)$. Using the coordinates of Q in the function, we obtain

$$(y_1 + \Delta y) = 4(x_1 + \Delta x) - (x_1 + \Delta x)^2$$
$$= 4x_1 + 4\,\Delta x - x_1^2 - 2x_1\,\Delta x - (\Delta x)^2.$$

Using the coordinates of P, we obtain

$$y_1 = 4x_1 - x_1^2.$$

Subtracting the second of these expressions from the first, in order to solve for Δy, we obtain

$$(y_1 + \Delta y) - y_1 = (4x_1 + 4\,\Delta x - x_1^2 - 2x_1\,\Delta x - (\Delta x)^2) - (4x_1 - x_1^2),$$

or

$$\Delta y = 4\,\Delta x - 2x_1\,\Delta x - (\Delta x)^2.$$

Dividing through by Δx in order to obtain an expression for $\Delta y/\Delta x$, we obtain the result

$$\frac{\Delta y}{\Delta x} = 4 - 2x_1 - \Delta x.$$

In this last equation, the desired expression is on the left, but all we can determine from $\Delta y/\Delta x$ itself is that the ratio will become one very small number divided by another very small number as $\Delta x \to 0$. The right side, however, approaches $4 - 2x_1$ as $\Delta x \to 0$. This indicates that the slope of a tangent at

the point (x_1, y_1) is given by

$$m_{\tan} = 4 - 2x_1.$$ *General expression of a slope of the curve*

The advantage this method has over that of Example A is that we now have a general expression for the slope of a tangent line for any value x_1. If $x_1 = -1$, $m_{\tan} = 6$, or if $x_1 = 3$, $m_{\tan} = -2$. These tangent lines are indicated in Fig. 2–4. *at $x_1 = 1$ $m_{\tan} = 2$ at $x_1 = 2$ $m_{\tan} = 0$*

FIGURE 2–4

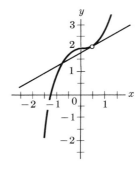

FIGURE 2–5

Example C. Find the expression for the slope of a line tangent to the curve $y = x^3 + 2$ at the general point (x_1, y_1), and by using this expression determine the slope when $x = \frac{1}{2}$.

Using the coordinates of the point $Q(x_1 + \Delta x, y_1 + \Delta y)$ in the function, we obtain

$$y_1 + \Delta y = (x_1 + \Delta x)^3 + 2 = x_1^3 + 3x_1^2 \Delta x + 3x_1 (\Delta x)^2 + (\Delta x)^3 + 2,$$

and using the coordinates of the point $P(x_1, y_1)$, we obtain $y_1 = x_1^3 + 2$. Subtracting this second expression from the first, we have

$$\Delta y = 3x_1^2 \Delta x + 3x_1 (\Delta x)^2 + (\Delta x)^3.$$

Dividing by Δx, we have

$$\frac{\Delta y}{\Delta x} = 3x_1^2 + 3x_1 \Delta x + (\Delta x)^2.$$

As $\Delta x \to 0$, the right side approaches the value $3x_1^2$. This means that

$$m_{\tan} = 3x_1^2.$$

When $x_1 = \frac{1}{2}$, we find that the slope of the tangent is $3(\frac{1}{4}) = \frac{3}{4}$. The curve and this tangent line are indicated in Fig. 2–5.

In interpreting this analysis as the rate of change of a function, we see that if $\Delta x = 1$ and the corresponding value of Δy is found, it can be said that y changes by the amount Δy as x changes one unit. If x changed by some lesser amount, we could still calculate a ratio for the amount of change in y for the given change in x. Therefore, as long as x changes at all, there will be a corresponding change in y. In this way the ratio $\Delta y/\Delta x$ is looked on as the *average* rate of change of y, which is a function of x, with respect to x. As $\Delta x \to 0$ the limit of the ratio $\Delta y/\Delta x$ gives us the *instantaneous* rate of change of y with respect to x.

Exercises

In Exercises 1 through 4, by the method of Example A, calculate the slope of a line tangent to the curve of each of the given functions. Sketch the curves and tangent lines.

1. $y = x^2$ at $(2, 4)$ 2. $y = 2x + 1$ at $(1, 3)$
3. $y = 1 - x^2$ at $(2, -3)$ 4. $y = x^3 + 1$ at $(-1, 0)$

In Exercises 5 through 12, by the method of Example B find a general expression for the slope of a tangent to each of the indicated curves. Then find the slope for the given values of x. Sketch the curves and the tangent lines.

5. $y = x^2$, $x = 2, x = -1$ 6. $y = 3x - 2$, $x = -1, x = 4$
7. $y = 2 - x^2$, $x = -3, x = 2$ 8. $y = 4 - 3x^2$, $x = 0, x = 2$
9. $y = x^2 + 4x + 5$, $x = -3, x = 2$
10. $y = x^3 - 2x$, $x = -1, x = 0, x = 1$
11. $y = 4 - 2x^2$, $x = 1, x = 2, x = 3$
12. $y = 3x - x^3$, $x = -2, x = -1, x = 0, x = 1, x = 2$

2-4 The derivative

Making use of the terminology and techniques developed in the first three sections of this chapter we are now ready to establish here one of the fundamental definitions of calculus. Generalizing on the method of Example B of the preceding section, if we consider that the point $P(x, y)$ is held constant while $Q(x + \Delta x, y + \Delta y)$ approaches it, then both Δx and Δy approach zero. The points P and Q both lie on the curve of the function $f(x)$, which in turn means that the co-ordinates of each point must satisfy the function. For the point P this means that $y = f(x)$, and for the point Q this means that $y + \Delta y = f(x + \Delta x)$. Subtracting the first expression from the second, we have

$$(y + \Delta y) - y = f(x + \Delta x) - f(x)$$

or

$$\Delta y = f(x + \Delta x) - f(x). \tag{2-19}$$

From the discussion of the previous section, we saw that the slope of a line tangent to $f(x)$ at point $P(x, y)$ was found as the limiting value of the ratio $\Delta y/\Delta x$ as Δx approaches zero. Formally, this limiting value of the ratio of $\Delta y/\Delta x$ is known as the *derivative* of the function. Therefore, the derivative of a function $f(x)$ is defined by the relation

$$\lim_{\Delta x \to 0} \frac{\Delta y}{\Delta x} = \lim_{\Delta x \to 0} \frac{f(x + \Delta x) - f(x)}{\Delta x}. \qquad (2\text{-}20)$$

The process of finding the derivative of a function from its definition is called the Δ-process. In general, the process of finding a derivative is called *differentiation*.

Example A. Find the derivative of the function $y = 2x^2 + 3x$ by means of the delta process.

In order to find Δy, we must first derive the quantity $f(x + \Delta x) - f(x)$. Thus we find $y + \Delta y = f(x + \Delta x)$ first:

$$y + \Delta y = 2(x + \Delta x)^2 + 3(x + \Delta x).$$

Then we subtract the original function:

$$y + \Delta y - y = 2(x + \Delta x)^2 + 3(x + \Delta x) - 2x^2 - 3x.$$

Simplifying, we find that the result is

$$\Delta y = 4x\,\Delta x + 2\,(\Delta x)^2 + 3\,\Delta x.$$

Next, dividing through by Δx, we obtain

$$\frac{\Delta y}{\Delta x} = 4x + 2\,\Delta x + 3.$$

When we find the limit as Δx approaches zero, we see that the $2\,\Delta x$ term on the right approaches zero. Thus

$$\lim_{\Delta x \to 0} \frac{\Delta y}{\Delta x} = 4x + 3.$$

Therefore we find that the derivative of the function $y = 2x^2 + 3x$ is the function $4x + 3$. This means that we can calculate the slope of a tangent line for any point on the graph of $y = 2x^2 + 3x$ by substituting the x-coordinate into the expression $4x + 3$. For example, the slope of a tangent line is 7, if $x = 1$.

Example B. Find the derivative of $y = 1/x$ by the Δ-process.

We write

$$y + \Delta y = \frac{1}{x + \Delta x}.$$

Then we find that

$$y + \Delta y - y = \frac{1}{x + \Delta x} - \frac{1}{x},$$

$$\Delta y = \frac{x - (x + \Delta x)}{x(x + \Delta x)} = \frac{-\Delta x}{x(x + \Delta x)};$$

$$\frac{\Delta y}{\Delta x} = \frac{-1}{x(x + \Delta x)},$$

$$\lim_{\Delta x \to 0} \frac{\Delta y}{\Delta x} = \lim_{\Delta x \to 0} \frac{-1}{x(x + \Delta x)},$$

$$\lim_{\Delta x \to 0} \frac{\Delta y}{\Delta x} = \frac{-1}{x^2}.$$

Example C. Find the derivative of $y = x^2 + \dfrac{1}{x + 1}$ by the Δ-process.

$$y + \Delta y = (x + \Delta x)^2 + \frac{1}{x + \Delta x + 1},$$

$$y + \Delta y - y = x^2 + 2x \Delta x + (\Delta x)^2 + \frac{1}{x + \Delta x + 1} - x^2 - \frac{1}{x + 1}.$$

The problem is most easily handled algebraically if the fractions are combined and the other terms are handled separately:

$$\Delta y = 2x \Delta x + (\Delta x)^2 + \frac{1}{x + \Delta x + 1} - \frac{1}{x + 1}$$

$$= 2x \Delta x + (\Delta x)^2 + \frac{(x + 1) - (x + \Delta x + 1)}{(x + \Delta x + 1)(x + 1)}$$

$$= 2x \Delta x + (\Delta x)^2 - \frac{\Delta x}{(x + \Delta x + 1)(x + 1)};$$

$$\frac{\Delta y}{\Delta x} = 2x + \Delta x - \frac{1}{(x + \Delta x + 1)(x + 1)},$$

$$\lim_{\Delta x \to 0} \frac{\Delta y}{\Delta x} = 2x - \frac{1}{(x + 1)^2}.$$

Several shorter notations are used for the derivative. The notation of the definition is clumsy for general use, so the notations

$$y', \quad D_x y, \quad f'(x), \quad \text{and} \quad dy/dx$$

are commonly used. Thus the answer to Example A could have been written as $y' = 4x + 3$, or as $dy/dx = 4x + 3$.

One might ask why, when we are finding a derivative, we take a limit as Δx approaches zero, and do not simply let Δx equal zero. If we did this, the ratio $\Delta y/\Delta x$ would be exactly $0/0$, which would then require division by zero. As we know, this is an undefined operation in mathematics, and therefore Δx cannot *equal* zero. However, it can equal any value just as near zero as necessary. This idea is inherent in the meaning of the word limit.

Example D. Find dy/dx of the function $y = \sqrt{x}$ by the Δ-process.

We shall first square both sides of the equation, thus obtaining $y^2 = x$. Substituting the coordinates of the point $(x + \Delta x, y + \Delta y)$ into this equation, we have

$$(y + \Delta y)^2 = x + \Delta x.$$

Expanding the left side and then subtracting the equation $y^2 = x$, we have

$$(y^2 + 2y\,\Delta y + (\Delta y)^2) - y^2 = (x + \Delta x) - x$$

or

$$2y\,\Delta y + (\Delta y)^2 = \Delta x.$$

Next, dividing through by Δx, we obtain

$$2y\frac{\Delta y}{\Delta x} + \Delta y\frac{\Delta y}{\Delta x} = 1.$$

Solving for $\Delta y/\Delta x$, we have

$$\frac{\Delta y}{\Delta x} = \frac{1}{2y + \Delta y}.$$

Finally, taking the limit as $\Delta x \to 0$, we obtain

$$\lim_{\Delta x \to 0} \frac{\Delta y}{\Delta x} = \lim_{\Delta x \to 0} \frac{1}{2y + \Delta y} = \frac{1}{2y}.$$

The Δy is omitted, since $\Delta y \to 0$ as $\Delta x \to 0$. Now, substituting in the original function, we obtain the final result:

$$\frac{dy}{dx} = \frac{1}{2\sqrt{x}}.$$

Exercises

By using the delta process, find the derivative of each of the functions in Exercises 1 through 15.

1. $y = 3x - 1$ 2. $y = 2 - 5x$ 3. $y = x^2 - 1$
4. $y = 4 - x^2$ 5. $y = x^2 - 7x$ 6. $y = 3x - 5x^2$

7. $y = x^3 + 4x - 6$ 8. $y = 2x - 4x^3$ 9. $y = x + \dfrac{1}{x}$

10. $y = \dfrac{1}{x + 1}$ 11. $y = \dfrac{x}{x - 1}$ 12. $y = \dfrac{2}{3 - x}$

13. $y = x^4 - \dfrac{2}{x}$ 14. $y = \dfrac{2}{x^2}$ 15. $y = x^4 + x^3 + x^2 + x + 1$

By the method of Example D, find dy/dx for the functions given in Exercises 16 through 18.

16. $y = \sqrt{x + 1}$ 17. $y = \sqrt{1 - 3x}$ 18. $y = \sqrt{x^2 + 3}$

2–5 The meaning of the derivative

In Section 2–3, we saw that the slope of a curve was the limiting value of the slope of the line through points P and Q as Q approaches P. At the end of the section, we discussed the idea that $\Delta y/\Delta x$ indicated the rate of change of y with respect to x. In Section 2–4, we defined the limit of the ratio of $\Delta y/\Delta x$ as $\Delta x \to 0$ as the derivative. Thus the derivative is a measure of the rate of change of y with respect to x at point P. However, P may represent any point, which means that the value of the derivative changes from one point on a curve to another point. We therefore interpret the derivative as the *instantaneous* rate of change of y with respect to x.

Example A. In Example A of Section 2–3, y is changing at the rate of 7 units for every change of 1 unit in x, *when x is 2, and only when x is 2.* In Example B of Section 2–3, y is changing 6 units for every change of 1 unit of x *when $x = -1$. When $x = 3$, y is falling 2 units for 1 unit of increase in x.*

If a functional relationship exists between any two variables, then one can be thought of as varying with respect to the other. There are many applications of this principle, one of them being the velocity of an object. We shall consider here the case of rectilinear motion, that is, motion along a straight line.

As we have seen, the velocity of an object is found by dividing the distance traversed by the time required to travel this distance. This, however, gives a value only for the *average velocity* for the specified time interval. If the time interval considered becomes smaller and smaller, then the average velocity which is calculated more nearly approximates the *instantaneous velocity* at some particular time. In the limit, the value of the average velocity gives the value of the instantaneous velocity. Using the symbols as defined for the derivative, the instantaneous velocity of an object moving in rectilinear motion at a particular time t is given by

$$v = \lim_{\Delta t \to 0} \frac{\Delta s}{\Delta t}. \qquad\qquad (2\text{–}21)$$

Example B. Find the velocity of an object for which the distance s (in feet) from some specified point is given by $s = 16t^2$, where t represents time in seconds.

Applying the Δ-process to this function, we can find the derivative of s with respect to t:

$$s + \Delta s = 16(t + \Delta t)^2 = 16t^2 + 32t\,\Delta t + 16\,(\Delta t)^2,$$

$$\Delta s = 32t\,\Delta t + 16\,(\Delta t)^2,$$

$$\frac{\Delta s}{\Delta t} = 32t + 16\,\Delta t,$$

$$v = \lim_{\Delta t \to 0} \frac{\Delta s}{\Delta t} = \frac{ds}{dt} = 32t.$$

If $t = 2$ sec, the velocity is 64 ft/sec. When $t = 4$ sec, the velocity is 128 ft/sec. These velocities are the instantaneous values at the specified times.

By finding $\lim_{\Delta x \to 0} \Delta y / \Delta x$, we can find the instantaneous rate of change of y with respect to x. The expression $\lim_{\Delta t \to 0} \Delta s / \Delta t$ gives the velocity, or instantaneous rate of change of distance with respect to time. Generalizing, we can say that the derivative can be interpreted as giving the instantaneous rate of change of the dependent variable with respect to the independent variable. This is true no matter what the variables represent, so long as a function is defined between the variables.

Example C. Find an expression for the rate of change of the volume of a sphere with respect to its radius.

$$V = \frac{4}{3}\pi r^3, \qquad V + \Delta V = \frac{4\pi}{3}(r + \Delta r)^3$$

$$= \frac{4\pi}{3}[r^3 + 3r^2\,\Delta r + 3r\,(\Delta r)^2 + (\Delta r)^3],$$

$$\Delta V = \frac{4\pi}{3}[3r^2\,\Delta r + 3r\,(\Delta r)^2 + (\Delta r)^3],$$

$$\frac{\Delta V}{\Delta r} = \frac{4\pi}{3}[3r^2 + 3r\,\Delta r + (\Delta r)^2],$$

$$\lim_{\Delta r \to 0} \frac{\Delta V}{\Delta r} = 4\pi r^2.$$

We can see that, as the radius increases, the rate of change of the volume with respect to the radius also increases. This should be expected, since a sphere changing from a radius of 1 to a radius of 2 has an increase in volume from $4\pi/3$ to $32\pi/3$, whereas a change in the radius from 2 to 3 involves a volume increase from $32\pi/3$ to $108\pi/3$.

Example D. The power P produced by an electric current i in a resistor varies directly as the square of the current. Given that 1.2 watts of power are produced by a current of 0.5 amp in a particular resistor, find an expression for the rate of change of power with respect to current.

We must first find the functional relationship between power and current. This we can do by solving the indicated problem in variation:

$$P = ki^2, \quad 1.2 = k(0.5)^2, \quad k = \frac{1.2}{0.25} = \frac{6}{5}(4) = \frac{24}{5} \text{ watts/amp}^2; \quad P = \frac{24}{5}i^2.$$

Now, knowing the function, we may determine the expression for the rate of change of P with respect to i by use of the Δ-process:

$$P + \Delta P = \frac{24}{5}(i + \Delta i)^2 = \frac{24}{5}[i^2 + 2i(\Delta i) + (\Delta i)^2],$$

$$\Delta P = \frac{24}{5}[2i(\Delta i) + (\Delta i)^2],$$

$$\frac{\Delta P}{\Delta i} = \frac{24}{5}(2i + \Delta i),$$

$$\lim_{\Delta i \to 0} \frac{\Delta P}{\Delta i} = \frac{48i}{5}.$$

This last expression tells us that as the current increases, the power changes at a rate of 48 i/5 watts/amp. For example, if the current is 2 amp, the power is changing at the rate of $\frac{96}{5}$ watts/amp. The larger the current, the greater the increase in power. This should be expected, since the power varies as the square of the current.

Exercises

Find the velocity of a particle moving with rectilinear motion according to each of the functions given in Exercises 1 through 5.

1. $s = 1 - 2t^2$
2. $s = 120t - 16t^2$
3. $s = t^3 - 6t + 2$
4. $s = \dfrac{1}{2t + 3}$
5. $s = s_0 + v_0 t - \frac{1}{2}at^2$ (s_0, v_0, and a are constants)

The instantaneous acceleration of an object is defined as the instantaneous rate of change of velocity of the object. In Exercises 6 through 10, find the acceleration if the velocity is indicated by the given functions.

6. $v = 6t^2 - 4t + 2$
7. $v = v_0 - gt$ (v_0 and g are constants)
8. Find the acceleration when an object moves according to the function given in Exercise 1. (Find v first, and then find the acceleration.)

9. Repeat Exercise 8 for the function of Exercise 3.

10. Repeat Exercise 8 for the function of Exercise 5.

11. Find a general expression for the rate of change of the area of a circle with respect to its radius. Then find the instantaneous rate of change of A with respect to r, when $r = 3$.

12. The centripetal acceleration a of an object moving in a circular path of radius r with a velocity v is given by $a = v^2/r$. Find the expression for the instantaneous rate of change of the acceleration with respect to the velocity for an object moving in a circular path of radius 2 ft. The acceleration is in ft/sec^2 and the velocity is in ft/sec.

13. The resistance of a certain resistor as a function of the temperature is given by the relation $R = 50(1 + 0.0053T + 0.00001T^2)$. Determine the instantaneous rate of change of resistance with respect to temperature (in ohms/°C) when the temperature is 20°C.

14. At very low temperatures, near absolute zero, the specific heat c of solids is given by the Debye equation $c = kT^3$, where T is the absolute temperature and k is a constant dependent on the material. Determine the expression for the instantaneous rate of change for the specific heat with respect to temperature. The units of the specific heat are cal/gm-°C and those of T are °C.

15. A 5-ohm resistor and a variable resistor R are placed in parallel. The expression for the resulting resistance R_T is given by $R_T = 5R/(5 + R)$. Determine the instantaneous rate of change of R_T with respect to R, and then evaluate this expression for $R = 8$ ohms.

16. The total energy supplied to an inductor while the current increases from 0 to I is proportional to the square of the current I. If 8 joules are supplied to a certain inductor as the current increases from 0 to 2 amps, evaluate the expression for the instantaneous rate of change of energy with respect to I when $I = 1.5$ amps.

17. The intensity of a light source varies inversely as the square of the distance from the source. Given that the intensity is 25 units at a distance of 200 cm, find the expression for the instantaneous rate of change of intensity with respect to distance. Calculate this rate for distances of 10 cm and 100 cm.

18. The frequency of vibration of a wire varies directly as the square root of the tension on the wire. Find the expression for the instantaneous rate of change of frequency with respect to tension. Find the value of this rate of change for $T = 10^5$ dynes if the frequency is 400/sec when $T = 10^5$ dynes.

19. The volume of a certain right circular cylinder is 100 in^3. Find the expression for the instantaneous rate of change of the total surface area of the cylinder with respect to the radius of the base.

2–6 Derivatives of polynomials

The task of finding the derivative of a function can be considerably shortened from that involved in the direct use of the Δ-process. We can use the Δ-process to derive certain basic formulas for finding derivatives of particular types of functions. These formulas will then be used to find the derivatives. In this section, we shall derive the formulas for finding derivatives of polynomial functions of the form $f(x) = a_0 x^n + a_1 x^{n-1} + \cdots + a_n$.

First we shall find the derivative of a constant. By letting $y = c$, and applying the Δ-process to this function, we can obtain the desired result:

$$y = c; \qquad y + \Delta y = c; \qquad \Delta y = 0, \qquad \frac{\Delta y}{\Delta x} = 0, \qquad \lim_{\Delta x \to 0} \frac{\Delta y}{\Delta x} = 0.$$

From this we conclude that the derivative of a constant is zero. No assumption was made as to the value of the constant, and thus this result holds for all constants. Therefore, if $y = c$, $dy/dx = 0$. This is more commonly written as

$$\frac{dc}{dx} = 0. \qquad\qquad (2\text{--}22)$$

Graphically this means that for any function of the type $y = c$ the slope is always zero. From our knowledge of straight lines, we know that $y = c$ represents a straight line parallel to the x-axis. From the definition of slope, we know that any line parallel to the x-axis has a slope of zero. We can see that the two results are consistent.

Next we shall find the derivative of any integral power of x. If $y = x^n$, where n is an integer, we have the following:

$$(y + \Delta y) = (x + \Delta x)^n$$
$$= x^n + nx^{n-1}\,\Delta x + (\text{a term in } x^{n-2})\,(\Delta x)^2 + \cdots + (\Delta x)^n.$$

(The right-hand side can be verified for any particular case by direct multiplication.) Then we have

$$\Delta y = nx^{n-1}\,\Delta x + (\text{a term in } x^{n-2})(\Delta x)^2 + \cdots + (\Delta x)^n,$$

$$\frac{\Delta y}{\Delta x} = nx^{n-1} + (\text{a term in } x^{n-2})\Delta x + \cdots + (\Delta x)^{n-1},$$

$$\lim_{\Delta x \to 0} \frac{\Delta y}{\Delta x} = nx^{n-1}.$$

Thus the derivative of the nth power of x is found to be

$$\frac{dx^n}{dx} = nx^{n-1}. \qquad\qquad (2\text{--}23)$$

$\dfrac{d\left(cx^n\right)}{dx} = ncx^{n-1}$

Example A. Find the derivative of the function $y = -5$.

Applying the result of Eq. (2--22), we have

$$\frac{d(-5)}{dx} = 0.$$

$\dfrac{d(c)}{dx} = 0$

$\dfrac{d(2.7)}{dx} \qquad y = 2.7x^0$

$\dfrac{dy}{dx} = 0 \times 2.7$

$\dfrac{dy}{dx} = y' = D_x y$

Example B. Find the derivative of the function $y = x$.

Applying the result of Eq. (2–23) (here $n = 1$), we have

$$\frac{d(x)}{dx} = (1)x^{1-1} = 1.$$

Thus the derivative of $y = x$ is 1, which means that the slope of the line $y = x$ is always 1. This is consistent with our previous discussion of the straight line.

Example C. Find the derivative of $y = x^3$.

We find that

$$\frac{d(x^3)}{dx} = 3x^{3-1} = 3x^2.$$

We can see that this result is consistent with results found in the examples and exercises of the previous sections in this chapter.

Example D. Find the derivative of $y = x^{10}$.

We find that

$$\frac{d(x^{10})}{dx} = 10x^{10-1} = 10x^9.$$

Next we shall find the derivative of a constant times a function of x. If $y = cu$, where $u = f(x)$, we have the following result:

$$y + \Delta y = c(u + \Delta u).$$

(As x increases by Δx, u increases by Δu, since u is a function of x.) Then

$$\Delta y = c\,\Delta u, \qquad \frac{\Delta y}{\Delta x} = c\,\frac{\Delta u}{\Delta x}, \qquad \lim_{\Delta x \to 0} \frac{\Delta y}{\Delta x} = c \lim_{\Delta x \to 0} \frac{\Delta u}{\Delta x}.$$

Therefore the derivative of the product of a constant and a function of x is the product of the constant and the derivative of the function of x. This is written as

$$\frac{d(cu)}{dx} = c\,\frac{du}{dx}. \tag{2–24}$$

Example E. Find the derivative of $y = 3x^2$.

In this case $c = 3$ and $u = x^2$. Thus $du/dx = 2x$. Therefore

$$\frac{dy}{dx} = 3(2x) = 6x.$$

Occasionally the derivative of a constant times a function of x is confused with the derivative of a constant (alone). The distinction between a constant multiplying a function and an isolated constant must be made.

Finally, if the types of functions for which we have found derivatives are added, the result is a polynomial function with more than one term. The derivative of such a function is found by letting $y = u + v$, where u and v are functions of x. Applying the Δ-process, we have the following result:

$$y + \Delta y = (u + \Delta u) + (v + \Delta v), \qquad \Delta y = \Delta u + \Delta v,$$

$$\frac{\Delta y}{\Delta x} = \frac{\Delta u}{\Delta x} + \frac{\Delta v}{\Delta x}, \qquad \lim_{\Delta x \to 0} \frac{\Delta y}{\Delta x} = \lim_{\Delta x \to 0} \frac{\Delta u}{\Delta x} + \lim_{\Delta x \to 0} \frac{\Delta v}{\Delta x}.$$

This tells us that the derivative of the sum of functions of x is the sum of the derivatives of the functions. This is written as

$$\frac{d(u + v)}{dx} = \frac{du}{dx} + \frac{dv}{dx}. \tag{2–25}$$

Example F. Find the derivative of $y = 4x^2 + 5$.

Here $u = 4x^2$ and $v = 5$. Thus $du/dx = 8x$ and $dv/dx = 0$. Hence we have $dy/dx = 8x$.

Example G. Find the derivative of $y = 5x^6 - 2x^3 - x + 7$.

$$\frac{dy}{dx} = \frac{d(5x^6)}{dx} - \frac{d(2x^3)}{dx} - \frac{dx}{dx} + \frac{d7}{dx} = 30x^5 - 6x^2 - 1.$$

Example H. Find the slope of a line tangent to the curve of the function $y = 4x^7 - x^4$ at the point $(1, 3)$.

We must find, and then evaluate, the derivative of the function for the value $x = 1$:

$$\frac{dy}{dx} = 28x^6 - 4x^3.$$

For evaluating this, we write

$$\left. \frac{dy}{dx} \right|_{x=1} = 28(1) - 4(1) = 24.$$

Thus the slope of the tangent line is 24.

Exercises

In Exercises 1 through 8, find the derivative of each of the given functions.

1. $y = x^4 - 6$
2. $y = 3x^5$
3. $y = 5x^3 - x - 1$
4. $y = 6x^2 - 6x + 5$
5. $y = x^8 - 4x^7 - x$
6. $y = 4x^4 - 2x + 9$

7. $y = \frac{1}{3}x^3 + \frac{1}{2}x^2$ 8. $y = \frac{1}{4}x^8 - \frac{1}{2}x^4 - \sqrt{3}$

In Exercises 9 and 10, evaluate the derivative of each of the given functions for the indicated value of x.

9. $y = 2x^6 - 6x^2$ $(x = 2)$ 10. $y = 3x^3 - 9x$ $(x = 1)$

If s represents distance in terms of time t, find an expression for the velocity for objects moving according to the functions given in Exercises 11 through 14.

11. $s = 6t^5 - 5t + 2$ 12. $s = 4t^2 - 7t$

13. $s = 120t - 16t^2$ 14. $s = s_0 + v_0 t + \frac{1}{2}at^2$

15. Find the slope of the curve $y = 4x^3 - x$ for the value $x = 3$.

16. Where is a tangent to the curve $y = 3x^2 - 6x$ parallel to the x-axis? (That is, where is the slope zero?)

17. If the radius of a right circular cylinder always equals its height, find an expression for the rate of change of volume with respect to the radius.

18. If the length of a pillar is constant, the crushing load varies as the fourth power of its radius. If 18 tons will crush a certain pillar 5 in. in radius, find an expression which gives the rate of change of crushing load with respect to a change in radius.

19. The voltage V produced by a certain thermocouple as a function of the temperature T is given by $V = 4.0T + 0.005T^2$. If the temperature changes slowly, find the rate of change of voltage with respect to temperature when the temperature is 200°C.

20. The ends of a 10-ft beam are supported at different levels. The deflection y of the beam is given by $y = kx^2(x^3 + 450x - 3500)$, where x is the horizontal distance from one end and k is a constant. Determine the expression for the instantaneous rate of change of deflection with respect to x.

2–7 Derivatives of products and quotients of functions

The formulas developed in the previous section are valid for polynomial functions. However, many functions are not polynomial in form. Some functions can best be expressed as the product of two or more simpler functions, others are the quotient of two simpler functions, and some are expressed as powers of a function. In this section, we shall develop formulas for the derivative of a product of functions and for the derivative of the quotient of two functions.

Example A. The functions $f(x) = x^2 + 2$ and $g(x) = 3 - 2x$ can be combined to form new functions which represent the types mentioned above. For example, the function $p(x) = f(x)g(x) = (x^2 + 2)(3 - 2x)$ is an example of a function expressed as the product of two simpler functions. The function

$$q(x) = \frac{g(x)}{f(x)} = \frac{3 - 2x}{x^2 + 2}$$

is an example of a rational fraction which is the quotient of two other functions.

The function $F(x) = (g(x))^3 = (3 - 2x)^3$ is an example of a power of a function.

If u and v both represent functions of x, the derivative of the product of u and v is found by applying the Δ-process. This leads to the following result:

$$y = u \cdot v, \qquad y + \Delta y = (u + \Delta u)(v + \Delta v).$$

(Since u and v are functions of x, each has an increment corresponding to an increment in x.) Then we have

$$\Delta y = u\, \Delta v + v\, \Delta u + \Delta u\, \Delta v,$$

$$\frac{\Delta y}{\Delta x} = u \frac{\Delta v}{\Delta x} + v \frac{\Delta u}{\Delta x} + \Delta u \frac{\Delta v}{\Delta x},$$

$$\lim_{\Delta x \to 0} \frac{\Delta y}{\Delta x} = u \lim_{\Delta x \to 0} \frac{\Delta v}{\Delta x} + v \lim_{\Delta x \to 0} \frac{\Delta u}{\Delta x} + \lim_{\Delta x \to 0} \left(\Delta u \frac{\Delta v}{\Delta x} \right).$$

(The functions u and v are not affected by Δx approaching zero, but Δu and Δv both approach zero as Δx approaches 0.) Thus

$$\frac{dy}{dx} = u \frac{dv}{dx} + v \frac{du}{dx} + 0 \frac{dv}{dx}.$$

We conclude that the derivative of the product of two functions equals the first function times the derivative of the second function plus the second function times the derivative of the first function. This is written as

$$\frac{d(uv)}{dx} = u \frac{dv}{dx} + v \frac{du}{dx}. \qquad (2\text{-}26)$$

Example B. For the product function in Example A, the derivative is found as follows:

$$y = (x^2 + 2)(3 - 2x), \qquad u = x^2 + 2, \qquad v = 3 - 2x,$$

$$\frac{dy}{dx} = (x^2 + 2)(-2) + (3 - 2x)(2x) = -2x^2 - 4 + 6x - 4x^2$$

$$= -6x^2 + 6x - 4.$$

Example C. Find the derivative of the function $y = (3 - x - 2x^2)(x^4 - x)$.

In this problem, $u = 3 - x - 2x^2$ and $v = x^4 - x$. Hence

$$\frac{dy}{dx} = (3 - x - 2x^2)(4x^3 - 1) + (x^4 - x)(-1 - 4x)$$

$$= 12x^3 - 3 - 4x^4 + x - 8x^5 + 2x^2 - x^4 - 4x^5 + x + 4x^2$$

$$= -12x^5 - 5x^4 + 12x^3 + 6x^2 + 2x - 3.$$

In both these examples, we could have multiplied the functions first, and then taken the derivative as a polynomial. However, we shall soon meet functions for which this latter method would not be applicable.

We shall now find the derivative of the quotient of two functions. We apply the Δ-process to the function $y = u/v$, and obtain the result as follows:

$$y + \Delta y = \frac{u + \Delta u}{v + \Delta v}, \qquad \Delta y = \frac{u + \Delta u}{v + \Delta v} - \frac{u}{v} = \frac{vu + v\,\Delta u - uv - u\,\Delta v}{v(v + \Delta v)},$$

$$\frac{\Delta y}{\Delta x} = \frac{v\,(\Delta u/\Delta x) - u\,(\Delta v/\Delta x)}{v(v + \Delta v)},$$

$$\lim_{\Delta x \to 0} \frac{\Delta y}{\Delta x} = \frac{v\,\lim_{\Delta x \to 0}(\Delta u/\Delta x) - u\,\lim_{\Delta x \to 0}(\Delta v/\Delta x)}{\lim_{\Delta x \to 0} v(v + \Delta v)}.$$

Thus

$$\frac{dy}{dx} = \frac{v\,(du/dx) - u\,(dv/dx)}{v^2}.$$

This last result says that the derivative of the quotient of two functions equals the denominator times the derivative of the numerator minus the numerator times the derivative of the denominator, all divided by the square of the denominator. This is written as

$$\frac{d\,\dfrac{u}{v}}{dx} = \frac{v\,\dfrac{du}{dx} - u\,\dfrac{dv}{dx}}{v^2}. \tag{2--27}$$

Example D. Find the derivative of the quotient indicated in Example A.

$$y = \frac{3 - 2x}{x^2 + 2}, \qquad u = 3 - 2x, \qquad v = x^2 + 2,$$

$$\frac{dy}{dx} = \frac{(x^2 + 2)(-2) - (3 - 2x)(2x)}{(x^2 + 2)^2} = \frac{-2x^2 - 4 - 6x + 4x^2}{(x^2 + 2)^2}$$

$$= \frac{2(x^2 - 3x - 2)}{(x^2 + 2)^2}.$$

Example E. Find the derivative of $y = \dfrac{x^3 - x - 1}{1 - 2x^2}$.

$$\frac{dy}{dx} = \frac{(1 - 2x^2)(3x^2 - 1) - (x^3 - x - 1)(-4x)}{(1 - 2x^2)^2}$$

$$= \frac{3x^2 - 1 - 6x^4 + 2x^2 + 4x^4 - 4x^2 - 4x}{(1 - 2x^2)^2} = \frac{-2x^4 + x^2 - 4x - 1}{(1 - 2x^2)^2}.$$

Exercises

In Exercises 1 through 12, find the derivative of each of the given functions.

1. $y = x^2(2 + 3x)$ use $\dfrac{d(uv)}{dx} = u\dfrac{dv}{dx} + v\dfrac{du}{dx}$

[Use Eq. (2–26), and then check by multiplying out, treating the function as a polynomial.]

2. $y = (x^3 - 6x)(2 - 4x^3)$ (Same instructions as for Exercise 1.)

3. $y = (x^4 - 3x^2 + 3)(1 - 2x^3)$ (Same instructions as for Exercise 1.)

4. $y = \dfrac{x}{x + 1}$

5. $y = \dfrac{1}{x^2 + 1}$

6. $y = \dfrac{x + 2}{x + 3}$

7. $y = \dfrac{x^2}{3 - 2x}$

8. $y = \dfrac{x + 8}{x^2 + x + 2}$

9. $y = \dfrac{3}{4x^5 - 3x - 4}$

10. $y = \dfrac{x^2(1 - 2x)}{3x - 7}$

(Do not multiply out numerator before taking the derivative. Treat numerator as a product.)

11. $y = 4x^2 - \dfrac{1}{x - 1}$ (Do not combine before taking the derivative.)

12. Repeat Exercise 11, combining fractions before taking the derivative.

13. If the distance traveled by a particle in a given time is found from the expression $s = 2/t^2$, find the velocity after 4 sec. (Use the quotient rule.)

14. Find the slope of a line tangent to the curve of the function $y = (x + 4)/(1 - 2x)$ at the point $(2, -2)$.

15. For what value(s) of x is the slope of a tangent to the curve $y = x/(x^2 + 1)$ equal to zero?

16. Determine the sign of the derivative of the function $y = (2x - 1)/(1 - x^2)$ for the following values of x: $-2, -1, 0, 1, 2$. Is the slope of a tangent to this curve ever negative?

17. The voltage across a resistor in an electric circuit is the product of the resistance and the current. If the current I, in amperes, varies with time, in seconds, according to the relation $I = 5.00 + 0.01t^2$, and the resistance varies with time according to the relation $R = 15.00 - 0.10t$, find the time rate of change of the voltage when $t = 5$ sec.

18. In thermodynamics, an equation relating pressure p, volume V and temperature T is $(p + a/V^2)(V - b) = RT$, where a, b, and R are constants. This equation is known as the van der Waals equation. Solve this equation for p, and then find the expression for the rate of change of p with respect to V, assuming a constant temperature.

19. The electrical power produced by a certain source is given by

$$P = \dfrac{E^2 r}{R^2 + 2Rr + r^2},$$

where E is the voltage of the source, R is the resistance of the source and r is the resistance in the circuit. Find the expression for the rate of change of power with respect to the resistance in the circuit, assuming that the other quantities remain constant.

20. In the study of simple harmonic motion, under certain conditions the tangent of the angle by which the displacement lags the impress force is given by

$$\tan \varphi = \frac{30\omega}{600 - \omega^2},$$

where ω, in $\sec^{-1}$, is the frequency of vibration. Find the rate of change of $\tan \varphi$ with respect to ω when $\omega = 3 \sec^{-1}$.

2–8 The derivative of a power of a function

In Example A of Section 2–7, a power of a function was illustrated. To find the derivative of that particular function, the expression could be multiplied out, and then treated as a polynomial. However, there are a great many functions for which this would not work. The function $\sqrt{x^2 + 1}$ is one example. This is a power of a function, for it is required to take the square root (the one-half power) of the function $x^2 + 1$. Thus we find it necessary to find a formula for the derivative of a power of a function.

By using the Δ-process on the function $y = u^n$, where u is a function of x, we derive the desired formula. We write

$$y = u^n;$$

$$y + \Delta y = (u + \Delta u)^n$$

$$= u^n + nu^{n-1}\,\Delta u + (\text{term in } u^{n-2})(\Delta u)^2 + \cdots + (\Delta u)^n;$$

$$\Delta y = nu^{n-1}\,\Delta u + (\text{term in } u^{n-2})(\Delta u)^2 + \cdots + (\Delta u)^n,$$

$$\frac{\Delta y}{\Delta x} = nu^{n-1}\left(\frac{\Delta u}{\Delta x}\right) + (\text{term in } u^{n-2})(\Delta u)\left(\frac{\Delta u}{\Delta x}\right) + \cdots + (\Delta u)^{n-1}\left(\frac{\Delta u}{\Delta x}\right).$$

Now, taking the limit as $\Delta x \to 0$, we find that all terms on the right side, except the first, go to zero, due to the presence of the Δu's. Thus we have

$$\lim_{\Delta x \to 0} \frac{\Delta y}{\Delta x} = nu^{n-1} \lim_{\Delta x \to 0} \frac{\Delta u}{\Delta x}.$$

The derivative of a power of a function is found by multiplying the function by the exponent, subtracting 1 from the exponent, and *multiplying by the derivative of the function*. (Students often mistake the power of a function for the power of x. We must include the factor du/dx when we are taking the derivative.) We write this as

$$\frac{du^n}{dx} = nu^{n-1}\left(\frac{du}{dx}\right). \tag{2-28}$$

Example A. Find the derivative of $y = (1 - 3x^2)^4$.
In this example, $n = 4$ and $u = 1 - 3x^2$. Hence

$$\frac{dy}{dx} = 4(1 - 3x^2)^3(-6x) = -24x(1 - 3x^2)^3.$$

(We must not forget the $-6x$.)

Example B. Find the derivative of

$$y = \frac{(3x - 1)^3}{1 - x}.$$

Here we must use the quotient rule, in combination with the power rule. We find the derivative of the numerator by using the power rule.

$$\frac{dy}{dx} = \frac{(1 - x)3(3x - 1)^2(3) - (3x - 1)^3(-1)}{(1 - x)^2}$$

$$= \frac{(3x - 1)^2(9 - 9x + 3x - 1)}{(1 - x)^2} = \frac{(3x - 1)^2(8 - 6x)}{(1 - x)^2}$$

$$= \frac{2(3x - 1)^2(4 - 3x)}{(1 - x)^2}.$$

It is normally much better to have the derivative in a factored, simplified form, since this is the only form from which useful information may readily be obtained. In this form we can determine where the derivative is undefined (denominator equal to zero) or where the slope is zero (numerator equal to zero); we can also make other required analyses of the derivative. Thus all derivatives should be simplified.

The power rule [Eq. (2–28)] makes it possible to find derivatives of powers of y, as well as functions in terms of x. Direct application of the rule gives the desired result.

Example C. Find the derivative of the function $y^3 = (x^2 - 1)^2$.
Rather than solving directly for y, we find the derivative of this function (which is called an implicit function, since the direct solution for y is not explicitly stated, but only implied) by first taking derivatives of each side, then solving for dy/dx. Applying the power rule to y^3, we have

$$\frac{d(y^3)}{dx} = 3y^2\left(\frac{dy}{dx}\right).$$

Note that the derivative dy/dx appears as a result of finding the factor du/dx, since in this case $u = y$. Thus we have

$$3y^2 \left(\frac{dy}{dx}\right) = 2(x^2 - 1)(2x) = 4x(x^2 - 1),$$

$$\frac{dy}{dx} = \frac{4x(x^2 - 1)}{3y^2}.$$

In this form, the derivative contains both x and y. If possible, the original function should be solved for y, and this expression should then be substituted into the expression for the derivative. In this example, $y^2 = (x^2 - 1)^{4/3}$, which is found by taking the $\frac{2}{3}$ power of each side of the function. Thus

$$\frac{dy}{dx} = \frac{4x(x^2 - 1)}{3(x^2 - 1)^{4/3}} = \frac{4x}{3(x^2 - 1)^{1/3}}.$$

So far, we have derived the formulas for the derivatives of powers of x and for functions of x for integral powers. We shall now establish that these formulas are also valid for any rational number used as an exponent. If $y = u^{p/q}$, and if each side is raised to the qth power, we have $y^q = u^p$. Applying the power rule to each side of this equation, we have

$$qy^{q-1}\left(\frac{dy}{dx}\right) = pu^{p-1}\left(\frac{du}{dx}\right).$$

Solving for dy/dx, we have

$$\frac{dy}{dx} = \frac{pu^{p-1}\,(du/dx)}{qy^{q-1}} = \frac{p}{q}\frac{u^{p-1}}{(u^{p/q})^{q-1}}\frac{du}{dx} = \frac{p}{q}\frac{u^{p-1}}{u^{p-p/q}}\frac{du}{dx} = \frac{p}{q}u^{p-1-p+(p/q)}\frac{du}{dx}.$$

Thus

$$\frac{dy}{dx} = \frac{p}{q}u^{(p/q)-1}\frac{du}{dx}.$$

We see that in finding the derivative we multiply the function by the rational exponent and subtract 1 from it to find the exponent of the function in the derivative. This, of course, is the same rule derived for integral exponents. Since the only restriction on the values of p and q is that they are integers ($q \neq 0$), the power rule can be used for all rational exponents, positive and negative.

Example D. We can now find the derivative of $y = \sqrt{x^2 + 1}$, a function mentioned at the beginning of this section. Writing the square root as the fractional exponent $\frac{1}{2}$, we can easily derive the result:

$$y = (x^2 + 1)^{1/2}, \qquad \frac{dy}{dx} = \frac{1}{2}(x^2 + 1)^{-1/2}(2x) = \frac{x}{(x^2 + 1)^{1/2}}.$$

In order not to introduce apparently significant factors into the numerator, we do not usually rationalize such fractions.

Example E. Find the derivative of

$$y = \frac{1}{(1 - 4x)^2}.$$

We can handle this more easily by direct use of the power rule, rather than the quotient rule. By writing the function as $y = (1 - 4x)^{-2}$, we can easily find the derivative:

$$\frac{dy}{dx} = (-2)(1 - 4x)^{-3}(-4) = \frac{8}{(1 - 4x)^3}.$$

(Remember, subtracting 1 from -2 gives -3.)

We can now see the value of fractional exponents in calculus. They are useful in algebraic operations, but are almost essential in calculus. Without fractional exponents, it would be necessary to develop more formulas to find derivatives of radicals. To find the derivative of an algebraic function, we need only use those equations which we have already developed. Often it is necessary to combine these, as we saw in Example B. Actually, most derivatives are combinations. It is the problem of the person finding the derivative to recognize the form of the function with which he is dealing. When he has recognized the form, completing the problem is only a matter of mechanics and algebra. The reader should now see the importance of being able to handle algebraic operations with facility.

Example F. Find the derivative of

$$y^2 = \frac{x}{\sqrt{1 - 4x}}.$$

The left side is a power of y, which means that we must use the power rule to find its derivative. The right side is a quotient, but in order to find the derivative of this quotient, we must again use the power rule (and a derivative of a polynomial form). With sufficient practice in taking derivatives, we can achieve these recognitions almost automatically. Thus we find the derivative:

$$2y \frac{dy}{dx} = \frac{(1 - 4x)^{1/2}(1) - x(\tfrac{1}{2})(1 - 4x)^{-1/2}(-4)}{1 - 4x}$$

$$= \frac{[(1 - 4x) + 2x]/(1 - 4x)^{1/2}}{1 - 4x} = \frac{1 - 2x}{(1 - 4x)^{3/2}}.$$

Substituting $\pm[x^{1/2}/(1 - 4x)^{1/4}]$ for y, we have

$$\frac{dy}{dx} = \frac{(1 - 2x)/(1 - 4x)^{3/2}}{\pm 2x^{1/2}/(1 - 4x)^{1/4}} = \pm \frac{1 - 2x}{2x^{1/2}(1 - 4x)^{5/4}}.$$

Exercises

In Exercises 1 through 17, find the derivative of each of the given functions.

1. $y = (x^2 + 1)^5$ 2. $y = (1 - 2x)^4$ 3. $y = \sqrt{x}$

4. $y = x\sqrt{x}$ 5. $y = \dfrac{1}{x^2}$ 6. $y = \dfrac{1}{\sqrt{x}}$

7. $y = x^2\sqrt{x} - \dfrac{1}{x}$ 8. $y = (1 - 6x)^{3/2}$ 9. $y = 2x^{-3} - x^{-1}$

10. $y = \dfrac{1}{\sqrt{1 - x}}$ 11. $y = \dfrac{1}{(1 - x^2)^4}$ 12. $y = x\sqrt{x - 1}$

13. $y = \sqrt[4]{1 - 8x^2}$ 14. $y = \dfrac{x\sqrt{x - 1}}{2x + 1}$ 15. $y^2 = x^2 - 1$

16. $y^2 + y = x^2 - 4$ (Express answer in x and y.)

17. $y^2x - x^2y = 2$ (Treat y^2x and x^2y as products.)

18. Find the velocity at $t = 4$, given that the distance in terms of the time for a particular object is $s = (t^3 - t)^{4/3}$.

19. Find the slope of a line tangent to the parabola $y^2 = 4x$ at the point $(1, 2)$.

20. Find the slope of a tangent to the circle $x^2 + y^2 = 25$ at the point $(4, 3)$.

21. Find any values of x for which the derivative of $y = x/\sqrt{4x - 1}$ is zero.

22. The period of a pendulum is directly proportional to the square root of its length. Find the derivative of the period with respect to the length for a pendulum 2 ft long which has a period of $\pi/2$ sec.

23. When the volume of a gas changes very rapidly, an approximate relation is that the pressure varies inversely as the $\frac{3}{2}$ power of the volume. If P is 3 atm when $V = 100$ cm^3, find the derivative of P with respect to V. Evaluate this derivative for $V = 100$ cm^3.

24. Under certain conditions, the velocity of an object moving with simple harmonic motion is given by $v = k\sqrt{A^2 - x^2}$, where x is the x-coordinate of the position of the object, A is the amplitude and k is a constant. Find the derivative of v with respect to x.

25. Under certain conditions, due to the presence of a charge q, the electric potential V along a line is given by $V = kq/\sqrt{x^2 + b^2}$, where k is a constant and b is the minimum distance from the charge to the line. Find the expression for the rate of change of V with respect to x.

26. The current in a circuit containing a resistance R and an inductance L is found from the expression $I = V/\sqrt{R^2 + (\omega L)^2}$. Find the expression for the rate of change of current with respect to L, assuming that the other quantities remain constant.

27. The magnetic field H due to a magnet of length l at a distance r is given by

$$H = \frac{k}{[r^2 + (l/2)^2]^{3/2}},$$

where k is a constant for a given magnet. Find the expression for the derivative of H with respect to r.

28. Under certain circumstances the velocity of a water wave is given by

$$v = \sqrt{a/\lambda + b\lambda},$$

where λ is the wavelength and a and b are constants. Find the derivative of v with respect to λ.

2–9 Graphical differentiation

In the previous sections of this chapter we developed certain important formulas by which we can differentiate (find the derivative of) the algebraic functions described in Section 2–1. Also, as we mentioned in that section, we

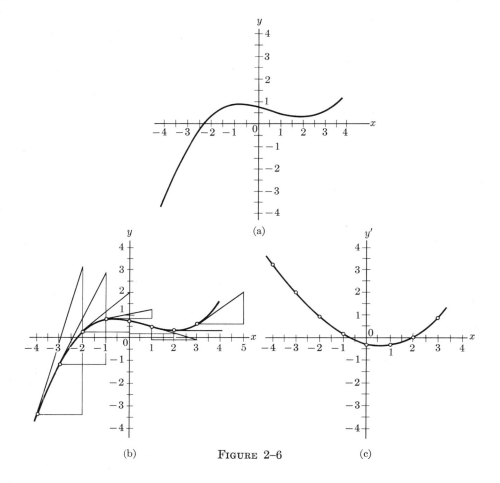

FIGURE 2–6

will take up the derivatives of certain important transcendental functions in later chapters. However, these formulas can be used only when we know the equation relating the variables. Often empirical data may be known, but the exact equation is not known. Under these circumstances it is possible to plot the graph and then use techniques based on the definition of the derivative to obtain values of the rate of change of one variable with respect to the other. Such methods are referred to as *graphical differentiation*. In this section one of the principal methods of graphical differentiation will be developed.

First, by means of the following example, we shall show how the interpretation of the derivative as the slope of a tangent line can be used to obtain the graph of a derivative of a given curve of a function.

Example A. Determine the graph of the derivative of the function whose graph is shown in Fig. 2–6(a).

x	Δy	$\dfrac{\Delta y}{\Delta x} = y'$
−4	$3.0 - (-3.4) = 6.4$	3.2
−3	$2.8 - (-1.2) = 4.0$	2.0
−2	$2.0 - 0.2 = 1.8$	0.9
−1	$1.2 - 0.8 = 0.4$	0.2
0	$0.1 - 0.7 = -0.6$	−0.3
1	$-0.1 - 0.5 = -0.6$	−0.3
2	$0.3 - 0.3 = 0$	0
3	$2.2 - 0.6 = 1.6$	0.8

First draw tangent lines (this must be done carefully) at various points along the curve. Then draw a triangle for each with the tangent line along the hypotenuse and sides parallel to each of the axes. Then measure the length of these sides to calculate $\Delta y/\Delta x$ for each tangent line. In Fig. 2–6(b) tangent lines have been drawn at each of the points where x is an integer. Triangles have been constructed such that Δx is 2 in each case. This is done for convenience of calculation. In this way the following table is constructed, and then used to plot the graph of y' vs. x in Fig. 2–6(c), which is the desired curve.

Example A demonstrates how a derivative curve can be found from the definition of the derivative. It is possible to modify this method by eliminating the actual calculation of $\Delta y/\Delta x$ and make the method a completely graphical one. Example B demonstrates the method for a curve which exists only for positive x-values. This is done so that the method may be followed easily in the figure. Also, most physical problems involve only positive values for the variables involved, particularly the independent variable.

Example B. Determine the graph of the derivative of the function, curve F, given in Fig. 2–7.

Tangent lines have been drawn to the given curve F at the points where x is integral. Here, the only thing which matters is that enough points are picked. Then a point on the negative x-axis is chosen and called the *pole*. In Fig. 2–7, the point where $x = -2$ is chosen. Next, lines parallel to each of the tangent lines are drawn through the pole until they cross the y-axis. A line is then drawn through this y-intercept, of each line from the pole, parallel to the x-axis until it crosses a line through the point on curve F drawn parallel to the y-axis. This point of intersection is a point on the curve D of the derivative.

Since the lines through the pole are parallel to the tangent lines, they have the same slopes. The slopes of the lines through the pole are the values of the y-intercept divided by the absolute value of the x-value of the pole. In this case, by dividing each y-intercept by 2, we have the proper values of the slopes. This scale for curve D is indicated at the right of Fig. 2–7. Thus, the derivative curve D is drawn through the derived points.

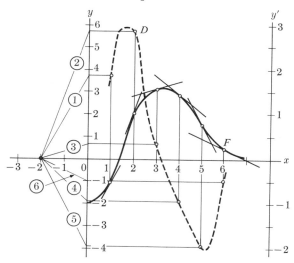

FIGURE 2–7

A final example will now be given to show the use of graphical differentiation of a curve found from empirical data.

Example C. An experiment which measured plate current i (in milliamperes) and plate voltage e (in volts) for a certain vacuum tube under specified conditions gave the following results.

i	0	5	13	26	52	90
e	250	275	300	325	350	375

FIGURE 2-8

Plot plate current vs. plate voltage and then determine the derivative curve. From this curve find the rate of change of i with respect to e when e is 360 volts.

Plotting the curve of i vs. e and then following the method of Example B, the solution is indicated in Fig. 2-8. The value of the derivative for $e = 360$ volts is read directly from the derivative curve and gives the desired result, 1.45 ma/volt, for the rate of change of i with respect to e. Note that the pole is 50 units to the left of the i-axis.

Exercises

By the method of Example A, find the derivative curve for the curves of Exercises 1 and 2.

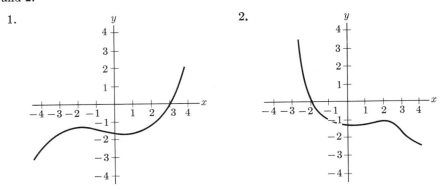

1.   2.

In Exercises 3 and 4, (a) sketch the graph of the given equation and then determine its derivative curve by means of the method of Example B, (b) find the derivative directly by formulas of the previous sections and then sketch the graph of the derivative, and (c) compare the results of (a) and (b). Use only positive values of x.

3. $y = x^2 - 4x$ 4. $y = 4/x$

In Exercises 5 and 6, the distance s is given as a function of the time t. Repeat the instructions for Exercises 3 and 4, noting that the derivative curve represents the velocity. The distance is in feet and the time is in seconds.

5. $s = t - t^3/3$ 6. $s = 60t - 16t^2$

In Exercises 7 through 12 use the method of Example B to find the derivative curve of the given sets of empirical data. In Exercises 10 through 12 evaluate the derivative for the indicated value.

7. The power P (in watts) measured as a function of the load resistance R (in ohms) for a certain electric circuit give the following results:

P	50.0	44.4	32.0	24.5	19.8	16.5	9.1
R	0.5	1.0	2.0	3.0	4.0	5.0	10.0

8. The vapor pressure (in atm) of ethane gas as a function of temperature (in °C) was measured as follows:

Pressure	2.6	3.8	5.6	7.8	10.5	14.1	18.2	23.6	32.3
Temperature	−70	−60	−50	−40	−30	−20	−10	0	15

9. The density (in gm/cm³) of water from 0°C to 10°C is given in the following table:

Density	0.99985	0.99990	0.99994	0.99996	0.99997	0.99996
Temperature	0	1	2	3	4	5

Density	0.99994	0.99990	0.99985	0.99978	0.99969
Temperature	6	7	8	9	10

10. The voltage (in volts) across a certain portion of an electric circuit as a function of time (in milliseconds) was measured as follows:

Voltage	0	110	160	180	195	200
Time	0	4	8	12	16	20

Evaluate dv/dt for $t = 15$ milliseconds.

11. The force (in pounds) applied to an object in a certain experiment as a function of time (in seconds) was measured as follows:

Force	6.0	6.0	6.0	4.6	3.7	3.0	2.5	2.1	1.8	1.6	1.5
Time	0	1	2	3	4	5	6	7	8	9	10

Evaluate the time rate of change of force when $t = 8.5$ sec.

12. When a certain photoelectric surface is illuminated with light of various wavelengths (in angstroms), the stopping potential (the voltage necessary to stop the emission of photoelectrons) is measured as follows:

Wavelength	3600	4000	4300	4900	5400	5800
Potential	1.45	1.10	0.90	0.60	0.35	0.25

Find the derivative of the wavelength with respect to the stopping potential, when the stopping potential is 0.75 volt.

Miscellaneous exercises for Chapter 2

In Exercises 1 through 6, evaluate the given limits.

1. $\lim\limits_{x \to 4} (8 - 3x)$

2. $\lim\limits_{x \to \infty} \left(7 - \dfrac{1}{x+1}\right)$

3. $\lim\limits_{x \to 2} \dfrac{x^2 + 3x - 10}{x^2 - x - 2}$

4. $\lim\limits_{x \to 3} \dfrac{x^2 - x - 6}{x - 3}$

5. $\lim\limits_{x \to \infty} \dfrac{x - 2x^3}{1 + x^3}$

6. $\lim\limits_{x \to \infty} \dfrac{2x + 5}{3x^3 - 2x}$

In Exercises 7 through 10, use the delta process to find the derivative of each of the given functions.

7. $y = 6 - 2x^2$ 8. $y = 2x^2 - x^3$ 9. $y = \dfrac{2}{x^2}$ 10. $y = \dfrac{1}{\sqrt{x}}$

In Exercises 11 through 20, find the derivative of each of the given functions.

11. $y = 2x^7 - 3x^2 + 5$ 12. $y = \dfrac{2x - 1}{x^2 + 1}$ 13. $y = (2 - 3x)^4$

14. $y = \dfrac{x}{1 - x}$ 15. $y = (x - 1)^3(x^2 - 2)^2$ 16. $y = \dfrac{x}{\sqrt{x^2 + 1}}$

17. $y = \dfrac{3}{(5 - 2x^2)^{3/4}}$ 18. $x^2 y^2 = x^2 + y^2$ 19. $(2x - 3y)^3 = x^2 - y$

20. $\dfrac{1}{y} - \dfrac{1}{x} = 1$

21. The combined capacitance for two capacitors connected in series is given by

$$C_T = \frac{C_1 C_2}{C_1 + C_2}.$$

Find $\lim_{C_1 \to C_2} C_T$ and $\lim_{C_1 \to 0} C_T$.

22. The intensity I of illumination is inversely proportional to the square of the distance x from the source. Find $\lim_{x \to 0} I$.

23. The voltage induced in an inductor L is given by

$$E = L \frac{dI}{dt},$$

where I is the current in the circuit and t is the time. Find the voltage induced in a 0.4-henry inductor if the current I (in amperes) is related to the time (in seconds) by $I = 0.1t + 5.0$.

24. The specific heat c_p of a certain gas as a function of the temperature T is given by

$$c_p = 6.50 + 0.01T + 0.000002T^2.$$

Find the expression for the rate of change of the specific heat with respect to temperature.

25. The electric field E at a distance r from a point charge is $E = k/r^2$, where k is a constant. Find an expression for the rate of change of the electric field with respect to r.

26. The distance d between ion layers of a crystalline solid such as table salt is given by

$$d = \sqrt[3]{M/2N\rho},$$

where M is the molecular weight, N is called Avogadro's number, and ρ is the density. Find the rate of change of d with respect to ρ.

27. The velocity of an object moving with constant acceleration can be found from the equation $v = \sqrt{v_0^2 + 2as}$, where v_0 is the initial velocity, a is the acceleration, and s is the distance traveled. Find dv/ds.

28. The time rate of change of angular velocity is angular acceleration. If a wire is moving through a magnetic field in a circular path such that its angular velocity is given by

$$\omega = \frac{2t^2}{1+t},$$

where t is the time (in seconds), find the expression for the angular acceleration (in rad/sec^2). What is the value of the angular acceleration when $t = 2$ sec?

29. Under certain conditions, the efficiency of an internal combustion engine is given by

$$\text{eff (in percent)} = 100\left(1 - \frac{1}{(V_1/V_2)^{0.4}}\right),$$

where V_1 and V_2 are, respectively, the maximum and minimum volumes of air in a cylinder. Assuming that V_2 is kept constant, find the expression for the rate of change of efficiency with respect to V_1.

30. In the production of steel, the rate at which the temperature of the furnace changes is important. In studying this relationship, the following results were obtained:

Temperature (°C)	25	290	480	700	790	770	710	650	610
Time (min)	0	1	2	3	4	5	6	7	8

By graphical differentiation, determine the graph of the derivative curve. Find the rate of change of temperature when t is 3.5 min.

31. In an experiment to study the pressure and volume of a gas under the condition of
    constant temperature, the following results were obtained:

Pressure (atm)	1.40	1.55	1.62	1.74	1.80	1.91	2.00
Volume (cm^3)	43.0	39.0	37.2	34.8	33.0	31.2	30.3

    By graphical differentiation, determine the derivative curve of pressure with
    respect to volume. Evaluate this derivative when $V = 36.0$ cm^3.

32. An airplane flies over an observer with a velocity of 400 mi/hr at an altitude of
    2640 ft. If the plane flies horizontally in a straight line, find the rate at which the
    distance from the observer to the plane is changing 0.6 min after the plane passes
    over the observer.

33. A rectangle is inscribed in the first quadrant under the parabola $y = 4 - x^2$.
    Express the area of the rectangle in terms of x. Then find the expression for dA/dx.

3 Applications of the derivative

3-1 Tangents and normals

In Chapter 2 we developed the meaning of the derivative of a function and then went on to find several formulas by which we can differentiate functions. In establishing the concept of the derivative as an instantaneous rate of change, numerous applications of the derivative were indicated in the examples and exercises. It was not necessary to develop any of these applications in any detail since the finding of a derivative was the primary concern. There are, however, certain types of problems in geometry and technology in which the derivative plays a key role in the solution, although other concepts also are involved. The first of these problems involves finding the equations of lines tangent and lines normal (perpendicular) to a given curve.

To find the equation of a line tangent to a curve at a given point, we first find the derivative of the function. The derivative is then evaluated at the point, and this gives us the slope of a line tangent to the curve at the point. Then, by using the point-slope form of the equation of a straight line, we find the equation of the tangent line. The following examples illustrate the method.

Example A. Find the equation of the line tangent to the parabola $y = x^2 - 1$ at the point $(-2, 3)$.

The derivative of this function is

$$\frac{dy}{dx} = 2x.$$

The value of this derivative for the value $x = -2$ (the y-value of 3 is not used since the derivative does not directly contain y) is

$$\frac{dy}{dx} = -4,$$

85

which means that the slope of the tangent line at $(-2, 3)$ is -4. Thus, by using the point-slope form of the equation of the straight line we obtain the desired equation. Thus, we have

$y_1 = 3$
$x_1 = -2$
$m = -4$

$$y - y_1 = m(x - x_1)$$
$$y - 3 = -4(x + 2),$$
$$y - 3 = -4x - 8,$$

or

$$y = -4x - 5.$$

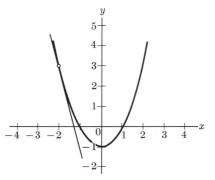

FIGURE 3–1

The parabola and the tangent line $y = -4x - 5$ are shown in Fig. 3–1.

Example B. Find the equation of the line tangent to the ellipse $4x^2 + 9y^2 = 40$ at the point $(1, 2)$.

The easiest method of finding the derivative of this equation is to treat it as an implicit function. In this way we have

implicit differentiation.

$$8x + 18yy' = 0 \quad \text{or} \quad y' = -4x/9y.$$

Evaluating this derivative at the point $(1, 2)$, we have

$$y' = -4/18 = -2/9.$$

Thus the slope of the desired tangent line is $-2/9$. Using the point slope form of the equation of the straight line we have

$$y - 2 = -\tfrac{2}{9}(x - 1),$$

or

$$9y - 18 = -2x + 2,$$

or

$$2x + 9y - 20 = 0.$$

The ellipse and the tangent line

$$2x + 9y - 20 = 0$$

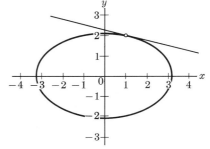

FIGURE 3–2

are shown in Fig. 3–2.

It might be noted that the derivative could have been found also by solving for y. In this way we would have to differentiate $y = (2\sqrt{10 - x^2})/3$.

If we wish to obtain the equation of a line normal (perpendicular to a tangent) to a curve, we recall that the slopes of perpendicular lines are negative reciprocals. Thus, the derivative is found and evaluated at the specified point. Since this gives the slope of a tangent line, we take the negative reciprocal of this number to find the slope of the normal line. Then, by using the point-slope form of the equation of a straight line we find the equation of the normal. The following examples illustrate the method.

Example C. Find the equation of the line normal to the hyperbola $y = 2/x$ at the point (2, 1).

The derivative of this function is $dy/dx = -2/x^2$, which evaluated at $x = 2$ gives $dy/dx = -1/2$. Therefore, the slope of a line normal to the curve at the point (2, 1) is 2. The equation of the normal is then

$$y - 1 = 2(x - 2) \qquad \text{or} \qquad y = 2x - 3.$$

The hyperbola and the normal line are shown in Fig. 3–3.

FIGURE 3–3

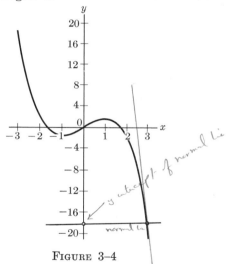

FIGURE 3–4

Example D. Find the y intercept of the line normal to the curve $y = 3x - x^3$ at $(3, -18)$.

The derivative of this function is $dy/dx = 3 - 3x^2$, which evaluated at $(3, -18)$ is

$$\frac{dy}{dx} = 3 - 3(9) = -24.$$

Therefore, the slope of a normal line is 1/24. The equation of the normal line is

$$y + 18 = \tfrac{1}{24}(x - 3) \qquad \text{or} \qquad 24y - x + 435 = 0.$$

To find the y intercept of this line we set $x = 0$. In this way we find the y intercept to be $-145/8$. The curve, normal line, and intercept are indicated in Fig. 3–4.

Many of the applications of tangents and normals are geometric. However, some of the areas of technology where they may be applied are indicated in the exercises.

Exercises

In Exercises 1 through 4, find the equations of the lines tangent to the indicated curves at the given points. In each, sketch the curve and the tangent line.

1. $y = x^2 + 2$ at $(2, 6)$ 2. $y = x^3 - 2x$ at $(2, 4)$

3. $y = \dfrac{1}{x^2 + 1}$ at $(1, \frac{1}{2})$ 4. $x^2 + y^2 = 25$ at $(3, 4)$

In Exercises 5 through 8, find the equations of the lines normal to the indicated curves at the given points. In each, sketch the curve and the normal line.

5. $y = 6x - x^2$ at $(1, 5)$ 6. $y = 2x^3 + 10$ at $(-2, -6)$

7. $y = \dfrac{1}{(x^2 + 1)^2}$ at $(1, \frac{1}{4})$ 8. $x^2 - y^2 = 8$ at $(3, 1)$

In Exercises 9 and 10, find the equations of the tangent lines and the normal lines to the indicated curves.

9. $y = \dfrac{1}{\sqrt{x^2 + 1}}$ where $x = \sqrt{3}$

10. The ellipse with focus at $(4, 0)$, vertex at $(5, 0)$ and center at $(0, 0)$ where $x = 2$.

11. Find the x-intercept of the line tangent to the parabola $y = 4x^2 - 8x$ at $(-1, 12)$.

12. Find the y-intercept of the line normal to the curve $y = x^{3/4}$ where $x = 16$.

13. A certain suspension cable with supports on the same level is closely approximated as being parabolic in shape. If the supports are 200 ft apart and the sag at the center is 30 ft, what is the equation of the line along which the tension acts (tangentially) at the right support? (Choose the origin of the coordinate system at the lowest point of the cable.)

14. In an electric field the lines of force are perpendicular to the curves of equal electric potential. A certain curve of equal electric potential is given by $y = 2x^{2/3}$. What is the equation of the line along which the force acts on an electron positioned on this curve where $x = 8$?

15. An object is moving in a horizontal circle of radius 2 ft at the rate of 2 rad/sec. If the object is on the end of a string, and the string breaks after $\pi/3$ sec, causing the object to travel along a line tangent to the circle, what is the equation of the path of the object after the string breaks? Sketch the path of the object. (Choose the origin of the coordinate system at the center of the circle and assume the object started on the positive x-axis moving counterclockwise.)

3–2 Curvilinear motion

A great many phenomena in technology involve the time rate of change of certain quantities. We encountered one of the most fundamental and most important of these when we discussed velocity, the time rate of change of distance, in Section 2–5. In this section we shall further develop the concept of velocity and certain other concepts necessary for the discussion. Other time-rate-of-change problems are discussed in the next section.

When velocity was introduced in Section 2–5, the discussion was limited to rectilinear motion, or motion along a straight line. A more general discussion of velocity is necessary when we discuss the motion of an object in a plane. There are many important applications of motion in the plane, a principal one among these being the motion of a projectile.

An important concept necessary in developing this topic is that of a *vector*. A good elementary definition of a vector is a quantity which has direction and magnitude. For example, velocity, acceleration, force, and momentum are vector quantities. Each is specified by giving both its magnitude and direction. For instance, we cannot determine the effect of a force unless we know the magnitude of the force as well as the direction in which it is acting. To represent a vector, we draw a line segment of length proportional to its magnitude, and in a direction which shows the direction of the vector.

FIGURE 3–5　　　　　　　　　FIGURE 3–6

The *addition* of two vectors **OA** and **AB**, directed from O to A and from A to B, respectively, gives the *resultant* vector **OB**, as shown in Fig. 3–5. The *initial point* is O and the *terminal point* is B. This is equivalent to making the two vectors being added the sides of a parallelogram, with the diagonal being the resultant. See Fig. 3–6. (Note: A vector quantity is represented by a letter printed in boldface type. The same letter in italic (lightface) type represents the magnitude only.) In general, a resultant is a single vector which can replace any number of other vectors and still produce the same physical effect.

Vectors may be subtracted by reversing the direction of the vector being subtracted, and then proceeding as in adding vectors.

Not only do we need to add vectors, but it is also frequently useful to consider a given vector as the sum of two vectors. These two vectors when added together give the original vector and are called *components* of the original vector.

In practice there are certain components of a vector which are of particular importance. If a vector is so placed that its initial point is at the origin and its direction is indicated by an angle with respect to the positive x-axis (standard position), we may find its components which are directed along the x-axis and along the y-axis. These are known as its x-component and its y-component.

Example A. Find the x- and y-components of a vector 10 units long and directed at an angle of 120°.

Placing the initial point of the vector at the origin, and putting the angle in standard position (Fig. 3–7) we see that the vector directed along the x-axis, $\mathbf{V}_x$, is related to the vector $\mathbf{V}$ of magnitude V by ← *magnitude of $\mathbf{V}$ vector*

$$V_x = V \cos 120° = -V \cos 60°.$$

FIGURE 3–7

(The minus sign indicates that the vector is directed in the negative direction; that is, to the left.) The vector directed along the y-axis, $\mathbf{V}_y$, is related to the vector $\mathbf{V}$ by

$$V_y = V \sin 120° = V \sin 60°.$$

Thus the vectors $\mathbf{V}_x$ and $\mathbf{V}_y$ have the magnitudes

$$V_x = -10(0.500) = -5.00,$$

$$V_y = 10(0.866) = 8.66.$$

Adding vectors by diagrams gives only approximate results. It is possible to find accurate numerical results for the sum of two vectors by the use of components. The method is to <u>resolve</u> (break into components) all vectors being added into their x- and y-components. These can then be added algebraically, since they are all directed along either the x- or the y-axis. The result will give us the component of the resultant in the x-direction and the component of the resultant in the y-direction. By addition we may then find the value of the resultant vector.

Example B. Find the resultant $\mathbf{R}$ of the two given vectors, $\mathbf{A}$ of magnitude 8 and direction 57° and $\mathbf{B}$ of magnitude 5 and direction 322°.

$$A_x = 8 \cos 57° = 8(0.5446) = 4.36,$$

$$A_y = 8 \sin 57° = 8(0.8387) = 6.71,$$

$$B_x = 5 \cos 38° = 5(0.7880) = 3.94,$$

$$B_y = -5 \sin 38° = -5(0.6157) = -3.08;$$

$$R_x = A_x + B_x = 4.36 + 3.94 = 8.30,$$

$$R_y = A_y + B_y = 6.71 - 3.08 = 3.63,$$

$$R = \sqrt{(8.30)^2 + (3.63)^2} = \sqrt{68.9 + 13.2} = \sqrt{82.1} = 9.06;$$

$$\tan \theta = \frac{R_y}{R_x} = \frac{3.63}{8.30} = 0.437, \qquad \theta = 23.6°.$$

Arctangent of =

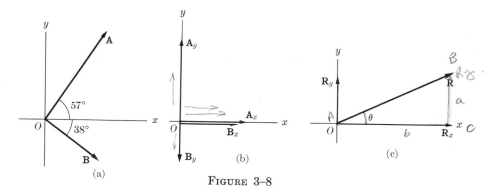

FIGURE 3–8

The resultant vector is 9.05 units long and is directed at an angle of 23.6° (see Fig. 3–8).

Some general formulas can be derived from Examples A and B. For a vector **A**, directed at an angle θ, of magnitude A, with components $\mathbf{A}_x$ and $\mathbf{A}_y$, we have the following relations:

$$A_x = A \cos \theta, \qquad A_y = A \sin \theta, \tag{3–1}$$

$$A = \sqrt{A_x^2 + A_y^2}, \tag{3–2}$$

$$\tan \theta = A_y/A_x. \tag{3–3}$$

Although vectors can be used to represent many physical quantities, we will restrict our attention to their use in describing the velocity and acceleration of an object moving in a plane along a specified path. Such motion is called _curvilinear motion._

In describing an object undergoing curvilinear motion, it is very common to express the x and y coordinates of its position separately as functions of time. Equations given in this form, that is, x and y both given in terms of a third variable (in this case t), are said to be in _parametric form._ The third variable, t, is called the parameter. The graph in rectangular coordinates is found by using values of t to find the corresponding values of x and y.

Example C. Plot the graph of the parametric equations

$$x = 1 + 2t \qquad \text{and} \qquad y = t^2 - 3t.$$

We assume various values of t, thus obtaining values of x and y shown in the following table.

t	0	1	2	3	4	5	— Parameter
x	1	3	5	7	9	11	
y	0	−2	−2	0	4	10	

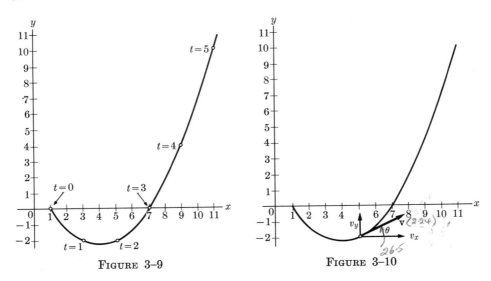

FIGURE 3–9   FIGURE 3–10

(Generally only positive values of t have physical significance.) Using the values of x and y the graph is constructed. (See Fig. 3–9.)

In order to find the velocity of an object whose coordinates are given in parametric form, we find its x-component of velocity v_x by determining dx/dt and its y-component of velocity v_y by determining dy/dt. These are then evaluated, and the resultant velocity is found from $v = \sqrt{v_x^2 + v_y^2}$. The direction in which the object is moving is found from $\tan \theta = v_y/v_x$. The following example illustrates the method.

Example D. Find the velocity and direction of motion when $t = 2$ of an object moving such that its x and y coordinates of position are given by $x = 1 + 2t$ and $y = t^2 - 3t$ (these are the same parametric equations as in Example C):

$$v_x = \frac{dx}{dt} = 2, \quad v_x|_{t=2} = 2,$$

$$v_y = \frac{dy}{dt} = 2t - 3, \quad v_y|_{t=2} = 1,$$

$$v|_{t=2} = \sqrt{4 + 1} = \sqrt{5} = 2.24, \quad \tan \theta = \tfrac{1}{2}, \quad \theta = 26.5°.$$

These quantities are shown in Fig. 3–10.

Acceleration is the time rate of change of velocity. Therefore, if the velocity, or its components, is known as a function of time, the acceleration of an object can be found by taking the derivative of the velocity with respect to time. For this reason it may be necessary to find the derivative of a derivative. This is called a second derivative. The notation for the second derivative of x with respect to t, for example, is d^2x/dt^2.

Example E. Find the magnitude and direction of the acceleration when $t = 2$ for an object moving such that its x and y coordinates of position are given by $x = t^3$ and $y = 1 - t^2$:

$$v_x = \frac{dx}{dt} = 3t^2, \qquad a_x = \frac{dv_x}{dt} = \frac{d^2x}{dt^2} = 6t, \qquad a_x|_{t=2} = 12,$$

$$v_y = \frac{dy}{dt} = -2t, \qquad a_y = \frac{dv_y}{dt} = \frac{d^2y}{dt^2} = -2, \qquad a_y|_{t=2} = -2,$$

$$a|_{t=2} = \sqrt{144 + 4} = \sqrt{148} = 12.2,$$

$$\tan \theta = \frac{a_y}{a_x} = -\tfrac{2}{12} = -\tfrac{1}{6}, \qquad \theta = -9.5°.$$

The quadrant in which θ lies is determined from the fact that a_y is negative and a_x is positive. Thus, θ must be a fourth quadrant angle. (See Fig. 3–11.)

If the curvilinear path which an object follows is given as y as a function of x, the velocity (and acceleration) is found by taking derivatives of each term of the equation with respect to time. In finding the derivatives we must be very careful to use the power rule for finding derivatives, Eq. (2–28), such that the general factor du/dx is not neglected. The following example illustrates the method.

FIGURE 3–11

FIGURE 3–12

Example F. A particle moves along the parabola $y = \tfrac{1}{3}x^2$ so that its vertical velocity v_y is always 8. Find the magnitude of the resultant velocity when the particle is at the point $(2, \tfrac{4}{3})$.

Since both y and x change with time, both can be considered functions of time. Thus we can take derivatives of $y = \tfrac{1}{3}x^2$ with respect to time. When we do this we obtain the following result:

$$\frac{dy}{dt} = \frac{2}{3} x \frac{dx}{dt}, \qquad v_y = \frac{2}{3} x v_x.$$

At the point $(2, \tfrac{4}{3})$ we have $8 = \tfrac{2}{3}(2)v_x$. Thus $v_x = 6$ at this point (see Fig. 3–12). Therefore the resultant velocity is

$$v = \sqrt{64 + 36} = 10.$$

Exercises

In Exercises 1 through 4, given that the x- and y-coordinates of a moving particle are given by the indicated parametric equations, find the magnitude and direction of the velocity for the specified value of t. Plot the curves and show the appropriate components of the velocity.

1. $x = 3t$, $y = 1 - t$, $t = 4$ 2. $x = 2t^3$, $y = 4t^2$, $t = 1$

3. $x = \dfrac{10}{2t + 3}$, $y = \dfrac{1}{t^2}$, $t = 2$ 4. $x = \sqrt{1 + 2t}$, $y = t - t^2$, $t = 4$

In Exercises 5 through 8, use the parametric equations and values of t of Exercises 1 through 4 to find the magnitude and direction of the acceleration in each case.

9. A particle moves along the curve $y = 5x^3$ with a constant x component of velocity equal to 20. Find the magnitude and direction of the velocity at the point $(1, 5)$.

10. A particle moves along the curve $y = 2\sqrt{x}$. What is the ratio of the x-component of velocity to the y-component at $(9, 6)$?

11. A particle moves along the upper half of the parabola $y^2 = 2x + 1$ such that $v_x = \sqrt{2x + 3}$. Find v_y when $x = 4$.

12. Find the magnitude and direction of the acceleration of the particle in Exercise 9.

13. A projectile moves according to the parametric equations $x = 120t$ and $y = 160t - 16t^2$, where distances are in feet and time is in seconds. Find the magnitude and direction of the velocity when $t = 3$ sec and when $t = 6$ sec.

14. A projectile moves according to the parametric equations $x = 100t$ and $y = -16t^2$, where distances are in feet and time is in seconds. Find the magnitude and direction of each of the velocity and acceleration when $t = 3$ sec.

15. Find the acceleration at the specified times for the projectile in Exercise 13.

16. An electron moves in an electric field according to the parametric equations $x = 2/\sqrt{1 + t^2}$ and $y = 2t/\sqrt{1 + t^2}$, where distances are in centimeters and time in milliseconds. Find the magnitude and direction of the velocity when $t = 10^{-3}$ sec.

17. A rocket follows a path given by $y = x - x^3/90$ (distances in miles). If the horizontal velocity is given by $v_x = x$, find the magnitude and direction of the velocity when the rocket hits the ground (assume level terrain) if time is in minutes.

18. A meteorite traveling toward the earth has a velocity inversely proportional to the square root of the distance from the earth's center. Show that its acceleration is inversely proportional to the square of the distance from the center of the earth.

3-3 Related rates

Any two variables which vary with respect to time, and between which a relation is known to exist, can have the time rate of change of one expressed in terms of the time rate of change of the other. We do this by taking the derivative with respect to time of the expression which relates the variables as we did in Example E of Section 3-2. Since the rates of change are related, this type of problem is referred to as a *related-rate* problem. The following examples illustrate the basic method of solution.

(handwritten at top: $E = y = \text{Voltage}$, $T = x = \text{temperature}$)

Example A. The voltage of a certain thermocouple as a function of temperature is given by $E = 2.800T + 0.006T^2$. If the temperature is increasing at the rate of 1°C/min, how fast is the voltage increasing when $T = 100°$ C?

Since we are asked to find the time rate of change of voltage, we first take derivatives with respect to time. This gives us

$$\frac{dE}{dt} = 2.800 \frac{dT}{dt} + 0.012T \frac{dT}{dt},$$

again being careful to include the factor dT/dt. From the given information we know that $dT/dt = 1°$C/min and that we wish to know dE/dt when $T = 100°$C. Thus,

$$\frac{dE}{dt}\bigg|_{T=100} = 2.800(1) + 0.012(100)(1) = 4 \text{ volts/min.}$$

(handwritten annotations: $1°/min$, 1.2, rate of change of voltage)

The derivative must be taken before values are substituted. In this problem we are finding the time rate of change of the voltage for a specified value of T. For other values of T, dE/dt would have different values.

Example B. The distance q that an image is from a certain lens in terms of p, the distance the object is from the lens, is given by

$$q = \frac{10p}{p - 10}.$$

(handwritten: $\frac{dp}{dt}$)

If the object distance is increasing at the rate of 0.2 cm/sec, how fast is the image distance changing when $p = 15$ cm?

Taking derivatives with respect to time, we have

$$\frac{dq}{dt} = \frac{(p - 10)\left(10\frac{dp}{dt}\right) - 10p\left(\frac{dp}{dt}\right)}{(p - 10)^2}.$$

(handwritten: $\frac{(15-10)(.2) + 10(15)(.2)}{(15-10)^2}$)

Now substituting $p = 15$ and $dp/dt = 0.2$, we have

$$\frac{dq}{dt}\bigg|_{p=15} = \frac{5(10)(0.2) - 10(15)(0.2)}{25} = -0.8 \text{ cm/sec.}$$

Thus the image distance is decreasing (the significance of the minus sign) at the rate of 0.8 cm/sec when $p = 15$ cm.

In many related-rate problems the function is not given, but must be set up according to the statement of the problem. The following examples illustrate this type of problem.

Example C. A spherical balloon is being blown up at the constant rate of 2 ft³/min. Find the rate at which the radius is increasing when it is 3 ft.

We are asked to find the relation between the rate of change of the volume of a sphere with respect to time and the corresponding rate of change of the radius. Thus we are to take derivatives of the expression for the volume of a sphere with respect to time.

$$V = \frac{4}{3}\pi r^3; \qquad \frac{dV}{dt} = 4\pi r^2 \left(\frac{dr}{dt}\right).$$

From the information given, we know the value of dV/dt to be 2. We want to find dr/dt when $r = 3$. Substituting these values, we have

$$2 = 4\pi(3)^2 \left(\frac{dr}{dt}\right) \qquad \text{or} \qquad \left.\frac{dr}{dt}\right|_{r=3} = \frac{1}{18\pi} = 0.0177 \text{ ft/min.}$$

Example D. Two ships, A and B, leave port at noon. Ship A travels north at 6 mi/hr, and ship B travels east at 8 mi/hr. How fast are they separating at 2 P.M.?

We are asked to find how fast the length of a line drawn directly from A to B is increasing at a particular time. First a relation must be found between the distances traveled. The Pythagorean theorem provides the necessary relation (see Fig. 3–13). If y is the distance traveled by A and x is the distance traveled by B, we can find the distance between them, z, from $z^2 = x^2 + y^2$. Taking derivatives of this expression, we find that

$$2z\frac{dz}{dt} = 2x\frac{dx}{dt} + 2y\frac{dy}{dt}.$$

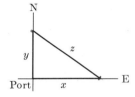

FIGURE 3–13

From the information given, we know that $dx/dt = 8$, $dy/dt = 6$, and for the specified time, $x = 16$, $y = 12$, and $z = 20$. Thus we have

$$\left.\frac{dz}{dt}\right|_{z=20} = \frac{16(8) + (12)(6)}{20} = 10 \text{ mi/hr.}$$

Exercises

1. The electric resistance of a certain resistor as a function of temperature is given by $R = 4.000 + 0.003T^2$, where R is measured in ohms and T in °C. If the temperature is increasing at the rate of 0.1°C/sec, find how fast the resistance changes when $T = 150$°C.

2. The kinetic energy of an object is given by KE $= \frac{1}{2}mv^2$, where m is the mass of the object and v is its velocity. If a 20-gm object is accelerating (remember that the time rate of change of velocity is acceleration) at 5 cm/sec^2, how fast is the kinetic energy (in ergs) changing when the velocity is 30 cm/sec?

3. The length of a pendulum is slowly decreasing at the rate of 0.1 in/sec. What is the rate of change of the period of the pendulum when the length is 16 in., if the relation between the period and length is $T = \pi\sqrt{L/96}$?

4. When air expands so that there is no change in heat (an adiabatic change) the relationship between the pressure and volume is $pv^{1.4} = k$, where k is a constant. At a certain instant, the pressure is 3 atm and the volume is 10 in^3. The volume is increasing at the rate of 2 in^3/sec. What is the time rate of change of pressure at this instant? $- \cdot 892$

5. The relation between the voltage V which produces a current I in a wire of radius r is $V = 0.03I/r^2$. If the current increases at the rate of 0.02 amp/sec in a wire of 0.04-in. radius, find the rate at which the voltage is increasing.

6. Two resistances in parallel vary with time. At a certain instant, R_1 is 8 ohms and is increasing at the rate of 0.5 ohm/sec. At the same instant, R_2 is 6 ohms and is increasing at the rate of 0.6 ohm/sec. What is the rate of change of the resistance R of the combination if $R = R_1R_2/(R_1 + R_2)$?

7. The side of a square is increasing at the rate of 5 ft/min. How fast is the area changing when the side is 10 ft long?

8. A circular plate is contracting by being cooled. Find the rate of decrease in area if the radius decreases at the rate of 0.1 ft/hr, when the radius is 4 ft.

9. The radius of a certain steam engine cylinder is 3 in. What is the speed of the piston if steam is entering the cylinder at 2 ft^3/sec? Assume no compression of the steam at this moment.

10. The intensity of heat varies directly as the strength of the source and inversely as the square of the distance from the source. If an object approaches a heated object of strength of 8 units at the rate of 50 cm/sec, how fast is the intensity changing when it is 100 cm from the source?

11. One statement of Boyle's law is that the pressure of a gas varies inversely as the volume for constant temperature. If a certain gas occupies 600 in^3 when the pressure is 2 atm and the volume is increasing at the rate of 20 in^3/min, how fast is the pressure changing when the volume is 800 in^3?

12. A ladder is slipping down along a vertical wall. If the ladder is 10 ft long, and the top of it is slipping at the constant rate of 10 ft/sec, how fast is the bottom of the ladder moving along the ground when the bottom is 6 ft from the wall?

13. A rope attached to a boat is being pulled in at a rate of 10 ft/sec. If the water is 20 ft below the level at which the rope is being drawn in, how fast is the boat approaching the wharf when 36 ft of rope are yet to be pulled in?

14. A pile of sand in the shape of a cone has a radius which always equals the altitude. If 100 ft^3 of sand are poured onto the pile each minute, how fast is the radius increasing when the pile is 10 ft high?

15. A man 6 ft tall approaches a street light 15 ft above the ground at the rate of 5 ft/sec. How fast is the end of the man's shadow moving when he is 10 ft from the base of the light?

16. Side a of a triangle is increasing at the rate of 2 in/min and side b is increasing at the rate of 3 in/min. If the angle between sides a and b is always 60°, find the rate of change of side c when $a = 5$ and $b = 8$.

3–4 The use of derivatives in curve sketching

Derivatives can be used effectively in the sketching of curves. An analysis of the first two derivatives can provide useful information as to the graph of a function. This information, possibly along with two or three key points on the curve, is often sufficient to obtain a good, although approximate, graph of the function. Graphs where this information must be supplemented with other analyses are the subject of the next section.

Considering the function $f(x)$ as shown in Fig. 3–14, we see that as x increases (from left to right) the y-values also increase until the point M is reached. From M to m the values of y decrease. To the right of m the values of y again increase. We also note that any tangent line to the left of M and to the right of m will have a positive slope. Any tangent line between M and m will have a negative slope. Since the derivative of a function determines the slope of a tangent line, we can conclude that, as x increases, y increases if the derivative is positive, and decreases if the derivative is negative. This can be stated as

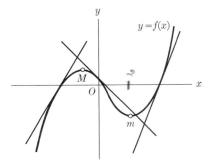

$$y = f(x) \text{ increases if } f'(x) > 0$$

and

$$y = f(x) \text{ decreases if } f'(x) < 0.$$

It is always assumed that x is increasing.

FIGURE 3–14

Example A. Determine for which values of x the function $f(x) = x^3 - 3x^2$ is increasing, and those values for which it is decreasing.

We find the solution to this problem by determining the values of x for which the derivative is positive and those for which it is negative. Finding the derivative, we have

$$f'(x) = 3x^2 - 6x = 3x(x - 2).$$

This now becomes a problem of solving an inequality. To find the values of x for which $f(x)$ is increasing we must solve the inequality

$$3x(x - 2) > 0.$$

We now recall that the solution of an inequality consists of *all* values of x which may satisfy it. Normally, this consists of certain *ranges* of values of x. These ranges are found by first setting the left side of the inequality equal to zero, thus obtaining the *critical values* of x. The function on the left will have the same *sign* for all values of x less than the leftmost critical value. The sign of the function will also be the same within any given region between critical values and to the right of the rightmost critical value. Those regions which give the proper sign will satisfy the inequality. In this case the critical values are $x = 0$ and $x = 2$. Therefore we have the following analysis.

slope of tangent = m

If $x < 0$, $3x(x - 2) > 0$, or $f'(x) > 0$.

If $0 < x < 2$, $3x(x - 2) < 0$, or $f'(x) < 0$. *if $0 > x > 2$ then $f'x > 0$*

If $x > 2$, $3x(x - 2) > 0$, or $f'(x) > 0$. *if $0 < x < 2$ then $f'x < 0$*

Therefore the solution of the above inequality is $x < 0$ and $x > 2$, which means that for these values $f(x)$ is increasing. We can also see that for $0 < x < 2$, $f'(x) < 0$, which means that $f(x)$ is decreasing for these values of x. The solution is now complete.

The points M and m in Fig. 3–14 are called a *relative maximum point* and a *relative minimum point*, respectively. This means that M has a greater y-value than any other point near it, and that m has the least y-value of any point near it. This does not necessarily mean that M has the greatest y-value of any point on the curve, or that m has the least y-value of any point on the curve. However, the points M and m are the greatest or least values of y for that part of the curve (that is why we use the word "relative"). Observation of Fig. 3–14 verifies this point. The characteristic of both M and m is that the derivative is zero at each point. (We see that this is so since a tangent line would have a slope of zero at each.) This is how relative maximum and relative minimum points are located. The derivative is found and then set equal to zero. The solutions of the resulting equation give the x-coordinates of the maximum and minimum points.

It remains now to determine whether a given value of x, for which the derivative is zero, is the coordinate of a maximum or a minimum point (or neither, which is also possible). From the discussion of increasing and decreasing values for y, we can see that the derivative changes sign from plus to minus when it passes through a relative maximum point, and from minus to plus when it passes through a relative minimum point. Thus we find maximum and minimum points by determining those values of x for which the derivative is zero and by properly analyzing the sign change of the derivative. If the sign of the derivative does not change, it is neither a maximum nor a minimum point. This is known as the first-derivative test for maxima and minima.

Example B. Find any maximum and minimum points of the function

$$y = 3x^5 - 5x^3.$$

when $x = 1$, $y = -2$
" $x = -1$, $y = 2$

Finding the derivative, and setting it equal to zero, we have

$$y' = 15x^4 - 15x^2 = 15x^2(x^2 - 1);$$

$$15x^2(x - 1)(x + 1) = 0 \quad \text{for} \quad x = 0, \quad x = 1, \quad \text{and} \quad x = -1.$$

Thus the sign of the derivative is the same for all points to the left of $x = -1$. For these values $y' > 0$ (thus y is increasing). For values of x between -1 and 0, $y' < 0$. For values of x between 0 and 1, $y' < 0$. For values of x greater than 1, $y' > 0$. Thus the curve has a maximum at $(-1, 2)$ and a minimum at $(1, -2)$. The point $(0, 0)$ is neither a maximum nor a minimum, since the sign of the derivative did not change for this value of x.

Looking again at the slope of tangents drawn to a curve (see Fig. 3–15a), we see that the slope goes from large to small positive values and then to negative values for this curve. At the point I the values of the slope again start to increase so that values of the slope again become positive after the point m. The conclusion is that the *slope decreases* as a point approaches I, and that the *slope increases* as a point moves to the right of I. The curve in Fig. 3–15(b) is that of the derivative, and therefore indicates the values of the slope of $f(x)$. If the slope changes, this means that we are dealing with the rate of change of slope, or the rate of change of the derivative. This function is the second derivative.

The curve in Fig. 3–15(c) is that of the second derivative. This means that we wish to be able to find an expression for the derivative of a derivative. We encountered this type of function before, in the discussion of acceleration. Where the second derivative of a function is negative, the slope is decreasing, or the curve is *concave down* (opens down). Where the second derivative is positive, the slope is increasing, or the curve is *concave up* (opens up). By the nature of the definition of maximum and minimum points, and of concavity, it is apparent that a curve is concave down at a maximum point and concave up at a minimum point. We can see these properties when we make a close analysis of the curves in Fig. 3–15 (the derivative curves can be obtained by recalling the method of graphical differentiation). The above results are summarized as follows:

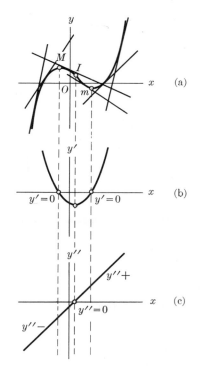

If $f''(x) > 0$, the curve is concave up.
If $f''(x) < 0$, the curve is concave down.
At a maximum point,

$$f'(x) = 0 \text{ and } f''(x) < 0.$$

At a minimum point,

$$f'(x) = 0 \text{ and } f''(x) > 0.$$

These statements comprise what is known as the second-derivative test for maxima and minima.

FIGURE 3–15

The points at which the curve changes from concave up to concave down, or from concave down to concave up, are known as *points of inflection*. Thus point I in the figure is a point of inflection. Inflection points are found by determining those values of x for which the second derivative changes sign. This is analogous to finding maximum and minimum points by the first-derivative test.

Example C. Determine the concavity and find any points of inflection of the function $y = x^3 - 3x$.
   This requires inspection and analysis of the second derivative. So we write

$$y' = 3x^2 - 3, \qquad y'' = 6x.$$

The second derivative is positive where the function is concave up, and this occurs if $x > 0$. The curve is concave down for $x < 0$, since y'' is negative. Thus $(0, 0)$ is a point of inflection, since the concavity changes there.

   At this point we shall summarize the information regarding the derivatives of a function.

$f(x)$ increases if $f'(x) > 0$; $f(x)$ decreases if $f'(x) < 0$;
$f'(x) = 0$ at a maximum point if $f'(x)$ changes from $+$ to $-$, or if $f''(x) < 0$.
$f'(x) = 0$ at a minimum point if $f'(x)$ changes from $-$ to $+$, or if $f''(x) > 0$.
$f''(x) > 0$ where $f(x)$ is concave up; $f''(x) < 0$ where $f(x)$ is concave down.
$f''(x) = 0$ at a point of inflection if $f''(x)$ changes from $+$ to $-$ or $-$ to $+$.

   The following examples illustrate how the above information is put together in order to obtain the graph of a function.

Example D. Sketch the graph of $y = 2x^3 + 3x^2 - 12x$.
   Finding the first two derivatives, we have

$$y' = 6x^2 + 6x - 12 = 6(x + 2)(x - 1)$$

and

$$y'' = 12x + 6 = 6(2x + 1).$$

We note that $y' = 0$ when $x = -2$ and $x = 1$. Using these values in the second derivative we find that y'' is negative (-18) for $x = -2$ and y'' is positive $(+18)$ when $x = 1$. When $x = -2$, $y = 20$; and when $x = 1$, $y = -7$. Therefore, $(-2, 20)$ is a maximum point and $(1, -7)$ is a minimum point.
   Next we see that $y' > 0$ if $x < -2$ and $x > 1$. Also, $y' < 0$ if $-2 < x < 1$. Therefore, y is increasing if $x < -2$ and $x > 1$, and y is decreasing if $-2 < x < 1$.
   Now we note that $y'' = 0$ when $x = -\frac{1}{2}$, and that $y'' < 0$ when $x < -\frac{1}{2}$, and $y'' > 0$ when $x > -\frac{1}{2}$. When $x = -\frac{1}{2}$, $y = \frac{13}{2}$. Therefore, there is a point of inflection at $(-\frac{1}{2}, \frac{13}{2})$, the curve is concave down if $x < -\frac{1}{2}$ and the curve is concave up if $x > -\frac{1}{2}$.

Finally, by locating the points $(-2, 20)$, $(-\frac{1}{2}, \frac{13}{2})$, and $(1, -7)$, we draw the curve *up* to $(-2, 20)$ and then *down* to $(-\frac{1}{2}, \frac{13}{2})$, with the curve *concave down*. Continuing *down*, but *concave up*, we draw the curve to $(1, -7)$ at which point we start *up* and continue up. This gives us an excellent graph indicating the shape of the curve. If more precision is required, additional points may be used. See Fig. 3–16.

FIGURE 3–16

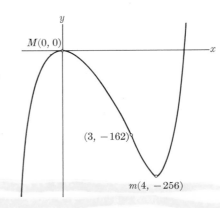

FIGURE 3–17

Example E. Sketch the graph of $y = x^5 - 5x^4$.

The first two derivatives are

$$y' = 5x^4 - 20x^3 = 5x^3(x - 4) \qquad \text{and} \qquad y'' = 20x^3 - 60x^2 = 20x^2(x - 3).$$

We now see that $y' = 0$ when $x = 0$ and $x = 4$. When $x = 0$, $y'' = 0$ also, which means we cannot use the second derivative test for maximum and minimum points for this value of x. When $x = 4$, y'' is positive ($+320$) which means $(4, -256)$ is a minimum point. Next we note that $y' > 0$ if $x < 0$ and $x > 4$ and $y' < 0$ if $0 < x < 4$. Thus, by the first derivative test, there is a maximum at $(0, 0)$. Also we see that y is increasing if $x < 0$ and $x > 4$ and decreasing if $0 < x < 4$. The second derivative indicates that there is a point of inflection at $(3, -162)$. It also indicates that the function is concave down if $x < 3$ $(x \neq 0)$ and concave up if $x > 3$. There is no point of inflection at $(0, 0)$ since the second derivative does not change sign when $x = 0$. From this information we sketch the curve in Fig. 3–17.

Exercises

In Exercises 1 through 6, determine those values of x for which the given functions are increasing and those values of x for which they are decreasing.

1. $y = x^2 - 2x$
2. $y = 6x - x^3$
3. $y = x^4 - 2x^2$
4. $y = x^5 - \frac{25}{3} x^3 + 20x$
5. $y = 4x^3 - 3x^4$
6. $y = x^5 + 20x^2$

In Exercises 7 through 12, find any maximum or minimum points of the functions given in Exercises 1 through 6 above.

In Exercises 13 through 18, determine the concavity and points of inflection of the functions given in Exercises 1 through 6 above.

In Exercises 19 through 24, sketch each of the functions given in Exercises 1 through 6 above, using the information obtained in Exercises 1 through 18.

25. A certain projectile follows a path given by $y = x - 0.00025x^2$, where distances are measured in feet. By the methods of this section sketch the graph of the path of the projectile.

26. The deflection y of a beam at a horizontal distance x from one end is given by $y = k(x^3 - 60x^2)$. Sketch the curve representing the beam if it is 10 ft long and $k = 1/5000$.

27. A rectangular box is made from a piece of cardboard 8 in. by 12 in., by cutting a square from each corner and bending up the sides. Express the volume of the box as a function of the side of the square which is cut out, and then sketch the curve of the resulting equation.

28. A tool box whose end is square is to be made from 600 in^2 of sheet metal. Express the volume of the box as a function of the side of the square of the end. Sketch the curve of the resulting function.

3–5 More on curve sketching

We are now in a position to combine the information from the derivative with information obtainable from the function itself for the purpose of sketching the graph of a function. The information obtainable from the function includes topics introduced in the first two chapters. They consist of intercepts, symmetry, the behavior of the curve as x becomes large, and the vertical asymptotes of the curve. The examples which follow demonstrate how these concepts are used, along with the information from the derivatives, to sketch the graph of a function. We will find that some of these considerations are of much more value than others in graphing any particular curve.

Example A. Sketch the graph of

$$y = \frac{2}{x^2 + 1}.$$

Intercepts: If $x = 0$, $y = 2$ which means that $(0, 2)$ is an intercept. We see that if $y = 0$, there is no corresponding value of x, since $2/(x^2 + 1)$ is a fraction greater than zero for all x.

Symmetry: The curve is symmetric to the y-axis since

$$y = \frac{2}{(-x)^2 + 1} \quad \text{is the same as} \quad y = \frac{2}{x^2 + 1}.$$

The curve is not symmetric to the x-axis since

$$-y = \frac{2}{x^2 + 1} \quad \text{is not the same as} \quad y = \frac{2}{x^2 + 1}.$$

The value in knowing the symmetry is that we should find those portions of the curve on either side of the y-axis reflections of the other. It is possible to use this fact directly or use it as a check.

Behavior as x becomes large: We note that as $x \to +\infty$, $y \to 0$ since $2/(x^2 + 1)$ is always a fraction greater than zero, but which becomes smaller as x becomes larger. Therefore we see that $y = 0$ is an asymptote. Either from the symmetry or the function, we also see that $y \to 0$ as $x \to -\infty$.

Vertical asymptotes: From the discussion of the hyperbola we recall that an asymptote is a line which a curve approaches. We have already noted that $y = 0$ is an asymptote for this curve. This asymptote, the x-axis, is a horizontal line. Vertical asymptotes, if any exist, are found by determining those values of x for which the denominator of any term is zero. Such a value of x makes y undefined. Since $x^2 + 1$ cannot be zero, this curve has no vertical asymptotes. The next example illustrates a curve which has a vertical asymptote.

Derivatives: Since

$$y = \frac{2}{x^2 + 1} = 2(x^2 + 1)^{-1}, \qquad$$

then

$$y' = -2(x^2 + 1)^{-2}(2x) = \frac{-4x}{(x^2 + 1)^2}.$$

Since $(x^2 + 1)^2$ is positive for all values of x, the sign of y' is determined by the numerator. Thus, we note that $y' = 0$ for $x = 0$ and that $y' > 0$ for $x < 0$ and $y' < 0$ for $x > 0$. The curve, therefore, is increasing for $x < 0$, decreasing for $x > 0$ and has a maximum point at $(0, 2)$. Now,

$$y'' = \frac{(x^2 + 1)^2(-4) + 4x(2)(x^2 + 1)(2x)}{(x^2 + 1)^4} = \frac{-4(x^2 + 1) + 16x^2}{(x^2 + 1)^3}$$

$$= \frac{12x^2 - 4}{(x^2 + 1)^3} = \frac{4(3x^2 - 1)}{(x^2 + 1)^3}.$$

We note that y'' is negative for $x = 0$, which confirms that $(0, 2)$ is a maximum point. Also, points of inflection are found for the values of x satisfying $3x^2 - 1 = 0$. Thus, $(-\sqrt{3}/3, \frac{3}{2})$ and $(\sqrt{3}/3, \frac{3}{2})$ are points of inflection. The curve is concave up if $x < -\sqrt{3}/3$ and $x > \sqrt{3}/3$ and concave down if $-\sqrt{3}/3 < x < \sqrt{3}/3$.

Putting this information together we sketch the curve shown in Fig. 3–18. It might be noted that this curve could have been sketched primarily by use of the fact that $y \to 0$ as $x \to +\infty$ and as $x \to -\infty$, and the fact that a maxi-

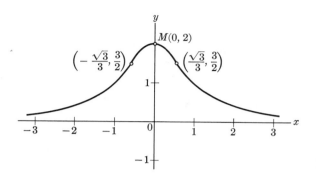

FIGURE 3–18

mum point exists at $(0, 2)$. However, the other parts of the analysis, such as symmetry and concavity, serve as excellent checks and also make the curve more accurate.

$$\frac{x+4}{x} = \frac{(x^2+4)}{x}$$

Example B. Sketch the graph of $y = x + 4/x$.

Intercepts: If we set $x = 0$, y is undefined. This means there are no y-intercepts. If we set $y = 0$, $x + 4/x = (x^2 + 4)/x$ cannot be zero since $x^2 + 4$ cannot be zero. Therefore, there are no intercepts. This may seem to be of little value, but we must realize *this curve does not cross either axis.* This, in itself, is of value in sketching the graph.

Symmetry: In testing for symmetry, we find that it is not symmetric to either axis. However, this curve does possess symmetry to the origin. This is determined by the fact that when $-x$ replaces x and at the same time $-y$ replaces y, the equation does not change. The meaning of this symmetry is that the origin is the midpoint of any two points (x, y) and $(-x, -y)$ which are on the curve.

Behavior as x becomes large: As $x \to +\infty$, and as $x \to -\infty$, $y \to x$ since $4/x \to 0$. Thus, $y = x$ is an asymptote of the curve.

Vertical asymptotes: As we noted in Example A, vertical asymptotes exist for values of x for which y is undefined. In this equation, $x = 0$ makes the second term on the right undefined and therefore y is undefined. In fact as $x \to 0$ from the positive side, $y \to +\infty$, and as $x \to 0$ from the negative side, $y \to -\infty$. This is derived from the sign of $4/x$ in each case.

Derivatives: Finding the first derivative we have

$$y' = 1 - \frac{4}{x^2} = \frac{x^2 - 4}{x^2}.$$

The x^2 in the denominator indicates that the sign of the first derivative is the same as its numerator. The numerator is zero if $x = -2$ or $x = 2$. If $x < -2$ and $x > 2$, then $y' > 0$; and if $-2 < x < 2$, $x \neq 0$, $y' < 0$. Thus, y is increasing if $x < -2$ or $x > 2$, and y is decreasing if $-2 < x < 2$, except $x = 0$ where y is undefined. Also, $(-2, -4)$ is a maximum point and $(2, 4)$

is a minimum point. The second derivative is $y'' = 8/x^3$. This cannot be zero,
but it is negative if $x < 0$ and positive if
$x > 0$. Thus, the curve is concave down
if $x < 0$ and concave up if $x > 0$. Using
this information we have the graph shown
in Fig. 3–19.

Example C. Sketch the graph of

$$y = \frac{1}{\sqrt{1 - x^2}}.$$

Intercepts: If $x = 0$, $y = 1$. If $y = 0$,
$1/\sqrt{1 - x^2}$ would have to be zero, but
it cannot since it is a fraction with 1 as
the numerator for all values of x. Thus
$(0, 1)$ is an intercept.

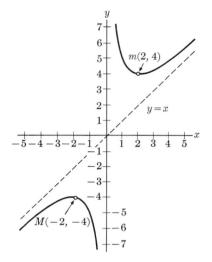

FIGURE 3–19

Symmetry: The curve is symmetric to
the y-axis.

Behavior as x becomes large: The values of x cannot be considered beyond
1 or -1, for any value of $x < -1$ or $x > 1$ gives imaginary values for y.
Thus, the curve does not exist for values of $x < -1$ or $x > 1$.

Vertical asymptotes: If $x = 1$ or $x = -1$, y is undefined. In each case as
$x \to 1$ and as $x \to -1$, $y \to +\infty$.

Derivatives:

$$y' = -\tfrac{1}{2}(1 - x^2)^{-3/2}(-2x) = \frac{x}{(1 - x^2)^{3/2}}.$$

We see that $y' = 0$ if $x = 0$. If $-1 < x < 0$, $y' < 0$ and if $0 < x < 1$,
$y' > 0$. Thus the curve is decreasing if $-1 < x < 0$ and increasing if
$0 < x < 1$. There is a minimum point at $(0, 1)$:

$$y'' = \frac{(1 - x^2)^{3/2} - x(\tfrac{3}{2})(1 - x^2)^{1/2}(-2x)}{(1 - x^2)^3}$$

$$= \frac{(1 - x^2) + 3x^2}{(1 - x^2)^{5/2}} = \frac{2x^2 + 1}{(1 - x^2)^{5/2}}.$$

The second derivative cannot be zero since
$2x^2 + 1$ is positive for all values of x. The
second derivative is also positive for all
permissible values of x which means the
curve is concave up for these values.

Using this information we sketch the
graph in Fig. 3–20.

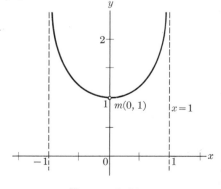

FIGURE 3–20

Exercises

In Exercises 1 through 6, use the method of the examples of this section to sketch the graph of the given function.

1. $y = \dfrac{4}{x^2}$

2. $y = \dfrac{x}{x - 2}$

3. $y = x^2 + \dfrac{2}{x}$

4. $y = x + \dfrac{4}{x^2}$

5. $y = \dfrac{1}{x^2 - 1}$

6. $y = x\sqrt{1 - x^2}$

7. Sketch R_T as a function of R for the function relating the combined resistance of the circuit given in Exercise 15 of Section 2–5.

8. A chain fence is to be constructed to enclose a rectangular area of 20,000 ft². A previously constructed wall is to be used for one side. Sketch the length of fence to be built as a function of the side of the fence parallel to the wall.

9. A cylindrical oil drum is to be made such that it will contain 20 ft³. Sketch the area of sheet metal required for construction as a function of the radius of the drum.

10. Sketch P as a function of r for the function relating power and resistance of the circuit given in Exercise 19 of Section 2–7. Assume values of $E = 6$ volts and $R = 1$ ohm.

3–6 Applied maximum and minimum problems

In geometry and in other fields, problems frequently occur which require finding a maximum or minimum value of some function. The methods we have already discussed regarding the finding of maximum or minimum values are valid in these problems. The principal difficulty which arises in these problems is the finding of the proper functions to maximize or minimize. Once we determine this function, we take a derivative with respect to a variable in which it is expressed, and then set the derivative equal to zero. Sufficient information must be given so that a unique solution is possible. Often this information is available, but we must analyze the wording of the problem carefully in order to find it. Also, many times it is more convenient to set up more than one function, based on the given information, and to find a derivative of each, with respect to the same variable. We can then eliminate, by substitution, any undesired variables or derivatives which appear in each. The following examples illustrate these methods.

Example A. Find the number which exceeds its square by the greatest amount.

We must set up a function which expresses the difference between a number and its square. Let the number be x, and let the difference be D. Then $D = x - x^2$. Taking a derivative, we have

$$\frac{dD}{dx} = 1 - 2x.$$

Setting the derivative equal to zero, we have $0 = 1 - 2x$. Solving for x, we obtain the result $x = \frac{1}{2}$. The second derivative gives $d^2D/dx^2 = -2$, which states that the second derivative is always negative. This means that whenever the first derivative is zero, it represents a maximum. Usually it is not necessary to test for maximum or minimum, since the nature of the problem will indicate which must be the case. For example, in this problem we know that numbers greater than 1 do not exceed their squares at all. The same is true for all negative numbers. Thus the answer must lie between 0 and 1.

Example B. Find the maximum possible area of a rectangle whose perimeter is 16 units.

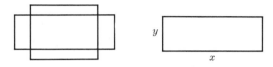

FIGURE 3–21

When we reflect on this problem, we see that there are limitless possibilities for rectangles of a perimeter of 16 units and differing areas (Fig. 3–21). For example, if the sides are 7 and 1, the area is 7. If the sides are 6 and 2, the area is 12. Therefore we set up a function for the area of a rectangle in terms of its sides x and y:

$$A = xy.$$

We know, however, one other important fact: that the perimeter is 16. Thus $2x + 2y = 16$. Solving for y, we have $y = 8 - x$. Substituting this equation into the expression for the area, we have $A = x(8 - x) = 8x - x^2$. Taking a derivative of this, we obtain $dA/dx = 8 - 2x$. Setting this derivative equal to zero, we arrive at the final result of $x = 4$. Thus $x = 4$ and $y = 4$ give the maximum area of 16.

Example C. Find the point on the parabola $y = x^2$ which is nearest the point $(6, 3)$.

In this example we must set up a function for this distance between a general point (x, y) on the parabola and the point $(6, 3)$. This relation is

$$D = \sqrt{(x - 6)^2 + (y - 3)^2}.$$

However, to make it easier for us to take derivatives, we shall square both sides of this expression. If a function is a minimum, then so is its square. We shall also use the fact that the point (x, y) is on $y = x^2$ by replacing y by x^2. Thus we have

$$D^2 = (x - 6)^2 + (x^2 - 3)^2 = x^2 - 12x + 36 + x^4 - 6x^2 + 9$$
$$= x^4 - 5x^2 - 12x + 45;$$
$$\frac{dD^2}{dx} = 4x^3 - 10x - 12, \qquad 0 = 2x^3 - 5x - 6.$$

Using synthetic division or some similar method, we find that the solution to this equation is $x = 2$. Thus the required point on the parabola is $(2, 4)$. (See Fig. 3–22.)

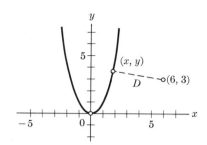

FIGURE 3–22

Example D. Find the most economical dimensions for a cylindrical cup which holds a specified volume.

When we analyze the wording of the problem carefully, we see that we are to minimize the surface area of a right circular cylinder which has a bottom, but no top. Also the volume is to be considered as constant. Thus we set up expressions for the surface area and volume:

$$A = \pi r^2 + 2\pi rh, \qquad V = \pi r^2 h.$$

Since the volume is not specified numerically, it is easier to take the derivative of each of these formulas separately. The derivatives may be taken with respect to either r or h. Let us choose r, and write

$$\frac{dA}{dr} = 2\pi r + 2\pi r\frac{dh}{dr} + 2\pi h, \qquad \frac{dV}{dr} = 0 = 2\pi rh + \pi r^2\left(\frac{dh}{dr}\right).$$

Setting dA/dr equal to zero, and at the same time eliminating the derivative dh/dr by substitution, we have

$$0 = 2\pi r + 2\pi r\left(-\frac{2h}{r}\right) + 2\pi h$$

or

$$0 = r - 2h + h.$$

This last equation tells us that $h = r$, which is the relation between dimensions for the most economical cup. (See Fig. 3–23.)

FIGURE 3–23

Example E. The intensity of illumination from a light source at any point varies directly as the strength of the source and inversely as the square of the distance from the source. Given two sources, of strengths 8 units and 1 unit, respectively, which are 100 ft apart, determine at what point between them the intensity is the least, assuming that the intensity at any point is the sum of the intensities of the two sources.

Let $I =$ the sum of the intensities and
    $x =$ the distance from the source of strength 8.

Then we find that

$$I = \frac{8}{x^2} + \frac{1}{(100 - x)^2}$$

is the function between the intensity and the distance from the source of strength 8. We must now take a derivative of I with respect to x, set it equal to zero, and solve for x to find the point at which the intensity is a minimum:

$$\frac{dI}{dx} = -\frac{16}{x^3} + \frac{2}{(100 - x)^3} = \frac{-16(100 - x)^3 + 2x^3}{x^3(100 - x)^3}.$$

This function will be zero if the numerator is zero. Therefore we have

$$2x^3 - 16(100 - x)^3 = 0 \qquad \text{or} \qquad x^3 = 8(100 - x)^3.$$

Taking cube roots of each side, we have

$$x = 2(100 - x) \qquad \text{or} \qquad x = 66.7 \text{ ft.}$$

The point where the intensity is a minimum is 66.7 ft from the 8-unit source of intensity.

Exercises

1. The product of two positive numbers is 64. Find them if their sum is a minimum.
2. Find the dimensions of the largest rectangle which can be inscribed in a quarter-circle of radius 4.
3. If the hypotenuse of a right triangle is 10, what must the sides be so that the area is a maximum? $h = b$
4. A rectangular field bounded on one side by a river is to be fenced in. If no fencing is required along the river, what is the maximum area which can be enclosed if 2000 ft of fencing are used? 500×1000
5. A box with a square base is open at the top. If 108 ft^2 of material are used, what is the maximum volume possible for the box? $s = 2h$
6. What is the area of the largest rectangle which can be inscribed in the first quadrant under the parabola $y = 4 - x^2$?
7. What is the maximum *slope* of the curve $y = 6x^2 - x^3$?
8. The x- and y-components of a projectile are given by $x = 120t$ and $y = 160t - 16t^2$. Find the greatest height the projectile reaches.
9. An open box is to be made from a square piece of cardboard whose sides are 8 in. long by cutting equal squares from the corners and bending up the sides. Determine the side of the square which is to be cut out in order that the volume of the box may be a maximum. quadratic equation
10. Find the relation between the radius and the height of a right circular cylinder for which the surface area is to be a minimum for a given volume.

—11. A certain area is a rectangle with a semicircle at each end. Find the open side of the rectangle if the perimeter is 8 units and the area of the rectangle is to be a maximum.

— 12. A company finds that there is a net profit of \$10 for each of the first 1000 units produced each week. For each unit over 1000 produced, there is 2 cents less profit per unit. How many units should be produced each week to net the greatest profit?   *1250 units*

13. The deflection y of a beam of length L at a horizontal distance x from one end is given by $y = k(2x^4 - 5Lx^3 + 3L^2x^2)$, where k is a constant. For what value of x does the maximum deflection occur?

14. The electrical power (in watts) produced by a certain source is given by

$$P = \frac{144r}{(r + 0.6)^2},$$

where r is the resistance in the circuit. For what value of r is the power a maximum?

15. The strength of a rectangular beam is proportional to the product of its width and the square of its depth. Find the dimensions of the strongest beam that can be cut from a circular log 16 in. in diameter.

16. A specially made cylindrical container is made of stainless steel sides and bottom and a silver top. If silver is ten times as expensive as stainless steel, what are the most economical dimensions of the container if it is to hold 10π in^3?

Miscellaneous exercises for Chapter 3

1. Find the equation of the line tangent to the parabola $y = 3x - x^2$ at the point $(-1, -4)$.

2. Find the equation of the line tangent to the curve

$$y = x^2 - \frac{2}{x}$$

at the point $(2, 3)$.

3. Find the equation of the line normal to

$$y = \frac{x}{4x - 1}$$

at the point $(1, 1/3)$.

4. Given that the x- and y-coordinates of a moving particle are given as a function of time by the parametric equations $x = t^4 - t$, $y = 1/t$, find the magnitude and direction of the velocity when $t = 2$.

5. Find the magnitude and direction of the acceleration for the particle in Exercise 4.

6. A particle moves along the curve of $y = 1/(x + 2)$ with a constant velocity in the x-direction of 4 cm/sec. Find v_y at $(2, 1/4)$.

In Exercises 7 through 9 sketch the graph of the given function by use of information obtained from the function as well as information obtained from the derivatives.

7. $y = 27x - x^3$ 8. $y = x^4 - 32x$ 9. $y = \dfrac{x}{x + 1}$

10. The parabolas $y = x^2 + 2$ and $y = 4x - x^2$ are tangent to each other. Find the equation of the line tangent to them at the point of tangency.

11. An electron is moving along the path $y = 1/x$ at the constant velocity of 10^4 cm/sec. Find the velocity in the x-direction when the electron is at the point $(2, 1/2)$.

12. Sketch a continuous curve having the following characteristics.

$$f(0) = 1, \qquad\qquad f'(0) = 0,$$

$$f''(x) < 0 \quad\text{for } x < 0, \qquad f'(x) > 0 \quad\text{for } |x| > 0,$$

$$f''(x) > 0 \quad\text{for } x > 0.$$

13. A machine part is to be in the shape of a circular sector of radius r and central angle θ. Find r and θ if the area is one unit and the perimeter is a minimum.

14. The current I through a circuit with a resistance R and a battery whose voltage is E and whose internal resistance is r is given by $I = E/(R + r)$. If R is a variable resistor, changing at the rate of 0.2 ohm/min, how fast is the current changing when $R = 6$ ohms, if $E = 3$ volts and $r = 0.2$ ohm?

15. A beam of rectangular cross section is to be cut from a log 2 ft in diameter. The stiffness varies as the width and the cube of the depth. What dimensions will give the beam maximum stiffness?

16. An alpha-particle moves through a magnetic field along the parabolic path $y = x^2 - 4$. Determine the closest that the particle comes to the origin.

17. Sketch a graph of van der Waals equation (see Exercise 18 of Section 2–7), assuming the following values: $R = T = a = 1$ and $b = 0$. For many gases the value of a is much greater than that for b. Even though the values of $R = T = 1$ are not realistic, the *shape* of the curve will be correct for the assumed value of $b = 0$.

18. The base of a conical machine part is being milled such that the height is decreasing at the rate of 0.05 in/min. If the part originally had a radius of 1 in. and height of 3 in., how fast is the volume changing when the height is 2.8 in.?

19. Two ships leave the same port at the same time, one traveling south at the rate of 12 mi/hr and the other traveling east at the rate of 5 mi/hr. At what rate is the distance between them changing two hours after they leave the port?

20. A Norman window has the form of a rectangle surmounted by a semicircle. Find the dimensions (radius of circular part and height of rectangular part) of the window that will admit the most light if the perimeter of the window is 12 ft.

4 Integration

4–1 Differentials

Physical investigations of phenomena often lead to information regarding the rate of change of a variable. Then in order to arrive at the functional relationship, we have to reverse the process of differentiation. Other applications of this reverse process involve finding areas under curves and finding volumes of solids. As we shall see, these basic problems, although apparently rather distinct, have a very similar mathematical interpretation.

We shall now define the *differential* of a function $y = f(x)$ as

$$dy = f'(x)\, dx. \tag{4–1}$$

In Eq. (4–1), the quantity dy is the differential of y, and dx is the differential of x. The differential dx is defined as equal to Δx, the increment in x. We define it purposely in this way, so that $f'(x) = dy/dx$. In this way we can interpret the derivative as the ratio of the differential of y to the differential of x. That is, now the derivative can be considered as a fraction.

Example A. Find the differential of $y = 3x^5 - x$.

$$\frac{dy}{dx} = f'\left(3x^5 - x\right)dx$$

In this example, $f(x) = 3x^5 - x$, which in turn means that $f'(x) = 15x^4 - 1$. Thus $dy = (15x^4 - 1)\, dx$.

Example B. Find the differential of $y = (2x^3 - 1)^4$.

$$dy = 4(2x^3 - 1)^3(6x^2)\, dx = 24x^2(2x^3 - 1)^3\, dx.$$

We shall find that this definition will clarify the connection between the various interpretations of the reverse process of differentiation. Although the principal purpose in introducing it here is to be able to utilize the notation, there are valuable direct applications of the differential.

113

The applications of the differential are based upon the fact that the differential of y, dy, closely approximates the increment in y, Δy, if the differential of x, dx, is small. To better understand this statement, let us look at Fig. 4–1. Recalling the meaning of Δx and Δy, we see that the points $P(x, y)$ and $Q(x + \Delta x, y + \Delta y)$ lie on the curve of $f(x)$. However, $f'(x) = dy/dx$ at P, which means if we draw a tangent line at P, its slope may be indicated by dy/dx. By choosing $\Delta x = dx$, we can see the difference between Δy and dy. It can be seen that as dx becomes smaller, Δy more nearly equals dy.

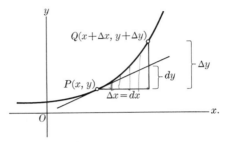

FIGURE 4–1

For given changes in x, it is necessary to use the Δ-process to find the exact change, Δy, in y. However, for small values of Δx, dy can be used to closely approximate Δy. Generally dy is much more easily determined than is Δy.

Example C. Calculate Δy and dy for $y = x^3 - 2x$ for $x = 3$ and $\Delta x = 0.1$.
By the Δ-process we find

$$\Delta y = 3x^2\, \Delta x + 3x(\Delta x)^2 + (\Delta x)^3 - 2\, \Delta x.$$

Using the given values we find

$$\Delta y = 3(9)(0.1) + 3(3)(0.01) + (0.001) - 2(0.1) = 2.591.$$

The differential of y is

$$dy = (3x^2 - 2)\, dx.$$

Since $dx = \Delta x$, we have

$$dy = [3(9) - 2](0.1) = 2.5.$$

Thus, $\Delta y = 2.591$ and $dy = 2.5$. We see that in this case dy is very nearly equal to Δy.

The fact that dy can be used to approximate Δy is useful in determining the error in a result, if the data is in error, or the equivalent problem of finding the change in a result if a change is made in the data. The following example illustrates the method.

Example D. The edge of a cube was determined to be 9.00 in. From this value the volume was found. Later it was discovered that the value of the edge was 0.20 in. too small. Approximately by how much was the volume in error?

The volume V of a cube, in terms of an edge, e, is $V = e^3$. Since we wish to find the change in V for a given change in e, this means we want the value of dV for $de = 0.2$ in. Thus,

$$dV = 3e^2 \, de,$$

$$dV = 3(9.00)^2(0.20) = 48.6 \text{ in}^3.$$

We see that the volume was in error by about 49 in^3.

Often when considering the error of a given value or result, the actual numerical value of the error, the *absolute error*, is not as important as its size is in relation to the size of the quantity itself. The ratio of the absolute error to the size of the quantity itself is known as the *relative error*. The relative error is commonly expressed as a percentage.

Example E. Referring to Example D, we see that the absolute error in the edge was 0.20 in. The relative error in the edge was $0.20/9.00 = 0.022 = 2.2\%$. The absolute error in the volume is 49 in^3, whereas the relative error in the volume is $49/729 = 0.067 = 6.7\%$.

Exercises

In Exercises 1 through 8, find the differential of each of the given functions.

1. $y = x^5 + x$ 2. $y = 3x^2 + 6$ 3. $y = (x^2 - 1)^4$ 4. $y = (4 + 3x)^{1/3}$
5. $y = x/(x + 1)$ 6. $y = x\sqrt{1 - 4x}$ 7. $y = 1/x^2$ 8. $y = 1/\sqrt{1 - x^3}$

In Exercises 9 and 10 find the values of Δy and dy for the given values of x and Δx.

9. $y = 7x^2 + 4x$, $x = 4$, $\Delta x = 0.2$ 10. $y = x^4$, $x = 2$, $\Delta x = 0.1$

In Exercises 11 and 12 determine dy for the given values of x and Δx.

11. $y = (1 - 3x)^5$, $x = 1$, $\Delta x = 0.1$ 12. $y = x/\sqrt{6x - 1}$, $x = 3$, $\Delta x = 0.2$

13. If the side of a square is measured to be 16 in., and an error of 1 in. is found in the measurement, approximately by how much is the original calculation of area in error?

14. If the radius of a circle is measured to be 8.00 in., and the measurement has a maximum possible error of 0.03 in., what is the maximum possible relative error in the area of the circle?

15. The voltage of a certain thermocouple as a function of temperature is given by $E = 6.2T + 0.0002T^3$. What is the approximate change in voltage if the temperature changes from 100°C to 101°C?

16. The velocity of an object rolling down a certain inclined plane is given by $v = \sqrt{100 + 16h}$, where h is the distance traveled along the plane by the object. What is the increase in velocity (in ft/sec) of an object in moving from 20 to 21 ft along the plane? What is the relative change in the velocity?

17. What is the volume of metal used to make a right circular cylindrical container of radius 3.0 in. and height 4.0 in., if the thickness of sheet metal from which it was made is 0.1 in.?

18. A precisely measured 10-ohm resistor (any error in its value will be considered negligible) is put in parallel with a variable resistor R. The combined resistance of the two resistors is $R_T = 10R/(10 + R)$. What is the relative error of the combined resistance, if R is measured at 40 ohms, with a possible error of 2 ohms?

19. Show that an error of 2% in the measurement of the side of a square results in an error of approximately 4% in the calculation of the area.

20. Show that the relative error in the calculation of the volume of a sphere is approximately three times the relative error in the measurement of the radius.

4–2 Inverse differentiation

Since many kinds of problems in technology can be solved by reversing the process of finding a derivative or a differential, we shall introduce the basic technique of this procedure in this section. This reverse process is known as *integration*. In the next section we shall formalize the process of integration, but it is only the basic idea that is the topic of this section. Many of the applications of integration are found in Chapter 5. The following example illustrates the method.

Example A. Find a function for which the derivative is $8x^3$.

We know that, when we set out to find the derivative of a polynomial, we reduce the power of x by 1. Also we multiply the coefficient by the power of x. Thus the power of the function must have been 4, since the power in the derivative is 3. A factor of 4 of the derivative must also be divided out in the process of finding the function. If we write the derivative as $2(4x^3)$, we recognize $4x^3$ as the derivative of x^4. Therefore the desired function is $y = 2x^4$. We can verify our result by finding the derivative.

In many applied problems, the differential of a function can be determined. It is then necessary to find the function. Using the same method as that used in Example A, the function can be found.

Example B. Find a function for which the differential is $(x^2 + 2x)\, dx$.

As for the x^2, we know that the power of x required in the function is 3. Also, to make the coefficient correct, we have to multiply by $\frac{1}{3}$. The $2x$ should be recognized as the derivative of x^2. Therefore the required function is

$y = \frac{1}{3}x^3 + x^2$. The factor dx no longer appears; since it is introduced in the process of finding the differential, we must exclude it in the reverse process.

A great many functions to which we must apply the process of inverse differentiation, integration, are not polynomials. It is these functions which may cause more difficulty in the process of integration. The reader is advised to pay special attention to the following example, for it illustrates a type of problem which will be found to be very important.

Example C. Find a function for which the differential is $3(x^3 - 1)^2(3x^2)\,dx$.

Noting that we have a power of $x^3 - 1$ in the differential, it is reasonable that the function itself may include a power of $x^3 - 1$. Since the differential has $x^3 - 1$ raised to the power 2, the function would then have $x^3 - 1$ raised to the power 3. Noting that the differential of $(x^3 - 1)^3$ is $3(x^3 - 1)^2(3x^2)\,dx$, the desired function is $(x^3 - 1)^3$. We note that the factor $3x^2\,dx$ does not appear in the function, for it was included from the process of finding a differential. It therefore must be present in order that $(x^3 - 1)^3$ may be the function, but it must also be excluded in the reverse process of differentiation.

Exercises

In Exercises 1 through 6, find a function for which each of the given expressions represents the derivative.

1. $3x^2$ 2. $5x^4$ 3. $6x^3 + 1$ 4. $-\dfrac{1}{x^2}$ 5. $x^4 - x$ 6. $6(2x + 1)^5(2)$

[handwritten annotations: over 1: x^3; over 3: $\frac{2}{3}x^4 + x$; over 5: $\frac{1}{5}x^5 - \frac{1}{2}x^2$]

In Exercises 7 through 15, find a function for which each of the given expressions represents the differential.

7. $6x^5\,dx$ 8. $9x^2\,dx$ 9. $(2x^2 - x)\,dx$

10. $(x^2 - 5)\,dx$ 11. $4(x^2 - 1)^3(2x)\,dx$ 12. $x(x^2 - 1)^3\,dx$

13. $(2x^4 + 1)\,dx$ 14. $5(2x^4 + 1)^4(8x^3)\,dx$ 15. $x^3(2x^4 + 1)^4\,dx$?

[handwritten annotations: over 7: x^6; after 8: $(x^2-1)^4$; over 9: $\frac{2}{3}x^3 - \frac{1}{2}x^2$; under 13: $\frac{2}{5}x^5 + x$; under 15: $f(x) = \dfrac{(2x^4 + 1)^5}{40}$]

4–3 The indefinite integral

Having developed the basic technique of integration as the inverse of differentiation, we now establish certain basic formulas for integration. First, one point in the process of integration should be mentioned.

In the previous section, when given the differential of a function, and then asked to find the function, we made no mention of the fact that the answers to the examples given there, and the answers to the exercises, are not unique. That is, we could have added any constant to the answers, and the result would still have been correct. This is due to the fact that the derivative of a constant is zero.

Example A. The differentials of x^3, $x^3 + 4$, $x^3 - 7$ and $x^3 + 4\pi$ are all $3x^2\,dx$. This means that any of the functions listed would be a proper answer to the problem of finding the function of which the differential is $3x^2\,dx$.

For the above reason, we define the *indefinite integral* of a function $f(x)$, for which $dF(x)/dx = f(x)$, as

$$\int f(x)\,dx = F(x) + C, \qquad (4\text{--}2)$$

where C is an arbitrary constant, called the *constant of integration*. We must have additional information, beyond a knowledge of the differential, in order to assign a value to C. Since C does not have a definite value without this additional information, we employ the term "indefinite integral." The symbol $\int$ is the *integral sign*, and indicates that the inverse of the differential is to be found.

Example B. $\int 5x^4\,dx = x^5 + C$.

We might think that the inclusion of this constant C would affect the derivative of the function x^5. However, the only effect of the C is to raise or lower the curve. The slope of $x^5 + 1$, $x^5 - 5$, or any function of the form $x^5 + C$ is the same for any given value of x. As Fig. 4–2 shows, tangents drawn to the curves are all parallel for the same value of x.

At this point we shall derive some basic formulas for integration. Since

$$\frac{d(cu)}{dx} = c\,\frac{du}{dx},$$

where u is a function of x, we can write

$$\int c\,du = c\int du = cu + C. \qquad (4\text{--}3)$$

Also, since the derivative of a sum of functions equals the sum of the derivatives, we write

$$\int (du + dv) = u + v + C. \qquad (4\text{--}4)$$

FIGURE 4–2

To find the derivative of a power of a function, we multiply by the power and subtract 1 from it. To find the integral, we reverse this by adding 1 to the power of $f(x)$ in $f(x)\,dx$, and dividing by this new power. The power formula for integration is therefore

$$\int u^n\,du = \frac{u^{n+1}}{n+1} + C, \qquad n \neq -1. \qquad (4\text{--}5)$$

When we use the above formulas, we must be able to recognize not only the proper form, but also all the component parts of the given formula. Unless you can do this, and unless you have a good knowledge of differentiation, you will have trouble in applying Eq. (4–5). Most of the difficulty, if it exists, arises from improper identification of du. The following examples illustrate the use of the above formulas.

$$\frac{6x^2}{2} = 3x^2 + C$$

Example C. Integrate: $\int 6x\, dx$.

First we must identify u, n, du, and any multiplying constants. By noting that 6 is a multiplying constant, we identify x as u, which in turn means that dx must be du and $n = 1$. Hence

$$\int 6x\, dx = 6 \int x\, dx = 6 \left(\frac{x^2}{2}\right) + C = 3x^2 + C.$$

Example D. Integrate: $\int (5x^3 - 6x^2 + 1)\, dx$.

In solving this problem, we have to use a combination of all three of the above formulas. Thus we have

$$\int (5x^3 - 6x^2 + 1)\, dx = \int 5x^3\, dx + \int (-6x^2)\, dx + \int dx$$
$$= 5 \int x^3\, dx - 6 \int x^2\, dx + \int dx.$$

In the first of these integrals, $u = x$, $n = 3$, and $du = dx$. In the second, $u = x$, $n = 2$, and $du = dx$. The third is a direct application of Eq. (4–3), with $c = 1$ and $du = dx$. Thus we have

$$5 \int x^3\, dx - 6 \int x^2\, dx + \int dx = 5 \left(\frac{x^4}{4}\right) - 6 \left(\frac{x^3}{3}\right) + x + C$$
$$= \frac{5}{4} x^4 - 2x^3 + x + C.$$

Example E. Integrate: $\int \left(\sqrt{x} - \frac{1}{x^3}\right) dx$.

We write

$$\int \left(\sqrt{x} - \frac{1}{x^3}\right) dx = \int x^{1/2}\, dx - \int x^{-3}\, dx = \frac{1}{3/2} x^{3/2} - \frac{1}{-2} x^{-2} + C$$
$$= \frac{2}{3} x^{3/2} + \frac{1}{2} x^{-2} + C = \frac{2}{3} x^{3/2} + \frac{1}{2x^2} + C.$$

Example F. Integrate: $\int (x^2 + 1)^3 (2x\, dx)$.

We first note that $n = 3$, for this is the power involved in the function being integrated. If $n = 3$, then $x^2 + 1$ must be u. If $u = x^2 + 1$, then $du = 2x\, dx$.

Thus the integral is in proper form for integration *as it stands*. Using the power formula, we have

apply (4-5) $$\int (x^2 + 1)^3 (2x\, dx) = \frac{(x^2 + 1)^4}{4} + C.$$ $f(x) = \frac{4(x^2+1)^3(2x)}{4}$

It is in this type of problem that recognition of the proper form of a differential is very important. Only a good knowledge of differential forms, along with sufficient experience, makes ready recognition of this type possible. It cannot be overemphasized that the entire quantity $(2x\, dx)$ must be equated to du, if we are to integrate properly. This illustrates that u and n are normally recognized first, and then the proper form of du is derived from u.

Example G. Integrate: $\int x^2 \sqrt{x^3 + 2}\, dx.$ $= \int x^2 (x^3+2)^{1/2}\, dx$

We first note that $n = \frac{1}{2}$ and u is then $x^3 + 2$. Since $u = x^3 + 2$, $\underline{du} = 3x^2\, dx$. In order to integrate properly, we must group the quantity $3x^2\, dx$ as $\underline{du}$, with other factors isolated from this quantity. Since there is no 3 under the integral sign, we introduce one. In order not to change the numerical value, we also introduce a $\frac{1}{3}$, normally before the integral sign. In this way we take full advantage of the fact that a constant (and only a constant) factor may be moved across the integral sign. The next form we should write is

$$\int x^2 \sqrt{x^3 + 2}\, dx = \tfrac{1}{3} \int \sqrt{x^3 + 2}\; (3x^2\, dx).$$

In this way we indicate the proper grouping to result in the correct form of Eq. (4–5). Thus

$$\int x^2 \sqrt{x^3 + 2}\, dx = \tfrac{1}{3} \cdot \tfrac{2}{3}(x^3 + 2)^{3/2} + C = \tfrac{2}{9}(x^3 + 2)^{3/2} + C.$$

The $1/\frac{3}{2}$ was written as $2/3$, since this form is generally more convenient when we are working with fractions.

We mentioned earlier that, in addition to knowing the differential, we need more information in order to find the constant of integration. Such information usually consists of a set of values which the function is known to satisfy. That is, a point through which the curve of the function passes would provide the necessary information.

Example H. Find y in terms of x, given that $dy/dx = 3x - 1$, and the curve passes through $(1, 4)$.

When we write the equation as $dy = (3x - 1)\, dx$, then indicate the integration $\int dy = \int (3x - 1)\, dx$, the result of this integration is $y = \frac{3}{2}x^2 - x + C$. We know that the required curve passes through $(1, 4)$, which means that the coordinates of this point must satisfy the equation. Thus $4 = \frac{3}{2} - 1 + C$, or

$C = \frac{7}{2}$. The complete solution is $y = \frac{3}{2}x^2 - x + \frac{7}{2}$, or

$$2y = 3x^2 - 2x + 7.$$

Example I. At each point of a certain curve, the slope is given by $x\sqrt{2 - x^2}$. Given that the curve passes through $(1, 2)$, find its equation.

We write

$$\frac{dy}{dx} = x\sqrt{2 - x^2}, \qquad y = \int x\sqrt{2 - x^2}\, dx.$$

To integrate this last expression, we recognize that $n = \frac{1}{2}$, $u = 2 - x^2$, and that therefore $du = -2x\, dx$. Hence

$$y = -\tfrac{1}{2}\int (2 - x^2)^{1/2}(-2x\, dx) = -\tfrac{1}{2} \cdot \tfrac{2}{3}(2 - x^2)^{3/2} + C$$

$$= -\tfrac{1}{3}(2 - x^2)^{3/2} + C.$$

Using the coordinates of the point $(1, 2)$, we have

$$2 = -\tfrac{1}{3}(2 - 1)^{3/2} + C \qquad \text{or} \qquad C = \tfrac{7}{3},$$

and

$$3y = 7 - (2 - x^2)^{3/2}.$$

Exercises

In Exercises 1 through 22, integrate each of the given expressions.

1. $\displaystyle\int 2x\, dx$

2. $\displaystyle\int x^5\, dx$

3. $\displaystyle\int x^{3/2}\, dx$

4. $\displaystyle\int x^{-4}\, dx$

5. $\displaystyle\int \sqrt[3]{x}\, dx$

6. $\displaystyle\int \frac{1}{\sqrt{x}}\, dx$

7. $\displaystyle\int (x^2 - x^5)\, dx$

8. $\displaystyle\int (1 - x)^2\, dx$

9. $\displaystyle\int (x\sqrt{x} - 5x^2)\, dx$

10. $\displaystyle\int \left(4x - \frac{2}{x^3}\right) dx$

11. $\displaystyle\int \sqrt{x}(x^2 - x)\, dx$

12. $\displaystyle\int (x^{1/3} + x^{1/5} + x^{-1/7})\, dx$

13. $\displaystyle\int (x^2 - 1)^5(2x\, dx)$

14. $\displaystyle\int (x^3 - 2)^6(3x^2\, dx)$

15. $\displaystyle\int (x^4 + 3)^4(4x^3\, dx)$

16. $\displaystyle\int (1 - 2x)^{1/3}(-2\, dx)$

17. $\displaystyle\int (x^5 + 4)^7 x^4\, dx$

18. $\displaystyle\int x^2(1 - x^3)^{4/3}\, dx$

19. $\displaystyle\int \frac{x\,dx}{\sqrt{6x^2 + 1}}$

20. $\displaystyle\int \frac{x^2\,dx}{\sqrt{2x^3 + 1}}$

21. $\displaystyle\int \frac{x - 1}{\sqrt{x^2 - 2x}}\,dx$

22. $\displaystyle\int (x^2 - x)(x^3 - \tfrac{3}{2}x^2)^8\,dx$

In Exercises 23 through 25, find y in terms of x.

23. $\dfrac{dy}{dx} = 6x^2,$ curve passes through $(0, 2)$

24. $\dfrac{dy}{dx} = x + 1,$ curve passes through $(-1, 4)$

25. $\dfrac{dy}{dx} = x^2(1 - x^3)^5,$ curve passes through $(1, 5)$

26. Find the equation of the curve whose slope is $-x\sqrt{1 - 4x^2}$ and which passes through $(0, 7)$.

27. Find the equation of the curve for which the second derivative is $12x^2$. The curve passes through $(1, 6)$ with a slope of 4.

4–4 The area under a curve

Another basic problem which can be solved by integration is that of finding the area under a curve. In geometry, there are methods and formulas for finding the area of regular figures. By means of the calculus we will find it possible to find the area between curves for which we know the equations. First let us look at an example which illustrates the basic idea behind the method we shall develop.

Example A. Approximate the area in the first quadrant under the parabola $y = x^2 + 1$ and to the left of the line $x = 4$. First make this approximation by inscribing two rectangles of equal width in the area and finding the sum of the areas of these rectangles. Then improve the approximation by repeating the process using eight rectangles.

The area to be approximated is shown in Fig. 4–3(a). The area with two rectangles inscribed under the curve is shown in Fig. 4–3(b). The first approximation, admittedly small, of the area can be found by adding the areas of the two rectangles. Both rectangles have a width of 2. The left rectangle is 1 unit high and the right rectangle is 5 units high. Thus, the area of the two rectangles is

$$A = 2(1 + 5) = 12 \text{ sq. units.}$$

A much better approximation is found by inscribing the eight rectangles as shown in Fig. 4–3(c). Each of these rectangles has a width of $\tfrac{1}{2}$. The leftmost

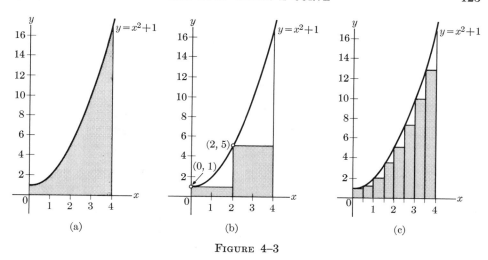

FIGURE 4–3

rectangle has a height of 1. The next has a height of $\frac{5}{4}$, which is determined by finding y for $x = \frac{1}{2}$. The next rectangle has a height of 2, which is found by evaluating y for $x = 1$. Finding the heights of all the rectangles and multiplying their sum by $\frac{1}{2}$ gives the area of the eight rectangles as

$$A = \tfrac{1}{2}(1 + \tfrac{5}{4} + 2 + \tfrac{13}{4} + 5 + \tfrac{29}{4} + 10 + \tfrac{53}{4})$$

$$= \tfrac{43}{2} = 21.5 \text{ sq. units.}$$

An even better approximation could be obtained by inscribing more rectangles under the curve. The greater the number of rectangles, the more nearly the sum of their areas equals the area under the curve. By a method involving integration developed later in this section we could determine the *exact* area to be $\frac{76}{3} = 25\frac{1}{3}$ sq. units.

We are now in a position to understand the basic method involved in finding an area under a curve as the sum of the areas of rectangles inscribed under the curve, as the number of rectangles is assumed to increase without bound. The reason for this last condition is that, as we saw in Example A, as the number of rectangles increases, the approximation of the area is better. Following is a specific example of this technique.

Example B. Find the area under the straight line $y = 2x$, above the x-axis, and to the left of the line $x = 4$.

We might mention at the beginning that this area can easily be found, since the figure is a triangle. However, the method we shall use here is the important concept at the moment. We first subdivide the interval from $x = 0$ to $x = 4$

# of rectangles

width

into n inscribed rectangles of Δx in width. Then
the extremities of the intervals are labeled a, x_1,
$x_2, \ldots , b \; (=x_n)$, as shown in Fig. 4-4, where

$$x_1 = \Delta x,$$
$$x_2 = 2\,\Delta x,$$
$$\vdots$$
$$x_{n-1} = (n-1)\,\Delta x,$$
$$b = n\,\Delta x.$$

FIGURE 4–4

We then find the area for each of the rectangles.
These areas are (for the respective rectangles):

First	$f(a)\,\Delta x,$	$f(a) \; = f(0) = 2(0) = 0$ equals length,
Second	$f(x_1)\,\Delta x,$	$f(x_1) = 2(\Delta x) = 2\,\Delta x$ equals length,
Third	$f(x_2)\,\Delta x,$	$f(x_2) = 2(2\,\Delta x) = 4\,\Delta x$ equals length,
Fourth	$f(x_3)\,\Delta x,$	$f(x_3) = 2(3\,\Delta x) = 6\,\Delta x$ equals length,
$\vdots$		
Last	$f(x_{n-1})\,\Delta x,$	$f[(n-1)\,\Delta x] = 2(n-1)\,\Delta x$ equals length.

These areas are now summed up as follows:

→ length of last rectangle

$$A_n = f(a)\,\Delta x + f(x_1)\,\Delta x + \cdots + f(x_{n-1})\,\Delta x$$
$$= f(0)\,\Delta x + f(\Delta x)\,\Delta x + \cdots + f[(n-1)\,\Delta x]\,\Delta x$$
$$= 0 + 2\,\Delta x(\Delta x) + 4\,\Delta x(\Delta x) + \cdots + 2[(n-1)\,\Delta x]\,\Delta x$$
$$= \{2\,\Delta x[(1+2+3+\cdots+(n-1)]\}\,\Delta x$$
$$= 2\,(\Delta x)^2[1+2+3+\cdots+(n-1)].$$

Now $b = n\,\Delta x$, or $4 = n\,\Delta x$, or $\Delta x = 4/n$. Thus

$$A_n = 2\left(\frac{4}{n}\right)^2 [1+2+3+\cdots+(n-1)].$$

The sum $1+2+3+\cdots+n-1$ is the indicated sum of an arithmetic
progression with the first term equal to 1 and the nth term equal to $n-1$.
This sum is

$$s = \frac{n-1}{2}(1+n-1) = \frac{n(n-1)}{2} = \frac{n^2-n}{2}\,.$$

Now the expression for the sum of the areas can be set forth as

$$A_n = \frac{32}{n^2}\left(\frac{n^2-n}{2}\right) = 16\left(1-\frac{1}{n}\right).$$

This expression is an approximation to the actual area under consideration. The larger n becomes, the better the approximation. If we let $n \to \infty$ (which is equivalent to letting $\Delta x \to 0$), the limit of this sum will equal the area in question. Thus

$$A = \lim_{n \to \infty} 16 \left(1 - \frac{1}{n}\right) = 16.$$

(This checks with the geometric result.) The area under the curve can be considered as the limit of the sum of the inscribed rectangles as the number of rectangles approaches infinity.

The method indicated in Example B illustrates the interpretation of finding an area as a summation process, although it should not be considered as a proof. However, we shall find that integration proves to be a much more useful method for finding an area. Let us now see how integration can be used directly.

Let ΔA represent the area $BCEG$ under the curve, as indicated in Fig. 4–5. We see that the following inequality is true for the indicated areas:

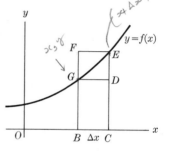

$$A_{BCDG} < \Delta A < A_{BCEF}.$$

If the point G is now designated as (x, y) and E as $(x + \Delta x, y + \Delta y)$, we have $y \Delta x < \Delta A < (y + \Delta y) \Delta x$. Dividing through by Δx, we have

$$y < \frac{\Delta A}{\Delta x} < y + \Delta y.$$

FIGURE 4–5

Now we take the limit as $\Delta x \to 0$ (Δy then also approaches 0). This results in the relation

$$\frac{dA}{dx} = y. \tag{4–6}$$

This is true since the left member of the inequality is y and the right member approaches y. Also remember that

$$\lim_{\Delta x \to 0} \frac{\Delta A}{\Delta x} = \frac{dA}{dx}.$$

We shall now use Eq. (4–6) to show the method of finding the complete area under a curve. We now let $x = a$ be the left boundary of the desired area, and $x = b$ be the right boundary (Fig. 4–6). The area under the curve to the right of $x = a$ and bounded on the right by the line GB is now designated as A_{ax}. From Eq. (4–6), we have

$$dA_{ax} = \Big[y\,dx \Big]_a^x \quad \text{or} \quad A_{ax} = \Big[\int y\,dx \Big]_a^x, \cdot$$

where $[\ ]_a^x$ is the notation used to indicate the boundaries of the area. Thus

$$A_{ax} = \left[\int f(x)\,dx\right]_a^x = \left[F(x) + C\right]_a^x. \quad (4\text{–}7)$$

But we know that if $x = a$, then $A_{aa} = 0$. Thus $0 = F(a) + C$, or $C = -F(a)$. Therefore

$$A_{ax} = \left[\int f(x)\,dx\right]_a^x = F(x) - F(a). \quad (4\text{–}8)$$

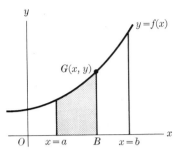

FIGURE 4–6

Now, to find the area under the curve that reaches from a to b, we write

$$A_{ab} = F(b) - F(a). \quad (4\text{–}9)$$

Thus the area under the curve that reaches from a to b is given by

$$A_{ab} = \left[\int f(x)\,dx\right]_a^b = F(b) - F(a). \quad (4\text{–}10)$$

This shows that the area under the curve may be found by integrating the function $f(x)$ to find the function $F(x)$, which is then evaluated at each boundary value. The area is the difference between these values of $F(x)$.

In Example B, we found an area under a curve by finding the limit of the sum of the inscribed rectangles as the number of rectangles approaches infinity. Equation (4–10) expresses the area under a curve in terms of integration. We can now see that we have obtained the area by summation and also expressed it in terms of integration. Thus we conclude that summations can be evaluated by integration. Also, we have grasped the connection between the problem of finding the slope of a tangent to a curve (differentiation) and the problem of finding an area (integration). We would not normally suspect that these two problems would have solutions which lead to reverse processes. We have also seen that the definition of integration has much more application than originally anticipated.

Example C. Find the area under the curve $y = x^2$ between the lines $x = 1$ and $x = 2$.

In Eq. (4–10), $f(x) = x^2$. Therefore

$$F(x) = \int x^2\,dx = x^3/3 + C;$$

$$A_{1,2} = F(2) - F(1) = \left(\frac{2^3}{3} + C\right) - \left(\frac{1^3}{3} + C\right)$$

$$= \tfrac{8}{3} - \tfrac{1}{3} = \tfrac{7}{3}.$$

Thus the required area is $\tfrac{7}{3}$ square units. This is the exact area, not an approximation. (See Fig. 4-7.) (The area as approximated by the sum of the areas of rectangles would have become exact when the limit as $n \to \infty$ ($\Delta x \to 0$) was taken.)

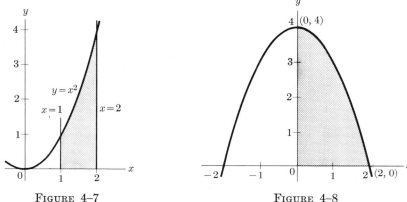

FIGURE 4-7　　　　　　　　　　FIGURE 4-8

Example D. Find the area under the curve $y = 4 - x^2$ which lies in the first quadrant.

By solving the equation $4 - x^2 = 0$, we determine that the area to be found extends from $x = 0$ to $x = 2$. (See Fig. 4-8.) Thus

$$\int (4 - x^2)\, dx = 4x - \frac{x^3}{3} + C;$$

$$A_{0,2} = (8 - \tfrac{8}{3} + C) - (0 - 0 + C) = \tfrac{16}{3}.$$

We can see from these examples that we do not have to include the constant of integration when we are finding areas. It cancels out when the values are subtracted.

Exercises

In each of Exercises 1 through 6, find the approximate area under the given curves by dividing the indicated intervals into n intervals, and adding the areas of the inscribed rectangles. The height of each rectangle may be found by evaluating the function for the proper value of x.

1. $y = x^2$　($x = 0$ to $x = 2$, $n = 4$)　　　　2. $y = 2x$　($x = 0$ to $x = 2$, $n = 4$)
3. $y = x^2 + 2$　($x = 1$ to $x = 4$, $n = 3$)
4. $y = 1 - x^3$　($x = 0$ to $x = 1$, $n = 2$)
5. $y = 4x - x^2$　($x = 1$ to $x = 4$, $n = 6$)
6. $y = \sqrt{x}$　($x = 1$ to $x = 4$, $n = 3$)

In Exercises 7 through 12, use the areas indicated in Exercises 1 through 6; find the exact value of each indicated area by use of Eq. (4-10).

4–5 The definite integral

Using reasoning similar to that in the preceding section, we define the *definite integral* of a function $f(x)$ as

$$\int_a^b f(x)\, dx = F(b) - F(a), \tag{4–11}$$

where $F'(x) = f(x)$. We call this a *definite integral* because the final result of integrating and evaluating is a number. (The *indefinite* integral had an arbitrary constant in the result.) The numbers a and b are called the *lower limit* and the *upper limit*, respectively. We can see that the value of a definite integral is found by evaluating the function (found by integration) at the upper limit and subtracting the value of this function at the lower limit.

We know, from the analysis in the preceding section, that this definite integral can be interpreted as a summation process, where the size of the subdivision approaches a limit of zero. This fact explains the choice of the $\int$ symbol for integration: It is an elongated S, representing the sum. It is this interpretation of integration which we shall apply to many kinds of problems.

Example A. Evaluate the integral $\int_0^2 x^4\, dx$.
  We write

$$\int_0^2 x^4\, dx = \left.\frac{x^5}{5}\right|_0^2 = \frac{2^5}{5} - 0 = \frac{32}{5}.$$

Note that a vertical line—with the limits written at the top and the bottom— is the way the value is indicated after integration, but before evaluation.

Example B. Evaluate $\int_1^3 (x^{-2} - 1)\, dx$.
  We set this forth as

$$\int_1^3 (x^{-2} - 1)\, dx = \left. -\frac{1}{x} - x \right|_1^3 = \left(-\frac{1}{3} - 3 \right) - (-1 - 1)$$

$$= 2 - \frac{10}{3} = -\frac{4}{3}.$$

Example C. Evaluate $\int_0^1 5x\,(x^2 + 1)^5\, dx$.
  For purposes of integration, $n = 5$, $u = x^2 + 1$, and $du = 2x\, dx$. Hence

$$\int_0^1 5x(x^2 + 1)^5\, dx = \frac{5}{2} \int_0^1 (x^2 + 1)^5 (2x\, dx) = \frac{5}{2} \cdot \frac{1}{6} (x^2 + 1)^6 \Big|_0^1$$

$$= \frac{5}{12} (2^6 - 1^6) = \frac{5(63)}{12} = \frac{105}{4}.$$

Example D. Evaluate $\int_{-1}^{3} x(1 - 3x^2)^{1/3}\, dx$.

For purposes of integration, $n = \frac{1}{3}$, $u = 1 - 3x^2$, and $du = -6x\, dx$. Thus

$$\int_{-1}^{3} x(1 - 3x^2)^{1/3}\, dx = -\tfrac{1}{6}\int_{-1}^{3} (1 - 3x^2)^{1/3}(-6x\, dx)$$

$$= -\tfrac{1}{6} \cdot \tfrac{3}{4}(1 - 3x^2)^{4/3}\Big|_{-1}^{3} = -\tfrac{1}{8}(-26)^{4/3} + \tfrac{1}{8}(-2)^{4/3}$$

$$= \tfrac{1}{8}(2\sqrt[3]{2} - 26\sqrt[3]{26}) = \tfrac{1}{4}(\sqrt[3]{2} - 13\sqrt[3]{26}).$$

Example E. Evaluate

$$\int_{0}^{4} \frac{x + 1}{(x^2 + 2x + 2)^3}\, dx.$$

For purposes of integration,

$$n = -3, \qquad u = x^2 + 2x + 2, \qquad \text{and} \qquad du = (2x + 2)\, dx.$$

Therefore

$$\int_{0}^{4} (x^2 + 2x + 2)^{-3}(x + 1)\, dx = \frac{1}{2}\int_{0}^{4} (x^2 + 2x + 2)^{-3}[2(x + 1)\, dx]$$

$$= \frac{1}{2} \cdot \frac{1}{-2} (x^2 + 2x + 2)^{-2}\Big|_{0}^{4}$$

$$= -\frac{1}{4}(16 + 8 + 2)^{-2} + \frac{1}{4}(0 + 0 + 2)^{-2}$$

$$= \frac{1}{4}\left(-\frac{1}{26^2} + \frac{1}{2^2}\right) = \frac{1}{4}\left(\frac{1}{4} - \frac{1}{676}\right)$$

$$= \frac{1}{4}\left(\frac{168}{676}\right) = \frac{21}{338}.$$

It should be pointed out that the definition of the definite integral is valid regardless of the source of $f(x)$. That is, we may apply the definite integral whenever we want to sum a function in a manner similar to that which we use to find an area.

Exercises

Evaluate the given definite integrals.

1. $\int_{0}^{1} 2x\, dx$ 2. $\int_{1}^{4} x^{5/2}\, dx$ 3. $\int_{1}^{5} \sqrt{2x - 1}\, dx$ 4. $\int_{4}^{9} (x\sqrt{x} - 1)\, dx$

5. $\displaystyle\int_{-1}^{1} (1 - x)^{1/3}\, dx$

6. $\displaystyle\int_{1}^{4} \frac{x^2 + 1}{\sqrt{x}}\, dx$

7. $\displaystyle\int_{0}^{3} (x^4 - x^3 + x^2)\, dx$

8. $\displaystyle\int_{0}^{3} x^2(x^3 + 2)^{3/2}\, dx$

9. $\displaystyle\int_{0}^{4} (1 - \sqrt{x})^2\, dx$

10. $\displaystyle\int_{0}^{1} x(3x^2 - 1)^3\, dx$

11. $\displaystyle\int_{0}^{4} \frac{x\, dx}{\sqrt{x^2 + 9}}$

12. $\displaystyle\int_{2}^{3} \frac{x^2 + 1}{(x^3 + 3x)^2}\, dx$

13. $\displaystyle\int_{3}^{7} 3\sqrt{4x - 3}\, dx$

14. $\displaystyle\int_{-1}^{0} x^3(1 - 2x^4)^2\, dx$

15. $\displaystyle\int_{0}^{1} (x^2 + 3)(x^3 + 9x + 6)\, dx$

4–6 Graphical integration

To this point we are limited to integrating algebraic functions, primarily by use of the power rule. There are many other kinds of functions and methods of integration. These methods, many of which are taken up later in Chapter 8, are based on the analytic use of the equation relating the variables. If empirical data are known, or we have a function which cannot be integrated by present methods, it is possible to plot the graph and develop methods of performing the integration graphically. In this section we shall develop a graphical method based upon the area under a curve. This method, which has similarities to the method of graphical differentiation presented in Chapter 2, is developed in the following example.

Example A. For the curve given in Fig. 4–9(a), find the curve of the integral by graphical means.

FIGURE 4–9

Let us first divide the area under the curve into equal (this is not essential, but is usually convenient) intervals along the x-axis as shown in Fig. 4–9(b). A horizontal line is then drawn through the leftmost vertical strip such that the area of the rectangle created is estimated as best possible as equal to the area under that portion of the curve. This requires that the area of the "triangle" above the curve equals the area of the "triangle" below the curve. A *pole*, k units from the origin, is chosen on the negative x-axis, just as in the case of graphical differentiation. A line, called a *ray*, is drawn from the pole to the point of the y-axis where the horizontal line cuts the y-axis. This is the line r_1. Finally a line is drawn from the origin to the right boundary of the rectangle such that it is parallel to the ray r_1. The two end points of this last line are points on the integral curve.

Since the ray and the line from the origin are parallel, two similar triangles are created. Referring to Fig. 4–9(b), we see that

$$\frac{y_1}{k} = \frac{a}{\Delta x}$$

or

$$y_1 \, \Delta x = ak.$$

However, $y_1 \, \Delta x$ is the area of the rectangle and therefore ak equals this area. Since the area under the curve equals the area of the rectangle, ak equals the area under this portion of the curve. Thus, a scale k times the y-scale is indicated on the right. This is the proper scale for the area A, and therefore of the integral curve.

A horizontal line is now drawn through the second vertical strip such that the area of the rectangle equals the area under this portion of the curve. This line is then extended to the y-axis. A ray r_2 is drawn from the pole, and a line parallel to this ray is then drawn from the end of the similar line of the first area to the right boundary of the second rectangle. This gives another point on the integral curve. This process is kept up for the desired number of intervals. The result gives points on the integral curve which can then be joined by a smooth curve representing the area A under the given curve, which therefore represents the integral. See Fig. 4–9(c).

This method of integration is valuable, as was mentioned previously, for finding the integral curve for a set of empirical data or a function which cannot be integrated by methods developed thus far. The following examples illustrate the method of graphical integration in these cases.

Example B. By graphical integration, find the integral curve of the function defined by the following table. (Such values could easily be arrived at empirically.)

x	0.0	1.0	2.0	3.0	4.0	5.0	6.0	7.0
y	1.0	1.4	2.1	4.0	5.2	4.8	4.0	3.2

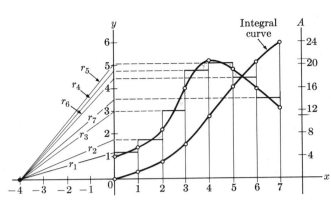

FIGURE 4–10

Observation of Fig. 4–10 indicates the curve found by plotting the data and the resulting curve. Since $k = 4$, the A-scale is four times that of the y-scale.

We might note that the integral curve can be used to evaluate the definite integral $\int_0^c y \, dx$, where c is a particular value of x. The A-coordinate of the integral curve is the value of this integral. For example, in this case $\int_0^4 y \, dx = 11$, and $\int_0^6 y \, dx = 21$ approximately.

Example C. By graphical integration, find the value of $\int_0^5 \sqrt{x^2 + 1} \, dx$.

By letting $y = \sqrt{x^2 + 1}$, we plot the graph of y vs. x from the following table. See Fig. 4–11.

x	0	1	2	3	4	5
y	1.0	1.4	2.2	3.2	4.1	5.1

Thus, $\int_0^5 \sqrt{x^2 + 1} \, dx = 14.0$, since this is the estimated value of the A-coordinate for $x = 5$. Methods of direct integration of this function give the value 13.9.

FIGURE 4–11

Two other points deserve mention. First, if a definite integral with a lower limit of a value other than zero is to be evaluated, subtraction of the appropriate A-values gives the result. For example, in Example B, $\int_4^6 y\, dx = 10$ approximately. Second, the integral curve found is the graph of the function of the indefinite integral, where the constant of integration is evaluated such that the curve passes through the origin. For other constants of integration, the entire curve can be raised or lowered by the appropriate number of units. Applications of this method to problems in technology are found in Chapter 5.

Exercises

In Exercises 1 through 4 copy the given curve to a larger scale, and then find the integral curve.

1.

2.

3.

4.

In Exercises 5 through 8, plot the given sets of data, and then find the integral curve.

5.

x	0	2	4	6	8	10
y	5.0	3.8	1.4	0.6	1.5	2.8

6.

x	0	0.1	0.2	0.3	0.4	0.5
y	0.1	0.9	1.1	0.7	0.6	1.2

7.

x	0	15	30	45	60	75
y	5	40	75	65	45	20

8.

x	0	5	10	15	20	25
y	0	−1	−3	−2	2	10

In Exercises 9 through 12, use graphical integration to evaluate the given integrals. In Exercises 9 and 10 check the results by direct integration.

9. $\displaystyle\int_0^4 \sqrt{1+x}\, dx$ 10. $\displaystyle\int_2^5 \frac{2x\, dx}{\sqrt{x^2+5}}$ 11. $\displaystyle\int_1^3 \frac{dx}{x+1}$ 12. $\displaystyle\int_3^{15} \frac{x\, dx}{\sqrt{x+1}}$

13. By graphical integration, find the integral curve for

$$y = \frac{1}{x^2+1}.$$

Then draw a curve "parallel" to the given curve such that it passes through $(0, 2)$. In this way the constant of integration is 2 greater than that of the original integral curve.

14. By graphical integration, find the integral curve for

$$y = \frac{x^3 + 1}{x + 2}.$$

Then draw a curve "parallel" to the integral curve such that it passes through $(2, -4)$. Find the difference between the constants of integration.

15. By graphical integration, find the area in the first quadrant under the curve $y = (6x - x^2 - 5)^{3/2}$.

4–7 Numerical integration: the trapezoidal rule

For data and functions which cannot be directly integrated by present methods, it is possible to develop numerical methods of integration as well as graphical methods as shown in the last section. There are a great many such numerical techniques for approximating the value of an integral, but we shall develop only one of these, the trapezoidal rule. It is based upon the area under a curve.

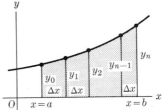

The area to be found is subdivided into n intervals of equal width. Perpendicular lines are then dropped from the curve (or points, if only a given set of numbers is available). If the points on the curve are joined by straight-line segments, the area of successive parts under the curve is then approximated by finding the area of each of the trapezoids formed. However, if these points are not too far apart, the approximation will be very good (see Fig. 4–12). From geometry we

FIGURE 4–12

recall that the area of a trapezoid equals one-half the product of the sum of the bases times the altitude. For these trapezoids the bases are the y-coordinates and the altitudes are Δx. When we thus indicate the sum of these trapezoidal areas, we have

$$A_T = \tfrac{1}{2}(y_0 + y_1)\,\Delta x + \tfrac{1}{2}(y_1 + y_2)\,\Delta x + \tfrac{1}{2}(y_2 + y_3)\,\Delta x + \cdots$$
$$+ \tfrac{1}{2}(y_{n-2} + y_{n-1})\,\Delta x + \tfrac{1}{2}(y_{n-1} + y_n)\,\Delta x.$$

We note, when this addition is performed, that the result is

$$A_T = (\tfrac{1}{2}y_0 + y_1 + y_2 + \cdots + y_{n-1} + \tfrac{1}{2}y_n)\,\Delta x. \qquad (4\text{–}12)$$

The y-values to be used are either derived from the function as $y_1 = f(x_1)$, or are the y-coordinates of a set of data.

Example A. Use the trapezoidal rule to find the approximate value of the area under the curve $xy = 1$, from $x = 1$ to $x = 3$. Let $n = 4$.

Figure 4–13 shows the graph. In this example

$$\Delta x = \frac{3 - 1}{4} = \frac{1}{2}, \qquad y_0 = f(a) = f(1) = 1,$$

$$y_1 = f\left(\frac{3}{2}\right) = \frac{2}{3}, \qquad y_2 = f(2) = \frac{1}{2},$$

$$y_3 = f\left(\frac{5}{2}\right) = \frac{2}{5}, \qquad \text{and} \qquad y_n = y_4 = f(b) = f(3) = \frac{1}{3}.$$

And so we write

$$A_T = \left[\frac{1}{2}(1) + \frac{2}{3} + \frac{1}{2} + \frac{2}{5} + \frac{1}{2}\left(\frac{1}{3}\right)\right]\frac{1}{2}$$

$$= \left(\frac{15 + 20 + 15 + 12 + 5}{30}\right)\frac{1}{2} = \frac{67}{30}\left(\frac{1}{2}\right) = \frac{67}{60}.$$

Note that we cannot perform this integration directly by methods developed up to this point.

FIGURE 4–13

FIGURE 4–14

Example B. Use the trapezoidal rule to find the approximate area under the curve $y = \sqrt{x^2 + 1}$ from $x = 0$ to $x = 1$. Let $n = 5$.

Figure 4–14 shows the graph. In this example,

$$\Delta x = \frac{1 - 0}{5} = 0.2.$$

Therefore

$$y_0 = f(0) = 1, \qquad y_1 = f(0.2) = \sqrt{1.04} = 1.02,$$

$$y_2 = f(0.4) = \sqrt{1.16} = 1.08, \qquad y_3 = f(0.6) = \sqrt{1.36} = 1.17,$$

$$y_4 = f(0.8) = \sqrt{1.64} = 1.28, \qquad y_5 = f(1) = \sqrt{2.00} = 1.41.$$

Hence we have

$$A_T = \left[\frac{1}{2}(1) + 1.02 + 1.08 + 1.17 + 1.28 + \frac{1}{2}(1.41)\right](0.2) = 1.15.$$

Example C. The following points were found empirically:

x	0	1	2	3	4	5
y	5.68	6.75	7.32	7.35	6.88	6.24

Find the area under the curve determined by these data.

We find the values of y_0, y_1, etc., directly from the table, and we sketch the graph in Fig. 4–15. Then we have

FIGURE 4–15

$$A_T = [\tfrac{1}{2}(5.68) + 6.75 + 7.32 + 7.35 + 6.88 + \tfrac{1}{2}(6.24)] = 34.26.$$

Exercises

In Exercises 1 through 8, use the trapezoidal rule to find the approximate area under each indicated curve, between the indicated values of x, for the given value of n.

1. $y = 2x^2$ $(x = 0 \text{ to } x = 2, n = 4)$ Check by direct integration.

2. $y = 1 - x^2$ $(x = 0 \text{ to } x = 1, n = 3)$ Check by direct integration.

3. $y = \dfrac{1}{2x}$ $(x = 2 \text{ to } x = 3, n = 2)$

4. $y = \dfrac{1}{x^2 + 1}$ $(x = 1 \text{ to } x = 4, n = 3)$

5. $y = \sqrt{4 - x^2}$ $(x = 0 \text{ to } x = 2, n = 4)$

6. $y = \sqrt{x^3 + 1}$ $(x = 0 \text{ to } x = 2, n = 4)$

7. $y = \dfrac{1}{x^2 + x}$ $(x = 1 \text{ to } x = 4, n = 3)$

8. $y = 2^x$ $(x = 0 \text{ to } x = 3, n = 6)$

In Exercises 9 through 11, find the approximate area under each of the curves defined by the given sets of data.

9.

x	3	4	5	6	7
y	1.08	1.65	3.23	3.67	2.97

10.

x	2	4	6	8	10	12	14
y	0.67	2.34	4.56	3.67	3.56	4.78	6.87

11.

x	1.4	1.7	2.0	2.3	2.6	2.9	3.2
y	0.18	7.87	18.23	23.53	24.62	20.93	20.76

Miscellaneous exercises for Chapter 4

In Exercises 1 through 11, evaluate the given integrals.

1. $\int (4x^3 - x)\, dx$

2. $\int x(x - 3x^4)\, dx$

3. $\int_1^4 \frac{1 + x}{\sqrt{x}}\, dx$

4. $\int x(1 - 2x^2)^5\, dx$

5. $\int \frac{dx}{(2 - 5x)^2}$

6. $\int_1^2 \frac{x^3 + 1}{x^2}\, dx$

7. $\int (7 - 2x)^{3/4}\, dx$

8. $\int_4^{25} \frac{dx}{2x\sqrt{x}}$

9. $\int_0^2 \frac{3x\, dx}{\sqrt[3]{1 + 2x^2}}$

10. $\int \frac{x^2 - 3}{\sqrt{6 + 9x - x^3}}\, dx$

11. $\int_1^3 (x^2 + x + 2)(2x^3 + 3x^2 + 12x)\, dx$

In Exercises 12 through 14, find the differential of each of the given functions.

12. $y = \dfrac{1}{(2x - 1)^2}$

13. $y = x\sqrt[3]{1 - 3x}$

14. $y = \dfrac{3 + x}{4 - x^2}$

15. Find the equation of the curve which passes through $(-1, 3)$ for which the slope is given by $3 - x^2$.

16. By use of Eq. (4–10), find the area in the first quadrant under the curve $y = 8x - x^4$.

For Exercises 17 and 18 use the following set of points.

x	0.0	3.0	6.0	9.0	12	15	18	21
y	1.8	2.5	2.0	1.2	0.2	1.0	6.0	12

17. Find the integral curve by graphical integration. Evaluate the area under the curve from $x = 6$ to $x = 21$.

18. Find the area under the curve from $x = 6$ to $x = 21$ by use of the trapezoidal rule, with $n = 5$.

For Exercises 19 through 21, use the function

$$y = \frac{x}{x^2 + 2}.$$

Approximate the area under the curve in the first quadrant to the left of the line $x = 5$ by the indicated method.

19. Inscribe five rectangles and find the sum of the areas of the rectangles.

20. Use graphical integration.

21. Use the trapezoidal rule with $n = 5$.

22. Evaluate $\Delta y - dy$ for $y = x^3$ if $x = 2$ and $\Delta x = 0.1$.

23. A ball bearing 4.00 mm in radius is coated with a special metal of thickness 0.02 mm. Approximately what volume of the special metal is used?

24. The electric resistance of a certain resistor as a function of temperature is given by $R = 12.00 + 0.06T + 0.0001T^2$. Approximately by how much does the resistance (in ohms) change as T changes from 100°C to 102°C?

25. The impedance Z of an electric circuit as a function of the resistance R and the reactance X is given by $Z = \sqrt{R^2 + X^2}$. Derive an expression for the relative error in impedance for an error in R and given value of X.

26. Show that the relative error of the nth root of a given measurement equals approximately $1/n$ of the relative error of the measurement.

5 Applications of integration

5-1 Applications of the indefinite integral

The applications of integration in engineering and technology are numerous. In this section we shall present two basic applications of the indefinite integral, with other applications being indicated in the exercises. In the sections which follow are found many of the basic applications of the definite integral.

The first of these applications deals with velocity and acceleration. The concepts of velocity as a first derivative and acceleration as a second derivative were introduced in Chapters 2 and 3. Here we shall apply integration to the problem of finding the distance as a function of time, when we know the relationship between acceleration and time, as well as certain specific values of distance and velocity. These latter values are necessary for determining the values of the constants of integration which are introduced. Recalling now that the acceleration a is given by $a = dv/dt$, we can find the expression for the velocity in terms of a, t, and the constant of integration. We write

$$dv = a\,dt \qquad \text{or} \qquad v = \int a\,dt. \tag{5-1}$$

If the acceleration is constant, we have

$$v = at + C_1. \tag{5-2}$$

Of course, Eq. 5-1 can be used in general to find the velocity as a function of time so long as we know the acceleration as a function of time. However, since the case of constant acceleration is often encountered, Eq. (5-2) is often encountered. If the velocity is known for some specified time, the constant C_1 may be evaluated.

Example A. Find the expression for the velocity if $a = 12t$, given that $v = 8$ when $t = 1$.

Using Eq. (5–1), we have

$$v = \int (12t) \, dt = 6t^2 + C_1.$$

Substituting the known values, we obtain

$$8 = 6 + C_1 \quad \text{or} \quad C_1 = 2.$$

Thus $v = 6t^2 + 2$.

Example B. For an object falling under the influence of gravity, the acceleration due to gravity is essentially constant. Its value is -32 ft/sec^2. (The minus sign is chosen so that all quantities directed up are positive, and all quantities directed down are negative.) Find the expression for the velocity of an object under the influence of gravity if $v = v_0$ when $t = 0$.

We write

$$v = \int (-32) \, dt = -32t + C_1, \quad v_0 = 0 + C_1; \quad v = v_0 - 32t.$$

The velocity v_0 is called the initial velocity.

Once we obtain the expression for velocity, we can integrate to find the expression for distance in terms of the time. That is,

$$s = \int v \, dt . \tag{5–3}$$

Example C. Find the expression for distance in terms of time, if $a = 6t^2$, $v = 0$ when $t = 2$, and $s = 4$ when $t = 0$.

$$v = \int 6t^2 \, dt = 2t^3 + C_1; \quad 0 = 2(2^3) + C_1; \quad C_1 = -16;$$

$$v = 2t^3 - 16.$$

$$s = \int (2t^3 - 16) \, dt = \tfrac{1}{2}t^4 - 16t + C_2; \quad 4 = 0 - 0 + C_2; \quad C_2 = 4;$$

$$s = \tfrac{1}{2}t^4 - 16t + 4.$$

Example D. Find the expression for the distance above the ground of an object, given a vertical velocity of v_0 from the ground.

From Example B, we know that $v = v_0 - 32t$. In this problem we know that $s = 0$ when $t = 0$ (given velocity v_0 *from the ground*) if distances are measured from ground level. Therefore

$$s = \int (v_0 - 32t) \, dt = v_0 t - 16t^2 + C_2; \quad 0 = 0 - 0 + C_2; \quad C_2 = 0;$$

$$s = v_0 t - 16t^2.$$

The second basic application of the indefinite integral which we shall discuss comes from the field of electricity. By definition, the current i in an electric circuit equals the time rate of change of the charge q (in coulombs) which passes a given point in the circuit, or

$$i = \frac{dq}{dt}.$$ (5–4)

Rewriting this expression in differential notation as $dq = i\,dt$ and integrating both sides of the equation we have

$$q = \int i\,dt.$$ (5–5)

Now, the voltage V_C across a capacitor C is given by $V_C = q/C$. By combining equations, the voltage V_C is given by

$$V_C = \frac{1}{C} \int i\,dt.$$ (5–6)

Here, V_C is measured in volts, C in farads, i in amperes, and t in seconds.

Example E. The current in a certain electric circuit as a function of time is given by $i = 6t^2 + 4$. Find an expression for the amount of charge which passes a point in the circuit as a function of time. Assuming that $q = 0$ when $t = 0$, determine the total charge which passes the point in two seconds.

Since $q = \int i\,dt$, we have

$$q = \int (6t^2 + 4)\,dt$$
$$= 2t^3 + 4t + C.$$

This last expression is the desired expression giving charge as a function of time. We note that when $t = 0$, then $q = C$, which means that the constant of integration represents the initial charge, or the charge which passed a given point before we started timing. Using q_0 to represent this charge, we have

$$q = 2t^3 + 4t + q_0.$$

Now, returning to the second part of the problem, we see that $q_0 = 0$. Therefore, evaluating q for $t = 2$ sec, we have

$$q = 2(8) + 4(2) = 24 \text{ coulombs.}$$

This is the charge which passes any specified point in the circuit in two seconds.

Example F. A certain capacitor is measured to have a voltage of 100 volts across it. At this instant a current as a function of time given by $i = 0.06\sqrt{t}$ is sent through the circuit. After 0.25 sec, the voltage across the capacitor is measured to be 140 volts. What is the capacitance of the capacitor?

From Eq. (5–6) we have

$$V_C = \frac{1}{C} \int i \, dt.$$

Substituting $i = 0.06\sqrt{t}$, we find that

$$V_C = \frac{1}{C} \int (0.06\sqrt{t} \, dt) = \frac{0.06}{C} \int t^{1/2} \, dt$$

$$= \frac{0.04}{C} t^{3/2} + C_1.$$

From the given information we know that $V_C = 100$ volts when $t = 0$. Thus,

$$100 = \frac{0.04}{C}(0) + C_1 \qquad \text{or} \qquad C_1 = 100 \text{ volts.}$$

This means that

$$V_C = \frac{0.04}{C} t^{3/2} + 100.$$

We also know that $V_C = 140$ volts when $t = 0.25$ sec. Therefore,

$$140 = \frac{0.04}{C} (0.25)^{3/2} + 100,$$

$$40 = \frac{0.04}{C} (0.125),$$

or

$$C = 1.25 \times 10^{-4} \text{ farad.}$$

Exercises

1. Find the distance above the ground of an object after 3 sec, if the object is given an initial upward velocity of 120 ft/sec.

2. The acceleration of a certain particle is given by $a = t^4$. Find the distance traveled in 2 sec if $v = 6$ and $s = 0$ when $t = 0$.

3. Find the velocity (in ft/sec) after 8 sec of an object which starts from rest and is given an acceleration of $a = \sqrt{t+1}$.

4. The acceleration of an object is given by $6t$. What is the relation between s and t for this object if $s = 8$ when $t = 1$ and $s = 4$ when $t = 2$?

5. Standing on a cliff, a man throws a ball with a vertical velocity of 64 ft/sec upward. If the ball hits the ground at the base of the cliff 7 sec after it is released, how far is it from the top of the cliff to the ground below?

6. A man wishes to throw an object to a height 100 ft above him. What initial vertical velocity must he give the object?

7. The current in a certain wire changes with time according to the relation $i = \sqrt[3]{1 + 3t}$. How many coulombs of charge pass a specified point in the first 3 seconds?

8. The current in a certain circuit as a function of time is given by $i = 8 - t$. If $q_0 = 0$, for what value of t, greater than zero, is $q = 0$? What interpretation can be given to this result?

9. The voltage across a 1.5×10^{-4} farad capacitor is 50 volts. What is the voltage after 1 second if a current $i = 0.012t^{1/5}$ further charges the capacitor?

10. A current $i = t/\sqrt{t^2 + 1}$ is sent into a circuit containing a previously uncharged 4×10^{-6} farad capacitor. How long does it take for the capacitor voltage to be 100 volts?

11. The angular velocity ω is the time rate of change of the angular displacement θ of a rotating object. If the angular velocity of an object is given by $\omega = 4t$, find an expression for the angular displacement θ if $\theta = 0$ when $t = 0$.

12. The angular acceleration α is the time rate of change of the angular velocity. If the angular acceleration of a rotating object is given by $\alpha = \sqrt{2t + 1}$, find the expression for the angular displacement if $\omega = 0$ and $\theta = 0$ when $t = 0$.

13. An inductor in an electric circuit is essentially a coil of wire in which the voltage is affected by a changing current. By definition, the voltage caused by the changing current is given by

$$V_L = L \frac{di}{dt},$$

where L is the inductance and is measured in henries. If $V_L = 12.0 - 0.2t$ for a 3-henry inductor, find the current in the circuit after 10 seconds if the initial current was zero.

14. If the inner and outer walls of a container are at different temperatures, the rate of change of temperature with respect to the distance from one wall is a function of the distance from the wall. Symbolically this is stated as $dT/dx = f(x)$, where T is the temperature. If x is measured from the outer wall, at 20°C, and $f(x) = 72x^2$, find the temperature at the inner wall if the container walls are 0.5 in. thick.

15. Surrounding an electrically charged particle is an electric field. The rate of change of electric potential with respect to the distance from the particle creating the field equals the negative of the value of the electric field. That is $dV/dx = -E$, where E is the electric field. If $E = k/x^2$, where k is a constant, find the electric potential at a distance x_1 from the particle, if $V = 0$ when $x = \infty$.

16. The rate of change of the vertical deflection y with respect to the horizontal distance x from one end of a beam is a function of x. For a particular beam, this function is $k(x^5 + 1350x^3 - 7000x^2)$, where k is a constant. Find y as a function of x.

17. Fresh water is flowing into a brine solution, with an equal volume of mixed solution flowing out. The amount of salt in the solution decreases, but more slowly as time increases. Under certain conditions the time rate of change of mass of salt, in gm/min, is given by $-1/\sqrt{t + 1}$. Find the mass of salt as a function of time if 1000 gm were originally present. Under these conditions, how long would it take for all the salt to be removed?

18. The rate of change of resistance of a certain electric resistor with respect to the temperature is given by $0.002T/\sqrt[3]{3T^2 + 1}$. Find the resistance as a function of temperature if $R = 0.0005$ ohms when $T = 0$°C.

5–2 Areas by integration

In Section 4–4 we introduced the method of finding the area under a curve by means of integration. In the same section we also showed that the area under a curve can be found by a summation process performed on the rectangles inscribed under the curve. In this way it was shown that integration can be interpreted as a summation process. The basic applications of the definite integral use this summation interpretation of the integral. In this section we shall formulate a general procedure for finding the area for which the bounding curves are known. The method is based on the summing of the areas of inscribed rectangles and using integration for the summation.

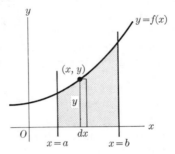

FIGURE 5–1

The first step in finding any area is to make a sketch of the area to be found. Next a "representative element" of area dA (a typical rectangle) should be drawn. In Fig. 5–1 the width of the element is dx. The length of the element is determined by the y-coordinate (of the vertex of the element) of the point on the curve. Thus, we call the length y. The area of this element is $y\,dx$, which in turn means that $dA = y\,dx$, or

$$A = \int_a^b y\,dx = \int_a^b f(x)\,dx. \tag{5–7}$$

This equation states that the elements are to be summed (this is the meaning of the integral sign) from a (the leftmost element) to b (the rightmost element).

Example A. Find the area bounded by the curves $y = 2x^2$, $y = 0$, $x = 1$, and $x = 2$.

The desired area is shown in Fig. 5–2. The rectangle shown is the representative element. Its area is $y\,dx$. The elements are to be summed from $x = 1$ to $x = 2$. Thus

$$A = \int_1^2 y\,dx = \int_1^2 2x^2\,dx = \tfrac{2}{3}x^3\Big|_1^2 = \tfrac{2}{3}(8 - 1) = \tfrac{14}{3}.$$

In Figs. 5–1 and 5–2 the elements are vertical. It is also possible to use horizontal elements, and many problems are simplified by using them. The dif-

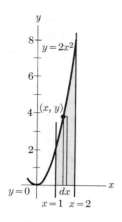

FIGURE 5–2

FIGURE 5–3

ference is that the length (longest dimension) is now measured in terms of the x-coordinate of the point on the curve, and the width becomes dy. In the following example, the area is found by both types of elements.

Example B. Find the area in the first quadrant bounded by $y = 9 - x^2$.

The area to be found is shown in Fig. 5–3. Using first the vertical element of length y and width dx, we have

$$A = \int_0^3 y \, dx = \int_0^3 (9 - x^2) \, dx = \left(9x - \frac{x^3}{3}\right)\Bigg|_0^3 = (27 - 9) - 0 = 18.$$

Now using the horizontal element of length x and width dy, we have

$$A = \int_0^9 x \, dy = \int_0^9 \sqrt{9 - y} \, dy = -\int_0^9 (9 - y)^{1/2}(-dy)$$

$$= -\tfrac{2}{3}(9 - y)^{3/2}\Big|_0^9 = -\tfrac{2}{3}(9 - 9)^{3/2} + \tfrac{2}{3}(9 - 0)^{3/2} = \tfrac{2}{3}(27) = 18.$$

Note that the limits for the vertical elements were 0 and 3, while those for the horizontal elements were 0 and 9. These limits are determined by the direction in which the elements are summed. By definition, vertical elements are summed from left to right, and horizontal elements are summed from bottom to top. Doing it this way means that the summation will be in a positive direction.

The choice of vertical or horizontal elements is determined by (1) which one leads to the simplest solution, or (2) the form of the resulting integral. In some problems it makes little difference which is chosen. However, our present methods of integration do not include many types of integrals. These will be discussed later.

It is also possible to find the area between two curves if one is not an axis. In such a case, the length of the element becomes the difference in the y- or x-coordinates, depending on which element is used. The following examples show how we find this type of area.

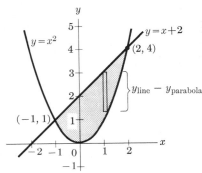

FIGURE 5–4

Example C. Find the area bounded by $y = x^2$ and $y = x + 2$.

This area is indicated in Fig. 5–4. Here we choose vertical elements, since they are all bounded on the top by the line and on the bottom by the parabola. If we choose horizontal elements, the bounding curves are different above $(-1, 1)$ (points of intersection are found by solving equations simultaneously) than below this point. Thus choosing horizontal elements would require two separate integrals for solution. Therefore, using vertical elements, we have

$$A = \int_{-1}^{2} (y \text{ of line} - y \text{ of parabola}) \, dx.$$

(The difference in y's is taken so that it is positive.) Continuing, we have

$$A = \int_{-1}^{2} (x + 2 - x^2) \, dx = \left(\frac{x^2}{2} + 2x - \frac{x^3}{3} \right) \Big|_{-1}^{2}$$

$$= \left(2 + 4 - \frac{8}{3} \right) - \left(\frac{1}{2} - 2 + \frac{1}{3} \right)$$

$$= \frac{10}{3} + \frac{7}{6} = \frac{27}{6} = \frac{9}{2}.$$

Example D. Find the area between $y = x^2$ and $y = x^3$.

Either horizontal or vertical elements may be used equally well (see Fig. 5–5). If we use horizontal elements, we have

$$A = \int_{0}^{1} (y^{1/3} - y^{1/2}) \, dy = \frac{3}{4} y^{4/3} - \frac{2}{3} y^{3/2} \Big|_{0}^{1} = \frac{3}{4} - \frac{2}{3} = \frac{1}{12}.$$

It is important that the length of the element be positive. If the difference is taken incorrectly, the result will be negative. This becomes of definite importance

FIGURE 5–5

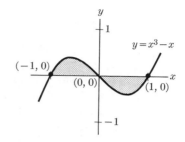

FIGURE 5–6

if part of the area considered is above, and the remainder below, the x-axis. In such a case, the area is found by two integrals. The following example illustrates the necessity of this procedure.

Example E. Find the area between $y = x^3 - x$ and the x-axis.

We note from Fig. 5–6 that the area to the left of the origin is above the axis and the area to the right is below. If we find the area from

$$A = \int_{-1}^{1} (x^3 - x)\, dx = \frac{x^4}{4} - \frac{x^2}{2}\bigg|_{-1}^{1} = (\tfrac{1}{4} - \tfrac{1}{2}) - (\tfrac{1}{4} - \tfrac{1}{2}) = 0,$$

we see that the apparent area is zero. This we know, from the figure, is not correct. Noting that the y-values (of the area) are negative to the right of the origin, we set up the integrals

$$A = \int_{-1}^{0} (x^3 - x)\, dx + \int_{0}^{1} -(x^3 - x)\, dx$$

$$= \left(\frac{x^4}{4} - \frac{x^2}{2}\right)\bigg|_{-1}^{0} - \left(\frac{x^4}{4} - \frac{x^2}{2}\right)\bigg|_{0}^{1}$$

$$= 0 - \left(\frac{1}{4} - \frac{1}{2}\right) - \left(\frac{1}{4} - \frac{1}{2}\right) + 0 = \frac{1}{2}.$$

Exercises

In Exercises 1 through 16, find the areas bounded by the indicated curves.

1. $y = x^2$, $y = 0$, $x = 1$ 2. $y = 2x$, $y = 0$, $x = 2$

3. $y = 2x$, $x = 0$, $y = 2$ 4. $y = x^2 - 2x$, $y = 0$

5. $y = 1 - x$, $x = 0$, $y = 0$ 6. $y = x$, $y = 2 - x$, $x = 0$

7. $y = x^{-2}$, $x = 1$, $x = 2$, $y = 0$ 8. $x = y^2 - y$, $x = 0$

9. $y = x^2$, $y = 2 - x$, $x = 0$ (smaller)

10. $y = x^2$, $y = 2 - x$, $y = 2$ (smallest)

11. $y = x^4$, $y = 16$ 12. $y = x^4 - 8x^2 + 16$, $y = 0$

13. $y = x^2$, $y = \sqrt{x}$ 14. $y = 8 - x^3$, $y = 7x$, $x = 0$

15. $y = x$, $x = -1$, $x = 1$, $y = 0$ 16. $y = x^2 + 2x - 8$, $y = x + 4$

17. Certain physical quantities are often represented as an area under a curve. By definition, power is defined as the time rate of change of performing work. Thus, $p = dw/dt$, or $dw = p\, dt$. Therefore, if $p = 12t - 4t^2$, find the work (in joules) performed in 3 seconds by finding the area under the curve of p versus t.

18. When considering the expansion of a gas, the expression for the work done in the expansion is $w = \int_{V_1}^{V_2} p\, dV$, where p is the pressure of the gas and V is its volume. For an adiabatic (no *heat* gained or lost) change, an approximate relation is $p = kV^{-1.4}$. Given that $k = 1$, find a numerical value for the work done if V changes from 1 to 4 units.

19. It is also possible to represent the change in distance as an area. Since $s = \int v\, dt$, if $v = t^{2/3} + 1$, determine the distance (in feet) that an object moves from $t = 1$ sec to $t = 8$ sec, by finding the area under the curve of v versus t.

20. Find the work (in ergs) done in expanding a gas from 1 cm³ to 5 cm³ if the pressure-volume relation is indicated in Fig. 5–7. Use graphical integration.

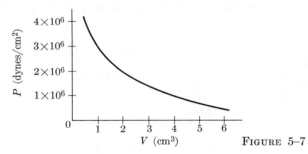

FIGURE 5–7

21. An experiment was performed by expanding a gas under the condition of constant temperature. The data found are tabulated below. How much work (in ergs) was done in the expansion? Use the trapezoidal rule, with $n = 4$.

p (dynes/cm²)	1.02	0.77	0.60	0.47	0.43
V (cm³)		6.0	8.0	10.0	12.0	14.0

(Multiply all values of p by 10^6).

22. A certain tract of land is bounded by a bend in a river and a straight fence. If the distances y from the fence to the river are given for various distances x along the fence from one end to the other as in the following table, find the approximate area of the piece of land by use of the trapezoidal rule, with $n = 8$.

y (ft)	0	15	50	70	95	80	35	20	0
x (ft)	0	10	20	30	40	50	60	70	80

23. Find the area indicated in Exercise 22 by use of graphical integration.

5–3 Volumes by integration

Consider the area, and its representative element (Fig. 5–8) to be rotated about the x-axis. When an area is rotated in this manner, it is said to generate a volume, which is also indicated in the figure. We shall now show methods of finding volumes which are generated in this manner.

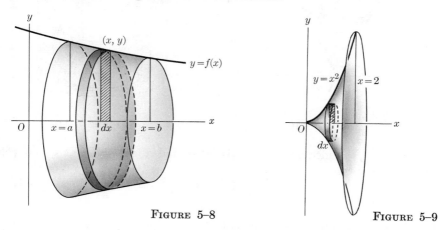

FIGURE 5–8   FIGURE 5–9

As the area rotates about the x-axis, so does its representative element. The element generates a solid for which the volume is known. This is a thin right circular cylinder. We know that the volume of a right circular cylinder is π times the square of the radius times the height of the cylinder. We must now determine the radius and height of this cylinder. Since the element is rotated about the x-axis, the y-coordinate of the point on the curve which touches the element must represent the radius. Also it can be seen that the height is dx (the cylinder is on its side). The representative *element of volume*, a circular *disk*, is $dV = \pi y^2\, dx$. Summing these elements of volume from left to right, we have the total volume V as

$$V = \pi \int_a^b y^2\, dx = \pi \int_a^b [f(x)]^2\, dx. \qquad (5\text{–}8)$$

Thus, by use of Eq. (5–8), we can find the volume generated by an area bounded by the x-axis, which is rotated about the x-axis.

Example A. Find the volume generated by rotating the area bounded by $y = x^2$, $x = 2$, and $y = 0$ about the x-axis.

See Fig. 5–9. By Eq. (5–8), we have

$$V = \pi \int_0^2 (x^2)^2\, dx = \pi \int_0^2 x^4\, dx = \frac{\pi}{5} x^5 \Big|_0^2 = \frac{32\pi}{5}.$$

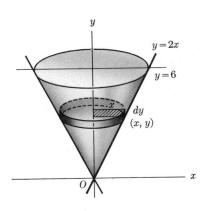

FIGURE 5–10   FIGURE 5–11

If an area bounded by the y-axis is rotated about the y-axis, the volume generated is given by

$$V = \pi \int_c^d x^2 \, dy. \tag{5–9}$$

In this case the radius of the element of volume is the x-coordinate of the point on the curve, and the height of the disk is dy. One should always make a point of properly identifying the radius and height.

Example B. Find the volume generated by rotating the area bounded by $y = 2x$, $y = 6$, and $x = 0$ about the y-axis.

Figure 5–10 shows the volume to be found. We write

$$V = \pi \int_0^6 x^2 \, dy = \pi \int_0^6 \left(\frac{y}{2}\right)^2 \, dy = \frac{\pi}{4} \int_0^6 y^2 \, dy = \frac{\pi}{12} y^3 \Big|_0^6 = 18\pi.$$

Since this volume is a right circular cone, it is possible to check the result:

$$V = \tfrac{1}{3}\pi r^2 h = \tfrac{1}{3}\pi (3^2)(6) = 18\pi.$$

There is another method of finding a volume of a solid of revolution. If the area in Fig. 5–9 is rotated about the y-axis, the element of area $y \, dx$ generates a different element of volume from that generated when it is rotated about the x-axis. We can see in Fig. 5–11 that this element of volume is a *cylindrical shell*. The total volume is made up of an infinite number of *concentric* shells. When the volumes of these shells are summed, we have the total volume generated. Thus we must now find the approximate volume dV of the representative shell. By finding the circumference of the base and multiplying this by the height, we can obtain an expression for the surface area of the shell. Then, by multiplying this by the thickness of the shell, we obtain its volume. The volume of the

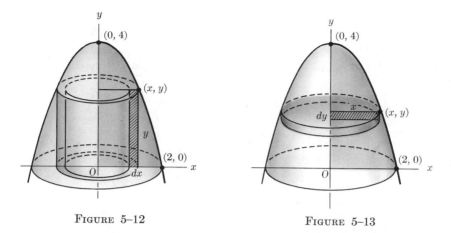

FIGURE 5–12   FIGURE 5–13

representative shell is

$$dV = 2\pi \,(\text{radius}) \cdot (\text{height}) \cdot (\text{thickness}). \qquad (5\text{--}10)$$

Similarly, the volume of a disk is given by

$$dV = \pi \,(\text{radius})^2 \cdot (\text{height}). \qquad (5\text{--}11)$$

The elements of volume should be remembered in the general forms given in Eqs. (5–10) and (5–11), and not in specific forms such as Eqs. (5–8) and (5–9). If we remember them in this manner, we can readily apply these methods to finding any such volume of a solid of revolution.

Example C. Using the method of cylindrical shells, find the volume generated by rotating the area bounded by

$$y = 4 - x^2, \qquad x = 0, \qquad \text{and} \qquad y = 0$$

about the y-axis.

From Fig. 5–12, we identify the radius, height, and thickness: $r = x$, $h = y$, $t = dx$ (this determines the limits as $x = 0$ and $x = 2$). And so

$$V = 2\pi \int_0^2 xy \, dx = 2\pi \int_0^2 x(4 - x^2) \, dx = 2\pi \int_0^2 (4x - x^3) \, dx = 8\pi.$$

Example D. Using the disk method, find the indicated volume of Example C.

From Fig. 5–13, we identify the radius and height: $r = x$, $h = dy$ (which tells us that the limits are from $y = 0$ to $y = 4$). Thus

$$V = \pi \int_0^4 x^2 \, dy = \pi \int_0^4 (4 - y) \, dy = 8\pi.$$

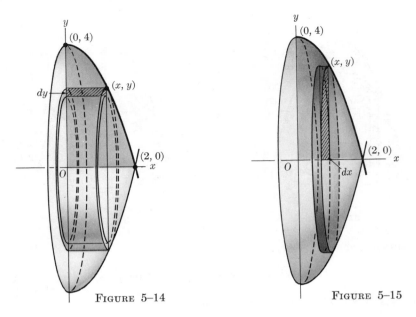

FIGURE 5–14   FIGURE 5–15

Example E. By the use of shells, find the volume if the area of Example C is rotated about the x-axis.

From Fig. 5–14, we see that $r = y$, $h = x$, $t = dy$ (thus the limits are $y = 0$ to $y = 4$). Hence

$$V = 2\pi \int_0^4 xy \, dy = 2\pi \int_0^4 \sqrt{4 - y} \, (y \, dy) = \frac{256\pi}{15}.$$

(The method of integrating this function has not yet been discussed. We present the answer here for the reader's information at this time.)

Example F. By the use of disks, find the volume indicated in Example E.

From Fig. 5–15, we see that $r = y$, $h = dx$ (the limits are $x = 0$ to $x = 2$). Therefore

$$V = \pi \int_0^2 y^2 \, dx = \pi \int_0^2 (4 - x^2)^2 \, dx = \pi \int_0^2 (16 - 8x^2 + x^4) \, dx = \frac{256\pi}{15}.$$

Example G. Find the volume generated if the area in Example C is rotated about the line $x = 2$.

Shells are convenient, since the volume of a shell can be expressed as a single integral. From Fig. 5–16, we see that

$$r = 2 - x, \qquad h = y, \qquad \text{and} \qquad t = dx.$$

Thus we have

$$V = 2\pi \int_0^2 (2 - x)y \, dx$$

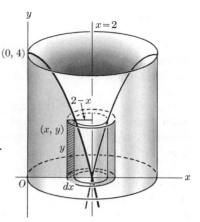

$$= 2\pi \int_0^2 (2 - x)(4 - x^2) \, dx$$

$$= 2\pi \int_0^2 (8 - 2x^2 - 4x + x^3) \, dx = \frac{40\pi}{3}.$$

(If the area had been rotated about the line $x = 3$, the only difference in the integral would have been that $r = 3 - x$. Everything else, including the limits, would have remained the same.)

FIGURE 5–16

Exercises

In Exercises 1 through 6, find the volume generated by the areas bounded by the given curves if they are rotated about the x-axis. Use the indicated method in each case.

1. $y = 1 - x$, $x = 0$, $y = 0$ (disks)
2. Area of Exercise 1   (shells)
3. $y = 2x - x^2$, $y = 0$ (disks)
4. $y = x^3$, $y = 8$, $x = 0$ (shells)
5. $y = x^2 + 1$, $x = 0$, $x = 3$, $y = 0$ (disks)
6. $y = x^2$, $y = x$ (shells)

In Exercises 7 through 12, find the volume generated by the areas bounded by the given curves if they are rotated about the y-axis.

7. Area of Exercise 1   (disks)
8. $y = \sqrt{4 - x^2}$ (first quadrant) (shells)
9. Area of Exercise 3   (shells)
10. $y^2 = x$, $y = 4$, $x = 0$ (disks)
11. Area of Exercise 10   (shells)
12. $x^2 + 4y^2 = 4$ (first quadrant) (disks)
13. Find the volume generated if the area of Exercise 3 is rotated about the line $x = 2$.
14. Find the volume generated if the area of Exercise 6 is rotated about the line $y = 4$.
15. Derive the expression for the volume of a right circular cone obtained by rotating the area bounded by $y = (r/h)x$, $y = 0$ and $x = h$ about the x-axis.

5–4 Centroids

In the study of mechanics, a very important property of an object is its center of mass. In this section we shall show the meaning of center of mass and then show how integration is used to determine it for areas and solids of rotation.

If a mass m is at a distance d from a specified point O, the moment of the mass about O is defined as md. If several masses $m_1, m_2, \ldots, m_n$ are at distances $d_1, d_2, \ldots, d_n$, respectively, from point O, their moment (as a group) about O is defined as

$$m_1 d_1 + m_2 d_2 + \cdots + m_n d_n.$$

If all the masses could be concentrated at one point $\bar{d}$ units from O, the moment would be $(m_1 + m_2 + \cdots + m_n)\bar{d}$. This is, however, what is meant by the above expression. Therefore, we may write

$$m_1 d_1 + m_2 d_2 + \cdots + m_n d_n = (m_1 + m_2 + \cdots + m_n)\bar{d}. \qquad (5\text{–}12)$$

In Eq. (5–12), $\bar{d}$ is the distance from O to the *center of mass*. The moment of a mass is a measure of its tendency to rotate about a point. A weight far from the point of balance of a long rod is more likely to make the rod turn than if the same weight were placed near the point of balance. It is easier to open a door if you push near the door knob than if you push near the hinges. This is the type of physical property which the moment of a mass measures.

Example A. On the x-axis a mass of 3 units is placed at $(2, 0)$, another of 6 units at $(5, 0)$ and a third, 7 units, at $(6, 0)$. Find the center of mass of these three objects.

Center
of mass   FIGURE 5–17

Taking the reference point as the origin, we find $d_1 = 2, d_2 = 5$, and $d_3 = 6$. Thus $m_1 d_1 + m_2 d_2 + m_3 d_3 = (m_1 + m_2 + m_3)\bar{d}$ becomes

$$3(2) + 6(5) + 7(6) = (3 + 6 + 7)\bar{d} \qquad \text{or} \qquad \bar{d} = 4.88.$$

This means that the center of mass of the three objects is at $(4.88, 0)$. Therefore a mass of 16 units placed at this point has the same moment as the three masses as a unit. See Fig. 5–17.

Example B. Find the center of mass of the area indicated in Fig. 5–18.

We first note that the center of mass is not *on* either axis. This can be seen from the fact that the major portion of the area is in the first quadrant. We

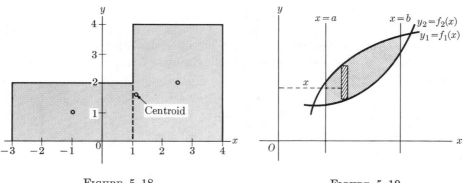

FIGURE 5–18   FIGURE 5–19

shall therefore measure the moments with respect to each axis to find the point which is the center of mass. This point is also called the *centroid* of the area.

The easiest method of finding the centroid is to divide the area into rectangles, as indicated by the dashed line, and assume that we may consider the mass of each rectangle to be concentrated at its center. In this way the left rectangle has its center at $(-1, 1)$ and the right rectangle has its center at $(\frac{5}{2}, 2)$. The mass of each rectangle, assumed uniform, is proportional to the area. The area of the left rectangle is 8 units and that of the right rectangle is 12 units. Thus, taking moments with respect to the y-axis, we have

$$8(-1) + 12(\tfrac{5}{2}) = (8 + 12)\bar{x},$$

where $\bar{x}$ is the x-coordinate of the centroid. Solving for $\bar{x}$ we have $\bar{x} = \frac{11}{10}$.

Now taking moments with respect to the x-axis we have

$$8(1) + 12(2) = (8 + 12)\bar{y},$$

where $\bar{y}$ is the y-coordinate of the centroid. Thus, $\bar{y} = \frac{8}{5}$. This means that the coordinates of the centroid, the center of mass, are $(\frac{11}{10}, \frac{8}{5})$. This may be interpreted that an area of this shape would balance on a single support under this point.

If an area is bounded by the curves of the functions $y_1 = f_1(x)$, $y_2 = f_2(x)$, $x = a$, and $x = b$, as shown in Fig. 5–19, the moment of the element of area about the y-axis is $(k\, dA)x$, where k is the mass per unit area. In this expression, $k\, dA$ is the mass of the element, and x is its distance (moment arm) from the y-axis. The element dA may be written as $(y_1 - y_2)\, dx$, which means that the moment may be written as $kx(y_1 - y_2)\, dx$. If we then sum up the moments of all the elements and write this as an integral (which, of course, means sum), we have $k\int_a^b x(y_1 - y_2)\, dx$. If we then considered all the mass of the area to be concentrated at one point $\bar{x}$ units from the y-axis, the moment would be $(kA)\bar{x}$, where kA is the mass of the entire area, and $\bar{x}$ is the distance the center of mass is from the y-axis. By the previous discussion these two expressions should be equal. This means $k \int_a^b x(y_1 - y_2)\, dx = kA\bar{x}$. Since k appears on each side of the equation, we may divide it out (we are assuming that the mass per unit area is constant). Also the area A is found by the integral $\int_a^b (y_1 - y_2)\, dx$. Therefore, we have

$$\bar{x} = \frac{\int_a^b x(y_1 - y_2)\, dx}{\int_a^b (y_1 - y_2)\, dx}. \qquad (5\text{--}13)$$

Equation (5–13) gives us the x-coordinate of the centroid of an area if vertical elements are used.

Following the same reasoning, if an area is bounded by $x_1 = g_1(y)$, $x_2 = g_2(y)$, $y = c$, and $y = d$ (Fig. 5–20), the y-coordinate of the centroid is

$$\bar{y} = \frac{\int_c^d y(x_2 - x_1)\, dy}{\int_c^d (x_2 - x_1)\, dy}. \qquad (5\text{--}14)$$

In this equation, horizontal elements are used.

In applying Eqs. (5–13) and (5–14), we should keep in mind that the denominators of the right-hand sides give the area, and once we have found this, we may use it for both $\bar{x}$ and $\bar{y}$. Also, we should utilize any symmetry a curve may have.

FIGURE 5–20

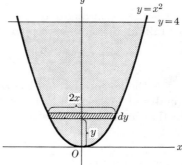

FIGURE 5–21

Example C. Find the coordinates of the centroid of the area bounded by $y = x^2$ and the line $y = 4$.

First we sketch a graph indicating the area and an element of area (Fig. 5–21). The curve is a parabola whose axis is the y-axis. Since the area is symmetrical to the y-axis, the centroid must be on this axis. This means that the x-coordinate of the centroid is zero, or $\bar{x} = 0$. To find the y-coordinate of the centroid, we use Eq. (5–14). For this area we have

$$\bar{y} = \frac{\int_0^4 y(2x)\,dy}{\int_0^4 2x\,dy} = \frac{\int_0^4 y(2\sqrt{y})\,dy}{\int_0^4 2\sqrt{y}\,dy} = \frac{2\int_0^4 y^{3/2}\,dy}{2\int_0^4 y^{1/2}\,dy} = \frac{2(\frac{2}{5})y^{5/2}\big|_0^4}{2(\frac{2}{3})y^{3/2}\big|_0^4} = \frac{\frac{4}{5}(32)}{\frac{4}{3}(8)}$$

$$= \frac{128}{5}\cdot\frac{3}{32} = \frac{12}{5}.$$

The coordinates of the centroid are $(0, \frac{12}{5})$. This area would balance if a single pointed support were to be put under this point.

Example D. Find the coordinates of the centroid of an isosceles right triangle with side a.

We must first set up this area in the xy-plane. One choice is to place the triangle with one vertex at the origin and the right angle on the x-axis (see Fig. 5–22). Since each side is a, the hypotenuse passes through the point (a, a). The equation of the hypotenuse is $y = x$. The x-coordinate of the centroid is

$$\bar{x} = \frac{\int_0^a xy\,dx}{\int_0^a y\,dx} = \frac{\int_0^a x(x)\,dx}{\int_0^a x\,dx}$$

$$= \frac{\int_0^a x^2\,dx}{\frac{1}{2}x^2\big|_0^a} = \frac{\frac{1}{3}x^3\big|_0^a}{a^2/2} = \frac{a^3/3}{a^2/2} = \frac{2a}{3}.$$

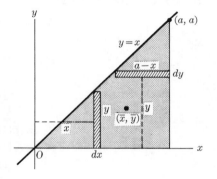

FIGURE 5–22

The y-coordinate of the centroid is

$$\bar{y} = \frac{\int_0^a y(a-x)\,dy}{a^2/2} = \frac{\int_0^a y(a-y)\,dy}{a^2/2} = \frac{\int_0^a (ay - y^2)\,dy}{a^2/2}$$

$$= \frac{ay^2/2 - y^3/3\big|_0^a}{a^2/2} = \frac{a^3/6}{a^2/2} = \frac{a}{3}.$$

Thus the coordinates of the centroid are $(2a/3, a/3)$. The results indicate that the center of mass is $a/3$ units from each of the equal sides.

Another important figure for which we wish to find the centroid is the solid of revolution. If the density of the solid is constant, the coordinates of the centroid will be on the axis of rotation. The problem which remains is to find just where on the axis the centroid is located.

If a given area bounded by the x-axis, as shown in Fig. 5–23, is revolved about the x-axis, a vertical element of area generates a disk element of volume. The center of mass of the disk is at its center, and therefore, for purposes of finding moments, we may consider its mass concentrated there. The moment about the y-axis of a typical element is $x(k)(\pi y^2\, dx)$, where x is the moment arm, k is the density, and $\pi y^2\, dx$ is the volume. The sum of the moments of the elements can be expressed as an integral; it equals the volume times the density times the x-coordinate of the centroid of the volume. Since the density k and the factor of π would appear on each side of the equation, they need not be written. Therefore

$$\bar{x} = \frac{\displaystyle\int_a^b xy^2\, dx}{\displaystyle\int_a^b y^2\, dx} \tag{5–15}$$

is the equation giving the x-coordinate of the centroid of a volume of a solid of revolution about the x-axis.

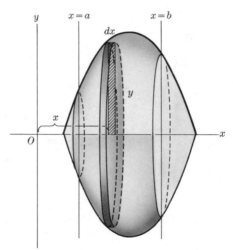

FIGURE 5–23

In the same manner we may find the y-coordinate of the centroid of a volume of a solid of revolution about the y-axis. It is

$$\bar{y} = \frac{\displaystyle\int_c^d yx^2\, dy}{\displaystyle\int_c^d x^2\, dy}. \tag{5–16}$$

Example E. Find the coordinates of the centroid of the volume generated by rotating the first-quadrant area under the curve $y = 4 - x^2$ about the x-axis.

Since the curve (see Fig. 5–24) is rotated about the x-axis, the centroid is on the x-axis, which means that $\bar{y} = 0$. We find the x-coordinate by using Eq. 5–15):

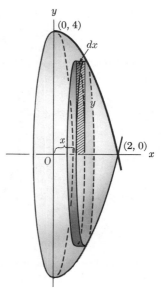

$$\bar{x} = \frac{\int_0^2 xy^2\, dx}{\int_0^2 y^2\, dx} = \frac{\int_0^2 x(4 - x^2)^2\, dx}{\int_0^2 (4 - x^2)^2\, dx}$$

$$= \frac{\int_0^2 (16x - 8x^3 + x^5)\, dx}{\int_0^2 (16 - 8x^2 + x^4)\, dx}$$

$$= \frac{8x^2 - 2x^4 + \frac{1}{6}x^6\Big|_0^2}{16x - \frac{8}{3}x^3 + \frac{1}{5}x^5\Big|_0^2} = \frac{32 - 32 + \frac{64}{6}}{32 - \frac{64}{3} + \frac{32}{5}} = \frac{5}{8}.$$

The coordinates of the centroid are $(\frac{5}{8}, 0)$.

FIGURE 5–24

Example F. Find the coordinates of the centroid of the volume generated by rotating the area of Example E about the y-axis.

Since the curve is rotated about the y-axis, $\bar{x} = 0$ (Fig. 5–25). The y-coordinate is found by using Eq. (5–16):

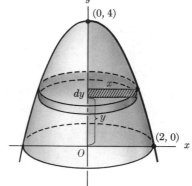

$$\bar{y} = \frac{\int_0^4 yx^2\, dy}{\int_0^4 x^2\, dy} = \frac{\int_0^4 y(4 - y)\, dy}{\int_0^4 (4 - y)\, dy}$$

$$= \frac{\int_0^4 (4y - y^2)\, dy}{\int_0^4 (4 - y)\, dy} = \frac{2y^2 - \frac{1}{3}y^3\Big|_0^4}{4y - \frac{1}{2}y^2\Big|_0^4}$$

$$= \frac{32 - \frac{64}{3}}{16 - 8} = \frac{4}{3}.$$

The coordinates of the centroid are $(0, \frac{4}{3})$.

FIGURE 5–25

Example G. Find the centroid of a right circular cone of radius a and altitude h.

To generate a right circular cone, we may rotate a right triangle about one of its legs (Fig. 5–26). Placing the leg of length h along the x-axis, we rotate the right triangle whose hypotenuse is given by $y = (a/h)x$ about the x-axis.

The x-coordinate of the centroid is

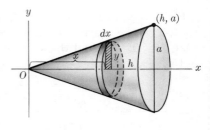

$$\bar{x} = \frac{\int_0^h xy^2 \, dx}{\int_0^h y^2 \, dx} = \frac{\int_0^h x[(a/h)x]^2 \, dx}{\int_0^h [(a/h)x]^2 \, dx}$$

$$= \frac{(a^2/h^2)(\frac{1}{4}x^4)\Big|_0^h}{(a^2/h^2)(\frac{1}{3}x^3)\Big|_0^h} = \frac{3}{4}h.$$

FIGURE 5–26

Therefore, the centroid is located along the altitude $\frac{3}{4}$ of the way from the vertex, or $\frac{1}{4}$ of the way from the base.

Exercises

In Exercises 1 through 3 find the center of mass of the particles of the given masses located at the given points.

1. 5 units at $(1, 0)$, 10 units at $(4, 0)$, 3 units at $(5, 0)$
2. 2 units at $(2, 0)$, 9 units at $(3, 0)$, 3 units at $(8, 0)$, 1 unit at $(12, 0)$
3. 4 units at $(-3, 0)$, 2 units at $(0, 0)$, 1 unit at $(2, 0)$, 8 units at $(3, 0)$
4. Find the coordinates of the centroid of the area in Fig. 5–27(a).
5. Find the coordinates of the centroid of the area in Fig. 5–27(b).
6. Find the coordinates of the centroid of the area in Fig. 5–27(c).

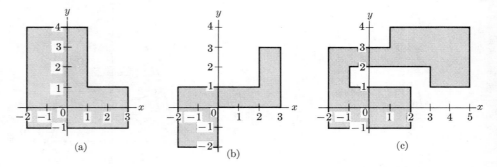

(a)   (b)   (c)

FIGURE 5–27

7. Find the coordinates of the centroid of the area bounded by $y = x^2$ and $y = 2$.
8. Find the coordinates of the centroid of a semicircular area.
9. Find the coordinates of the centroid of the area bounded by $y = 4 - x$ and the axes.
10. Find the coordinates of the centroid of the area bounded by $y = x^3$, $x = 2$, and the x-axis.

11. Find the coordinates of the centroid of the area bounded by $y = x^2$ and $y = x^3$.

12. Find the coordinates of the centroid of the volume generated by rotating the area bounded by $y = x^2$, $x = 2$, and the x-axis about the x-axis.

13. Find the coordinates of the centroid of the volume generated by rotating the area bounded by $y^2 = 4x$ and $x = 1$ about the x-axis.

14. Find the coordinates of the centroid of the volume generated by rotating the area bounded by $x^2 - y^2 = 9$, $y = 4$, and the x-axis about the y-axis.

15. Find the coordinates of the centroid of the volume generated by rotating the area bounded by $y = 4/x^2$, $x = 1$, $x = 2$, and the x-axis about the x-axis.

16. Find the coordinates of the centroid of the volume generated by rotating the first-quadrant area bounded by the ellipse $4x^2 + 9y^2 = 36$ around the y-axis.

17. Find the location of the centroid of a right triangle with legs a and b.

18. Find the coordinates of the centroid of an isosceles trapezoid with bases b_1 and b_2 and altitude a.

19. Find the location of the centroid of a hemisphere of radius a.

20. Find the location of the centroid of the frustrum of a right circular cone if the radii are 2 and 6 in., and the altitude is 5 in.

5–5 Moments of inertia

In applying the laws of physics, we encounter an important quantity when we are discussing the rotation of an object: its *moment of inertia*. The moment of inertia of an object rotating about an axis is analogous to the mass of an object moving through space in reference to some point. In each case the quantity (moment of inertia or mass) is the measure of the tendency of an object to resist the motion.

Suppose that a particle of mass m is rotating about some point; we define its moment of inertia as md^2, where d is the distance from the particle to the point. If a group of particles of masses $m_1, m_2, \ldots, m_n$ are rotating about some axis, the moment of inertia of the group with respect to that axis is

$$m_1 d_1^2 + m_2 d_2^2 + \cdots + m_n d_n^2,$$

where the d's are the respective distances of the particles from the axis. If all of the masses were at the same distance R from the axis of rotation, so that the total moment of inertia were the same, we would have

$$m_1 d_1^2 + m_2 d_2^2 + \cdots + m_n d_n^2 = (m_1 + m_2 + \cdots + m_n) R^2, \quad (5\text{–}17)$$

where R is called the *radius of gyration*.

Example A. Find the moment of inertia and radius of gyration of three masses, one of 3 units at $(-2, 0)$, the second of 5 units at $(1, 0)$, and the third of 4 units at $(4, 0)$ with respect to the origin. See Fig. 5–28.

FIGURE 5–28

The moment of inertia, I, of the group is

$$I = 3(-2)^2 + 5(1)^2 + 4(4)^2 = 81.$$

The radius of gyration is found from $I = (m_1 + m_2 + m_3)R^2$. Thus,

$$81 = (3 + 5 + 4)R^2, \qquad R^2 = \tfrac{81}{12}, \qquad \text{or} \qquad R = 2.60.$$

This means that a mass of 12 units placed at $(2.60, 0)$ [or at $(-2.60, 0)$] would have the same rotational inertia about the origin as the three objects as a unit.

FIGURE 5–29

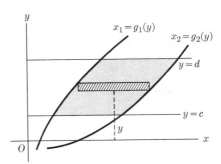

FIGURE 5–30

If an area is bounded by the curves of the functions $y_1 = f_1(x)$, $y_2 = f_2(x)$, and $x = a$ and $x = b$, as shown in Fig. 5–29, the moment of inertia of this area with respect to the y-axis, I_y, is given by the sum of the moments of inertia of the individual elements. The mass of each element is $k(y_1 - y_2)\,dx$ where k is the mass per unit area, and $(y_1 - y_2)\,dx$ is the area of the element. The distance of the element from the y-axis is x. Representing this sum as an integral, we have

$$I_y = k\int_a^b x^2(y_1 - y_2)\,dx. \tag{5–18}$$

To find the radius of gyration of the area with respect to the y-axis, R_y, we would first find the moment of inertia, divide this by the mass of the area, and take the square root of this result.

In the same manner, the moment of inertia of an area, with respect to the x-axis, bounded by $x_1 = g_1(y)$ and $x_2 = g_2(y)$ is given by

$$I_x = k\int_c^d y^2(x_2 - x_1)\,dy. \tag{5–19}$$

We find the radius of gyration of the area with respect to the x-axis, R_x, in the same manner as we find it with respect to the y-axis (see Fig. 5–30).

Example B. Find the moment of inertia and the radius of gyration of the area bounded by $y = 4x^2$, $x = 1$, and the x-axis with respect to the y-axis.

We find the moment of inertia of the area (Fig. 5–31) by using Eq. (5–18):

$$I_y = k\int_0^1 x^2 y \, dx$$

$$= k\int_0^1 x^2(4x^2) \, dx = 4k\int_0^1 x^4 \, dx$$

$$= 4k\left(\frac{1}{5}x^5\right)\Big|_0^1 = \frac{4k}{5}.$$

FIGURE 5–31

To find the radius of gyration, we first determine the mass of the area:

$$m = k\int_0^1 y \, dx = k\int_0^1 (4x^2) \, dx = 4k\left(\frac{1}{3}x^3\right)\Big|_0^1 = \frac{4k}{3};$$

$$R_y^2 = \frac{I_y}{m} = \frac{4k}{5} \cdot \frac{3}{4k} = \frac{3}{5}, \qquad R_y = \sqrt{3/5} = \frac{\sqrt{15}}{5}.$$

Example C. Find the moment of inertia of a right triangle with sides a and b with respect to the side b. Assume that $k = 1$.

Placing the triangle as shown in Fig. 5–32, we see that the equation of the hypotenuse is $y = (a/b)x$. The moment of inertia is

$$I_x = \int_0^a y^2(b - x) \, dy = \int_0^a y^2\left(b - \frac{b}{a}y\right) dy$$

$$= b\int_0^a \left(y^2 - \frac{1}{a}y^3\right) dy = b\left(\frac{1}{3}y^3 - \frac{1}{4a}y^4\right)\Big|_0^a$$

$$= b\left(\frac{a^3}{3} - \frac{a^3}{4}\right) = \frac{ba^3}{12}.$$

FIGURE 5–32

Among the most important moments of inertia are those of solids of revolution. Since all parts of an element of mass should be at the same distance from the axis, the most convenient element of volume to choose is the cylindrical shell (Fig. 5–33). If the area bounded by the curves $y = f(x)$, $x = a$, $x = b$, and the x-axis is rotated about the y-axis, the moment of inertia of the element of volume is $k(2\pi xy \, dx)(x^2)$, where k is the density, $2\pi xy \, dx$ is the volume of the

FIGURE 5–33

element, and x^2 is the square of its distance from the y-axis. Expressing the sum of the moments of the elements as an integral, the moment of inertia of the volume with respect to the y-axis, I_y, is

$$I_y = 2\pi k \int_a^b yx^3 \, dx. \qquad (5\text{–}20)$$

The radius of gyration of the volume with respect to the y-axis R_y is found by determining (1) the moment of inertia, (2) the mass of the volume, and (3) the square root of the quotient of the moment of inertia divided by the mass.

The moment of inertia of the volume (Fig. 5–34) generated by rotating the area bounded by $x = g(y)$, $y = c$, $y = d$, and the y-axis about the x-axis, I_x, is given by

$$I_x = 2\pi k \int_c^d xy^3 \, dy. \qquad (5\text{–}21)$$

The radius of gyration of the volume with respect to the x-axis, R_x, is found in the same manner as R_y.

Example D. Find the moment of inertia and the radius of gyration of the solid (Fig. 5–35) generated by rotating the area bounded by $y^3 = x$, $y = 2$, and the y-axis about the x-axis. We write

$$I_x = 2\pi k \int_0^2 xy^3 \, dy = 2\pi k \int_0^2 (y^3)y^3 \, dy = 2\pi k \left(\frac{1}{7} y^7\right)\Big|_0^2 = \frac{256\pi k}{7} \; ;$$

$$m = 2\pi k \int_0^2 xy \, dy = 2\pi k \int_0^2 y^3 y \, dy = 2\pi k \left(\frac{1}{5} y^5\right)\Big|_0^2 = \frac{64\pi k}{5} \; ;$$

$$R_x^2 = \frac{256\pi k}{7} \cdot \frac{5}{64\pi k} = \frac{20}{7}, \qquad R_x = \sqrt{20/7} = \frac{2}{7}\sqrt{35}.$$

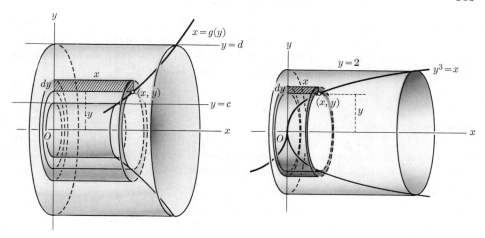

FIGURE 5–34   FIGURE 5–35

Example E. Find the moment of inertia of a disk of radius r with respect to its axis.

To generate a disk (Fig. 5–36) we shall rotate the area bounded by the axes, $x = r$ and $y = b$, about the y-axis. We then have

$$I_y = 2\pi k \int_0^r x^3 y \, dx = 2\pi k \int_0^r x^3 (b) \, dx$$

$$= 2\pi k b \int_0^r x^3 \, dx = 2\pi k b \left(\frac{1}{4} x^4\right)\Big|_0^r = \frac{\pi k b r^4}{2}.$$

The mass of the disk is $k(\pi r^2) b$. Rewriting the expression for I_y, we have

$$I_y = \frac{(\pi k b r^2) r^2}{2} = \frac{m r^2}{2}.$$

This is the usual way of expressing the moment of inertia of a particular solid. That is, the mass is usually included in the formula for the moment of inertia.

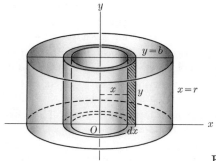

FIGURE 5–36

Due to the limited methods of integration available at this point, we cannot integrate the expressions for the moments of inertia of circular areas or of a sphere. These will be introduced in Section 8–8 in the exercises, by which point the proper method of integration will have been developed.

Exercises

In Exercises 1 through 4, find the moment of inertia and the radius of gyration with respect to the origin of the given masses at the given points.

1. 5 units at $(2, 0)$ and 3 units at $(6, 0)$
2. 3 units at $(-1, 0)$, 6 units at $(3, 0)$, 2 units at $(4, 0)$
3. 4 units at $(-4, 0)$, 10 units at $(0, 0)$, 6 units at $(5, 0)$
4. 6 units at $(-3, 0)$, 5 units at $(-2, 0)$, 9 units at $(1, 0)$, 2 units at $(8, 0)$
5. Find the moment of inertia of the area bounded by $y^2 = x$, $x = 4$, and the x-axis with respect to the x-axis.
6. Find the moment of inertia of the area bounded by $y = 2x$, $x = 1$, $x = 2$, and the x-axis with respect to the y-axis.
7. Find the radius of gyration of the area bounded by $y = x^3$, $x = 2$, and the x-axis with respect to the y-axis.
8. Find the radius of gyration of the first-quadrant area under the curve $y = 1 - x^2$ with respect to the y-axis.
9. Express the moment of inertia of the triangular area in Example C in terms of the mass of the area.
10. Find the moment of inertia of a rectangular area of sides a and b with respect to side a. Express the result in terms of the mass.
11. Find the radius of gyration of the area bounded by $y = x^2$, $x = 2$, and the x-axis with respect to the x-axis.
12. Find the radius of gyration of the area bounded by $y^2 = x^3$, $y = 8$, and the y-axis with respect to the y-axis.
13. Find the radius of gyration of the area of Exercise 12 with respect to the x-axis.
14. Find the moment of inertia with respect to its axis of the solid generated by rotating the area bounded by $y^2 = x$, $y = 2$, and the y-axis about the x-axis.
15. Find the radius of gyration with respect to its axis of the volume generated by rotating the first-quadrant area under the curve $y = 4 - x^2$ about the y-axis.
16. Find the radius of gyration with respect to its axis of the volume generated by rotating the area bounded by $y = 2x - x^2$ and the x-axis about the y-axis.
17. Find the radius of gyration with respect to its axis of the volume generated by rotating the area bounded by $y = 2x$ and $y = x^2$ about the y-axis.
18. Find the moment of inertia in terms of its mass of a right circular cone of radius r and height h with respect to its axis.
19. Find the moment of inertia in terms of its mass of a circular disk with a hole in the center with respect to its axis. Let the inner radius be r_1 and the outer radius be r_2.

5–6 Other applications

In order to illustrate the great variety of applications of integration, we shall demonstrate two more types of applied problems in this section. Certain other applications are shown in the exercises. The first application is to the physical problem of work done by a variable force.

Work, in its physical sense, is the product of a constant force times the distance through which it acts. When we consider the work done in stretching a spring, the first thing we recognize is that the more the spring is stretched, the greater is the force necessary to stretch it. Thus the force varies. However, if we are stretching the spring a distance Δx, where we are considering the limit as $\Delta x \to 0$, the force can be considered as approaching a constant. Adding the products of force$_1$ times Δx_1, force$_2$ times Δx_2, and so forth, we see that the total work is the sum of these products. Thus the work can be expressed as a definite integral in the form

$$W = \int_a^b f(x)\,dx, \tag{5–22}$$

where $f(x)$ is the force as a function of the distance the spring is stretched. The limits a and b refer to the initial and the final distances the spring is stretched *from its normal length.*

One problem remains: We must find the function $f(x)$. From physics we learn that the force required to stretch a spring is proportional to the amount it is stretched (Hooke's Law). If a spring is stretched x units from its normal length, then $f(x) = kx$. From conditions stated for a particular spring, the value of k may be determined. Thus $W = \int_a^b kx\,dx$ is the formula for finding the total work done in stretching a spring.

Example A. A spring, of natural length 12 in., requires a force of 6 lb to stretch it 2 in. (Fig. 5–37). Find the work done in stretching it 6 in.

From Hooke's Law, we have $F = kx$, or $6 = k2$, $k = 3$ lb/in. Thus

$$W = \int_0^6 3x\,dx = \tfrac{3}{2}x^2 \Big|_0^6 = 54 \text{ lb-in.}$$

FIGURE 5–37

Problems involving work by a variable force arise in many fields of technology. An illustration from electricity is found in the motion of an electric charge through an electric field created by another electric charge.

Electric charges are of two types, designated as positive and negative. A basic law is that charges of the same sign repel each other and charges of opposite signs attract each other. The force between charges is proportional to the product of their charges, and inversely proportional to the square of the distance between them. Thus, for this case

$$f(x) = \frac{kq_1q_2}{x^2}, \tag{5-23}$$

where q_1 and q_2 are the charges in coulombs, x is the distance in meters, the force is in newtons, and $k = 9 \times 10^9$ n·m²/coul². For other systems of units, the numerical value of k is different. We can find the work done when electric charges move toward each other or when they separate by use of Eq. (5–23) in Eq. (5–22).

Example B. Find the work done when two α-particles, $q = 3.2 \times 10^{-19}$ coul each, move until they are 10^{-8} m apart, if they were originally separated by one meter.

Applying Eqs. (5–22) and (5–23) we have

$$W = \int_1^{10^{-8}} \frac{9 \times 10^9 (3.2 \times 10^{-19})^2}{x^2} \, dx = 9.2 \times 10^{-28} \int_1^{10^{-8}} \frac{dx}{x^2}$$

$$= 9.2 \times 10^{-28} \left(-\frac{1}{x} \right) \Big|_1^{10^{-8}} = -9.2 \times 10^{-28}(10^8 - 1)$$

$$= -9.2 \times 10^{-20} \text{n} - \text{m}.$$

Since $10^8 \gg 1$, where $\gg$ means "much greater than," the 1 may be neglected in the calculation. The meaning of the minus sign in the result is that work must be done *on* the system to move the particles together. If free to move, they would tend to separate.

The second application of integration in this section is that of the average value of a function. In general an average is found by summing up the quantities to be averaged, and then dividing by the total number of them. Generalizing on this and using integration for the summation, the average value of a function y with respect to x is given by

$$y_{av} = \frac{\int_a^b y \, dx}{b - a}. \tag{5-24}$$

The following examples illustrate the applications of the average value of a function.

Example C. The velocity of an object falling under the influence of gravity as a function of time is given by $v = 32t$. What is the average velocity (in ft/sec) with respect to time for the first three seconds?

In this case, the average velocity with respect to t is

$$v_{av} = \frac{\int_0^3 v\,dt}{3-0} = \frac{\int_0^3 32t\,dt}{3} = \frac{16t^2}{3}\Big|_0^3 = 48 \text{ ft/sec.}$$

This result can be interpreted as meaning that an average velocity of 48 ft/sec for 3 sec would result in the same distance, 144 ft, being traveled as that with the variable velocity. Since $s = \int v\,dt$, the numerator represents the distance traveled.

Example D. The power developed in a certain resistor as a function of current is $P = 6i^2$. What is the average power (in watts) with respect to the current as the current changes from 2 to 5 amperes?

The average value of P with respect to i is

$$P_{av} = \frac{\int_2^5 P\,di}{5-2} = \frac{6\int_2^5 i^2\,di}{3} = \frac{2}{3}i^3\Big|_2^5 = \frac{2}{3}(125-8) = 78 \text{ watts.}$$

In general, it might be noted that the average value of y with respect to x is that value of y, which when multiplied by the length of the interval for x, gives the same area as that under the curve of y as a function of x.

Exercises

1. A spring, of natural length 10 in., measures 14 in. when a 12-lb weight is attached to it. How much work is required to stretch it 5 in. from its natural length?

2. How much work is required to stretch the spring in Exercise 1 from a length of 14 in. to a length of 19 in.?

3. It requires 500 lb to stretch a certain spring 1 ft. How much work is done on the spring if we attach a 300-lb weight to it?

4. If another 300-lb weight is attached to the spring in Exercise 3, how much work is done by the additional weight?

5. Find the work done in separating a 2×10^{-6} coul positive charge from a 4×10^{-6} coul negative charge to a distance of 0.06 m from a distance of 0.02 m.

6. The gravitational force of attraction between two objects is given by $F = k/x^2$. Given two objects which are 10 ft apart, find the work required to separate them further, until they are 100 ft apart. Express the result in terms of k.

7. Find the work done in winding up a 200-ft cable which weighs 100 lb.

8. Find the work done in pumping the water out of the top of a cylindrical tank 3 ft in radius and 10 ft high, if water weighs 62.4 lb/ft^3. (*Hint:* If horizontal slices dx ft thick are used, each element weighs $62.4(9\pi\,dx)$ lb, and each element must be raised $10 - x$ ft, if x is the distance from the base to the element. In this way the

force, the weight of the slice, and distance are determined. Thus, the products of force and distance are summed by integration.)

9. The electric current as a function of time for a certain circuit is given by $i = 4t - t^2$. Find the average value of the current (in amps), with respect to time, for the first 4 seconds.

10. Find the average value of the function $y = \sqrt{x}$, with respect to x, from $x = 1$ to $x = 9$.

11. An object moves along the x-axis according to the relation $x = t^3 - 3t$. Find the average value of the velocity with respect to t, as t changes from 1 to 3.

12. Find the average value of the volume of a sphere with respect to the radius.

13. The length of arc of a curve is given by

$$s = \int_a^b \sqrt{1 + (dy/dx)^2}\ dx.$$

Find the length of the curve $y = \frac{2}{3}x^{3/2}$ from $x = 0$ to $x = 3$.

14. Find the length of the curve $y = \frac{2}{3}(x^2 - 1)^{3/2}$ from $x = 1$ to $x = 3$.

15. The force on a vertical plane area below the surface of a liquid equals the product of the weight per unit volume of the liquid, the area of the plane, and the depth of the centroid of the area. Find the force on the area bounded by $y = x^2$ and $y = 4$ if the surface of the water is at $y = 20$. The weight per unit volume of water is 62.4 lb/ft^3. Assume all distances are in feet.

16. Find the force on the area bounded by $x = 2y - y^2$ and the y-axis if the upper point of the area is at the surface of the water. Assume all distances are in feet.

17. The area of a surface of revolution generated by rotating an arc about the x-axis is given by $S = 2\pi \int_a^b y\sqrt{1 + (dy/dx)^2}\ dx$. Find the area of the surface generated by rotating $y = \frac{3}{4}x$ from $x = 0$ to $x = 2$ about the x-axis.

18. Find the area of the surface generated by rotating $y = x^3$ from $x = 1$ to $x = 3$ about the x-axis.

Miscellaneous exercises for Chapter 5

1. What is the velocity after 5 sec of an object which is dropped and falls due to gravity?

2. Find an expression for the distance traveled by an object for which the velocity is given by $v = 3t/\sqrt{t^2 + 1}$, if $s = 0$ when $t = 0$.

3. The current in a certain electric resistor is given by $i = 5t^{2/3}$. Find the charge which passes a given point in the circuit during the third second.

4. What is the capacitance of a capacitor if a current $i = \sqrt[6]{3t + 1}$ charges it such that the voltage across it is 200 volts at $t = 0$ and 280 volts when $t = 0.7$ sec?

5. The distribution of weight on a cable is not uniform. If the slope of the cable at any point is given by $dy/dx = 20 + (x^2/40)$, and if the origin of the coordinate system is at the lowest point, find the equation which gives the curve described by the cable.

6. The acceleration of an object rolling down an inclined plane is 12 ft/sec^2. If it starts from rest at the top of the plane, find an expression for the distance the object travels from the top as a function of the time.

7. Find the area between $y = \sqrt{1 - x}$ and the coordinate axes.

8. Find the area bounded by $y = 1/(2x + 1)^2$, $y = 0$, $x = 1$, and $x = 2$.

9. Find the volume generated by rotating the area bounded by $y = 3 + x^2$ and the line $y = 4$ about the x-axis.

10. Find the volume generated by rotating the area bounded by $y = x$ and $y = 3x - x^2$ about the y-axis.

11. Find the centroid of the area bounded by $y^2 = x^3$ and $y = 2x$.

12. Find the centroid of the volume generated by rotating the area bounded by $yx^4 = 1$, $y = 1$, and $y = 4$ about the y-axis.

13. Find the moment of inertia of the area bounded by $y = 3x - x^2$ and $y = x$ with respect to the y-axis.

14. Find the radius of gyration with respect to its axis of the solid formed by rotating the area bounded by $xy = 1$, $x = 1$, $x = 3$, and $y = \frac{1}{3}$ about the x-axis.

15. A certain spring is 16 in. long when 12 lb are hung from it. It measures 12 in. when 4 lb are hung from it. How much work is done when the spring is stretched from its natural length by hanging 6 lb on it?

16. If the pressure of a gas is 4 atm when the volume is 243 in^3, how much work is done in compressing the gas to 32 in^3, if it undergoes an adiabatic change such that $pV^{1.4} = c$?

17. The electric resistance of a wire is inversely proportional to the square of its radius. If a certain wire has a resistance of 0.3 ohms when its radius is 0.0020 m, find the average value of the resistance with respect to the radius if the radius changes from 0.0020 m to 0.0021 m.

18. The velocity of an object as a function of the distance fallen after being dropped is $v = 8\sqrt{s}$. Find the average value of v with respect to s during the third second, if $s = 16t^2$, and s is measured in feet?

19. The production rate, in lb/hr, of a certain chemical plant is given by the following table. Using the trapezoidal rule, determine the approximate daily production.

Time	12 M	4 AM	8 AM	12 N	4 PM	8 PM	12 M
Production rate	2000	2000	7000	12,000	12,000	8000	2000

20. The current as a function of time was measured in a particular circuit, with the results tabulated below. What charge, in coul, was transmitted across a given point in the first 6 sec? Use the trapezoidal rule.

i (amp)	0.0	1.5	4.0	7.2	7.5	4.3	1.6
t (sec	0.0	1.0	2.0	3.0	4.0	5.0	6.0

21. Solve Exercise 18 by use of graphical integration.

22. Solve Exercise 20 by use of graphical integration.

6 Derivatives of the trigonometric and inverse trigonometric functions

6–1 The trigonometric functions

Many important applications in technology are periodic in nature. That is, these phenomena have properties that repeat after definite periods of time. Applications of this type arise in alternating-current theory and harmonic motion analysis, as well as in many other fields. Such phenomena may be represented by the use of the trigonometric functions, especially the sine and cosine functions. It is assumed that the reader has a background which includes basic trigonometry. However, it is the purpose in this section and the next to present a summary of the trigonometric functions and their properties for purposes of review and reference. This material is essential to the development of later topics in this chapter and later chapters.

An angle in *standard position* is one with its vertex at the origin and its initial side the positive x-axis. If the angle is measured counterclockwise it is positive, and if it is measured clockwise it is negative. See Fig. 6–1.

The six trigonometric functions defined in terms of the coordinates (x, y) of a point on its terminal side, at a distance r (considered positive) from the origin are as follows:

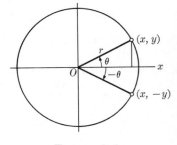

FIGURE 6–1

$$\sin \theta = \frac{y}{r}, \qquad \cos \theta = \frac{x}{r}, \qquad \tan \theta = \frac{y}{x},$$
$$\cot \theta = \frac{x}{y}, \qquad \sec \theta = \frac{r}{x}, \qquad \csc \theta = \frac{r}{y}. \tag{6–1}$$

There are two widely used measurements of angles. These are the *degree* and the *radian*. The degree, defined as $\frac{1}{360}$ of a complete revolution, is used primarily in triangle solution. The degree is divided into 60 equal parts called minutes, and each minute is divided into 60 equal parts called seconds. Degrees and decimal parts are also widely used.

The radian is a more convenient measure of an angle for theoretical discussion. Since it is our purpose to develop mathematics, which has wide application in technology, we shall restrict our attention largely to radian measure. A radian is the measure of an angle, with vertex at the center of a circle, whose intercepted arc is equal in length to the radius of the circle.

Since the circumference of a circle is given by $c = 2\pi r$, the ratio of the circumference to the radius is 2π. This means that the radius may be laid off 2π times along the circumference, or that an angle of 360° equals an angle of 2π radians. Therefore,

$$\pi \text{ rad} = 180°. \tag{6--2}$$

Due to the nature of the definition of a radian, it is common to express angles measured in radians in terms of π.

Example A.

$$1° = \frac{\pi}{180} \text{ rad} = 0.01745 \text{ rad}; \qquad 1 \text{ rad} = \frac{180°}{\pi} = 57.3°;$$

$$\frac{\pi}{4} \text{ rad} = \frac{180°}{4} = 45°; \qquad \frac{\pi}{3} \text{ rad} = \frac{180°}{3} = 60°; \qquad \frac{\pi}{10} \text{ rad} = \frac{180°}{10} = 18°.$$

One point should be emphasized here. Since π is simply a particular way of writing the *number* which is the ratio of the circumference of a circle to the diameter, *radian measure amounts to measuring angles in terms of numbers.* For this reason radian measure is used in theoretical work, since radians are numbers and can represent numerical quantities without any special conversions. Also, for the same reason, when radians are used, it is common practice not to indicate any units.

Example B.

$$\frac{\pi}{6} = 30°; \qquad \frac{2\pi}{3} = 120°; \qquad \sin 1 = \sin 57.3°;$$

$$\frac{\pi}{6} = 0.524, \quad \text{which means that } \sin \frac{\pi}{6} = \sin 0.524.$$

Tables of values of the trigonometric functions are found in the Appendix. In Table 6–1 we present a short list of commonly used angles and the exact values of trigonometric functions of these angles.

Since the tables include the values of functions only for angles between 0° and 90°, it is necessary to be able to determine the values of the functions of angles greater than 90°.

TABLE 6–1

Degrees	0°	30°	45°	60°	90°	180°	270°	360°
Radians	0	$\pi/6$	$\pi/4$	$\pi/3$	$\pi/2$	π	$3\pi/2$	2π
Sine	0	1/2	$\sqrt{2}/2$	$\sqrt{3}/2$	1	0	−1	0
Cosine	1	$\sqrt{3}/2$	$\sqrt{2}/2$	1/2	0	−1	0	1
Tangent	0	$\sqrt{3}/3$	1	$\sqrt{3}$	Undef.	0	Undef.	0

An angle in standard position has the same terminal side as some positive angle less than 360°. Since the trigonometric functions of angles with the same terminal side are equal, we need consider only the problem of finding values of the trigonometric functions of positive angles less than 360°.

We note that the *signs* of the functions differ, depending on the quadrant in which the terminal side of the angle lies. Noting the definitions, Eqs. (6–1), we see that all the functions are positive for first quadrant angles, $\sin\theta$ and $\csc\theta$ are positive for second quadrant angles, $\tan\theta$ and $\cot\theta$ are positive for third quadrant angles, $\cos\theta$ and $\sec\theta$ are positive for fourth quadrant angles, and all other functions are negative. An analysis of the signs of x and y in the various quadrants will verify this.

From Fig. 6–2 we see that the point (x_1, y_1) is on the terminal side of θ_1 and the point $(-x_1, y_1)$ is on the terminal side of θ_2. This means that if the terminal side of the angle θ_2 lies in the second quadrant, the functions of θ_2 are numerically equal to the corresponding functions of the angle θ_1, in the first quadrant. Thus, r is the same for the two angles, and $\alpha = \theta_1$, where α is called the *reference angle*. However, $\alpha = 180° - \theta_2$. Letting F represent any of the trigonometric functions we conclude that

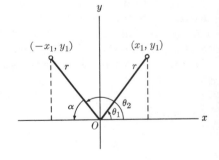

FIGURE 6–2

$$F(\theta_2) = \pm F(180° - \theta_2) = \pm F(\pi - \theta_2).$$

$$(6–3)$$

The sign to be used depends on whether the function is positive or negative in the second quadrant.

In the same way, we may derive the formulas for finding the trigonometric functions of a third- or fourth-quadrant angle (see Figs. 6–3 and 6–4):

$$F(\theta_3) = \pm F(\theta_3 - 180°) = \pm F(\theta_3 - \pi);$$
$$F(\theta_4) = \pm F(360° - \theta_4) = \pm F(2\pi - \theta_4).$$

$$(6–4)$$

FIGURE 6-3

FIGURE 6-4

Example C. Let $\theta_2 = 135°$.

$$\sin 135° = \sin (180° - 135°) = \sin 45° = \sqrt{2}/2,$$

$$\tan 135° = -\tan (180° - 135°) = -\tan 45° = -1.$$

Let $\theta_3 = 210°$.

$$\tan 210° = \tan (210° - 180°) = \tan 30° = \sqrt{3}/3,$$

$$\cos 210° = -\cos (210° - 180°) = -\cos 30° = -\sqrt{3}/2.$$

Let $\theta_4 = 330°$.

$$\sin 330° = -\sin (360° - 330°) = -\sin 30° = -\tfrac{1}{2},$$

$$\cos 330° = \cos (360° - 330°) = \cos 30° = \sqrt{3}/2.$$

One of the clearest ways to demonstrate the variation in the trigonometric functions is by means of their graphs. Since the graphs of the sine and cosine functions are of primary importance, we shall restrict our attention here to them.

In plotting the trigonometric functions, it is normal to express the angle in radians. In this way both x and y are expressed as numbers.

In the equations $y = a \sin (bx + c)$ and $y = a \cos (bx + c)$ we recall that a represents the *amplitude* of the curve. This is the maximum number of units the curve may be from the x-axis. The *period* of each of these curves is $2\pi/b$. For any function F, we say that it has a period P if, for all x, $F(x) = F(x + P)$. The effect of the c in the equation is to shift the curve of $y = a \sin bx$ or

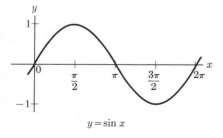

$y = \sin x$

FIGURE 6-5

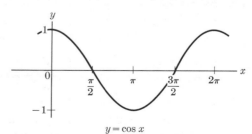

$y = \cos x$

FIGURE 6-6

$y = a \cos bx$ to the left if $c > 0$, and to shift it to the right if $c < 0$. The amount of the shift is given by c/b. The quantity c/b is called the *displacement*.

Thus, by knowing the basic shape of the sine and cosine curves, which are shown in Figs. 6–5 and 6–6, and the information obtained from the equation, we may sketch the graphs of sine and cosine functions. The following examples illustrate the method.

Example D. Sketch the graph of $y = 3 \sin (2x + \pi/4)$.

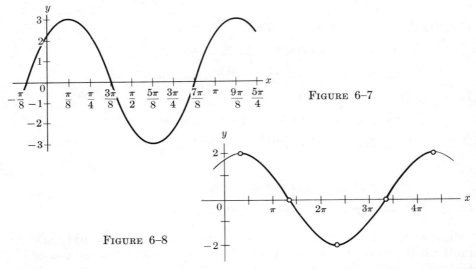

FIGURE 6–7

FIGURE 6–8

First we note that $a = 3$, which means that the amplitude of the curve is 3. Next we see that $b = 2$. This means that the period of the curve is $2\pi/2 = \pi$. Therefore points on the curve will "repeat" every π units along the x-axis. Finally $c = \pi/4$, which means the displacement is $(\pi/4)/2 = \pi/8$. This means the curve is displaced $\pi/8$ units to the left of the curve of $y = 3 \sin 2x$. Therefore, "starting" the curve at $x = -\pi/8$, we know it starts repeating at $x = 7\pi/8$ (π units to the right of $x = -\pi/8$), again at $15\pi/8$, etc. With this information we can construct the following table, from which the curve can quickly be sketched. (See Fig. 6–7).

x	$-\dfrac{\pi}{8}$	$\dfrac{\pi}{8}$	$\dfrac{3\pi}{8}$	$\dfrac{5\pi}{8}$	$\dfrac{7\pi}{8}$	$\dfrac{9\pi}{8}$
y	0	3	0	-3	0	3

Example E. Sketch the graph of the function $y = 2 \cos (x/2 - \pi/6)$; amplitude = 2, period = $2\pi/\frac{1}{2} = 4\pi$, displacement = $(\pi/6)/\frac{1}{2} = \pi/3$ (to the right).

We construct the table of values:

x	$\dfrac{\pi}{3}$	$\dfrac{4\pi}{3}$	$\dfrac{7\pi}{3}$	$\dfrac{10\pi}{3}$	$\dfrac{13\pi}{3}$
y	2	0	−2	0	2

And then we sketch the graph in Fig. 6–8. We note that when the coefficient of x is less than 1, the period is extended.

Exercises

In Exercises 1 through 4 express the given angle in terms of π.

1. 15°   2. 240°   3. −60°   4. 80°

In Exercises 5 through 10 find the indicated trigonometric functions.

5. $\sin\dfrac{7\pi}{18}$ 6. $\cos\dfrac{\pi}{20}$ 7. $\tan\dfrac{17\pi}{18}$

8. $\cot 2$ 9. $\cos 1.1$ 10. $\sin 3.9$

In Exercises 11 through 14 find θ for $0 \le \theta < 2\pi$.

11. $\sin\theta = 0.3420$ 12. $\cos\theta = 0.4384$
13. $\tan\theta = -1.192$ 14. $\cot\theta = -0.5095$

In Exercises 15 through 22 sketch the graph of each of the given functions.

15. $y = 3\sin x$ 16. $y = 2\cos 2x$ 17. $y = -4\sin 3x$

18. $y = 6\cos\pi x$ 19. $y = 2\sin\left(3x - \dfrac{\pi}{2}\right)$ 20. $y = 4\cos\left(\dfrac{x}{2} + \dfrac{\pi}{8}\right)$

21. $y = \cos\left(\pi x - \dfrac{\pi}{2}\right)$ 22. $y = \sin(\pi x + 1)$

23. The angular displacement θ of a pendulum bob is given in terms of its initial ($t = 0$) displacement θ_0 by the equation $\theta = \theta_0\cos\omega t$. If $\omega = 2$ rad/sec and $\theta_0 = \pi/30$ rad, draw two cycles for the resulting equation.
24. The displacement, as a function of time, from the position of equilibrium of an object on the end of a spring is given by $x = A\cos(\omega t + \alpha)$. Make a general graph representing this motion.
25. The voltage across a circuit in which there is an alternating current is given by $e = E_m\sin(\omega t + \alpha)$. If $E_m = 110$ volts, $\omega = 120\pi$ rad/sec, and $\alpha = -\pi/3$, what is the instantaneous voltage e after 0.01 sec? after 1 sec?
26. If the upper end of a spring is not fixed and is being moved with a sinusoidal motion, the motion of the bob at the end of the spring is affected. Plot the curve of the motion of the upper end of a spring which is being moved by an external force according to the equation $y = 4\sin 2t - 2\cos 2t$. This may be done graphically

by plotting $y_1 = 4 \sin 2t$ and $y_2 = 2 \cos 2t$ and then finding $y = y_1 - y_2$. This method is referred to as *addition of ordinates*.

27. The current in a certain electric circuit is given by $i = 4 \sin 60\pi t + 2 \cos 120\pi t$. Sketch the graph of i vs. t.

6–2 Basic trigonometric relations

Referring to the definitions of the trigonometric functions, Eqs. (6–1), we see that there are a number of relations which exist among the functions. Certain other important relationships may also be established. We shall find that these have very definite application, since certain problems rely on a change of form for solution. The ability to effectively use these basic relations depends to a large extent on being familiar with them, and recognizing them in different forms. Therefore, in this section we shall review the important trigonometric relations.

Directly from the definitions we observe that

$$\sin \theta = \frac{1}{\csc \theta}, \qquad \cos \theta = \frac{1}{\sec \theta}, \qquad \tan \theta = \frac{1}{\cot \theta}. \qquad (6-5)$$

Also, since

$$\tan \theta = \frac{y}{x} = \frac{y/r}{x/r},$$

we have

$$\tan \theta = \frac{\sin \theta}{\cos \theta}, \qquad \cot \theta = \frac{\cos \theta}{\sin \theta}. \qquad (6-6)$$

Certain important relations can be found by use of the definitions and the Pythagorean relation $x^2 + y^2 = r^2$. By dividing each term of the Pythagorean relation by r^2, we have

$$\sin^2 \theta + \cos^2 \theta = 1. \qquad (6-7)$$

By dividing each term of the Pythagorean relation by x^2, we obtain

$$1 + \tan^2 \theta = \sec^2 \theta. \qquad (6-8)$$

By dividing each term of the Pythagorean relation by y^2, we obtain

$$\cot^2 \theta + 1 = \csc^2 \theta. \qquad (6-9)$$

Many other relationships which exist among the trigonometric functions may be proven valid by the basic identities (6–5) to (6–9). The following example illustrates the method of proving such trigonometric identities.

Example A. Prove the identity $\sec^2 x + \csc^2 x = \sec^2 x \csc^2 x$.

Here we note the presence of $\sec^2 x$ and $\csc^2 x$ on each side. This suggests the possible use of the square relationships. By replacing the $\sec^2 x$ on the right-hand side by $1 + \tan^2 x$, we can create $\csc^2 x$ plus another term. The left-hand side is the $\csc^2 x$ plus another term, so this procedure should help. Thus

$$\sec^2 x + \csc^2 x = \sec^2 x \csc^2 x$$
$$= (1 + \tan^2 x)\,(\csc^2 x)$$
$$= \csc^2 x + \tan^2 x \csc^2 x.$$

Now we note that $\tan x = \sin x / \cos x$ and $\csc x = 1/\sin x$. Thus

$$\sec^2 x + \csc^2 x = \csc^2 x + \left(\frac{\sin^2 x}{\cos^2 x}\right)\left(\frac{1}{\sin^2 x}\right)$$
$$= \csc^2 x + \frac{1}{\cos^2 x}.$$

But $\sec x = 1/\cos x$, and therefore $\sec^2 x + \csc^2 x = \csc^2 x + \sec^2 x$, which proves the identity. We could have used many other variations of this procedure, and they would have been perfectly valid.

Referring to Fig. 6–1 and the definitions of the functions we see, for example, that $\sin \theta = y/r$ and $\sin (-\theta) = -y/r$. Thus, in this way we arrive at the following important relations concerning negative angles:

$$\sin (-\theta) = -\sin \theta, \qquad \cos (-\theta) = \cos \theta, \qquad \tan (-\theta) = -\tan \theta. \quad (6\text{--}10)$$

FIGURE 6–9

By use of the distance formula, Eq. (1–1), and Fig. 6–9, we may establish the *law of cosines*. Thus,

$$c^2 = (b \cos \theta - a)^2 + (b \sin \theta)^2$$
$$= b^2 \cos^2 \theta - 2ab \cos \theta + a^2 + b^2 \sin^2 \theta$$
$$= b^2 (\cos^2 \theta + \sin^2 \theta) + a^2 - 2ab \cos \theta,$$
$$c^2 = a^2 + b^2 - 2ab \cos \theta. \quad (6\text{--}11)$$

We shall now develop a number of important equations. We will be using the distance formula, the law of cosines and some of the other relations already established. Also, some of those we derive will be used in turn to derive others. Since there are numerous uses of the various equations of the section in the following material, the reader will gain facility in the use of the relationships by following the development.

From Fig. 6–10 we have

$$(r \cos \alpha - r \cos \beta)^2 + (r \sin \alpha - r \sin \beta)^2 = r^2 + r^2 - 2(r)(r) \cos (\alpha - \beta),$$

$$r^2 \cos^2 \alpha - 2r^2 \cos \alpha \cos \beta + r^2 \cos^2 \beta + r^2 \sin^2 \alpha - 2r^2 \sin \alpha \sin \beta + r^2 \sin^2 \beta$$
$$= 2r^2 - 2r^2 \cos (\alpha - \beta).$$

Dividing through by r^2 and collecting terms we have

$$\cos^2 \alpha + \sin^2 \alpha - 2(\cos \alpha \cos \beta + \sin \alpha \sin \beta) + \cos^2 \beta + \sin^2 \beta$$
$$= 2 - 2 \cos (\alpha - \beta).$$

Rearranging terms after using Eq. (6–7), we obtain

$$\cos (\alpha - \beta) = \cos \alpha \cos \beta + \sin \alpha \sin \beta. \tag{6–12}$$

Equation (6–12) is one of the important *addition formulas*, the remainder of which we shall now develop.

FIGURE 6–10

Writing $\cos (\alpha + \beta) = \cos [\alpha - (-\beta)]$, and using Eqs. (6–10) and (6–12), we have

$$\cos (\alpha + \beta) = \cos \alpha \cos \beta - \sin \alpha \sin \beta. \tag{6–13}$$

In Eq. (6–12), if we let $\alpha = 90°$, the result is

$$\cos (90° - \beta) = \cos 90° \cos \beta + \sin 90° \sin \beta.$$

Since $\sin 90° = 1$, $\cos 90° = 0$, we obtain

$$\cos (90° - \beta) = \sin \beta. \tag{6–14}$$

Since β is a general representation of an angle, and $\cos \beta$ is a function of β, we may substitute other expressions for angles for β. Therefore, replacing β by

$90° - \beta$ in Eq. (6–14) we have

$$\cos [90° - (90° - \beta)] = \sin (90° - \beta)$$

or

$$\sin (90° - \beta) = \cos \beta. \qquad (6\text{–}15)$$

Now, replacing β by $\alpha + \beta$ in Eq. (6–14) we obtain

$$\sin (\alpha + \beta) = \cos [(90° - \alpha) - \beta]$$
$$= \cos (90° - \alpha) \cos \beta + \sin (90° - \alpha) \sin \beta;$$

and by using Eqs. (6–14) and (6–15) we arrive at the equation

$$\sin (\alpha + \beta) = \sin \alpha \cos \beta + \cos \alpha \sin \beta. \qquad (6\text{–}16)$$

If we replace β by $-\beta$ in Eq. (6–16) we have

$$\sin (\alpha - \beta) = \sin \alpha \cos \beta - \cos \alpha \sin \beta. \qquad (6\text{–}17)$$

Example B. Show that

$$\sin \left(\frac{\pi}{4} + x\right) \cos \left(\frac{\pi}{4} + x\right) = \frac{1}{2} (\cos^2 x - \sin^2 x).$$

$$\sin \left(\frac{\pi}{4} + x\right) \cos \left(\frac{\pi}{4} + x\right)$$

$$= \left(\sin \frac{\pi}{4} \cos x + \cos \frac{\pi}{4} \sin x\right) \left(\cos \frac{\pi}{4} \cos x - \sin \frac{\pi}{4} \sin x\right)$$

$$= \sin \frac{\pi}{4} \cos \frac{\pi}{4} \cos^2 x - \sin^2 \frac{\pi}{4} \sin x \cos x$$

$$\quad + \cos^2 \frac{\pi}{4} \sin x \cos x - \sin^2 x \sin \frac{\pi}{4} \cos \frac{\pi}{4}$$

$$= \frac{\sqrt{2}}{2} \frac{\sqrt{2}}{2} \cos^2 x - \left(\frac{\sqrt{2}}{2}\right)^2 \sin x \cos x$$

$$\quad + \left(\frac{\sqrt{2}}{2}\right)^2 \sin x \cos x - \frac{\sqrt{2}}{2} \frac{\sqrt{2}}{2} \sin^2 x$$

$$= \tfrac{1}{2} \cos^2 x - \tfrac{1}{2} \sin^2 x = \tfrac{1}{2} (\cos^2 x - \sin^2 x).$$

Letting $A = \alpha + \beta$ and $B = \alpha - \beta$ leads to $\alpha = \frac{1}{2}(A + B)$ and $\beta = \frac{1}{2}(A - B)$. Using these in Eqs. (6–16) and (6–17), and subtracting, we obtain

$$\sin A - \sin B = 2 \cos \frac{A + B}{2} \sin \frac{A - B}{2}. \qquad (6\text{–}18)$$

We shall find this equation of use in the following section.

If $\alpha = \beta$ in Eq. (6–16) we have

$$\sin 2\alpha = 2 \sin \alpha \cos \alpha. \tag{6–19}$$

Also, if $\alpha = \beta$ in Eq. (6–13), we obtain

$$\cos 2\alpha = \cos^2 \alpha - \sin^2 \alpha. \tag{6–20}$$

Using Eq. (6–7), we may rewrite Eq. (6–20) in the form

$$\cos 2\alpha = 2 \cos^2 \alpha - 1 = 1 - 2 \sin^2 \alpha. \tag{6–21}$$

Equations (6–19), (6–20), and (6–21) are the *double-angle formulas*.
By replacing 2α by α in Eq. (6–21) we obtain

$$\sin \frac{\alpha}{2} = \pm \sqrt{\frac{1 - \cos \alpha}{2}} \tag{6–22}$$

and

$$\cos \frac{\alpha}{2} = \pm \sqrt{\frac{1 + \cos \alpha}{2}}. \tag{6–23}$$

Equations (6–22) and (6–23) are the *half-angle formulas*.

Example C. Given that $\cos \alpha = \frac{3}{5}$, where $3\pi/2 < \alpha < 2\pi$, find $\sin 2\alpha$ and $\cos \dfrac{\alpha}{2}$.

Knowing that $\cos \alpha = \frac{3}{5}$ for an angle in the fourth quadrant, we then determine that $\sin \alpha = -\frac{4}{5}$. Thus

$$\sin 2\alpha = 2(-\tfrac{4}{5})(\tfrac{3}{5}) = -\tfrac{24}{25}.$$

Also, since α is between $3\pi/2$ and 2π, $\alpha/2$ must be between $3\pi/4$ and π, which means that $\alpha/2$ is in the second quadrant and therefore $\cos \alpha/2$ is negative. Thus,

$$\cos \frac{\alpha}{2} = -\sqrt{\frac{1 + 3/5}{2}} = -0.8944.$$

Two other useful relations are found from the definition of the radian. From geometry we know that the length of an arc on a circle is proportional to the central angle, and that the length of the arc of a complete circle is the circumference. Letting s represent the length of arc, we may state that $s = 2\pi r$ for a complete circle, or

$$s = \theta r \tag{6–24}$$

for a circular arc with central angle θ, measured in radians. (See Fig. 6–11.)
Another geometric fact is that areas of sectors of circles are proportional to their central angles. The area of a complete circle is $A = \pi r^2$. This can be

Figure 6–11

Figure 6–12

written as $A = \frac{1}{2}(2\pi)r^2$. We now note that the angle for a complete circle is 2π, and therefore the area of a sector of a circle in terms of the radius and the central angle, in radians, is

$$A = \tfrac{1}{2}\theta r^2. \tag{6–25}$$

(See Fig. 6–12.)

Example D. Find the length of a circular arc if the central angle is 18° and the radius of the circle is 5 in. Also find the area of the corresponding circular sector.

First we must express θ in radians:

$$18° = \frac{\pi}{10}.$$

Now, solving for s, we have

$$s = \frac{\pi}{10}(5) = \frac{\pi}{2} = 1.57 \text{ in.}$$

The area is

$$A = \frac{1}{2}\left(\frac{\pi}{10}\right)(25) = \frac{5\pi}{4} = 3.93 \text{ in}^2.$$

A great many formulas have been developed in this section. As stated previously, however, these will be essential to the development of the material to come. The development of these formulas has been included, primarily to help the reader review the use of the equations.

Exercises

In Exercises 1 through 14 prove the given trigonometric identities.

1. $\tan x \csc x = \sec x$ 2. $\cos^2 x(1 + \tan^2 x) = 1$

3. $\sin x \tan x + \cos x = \sec x$ 4. $\tan x + \cot x = \sec x \csc x$

5. $\cos^2 x - \sin^2 x = 1 - 2\sin^2 x$ 6. $\tan^2 y \sec^2 y - \tan^4 y = \tan^2 y$

7. $\sin(x + y)\sin(x - y) = \sin^2 x - \sin^2 y$

8. $\cos(x + y)\cos(x - y) = \cos^2 x - \sin^2 y$

9. $\cos(x - y) + \sin(x + y) = (\cos x + \sin x)(\cos y + \sin y)$

10. $\cos^4 x - \sin^4 x = \cos 2x$

11. $2 \sin x + \sin 2x = \dfrac{2 \sin^3 x}{1 - \cos x}$

12. $\dfrac{\sin 3x}{\sin x} - \dfrac{\cos 3x}{\cos x} = 2$

13. $\sin \dfrac{\alpha}{2} = \dfrac{1 - \cos \alpha}{2 \sin (\alpha/2)}$

14. $\tan \dfrac{\alpha}{2} = \pm\sqrt{\dfrac{1 - \cos \alpha}{1 + \cos \alpha}}$

15. The displacements y_1 and y_2 of two waves traveling through the same medium are given by

$$y_1 = A \sin 2\pi(t/T - x/\lambda) \quad \text{and} \quad y_2 = A \sin 2\pi(t/T + x/\lambda).$$

Find an expression for the displacement $y_1 + y_2$ of the combination of the waves.

16. In the analysis of the angles of incidence i and reflection r of a light ray subject to certain conditions, the following expression is found:

$$E_2 \left(\frac{\tan r}{\tan i} + 1\right) = E_1 \left(\frac{\tan r}{\tan i} - 1\right).$$

Show that an equivalent expression is

$$E_2 = E_1 \frac{\sin (r - i)}{\sin (r + i)}.$$

17. The equation for the displacement of a certain object at the end of a spring is $y = A \sin 2t + B \cos 2t$. Show that this equation may be written as

$$y = C \sin (2t + \alpha),$$

where $C = \sqrt{A^2 + B^2}$ and $\tan \alpha = B/A$. [*Hint*: Let $A/C = \cos \alpha$ and $B/C = \sin \alpha$.]

18. A pendulum 5 ft long swings through an angle of 4.5°. Through what distance does the bob swing?

19. A horizontal water pipe has a radius of 6 ft. If the depth of water in the pipe is 3 ft, what percentage of the volume of the pipe is filled?

20. In developing an expression for the power in an alternating current circuit, the expression $\sin \omega t \sin(\omega t + \varphi)$ is found. Show that this expression can be written as $\frac{1}{2}[\cos \varphi - \cos(2\omega t + \varphi)]$.

6–3 Derivatives of the sine and cosine functions

In Chapter 2 we introduced the operation of differentiation. The functions we used, however, were algebraic functions in all cases. Now that we have developed the process of finding derivatives, and reviewed the properties of the trigonometric functions, we are in a position to develop the formulas necessary for finding the derivatives of the trigonometric functions.

After we utilize the Δ-process for finding the derivative of the sine function, it is possible to use this derivative as a basis for finding the derivatives of the other trigonometric and inverse trigonometric functions. Therefore we shall now find the derivative of the sine function.

Let $y = \sin u$, where u is a function of x and is expressed in radians. If u changes by Δu, y then changes by Δy. Thus

$$y + \Delta y = \sin (u + \Delta u),$$

$$\Delta y = \sin (u + \Delta u) - \sin u,$$

$$\frac{\Delta y}{\Delta u} = \frac{\sin (u + \Delta u) - \sin u}{\Delta u}.$$

Referring now to Eq. (6–18) we have

$$\frac{\Delta y}{\Delta u} = \frac{2 \sin \frac{1}{2}(u + \Delta u - u) \cos \frac{1}{2}(u + \Delta u + u)}{\Delta u}$$

$$= \frac{\sin (\Delta u/2) \cos [u + (\Delta u/2)]}{\Delta u/2}.$$

Looking ahead to the next step of letting $\Delta u \to 0$, we see that the numerator and denominator both approach zero. This situation is precisely the same as that in which we were finding the derivatives of the algebraic functions. In order to find the limit, it is necessary to find

$$\lim_{\Delta u \to 0} \frac{\sin (\Delta u/2)}{\Delta u/2},$$

since these are the factors which cause the numerator and the denominator to approach zero.

We have to use a geometric approach to find $\lim_{\theta \to 0} \sin \theta/\theta$ (for ease of notation we have let $\Delta u/2 = \theta$). Considering Fig. 6–13, we can see that the following inequality is true for the indicated areas:

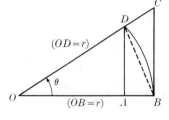

$(OD = r)$

$(OB = r)$

FIGURE 6–13

$$\text{Area triangle } OBD < \text{ area sector } OBD < \text{ area triangle } OBC,$$

$$\tfrac{1}{2}r(r \sin \theta) < \tfrac{1}{2}r^2\theta < \tfrac{1}{2}r(r \tan \theta), \quad \text{or} \quad \sin \theta < \theta < \tan \theta.$$

Remembering that we want to find the limit of $\sin \theta/\theta$, we next divide through by $\sin \theta$, and then take reciprocals:

$$1 < \frac{\theta}{\sin \theta} < \frac{1}{\cos \theta} \quad \text{or} \quad 1 > \frac{\sin \theta}{\theta} > \cos \theta.$$

When we consider the limit as $\theta \to 0$, we see that the left member remains 1 and the right member approaches 1. Thus $\sin \theta/\theta$ must approach 1. This means that

$$\lim_{\theta \to 0} \frac{\sin \theta}{\theta} = \lim_{\Delta u \to 0} \frac{\sin (\Delta u/2)}{\Delta u/2} = 1. \qquad (6\text{–}26)$$

Using the result expressed in Eq. (6–26) in the expression for $\Delta y/\Delta u$, we have

$$\lim_{\Delta u \to 0} \frac{\Delta y}{\Delta u} = \lim_{\Delta u \to 0} \left[\cos \left(u + \frac{\Delta u}{2} \right) \frac{\sin (\Delta u/2)}{\Delta u/2} \right] = \cos u$$

or

$$\frac{dy}{du} = \cos u. \tag{6–27}$$

However, what we want is the derivative of y with respect to x. This requires the use of the following expression:

$$\frac{\Delta y}{\Delta x} = \frac{\Delta y}{\Delta x} \frac{\Delta u}{\Delta u} = \frac{\Delta y}{\Delta u} \frac{\Delta u}{\Delta x},$$

$$\lim_{\Delta x \to 0} \frac{\Delta y}{\Delta x} = \lim_{\Delta x \to 0} \left(\frac{\Delta y}{\Delta u} \right) \left(\frac{\Delta u}{\Delta x} \right),$$

or

$$\frac{dy}{dx} = \frac{dy}{du} \frac{du}{dx}. \tag{6–28}$$

Combining Eqs. (6–27) and (6–28), we have ($y = \sin u$)

$$\frac{d (\sin u)}{dx} = \cos u \frac{du}{dx}. \tag{6–29}$$

Example A. Find the derivative of $y = \sin 2x$.
   In this example $u = 2x$. Thus

$$\frac{dy}{dx} = \cos 2x \left(\frac{d(2x)}{dx} \right) = 2 \cos 2x.$$

Example B. Find the derivative of $y = 2 \sin (x^2)$.
   In this example $u = x^2$, which means that $du/dx = 2x$. Hence

$$\frac{dy}{dx} = 2 \left[\cos (x^2) \right](2x) = 4x \cos (x^2).$$

It is important here, just as it is in finding the derivatives of powers of functions, to remember to include the factor du/dx.

Example C. Find the derivative of $y = \sin^2 x$.
   This example is a combination of the use of the power rule, Eq. (2–28), and the derivative of the sine function, Eq. (6–29). In the power rule, $u = \sin x$. Thus

$$\frac{dy}{dx} = 2 (\sin x) \frac{d \sin x}{dx} = 2 \sin x \cos x = \sin 2x.$$

Example D. Find the derivative of $y = 2 \sin^3 (2x^4)$.

In the general power rule, $u = \sin (2x^4)$. In the derivative of the sine function, $u = 2x^4$. Thus we have

$$\frac{dy}{dx} = 2(3) \sin^2 (2x^4) \frac{d (\sin 2x^4)}{dx}$$

$$= 6 \sin^2 (2x^4) \cos (2x^4) \frac{d(2x^4)}{dx} = 48x^3 \sin^2 (2x^4) \cos (2x^4).$$

To find the derivative of the cosine function, we write it in the form $\cos u = \sin [(\pi/2) - u]$. Thus, if $y = \sin [(\pi/2) - u]$, we have

$$\frac{dy}{dx} = \cos \left(\frac{\pi}{2} - u \right) \frac{d[(\pi/2) - u]}{dx} = \cos \left(\frac{\pi}{2} - u \right) \left(-\frac{du}{dx} \right)$$

$$= -\cos \left(\frac{\pi}{2} - u \right) \frac{du}{dx}.$$

Since $\cos [(\pi/2) - u] = \sin u$, we have

$$\frac{d (\cos u)}{dx} = -\sin u \frac{du}{dx}. \qquad (6\text{–}30)$$

Example E. Find the derivative of $y = \cos^2 (2x)$.

Using the power rule and Eq. (6–30), we have

$$\frac{dy}{dx} = 2 \cos (2x) (-\sin 2x)(2) = -4 \sin 2x \cos 2x = -2 \sin 4x.$$

Example F. Find the derivative of $y = \sin 2x \cos x^2$.

Using the product rule and the derivatives of the sine and cosine functions, we arrive at the following result:

$$\frac{dy}{dx} = \sin 2x (-\sin x^2)(2x) + \cos x^2 (\cos 2x)(2)$$

$$= -2x \sin 2x \sin x^2 + 2 \cos 2x \cos x^2.$$

Exercises

In Exercises 1 through 14, find the derivatives of the given functions.

1. $y = \sin (x + 2)$　　　　2. $y = 3 \sin 4x$　　　　3. $y = \sin^2 4x$

4. $y = \cos (1 - x)$　　　　5. $y = 3 \cos^3 (5x + 2)$　　　　6. $y = 4 \cos^2 \sqrt{x}$

7. $y = x \sin 3x$　　　　8. $y = x \cos 2x^3$　　　　9. $y = \dfrac{\sin 3x}{x}$

10. $y = \dfrac{5x}{\cos x}$ 11. $y = \sin^3 x - \cos 2x$ 12. $y = x \sin x + \cos x$

13. $y = x - \frac{1}{3} \sin^3 4x$ 14. $y = 2x \sin x + 2 \cos x - x^2 \cos x$

15. Show that
$$\frac{d^4 \sin x}{dx^4} = \sin x.$$

16. If $y = \cos 2x$, show that
$$\frac{d^2 y}{dx^2} = -4y.$$

17. Find the velocity after 2 sec, if the distance from a reference point of a particle is given by $s = 2 \sin 3t + t^2$, where s is in feet.

18. The current, in amperes, in a certain electric circuit, as a function of time, in sec, is given by $i = 10 \cos (120\pi t + \pi/6)$. Find the expression for the voltage across a 2-henry inductor. (See Exercise 13 of Section 5–1.)

6–4 Derivatives of the other trigonometric functions

We can find the derivatives of the other trigonometric functions by expressing the functions in terms of the sine and cosine. After we perform the differentiation, we use trigonometric relations to put the derivative in a convenient form.

We obtain the derivative of $\tan u$ by expressing $\tan u$ as $\sin u/\cos u$. Therefore, letting $y = \sin u/\cos u$, by employing the quotient rule we have

$$\frac{dy}{dx} = \frac{\cos u \,[\cos u \,(du/dx)] - \sin u \,[-\sin u \,(du/dx)]}{\cos^2 u}$$

$$= \frac{\cos^2 u + \sin^2 u}{\cos^2 u}\frac{du}{dx} = \frac{1}{\cos^2 u}\frac{du}{dx} = \sec^2 u \frac{du}{dx}.$$

Thus

$$\frac{d\,(\tan u)}{dx} = \sec^2 u \frac{du}{dx}. \qquad (6\text{–}31)$$

We find the derivative of $\cot u$ by letting $y = \cos u/\sin u$, and again using the quotient rule:

$$\frac{dy}{dx} = \frac{\sin u \,[-\sin u \,(du/dx)] - \cos u \,[\cos u \,(du/dx)]}{\sin^2 u}$$

$$= \frac{-\sin^2 u - \cos^2 u}{\sin^2 u}\frac{du}{dx}.$$

Thus

$$\frac{d\,(\cot u)}{dx} = -\csc^2 u \frac{du}{dx}. \qquad (6\text{–}32)$$

To obtain the derivative of sec u, we let $y = 1/\cos u$. Then

$$\frac{dy}{dx} = -(\cos u)^{-2}\left[(-\sin u)\left(\frac{du}{dx}\right)\right] = \frac{1}{\cos u}\frac{\sin u}{\cos u}\frac{du}{dx}.$$

Thus

$$\frac{d\,(\sec u)}{dx} = \sec u \tan u \frac{du}{dx}. \tag{6–33}$$

We obtain the derivative of csc u by letting $y = 1/\sin u$. And so

$$\frac{dy}{dx} = -(\sin u)^{-2}\left(\cos u \frac{du}{dx}\right) = -\frac{1}{\sin u}\frac{\cos u}{\sin u}\frac{du}{dx}.$$

Thus

$$\frac{d\,(\csc u)}{dx} = -\csc u \cot u \frac{du}{dx}. \tag{6–34}$$

Example A. Find the derivative of $y = \tan^2 4x$.
Using the power rule and Eq. (6–31), we have

$$\frac{dy}{dx} = 2 \tan 4x \,(\sec^2 4x)(4) = 8 \tan 4x \sec^2 4x.$$

Example B. Find the derivative of $y = \cot^4 2x$.
Using the power rule and Eq. (6–32), we have

$$\frac{dy}{dx} = 4 \,(\cot^3 2x) \,(-\csc^2 2x)(2) = -8 \cot^3 2x \csc^2 2x.$$

Example C. Find the derivative of $y = \sec^2 x$.
Using the power rule and Eq. (6–33), we have

$$\frac{dy}{dx} = 2 \sec x \,(\sec x \tan x) = 2 \sec^2 x \tan x.$$

Example D. Find the derivative of $y = x \csc^3 2x$.
Using the power rule, the product rule, and Eq. (6–34), we have

$$\frac{dy}{dx} = x(3 \csc^2 2x) \,(-\csc 2x \cot 2x)(2) + \csc^3 2x = \csc^3 2x(-6x \cot 2x + 1).$$

Example E. Find the derivative of $y = (\tan 2x + \sec 2x)^3$.
Using the power rule, Eqs. (6–31) and (6–33), we have

$$\frac{dy}{dx} = 3 \,(\tan 2x + \sec 2x)^2 \,[\sec^2 2x(2) + \sec 2x \tan 2x(2)]$$

$$= 6 \sec 2x \,(\tan 2x + \sec 2x)^3.$$

Exercises

In Exercises 1 through 14, find the derivatives of the given functions.

1. $y = \tan 5x$
2. $y = \sec^3 x$
3. $y = -3 \csc \sqrt{x}$
4. $y = \cot^2 (1 - x)$
5. $y = \cot (1 - x)^2$
6. $y = 2 \tan^2 (x^2)$
7. $y = \sqrt{\sec 4x}$
8. $y = \tan 2x - \sec 2x$
9. $y = \dfrac{\csc x}{x}$
10. $y = x^2 \tan x$
11. $y = \cot \sqrt{x - 2}$
12. $y = \frac{1}{2} \sin 2x \tan 2x$
13. $y = \frac{1}{3} \tan^3 x - \tan x$
14. $y = x - \tan x + \sec^2 2x$

15. Find the differential of the function $y = \tan 4x \sec 4x$.

16. Show that $y = \cos^3 x \tan x$ satisfies the equation

$$\cos x \frac{dy}{dx} + 3y \sin x - \cos^2 x = 0.$$

17. On observing the take-off of a rocket, the angle of elevation of the rocket with respect to the observer 1000 ft horizontally from the take-off position was found to be $\theta = 3t/(2t + 10)$ as a function of the time. Therefore, the height h of the rocket was

$$h = 1000 \tan \frac{3t}{2t + 10}.$$

Find the time rate of change of height after 5 seconds.

6–5 The inverse trigonometric functions

There are times when we wish to solve for the angle in trigonometric relations. Such occasions occur when we know the function of an angle and must find the angle. Also, if we wish to find the rate of change of an angle under certain conditions, it might be convenient to have an expression representing the angle, and not simply a function of it. Functions have been defined for this purpose, and as we shall see, they have significant application in calculus.

Therefore, we define the *inverse trigonometric* relations. The *inverse sine of* x is defined by

$$y = \arcsin x. \qquad (6\text{–}35)$$

(The notation $y = \sin^{-1} x$ is also used.) Similar relations exist for the other inverse trigonometric relations.

It is important to emphasize that $y = \arcsin x$ and $x = \sin y$ represent exactly the same relation between x and y. The advantage of having both forms is that a trigonometric relation may be expressed in terms of the function of an angle or in terms of the angle itself. The most useful way of reading Eq. (6–35) is "y is the angle whose sine is x."

Example A. If $y = \arcsin \frac{1}{2}$, we wish to find "the angle whose sine is $\frac{1}{2}$." Thus, $y = \pi/6$ is an acceptable answer. However, $-11\pi/6$, $13\pi/6$, and so forth, would also satisfy the equation.

Example B. Given that $y = \sec 2x$, and we wish to solve for x, we proceed as follows. First, $2x = \text{arcsec } y$ by the definition of the inverse relations. Then, $x = \frac{1}{2} \text{arcsec } y$ gives us the desired result.

Given that $4y = \text{arccot } 2x$, and we wish to find x we proceed as follows. First, $2x = \cot 4y$ and then $x = \frac{1}{2} \cot 4y$. We see that it is possible to change forms either way by the use of the inverse trigonometric relations.

We noted in Example A that it was possible to find many values of y, if we assumed some value of x in the relation $y = \arcsin x$. As we defined them, any one of the various possibilities would be considered correct. This, however, leads to ambiguity when values of x are assumed. In order to define inverse trigonometric *functions* such that this ambiguity does not exist, and so that there exists a single value of y for any given value of x, the following *principal values* are chosen for the given relations.

$$-\frac{\pi}{2} \leq \text{Arcsin } x \leq \frac{\pi}{2}, \qquad 0 \leq \text{Arccos } x \leq \pi, \qquad -\frac{\pi}{2} < \text{Arctan } x < \frac{\pi}{2}$$

$$(6\text{--}36)$$

This means that when we are looking for a value of y corresponding to a given value of x, we use *the* value of y as defined in Eq. (6–36). The capital letter designates the use of the principal value.

Example C. $\text{Arcsin}(\frac{1}{2}) = \pi/6$. This is the only value of the function which lies within the defined range. The value $5\pi/6$ is not acceptable, since it lies outside the defined range of values.

$\text{Arccos}(-\frac{1}{2}) = 2\pi/3$. Other values such as $4\pi/3$ and $-2\pi/3$ are not correct since they are not within the defined range of values for the Arccos x.

Example D. $\text{Arcsin }(-\sqrt{3}/2) = -\pi/3$, $\text{Arccos }(-1) = \pi$,

        $\text{Arctan } 0 = 0$, $\text{Arcsin }(-0.1564) \doteq -\pi/20$,

        $\text{Arccos }(-0.8090) = 4\pi/5$, $\text{Arctan }(\sqrt{3}) = \pi/3$.

One might logically ask why these values are chosen when there are so many different possibilities. The values are so chosen that, if x is positive, the resulting answer gives an angle in the first quadrant. We must, however, account for the possibility that x might be negative. We could not choose second-quadrant angles for the Arcsin x. This is due to the fact that the sine of second-quadrant angles is also positive, and this then would lead to ambiguity. The sine is negative for fourth-quadrant angles, and in order to have a continuous range of values of x, we express the fourth-quadrant angles in the form of negative angles. This range is also chosen for the Arctan x, for similar reasons. However, the Arccos x cannot be chosen in this way, since the cosine of fourth-quadrant angles is also positive. Thus, again to keep a continuous range of values for Arccos x, the second-quadrant angles are chosen for negative values of x.

As for principal values for the other functions, we choose values of these such that if x is positive, the result is an angle in the first quadrant. There is no general agreement on how values of these functions should be defined for negative values of x. In practice it rarely makes any difference, since either positive values of x arise, or we can use one of the functions for which ranges are defined for negative values of x. For these reasons we shall not define the ranges for these other functions for negative values of x.

If we know the value of x for one of the inverse functions, we can find the trigonometric functions of the angle. If general relations are desired, a representative triangle is very useful. The following examples illustrate these methods.

Example E. Find cos (Arcsin 0.5). [Remember again: the inverse functions are *angles*.]

We know Arcsin 0.5 is a first-quadrant angle, since 0.5 is positive. Thus we find Arcsin 0.5 $= \pi/6$. The problem now becomes one of finding cos $(\pi/6)$. This is, of course, $\sqrt{3}/2$ or 0.8660.

Example F. Find sin (Arctan x).

We know that Arctan x is another way of stating "the angle whose tangent is x." Thus let us draw a right triangle, as in Fig. 6–14, and label one of the acute angles θ, the side opposite θ as x, and the side adjacent θ as 1. In this way we see that, by defini-

FIGURE 6–14

tion, tan $\theta = x/1$, or $\theta =$ Arctan x, which means that θ is the desired angle. By the Pythagorean Theorem, the hypotenuse of this triangle is $\sqrt{x^2 + 1}$. Now we find that sin θ, which is the same as sin (Arctan x), is $x/\sqrt{x^2 + 1}$,

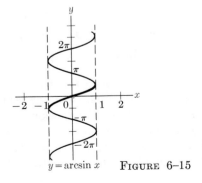

$y = \arcsin x$ FIGURE 6–15

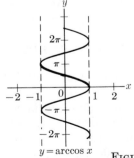

$y = \arccos x$ FIGURE 6–16

from the definition of the sine. Thus,

$$\sin (\text{Arctan } x) = \frac{x}{\sqrt{x^2 + 1}}.$$

Since $y = \arcsin x$ and $x = \sin y$ are equivalent equations, we can obtain the graph of the inverse sine by sketching the sine curve *along the y-axis*. The graphs of the other inverse functions are obtained in the same way. The darker portions of the graphs represent the principal values (see Figs. 6–15, 6–16, and 6–17).

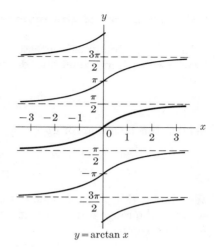

FIGURE 6–17　　　$y = \text{arctan } x$

Exercises

In Exercises 1 through 15, evaluate the given expressions.

1. Arccos $(\frac{1}{2})$
2. Arctan $(-\sqrt{3})$
3. Arcsin 1
4. Arctan $(\sqrt{3}/3)$
5. Arcsin $(-\frac{1}{2})$
6. Arcsec 2
7. Arcsin $(-\sqrt{2}/2)$
8. Arccot $\sqrt{3}$
9. Arccsc $\sqrt{2}$
10. Arcsin 0
11. Arccos (-0.5878)
12. cos [Arctan (-1)]
13. sin (Arctan $\sqrt{3}$)
14. sin (2 Arctan 2)
15. Arctan (Arcsin 1)

In Exercises 16 through 18, solve for x.

16. $y = \sin 3x$
17. $y = 1 + \sec 3x$
18. $y = 2 - \text{Arcsin } (x/6)$

In Exercises 19 through 24, find an algebraic expression for each expression.

19. tan (Arcsin x)
20. sin (Arccos x)
21. sin (Arcsin x)
22. cos (2 Arctan x)
23. sin (2 Arcsin x)
24. tan (Arcsin $2x$)

25. The magnitude of a certain ray of polarized light is given by

$$E = E_0 \cos \theta \sin \theta.$$

Solve for θ.

26. Show that

$$\text{Arcsin } \tfrac{3}{5} + \text{Arcsin } \tfrac{5}{13} = \text{Arcsin } \tfrac{56}{65}.$$

[*Hint:* Use the relation for sin $(\alpha + \beta)$.]

27. Under certain conditions, the current in an electric circuit is given by

$$i = I_m[\sin (\omega t + \alpha) \cos \varphi + \cos (\omega t + \alpha) \sin \varphi].$$

Solve for t.

6–6 Derivatives of the inverse trigonometric functions

In order to obtain the derivative of $y = \text{Arcsin } u$, we first solve for u in the form $u = \sin y$ and then take derivatives with respect to x:

$$\frac{du}{dx} = \cos y \frac{dy}{dx}.$$

Solving this equation for dy/dx, we obtain

$$\frac{dy}{dx} = \frac{1}{\cos y} \frac{du}{dx} = \frac{1}{\sqrt{1 - \sin^2 y}} \frac{du}{dx} = \frac{1}{\sqrt{1 - u^2}} \frac{du}{dx}.$$

We choose the positive square root since $\cos y > 0$ for $-\pi/2 < y < \pi/2$, which is the range of the principal values of Arcsin u. Therefore we obtain the following result:

$$\frac{d (\text{Arcsin } u)}{dx} = \frac{1}{\sqrt{1 - u^2}} \frac{du}{dx}. \tag{6–37}$$

We note here that the derivative of the inverse sine function is an algebraic function.

We can find the derivative of the inverse cosine function by letting $y = \text{Arccos } u$, and by following the same procedure as that used in finding the derivative of Arcsin u:

$$u = \cos y, \qquad \frac{du}{dx} = -\sin y \frac{dy}{dx},$$

$$\frac{dy}{dx} = -\frac{1}{\sin y} \frac{du}{dx} = -\frac{1}{\sqrt{1 - \cos^2 y}} \frac{du}{dx}.$$

Therefore

$$\frac{d (\text{Arccos } u)}{dx} = -\frac{1}{\sqrt{1 - u^2}} \frac{du}{dx}. \tag{6–38}$$

The positive square root is chosen in this case since $\sin y > 0$ for $0 < y < \pi$, which is the range of the principal values of Arccos u. We note that the derivative of the inverse cosine is the negative of the derivative of the inverse sine.

By letting $y = \text{Arctan } u$, solving for u, and taking derivatives, we find the derivative of the inverse tangent function:

$$u = \tan y, \qquad \frac{du}{dx} = \sec^2 y \frac{dy}{dx}, \qquad \frac{dy}{dx} = \frac{1}{\sec^2 y} \frac{du}{dx} = \frac{1}{1 + \tan^2 y} \frac{du}{dx}.$$

Therefore

$$\frac{d (\text{Arctan } u)}{dx} = \frac{1}{1 + u^2} \frac{du}{dx}. \tag{6–39}$$

We can see that the derivative of the inverse tangent is an algebraic function also.

The inverse sine and inverse tangent prove to be of the greatest importance in applications and in further development of mathematics. Therefore the formulas for the derivatives of the other inverse functions are not presented here, although they are included in the exercises.

Example A. Find the derivative of $y = \text{Arcsin } 4x$.
    We write

$$\frac{dy}{dx} = \frac{1}{\sqrt{1 - 16x^2}}\,(4) = \frac{4}{\sqrt{1 - 16x^2}}.$$

Example B. Find the derivative of $y = \text{Arccos }(1 - 2x)$.
    We write

$$\frac{dy}{dx} = \frac{-1}{\sqrt{1 - (1 - 2x)^2}}\,(-2) = \frac{2}{\sqrt{1 - 1 + 4x - 4x^2}}$$

$$= \frac{2}{\sqrt{4x - 4x^2}} = \frac{1}{\sqrt{x - x^2}}.$$

Example C. Find the derivative of $y = (x^2 + 1)\,\text{Arctan } x - x$.
    We have

$$\frac{dy}{dx} = (x^2 + 1)\frac{1}{1 + x^2} + \text{Arctan } x\,(2x) - 1 = 2x\,\text{Arctan } x.$$

Example D. Find the derivative of $y = x\,\text{Arctan}^2\, 2x$.
    We have

$$\frac{dy}{dx} = x(2)(\text{Arctan } 2x)\left(\frac{1}{1 + 4x^2}\right)(2) + \text{Arctan}^2\, 2x$$

$$= \text{Arctan } 2x \left(\frac{4x}{1 + 4x^2} + \text{Arctan } 2x\right).$$

Example E. Find the derivative of $y = x\,\text{Arcsin } 2x + \frac{1}{2}\sqrt{1 - 4x^2}$.
    We write

$$\frac{dy}{dx} = x\left(\frac{2}{\sqrt{1 - 4x^2}}\right) + \text{Arcsin } 2x + \frac{1}{2}\cdot\frac{1}{2}(1 - 4x^2)^{-1/2}(-8x)$$

$$= \frac{2x}{\sqrt{1 - 4x^2}} + \text{Arcsin } 2x - \frac{2x}{\sqrt{1 - 4x^2}} = \text{Arcsin } 2x.$$

Exercises

In Exercises 1 through 14, find the derivatives of the given functions.

1. $y = \text{Arcsin}\,(x^2)$

2. $y = \text{Arctan}\,(1 + x)$

3. $y = \text{Arccos}\,\frac{1}{2}x$

4. $y = \text{Arcsin}\,\sqrt{1 - x}$

5. $y = \text{Arctan}\,\sqrt{x}$

6. $y = \text{Arcsin}\,(1 - x^2)$

7. $y = x\,\text{Arcsin}\,x$

8. $y = \dfrac{\text{Arctan}\,2x}{x}$

9. $y = x^2\,\text{Arccos}\,x$

10. $y = \text{Arcsin}\,x - \sqrt{1 - x^2}$

11. $y = \text{Arctan}\left(\dfrac{1}{x}\right)$

12. $y = \sqrt{\text{Arcsin}\,(x - 1)}$

13. $y = \dfrac{1}{1 + 4x^2} - \text{Arctan}\,2x$

14. $y = \text{Arcsin}^2\,4x$

15. Find the differential of the function $y = \text{Arcsin}^3\,x$.

16. Find the second derivative of the function $y = \text{Arctan}\,2x$.

17. Show that

$$\frac{d\,(\text{Arccot}\,u)}{dx} = -\frac{1}{1 + u^2}\frac{du}{dx}.$$

18. Show that

$$\frac{d\,(\text{Arcsec}\,u)}{dx} = \frac{1}{u\sqrt{u^2 - 1}}\frac{du}{dx}.$$

19. Show that

$$\frac{d\,(\text{Arccsc}\,u)}{dx} = -\frac{1}{u\sqrt{u^2 - 1}}\frac{du}{dx}.$$

20. As a person approaches a building of height h, the angle of elevation of the top of the building is a function of his distance from the building. Express the angle of elevation θ in terms of h and the distance x from the building and then find $d\theta/dx$. Assume the person's height is negligible to that of the building.

6–7 Applications

With our development of the formulas for the derivatives of the trigonometric and inverse trigonometric functions, it is now possible for us to apply these derivatives in the same manner as we applied the derivatives of algebraic functions. We can now use trigonometric and inverse trigonometric functions to solve time-rate of change, tangent and normal, curve tracing, maximum and minimum, and differential application problems. The following examples illustrate the use of these functions in these types of problems.

FIGURE 6–18

Example A. Sketch the curve $y = \sin^2 x - \dfrac{x}{2}$ $(0 \le x \le 2\pi)$.

First we write

$$\frac{dy}{dx} = 2 \sin x \cos x - \frac{1}{2} = \sin 2x - \frac{1}{2}, \qquad \frac{d^2y}{dx^2} = 2 \cos 2x.$$

The only easily obtained intercept is $(0, 0)$. (See Fig. 6–18.) Maximum and minimum points will occur for $\sin 2x = \frac{1}{2}$. Thus maximum and minimum points occur if

$$2x = \frac{\pi}{6}, \frac{5\pi}{6}, \frac{13\pi}{6}, \frac{17\pi}{6}.$$

Thus the x-values are

$$x = \frac{\pi}{12}, \frac{5\pi}{12}, \frac{13\pi}{12}, \frac{17\pi}{12}.$$

Using the second derivative, we find that d^2y/dx^2 is positive for $x = \pi/12$ and $x = 13\pi/12$, and negative for $x = 5\pi/12$ and $x = 17\pi/12$. Thus the maximum points are $(5\pi/12, 0.278)$ and $(17\pi/12, -1.19)$. The minimum points are $(\pi/12, -0.064)$ and $(13\pi/12, -1.64)$. Inflection points occur for $\cos 2x = 0$, or

$$2x = \frac{\pi}{2}, \frac{3\pi}{2}, \frac{5\pi}{2}, \frac{7\pi}{2}, \qquad \text{or} \qquad x = \frac{\pi}{4}, \frac{3\pi}{4}, \frac{5\pi}{4}, \frac{7\pi}{4}.$$

Therefore the points of inflection are $(\pi/4, 0.11)$, $(3\pi/4, -0.68)$, $(5\pi/4, -1.47)$, and $(7\pi/4, -2.25)$. Using this information, we sketch the curve.

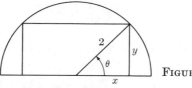

FIGURE 6–19

Example B. Find the area of the largest rectangle which can be inscribed in a semicircle of radius 2.

From Fig. 6–19, we see that $A = 2xy$, where $x = 2 \cos \theta$ and $y = 2 \sin \theta$. Thus $A = 8 \sin \theta \cos \theta = 4 \sin 2\theta$. We shall find the value of θ corresponding to the maximum area. Therefore

$$\frac{dA}{d\theta} = 8\cos 2\theta, \qquad 8\cos 2\theta = 0, \qquad 2\theta = \frac{\pi}{2}, \qquad \theta = \frac{\pi}{4}.$$

Thus the maximum area is $A = 4\sin 2(\pi/4) = 4$.

Example C. A rocket is taking off vertically at a distance of 600 ft from an observer. If, when the angle of elevation is $\pi/4$, it is changing at the rate of 0.5 rad/sec, how fast is the rocket ascending?

From Fig. 6–20, we see that

$$\theta = \text{Arctan}\,(x/600).$$

Taking derivatives with respect to time, we have

$$\frac{d\theta}{dt} = \frac{1}{1 + x^2/(3.6 \times 10^5)}\,\frac{dx/dt}{600}$$

$$= \frac{600\,dx/dt}{3.6 \times 10^5 + x^2}.$$

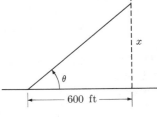

FIGURE 6–20

From the given information, we find that $d\theta/dt = 0.5$ rad/sec, $x = 600$ ft when $\theta = \pi/4$. Thus

$$0.5 = \frac{600\,dx/dt}{7.2 \times 10^5} \qquad \text{or} \qquad \frac{dx}{dt} = 600 \text{ ft/sec.}$$

Example D. A particle moves so that its x- and y-coordinates are given by $x = \cos 2t$ and $y = \sin 2t$. Find the magnitude and direction of its velocity when $t = \pi/8$.

We write

$$v_x = \frac{dx}{dt} = -2\sin 2t, \qquad v_y = \frac{dy}{dt} = 2\cos 2t,$$

$$v_x\big|_{t=\pi/8} = -2\sin 2\left(\frac{\pi}{8}\right) = -2\left(\frac{\sqrt{2}}{2}\right) = -\sqrt{2},$$

$$v_y\big|_{t=\pi/8} = 2\cos 2\left(\frac{\pi}{8}\right) = 2\left(\frac{\sqrt{2}}{2}\right) = \sqrt{2},$$

$$v = \sqrt{v_x^2 + v_y^2} = \sqrt{2+2} = 2, \qquad \tan\theta = \frac{v_y}{v_x} = \frac{\sqrt{2}}{-\sqrt{2}} = -1.$$

Since v_x is negative and v_y is positive, $\theta = 135°$. Note that in this example θ is the angle, in standard position, between the horizontal and the resultant velocity.

By plotting the curve we note that it is a circle (Fig. 6–21). Thus the object is moving about a circle in a counterclockwise direction. That the curve is a

FIGURE 6–21

circle can be determined in another way. If we square each of the expressions defining x and y, and then add these, we have $x^2 + y^2 = \cos^2 2t + \sin^2 2t = 1$. This is a circle of radius 1.

Example E. At a point 180 ft from the base of a building on level ground, the angle of elevation of the top of the building is 30°. What would be the error in the height of the building due to an error of 15′ in this angle?

   From Fig. 6–22 we see that $h = 180 \tan \theta$. Finding the differential of h, we have

$$dh = 180 \sec^2 \theta \, d\theta.$$

Since $\theta = 30°$, $\sec \theta = 2/\sqrt{3}$, or $\sec^2 \theta = 4/3$. The possible error in θ is 15′ which is 0.25°, which in turn is 0.00436 rad, which is the value we must use in the calculation. Thus,

$$dh = (180)(\tfrac{4}{3})(0.00436) = 1.05 \text{ ft.}$$

We see that an error of 15′ in the angle can result in an error of over 1 ft in the calculation of the height.

FIGURE 6–22

Exercises

1. Show that the slopes of the sine and cosine curves are negatives of each other at the points of intersection.
2. Show that the tangent curve, when defined, is always increasing.
3. Show that $y = \text{Arctan } x$ is always increasing.
4. Sketch the graph of $y = \sin x + \cos x \quad (0 \leq x \leq 2\pi)$.
5. Sketch the graph of $y = x - \tan x \quad (-\pi/2 < x < \pi/2)$.
6. Sketch the graph of $y = \sin x + \sin 2x \quad (0 < x < 2\pi)$.
7. Find the equation of the line tangent to the curve of $y = \sin 2x$ where $x = 5\pi/8$.
8. Find the equation of a line normal to the curve of $y = \text{Arctan } (x/2)$ where $x = 3$.

9. If the distance (in feet) a certain object travels as a function of time is given by $s = \sin t + \cos 2t$, find its velocity and acceleration when $t = \pi/6$ sec.

10. The *apparent* power P_a of an electric circuit whose power is P and impedance phase angle is θ is given by $P_a = P \sec \theta$. If P is constant at 12 watts, find the time rate of change of P_a if θ is changing at the rate of 0.05 rad/min, when $\theta = 2\pi/9$.

11. Find the magnitude and direction of the velocity of an object which moves so that its x- and y-coordinates are given by $x = \sin 2\pi t$ and $y = \cos 2\pi t$ when $t = \frac{1}{12}$.

12. Find the magnitude and direction of the velocity of an object which moves so that the x- and y-coordinates are given by $x = \cos 2t$ and $y = 2 \sin t$ when $t = \pi/6$.

13. Find the magnitude and direction of the acceleration of the particle in Example D when $t = \pi/8$.

14. Find the magnitude and direction of the acceleration of the object in Exercise 12.

15. A person observes an object dropped from the top of a building 100 ft away. If the building is 200 ft high, how fast is the angle of elevation of the object changing after 1 sec? (The distance the object drops is given by $s = 16t^2$.)

16. An airplane flying horizontally at 500 ft/sec passes directly over an observer 4000 ft below. How fast is the angle of elevation changing at this instant?

17. One leg of a right triangle is 6 units long. If the acute angle of which this side is the adjacent side is increasing at the rate of 0.1 rad/sec, how fast is the hypotenuse changing when it is 10 units in length?

18. If a block is placed on an inclined plane, inclined at an angle θ with the horizontal, such that it just moves down the plane, the coefficient of friction μ, is given by $\mu = \tan \theta$. By use of differentials, find the change in μ if θ changes from 20° to 21°.

19. The current (in amps) in a certain electric circuit is given by $i = \sin^2 2t$. Find the approximate change in i between $t = 1.00$ sec and $t = 1.05$ sec.

20. Two sides and the included angle of a triangle are measured to be 8.00 in., 7.50 in., and 40°. What is the error caused in the calculation of the third side by an error of 0.5° in the angle?

21. Using trigonometric functions, find the area of the largest rectangle with a perimeter of 12 in.

22. Find the angle between the equal sides of an isosceles triangle of greatest area for a given perimeter.

23. A wall is 6 ft high and 4 ft from a building. What is the length of the shortest pole that can touch the building and the ground beyond the wall? [*Hint:* $y = 6 \csc \theta + 4 \sec \theta$. See Fig. 6–23.]

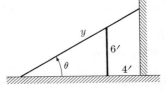

FIGURE 6–23

Miscellaneous exercises for Chapter 6

In Exercises 1 through 12 find the derivative of each of the given functions.

1. $y = 3 \cos (4x - 1)$ 2. $y = 2 \sin^3 \sqrt{x}$ 3. $y = \tan \sqrt{3 - x}$

4. $y = \dfrac{\text{Arcsin } x}{x}$ 5. $y = \sqrt{\csc 4x + \cot 4x}$ 6. $y = \cot^2 5x$

7. $y = 3 \operatorname{Arctan} \left(\dfrac{x}{3} \right)$

8. $y = \sin (\operatorname{Arctan} x)$

9. $y = x \operatorname{Arccos} x - \sqrt{1 - x^2}$

10. $x + \sec^2 (xy) = 1$

11. $x \sin 2y = y \cos 2x$

12. $y = x \operatorname{Arcsin}^2 x + 2\sqrt{1 - x^2} \operatorname{Arcsin} x - 2x$

13. Power can be defined as the time rate of doing work. If work is being done in an electric circuit according to $W = 10 \cos 2t$, find P as a function of t.

14. A particle moves on the circumference of a circle with constant angular velocity. The projection of its motion on the x-axis is given by

$$x = 4 \cos \left(\frac{\pi}{3} t + \frac{\pi}{6} \right).$$

Find the velocity of the projection when $t = 0$.

15. Find the equation of the line tangent to the curve $y = 4 \cos^2 (x^2)$ where $x = 1$.

16. The force which acts on a pendulum bob to restore it to its equilibrium position is given by $F = -mg \sin \theta$ where m is the mass of the bob, g is the acceleration of gravity, and θ is the angle between the string and the vertical. For a bob of 10 gm, find the approximate difference in the force for angles of 3.0° and 3.1° if $g = 980$ cm/sec².

17. In the study of polarized light, under certain conditions, the intensity of transmitted light is given by $I = I_m \cos^2 \theta$, where I_m is the maximum intensity and θ is the angle of transmission. If $I = 8$ units when $\theta = 60°$, and θ is changing at the rate of 0.03 rad/sec, find the rate of change of I when $\theta = 60°$.

18. In optics, the index of refraction of a liquid is defined as $n = \sin i / \sin r$, where i is the angle at which the light is incident on the liquid from the air, and r is the angle of the refracted light in the liquid. If the angle of incidence is increasing at the rate of 0.05 rad/min, what is the rate of change of the angle r when $i = 10°$ for benzene, for which $n = 1.50$?

19. A revolving light 300 ft from a straight wall makes 6 rev/min. Find the velocity of the beam along the wall at the instant it makes an angle of 45° with the wall.

20. Sketch the graph of $y = 4 \sin x + \cos 2x$.

21. A gutter is to be made from a sheet of metal 12 in. wide by turning up strips of width 4 in. along each side such that they make equal angles θ with the vertical. Sketch a graph of the cross-sectional area A as a function of θ. See Fig. 6–24.

4 in θ A θ 4 in

4 in

FIGURE 6–24

22. A force P at an angle θ above the horizontal drags a 50-lb box across a level floor. The coefficient of friction between the floor and box is constant and equals 0.2. The magnitude of the force P is given by

$$P = \frac{(0.2)(50)}{(0.2) \sin \theta + \cos \theta}.$$

Find θ such that P is a minimum.

23. The intensity of illumination of light from a source varies directly as the cosine of the angle of incidence (measured from the perpendicular) and inversely as the square of the distance r from the source. How high above the center of a circle of radius 10 in. should a light be placed so that the intensity at the circumference will be a maximum? (See Fig. 6–25.)

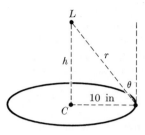

FIGURE 6–25

24. A metal bracket in the shape of a Y is to be made such that its height is 10 in. and width across the top is 6 in. What shape will require the least amount of material?

7 Derivatives of the exponential and logarithmic functions

7–1 Exponential and logarithmic functions

Another important function in many of the applications of technology, especially in mechanics and electricity, is the exponential function. Closely associated with the exponential function is the logarithmic function, which also has numerous applications. Therefore, in this section we shall review the properties of these functions, and in the remaining sections of this chapter we shall develop the derivatives of them.

By definition, the exponential function is of the form

$$y = b^x, \tag{7–1}$$

where b is the *base*, a *constant*, and x is the exponent, the independent *variable*. Restricting values of both variables to real numbers leads us to choose the base as a positive number other than 1. We know that 1 raised to any finite power will result in an answer of 1. Negative numbers for b would result in imaginary values for y, if x were any fractional exponent with an even integer as its denominator.

Example A. $y = 2^x$ is an exponential function, where we see that x is the exponent of 2. That is, 2 raised to any given power gives us the corresponding value of y. If $x = 2, y = 4$. If $x = -4, y = \frac{1}{16}$. If $x = \frac{1}{2}, y = \sqrt{2} = 1.41$. If $x = \frac{3}{2}, y = 2\sqrt{2} = 2.83$. By the definition of the exponential function, any real value of x may be assumed.

In Eq. (7–1), since y is a function of x, it is possible to define x as a function of y. Therefore, in Eq. (7–1) we *define x as the logarithm of the number y to the base b*, which is written as

$$x = \log_b y. \tag{7–2}$$

203

Equations (7–1) and (7–2) state precisely the same relationship, but in a different manner. Equation (7–1) is the exponential form, and Eq. (7–2) is the logarithmic form. In either case, x is a logarithm, and a logarithm is an exponent.

Example B. The equation $y = 2^x$ would be written as $x = \log_2 y$ if we put it in logarithmic form. When we choose values of y to find the corresponding values of x from this equation, we ask ourselves, "2 raised to what power gives y?" Hence if $y = 4$, we know that 2^2 is 4, and x would be 2. If $y = 8, 2^3 = 8$, or $x = 3$.

Example C. $3^2 = 9$ in logarithmic form is $2 = \log_3 9; 4^{-1} = \frac{1}{4}$ in logarithmic form is $-1 = \log_4 \left(\frac{1}{4}\right)$. Remember, the exponent may be negative, but the base must be positive.

If $-4 = \log_b \left(\frac{1}{81}\right)$, and if we write this in exponential form, we may find b. In exponential form it becomes $b^{-4} = \frac{1}{81}$ which means that $b = 3$.

When working with functions, we normally denote the dependent variable as y and the independent variable as x. For this reason, we define the logarithmic function to be

$$y = \log_b x. \tag{7–3}$$

Equations (7–2) and (7–3) may seem to have different meanings, due to the location of the variables. We must keep in mind that a function is defined by the operation being performed on the independent variable, and not by the letter chosen to represent it. These two equations express the same function, the logarithmic function.

We shall now show the graphs of the exponential function, Eq. (7–1), and the logarithmic function, Eq. (7–3). In this way we may demonstrate their properties. The following examples are used for this purpose.

Example D. Plot the graph of $y = 2^x$.

Assuming values for x and then finding the corresponding values for y, we obtain the values in the following table.

x	-3	-2	-1	0	1	2	3	4
y	$\frac{1}{8}$	$\frac{1}{4}$	$\frac{1}{2}$	1	2	4	8	16

From these values we plot the curve, as shown in Fig. 7–1.

Example E. Plot the graph of

$$y = \log_3 x.$$

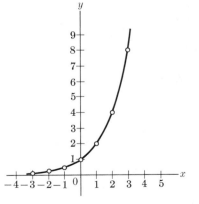

FIGURE 7–1

We can find the points for this graph more easily if we first put the equation in exponential form: $x = 3^y$. By assuming values for y, we can find the corresponding values for x.

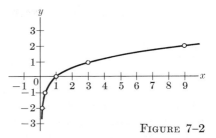

x	$\frac{1}{9}$	$\frac{1}{3}$	1	3	9	27
y	-2	-1	0	1	2	3

FIGURE 7–2

Using these values, we construct the graph seen in Fig. 7–2.

Any exponential or logarithmic curve, where $b > 1$, will be similar to those of Examples D and E. From these we can draw certain conclusions:

(1) If $0 < x < 1$, $\log_b x < 0$; $\log_b 1 = 0$; if $x > 1$, $\log_b x > 0$.
(2) If $x > 1$, x increases more rapidly than $\log_b x$.
(3) $b^x > 0$ for all values of x.
(4) If $x > 1$, b^x increases more rapidly than x.

Since a logarithm is an exponent, it must obey the laws of exponents. Those laws which are of the greatest importance at this time are listed here for reference.

$$b^u \cdot b^v = b^{u+v}, \tag{7–4}$$

$$b^u / b^v = b^{u-v}, \tag{7–5}$$

$$(b^u)^n = b^{nu}. \tag{7–6}$$

We shall now show how these laws for exponents give certain useful properties to logarithms.

If we let $u = \log_b x$ and $v = \log_b y$, and write these equations in exponential form, we have $x = b^u$ and $y = b^v$. Therefore, forming the product of x and y, we obtain

$$xy = b^u b^v = b^{u+v} \quad \text{or} \quad xy = b^{u+v}.$$

Writing this last equation in logarithmic form yields

$$u + v = \log_b xy$$

or

$$\log_b x + \log_b y = \log_b xy. \tag{7–7}$$

Equation (7–7) states the property that *the logarithm of the product of two numbers is equal to the sum of the logarithms of the numbers.*

Using the same definitions of u and v to form the quotient of x and y, we have

$$\frac{x}{y} = \frac{b^u}{b^v} = b^{u-v} \quad \text{or} \quad \frac{x}{y} = b^{u-v}.$$

Writing this last equation in logarithmic form, we have

$$u - v = \log_b \left(\frac{x}{y}\right)$$

or

$$\log_b x - \log_b y = \log_b \left(\frac{x}{y}\right). \tag{7-8}$$

Equation (7–8) states the property that *the logarithm of the quotient of two numbers is equal to the logarithm of the numerator minus the logarithm of the denominator.*

If we again let $u = \log_b x$ and write this in exponential form, we have $x = b^u$. To find the nth power of x, we write

$$x^n = (b^u)^n = b^{nu}.$$

Expressing this equation in logarithmic form yields

$$nu = \log_b (x^n)$$

or

$$n \log_b x = \log_b (x^n). \tag{7-9}$$

This last equation states that *the logarithm of the nth power of a number is equal to n times the logarithm of the number.* The exponent n may be integral or fractional and, therefore, we may use Eq. (7–9) for finding powers and roots of numbers.

Example F. By Eq. (7–7) we can see that

$$\log_2 6 = \log_2 (2 \cdot 3) = \log_2 2 + \log_2 3 = 1 + \log_2 3.$$

By Eq. (7–8) we have

$$\log_5 100 - \log_5 4 = \log_5 \left(\frac{100}{4}\right) = \log_5 25 = 2.$$

If we have

$$\log_b y = 2 \log_b x + \log_b a,$$

by Eqs. (7–9) and (7–7) we may write

$$\log_b y = \log_b x^2 + \log_b a = \log_b (ax^2).$$

Therefore,

$$y = ax^2.$$

There are two bases of logarithms that are used widely. Base 10 is used primarily for calculational purposes, and base e, an irrational number equal to about 2.718, is used primarily for theoretical purposes. In the next section we shall see why e is chosen for this purpose. Tables of logarithms in both bases are found in the Appendix.

It is assumed here that the reader is familiar with logarithms to the base 10 for calculations. The notation $\log x$, without any base indicated, will be used for logarithms to the base 10.

Since our primary purpose in this chapter is to develop the derivatives of the logarithmic and exponential functions, we shall be using the base e extensively. The notation $\ln x$ will be used for this purpose.

Since more than one base is important, it is occasionally useful to be able to change a logarithm in one base to another base. If $u = \log_b x$, $b^u = x$, and taking logarithms of each side to the base a, we have

$$u \log_a b = \log_a x, \qquad u = \frac{\log_a x}{\log_a b},$$

or

$$\log_b x = \frac{\log_a x}{\log_a b}. \tag{7–10}$$

Equation (7–10) allows us to transfer a logarithm in one base to another. The following example illustrates the procedure.

Example G. Since logarithms to the base 10 are commonly tabulated, it is normally necessary to change a logarithm from base 10 to the other base. Thus, let us change $\log 20 = 1.3010$ to the base e, that is, let us find $\ln 20$.

$$\ln 20 = \frac{\log 20}{\log e} = \frac{\log 20}{\log 2.718} = \frac{1.3010}{0.4343} = 2.996.$$

Exercises

In Exercises 1 through 10, change those in exponential form to logarithmic form, and those in logarithmic form to exponential form.

1. $4^4 = 256$ 2. $3^{-2} = \frac{1}{9}$ 3. $\log_8 16 = \frac{4}{3}$ 4. $\log_7 \left(\frac{1}{49}\right) = -2$
5. $8^{1/3} = 2$ 6. $\log_{0.5} 16 = -4$ 7. $\log_{243} 3 = \frac{1}{5}$
8. $(12)^0 = 1$ 9. $\left(\frac{1}{2}\right)^{-2} = 4$ 10. $\log_{1/32} \left(\frac{1}{8}\right) = \frac{3}{5}$

In Exercises 11 through 14, determine the value of the letter present.

11. $\log_7 y = 3$ 12. $\log_b 4 = \frac{2}{3}$ 13. $\log (10)^{0.2} = x$ 14. $\log_8 y = -\frac{2}{3}$

In Exercises 15 and 16 plot the graphs of the given functions.

15. $y = 3^x$ 16. $y = 2 \log_4 x$

In Exercises 17 through 20, express each as a single logarithm.

17. $\log_5 9 - \log_5 3$ 18. $\log_4 3^3 - \log_4 9$
19. $\log_b \sqrt{x} - \log_b x^2$ 20. $\log_b b^{-1} + \log_b \sqrt{b}$

By use of the table of logarithms to the base 10, evaluate the logarithms in Exercises 21 through 24.

21. ln 3   22. ln 0.9   23. $\log_7 42$ 24. $\log_{12} 122$

25. The atmospheric pressure at a given height is given by $p = p_0 e^{-kh}$, where p_0 and k are constants. If $p_0 = 1$ atm and $k = 10^{-5}$/ft, plot p (in atm) versus h (in ft) on semilogarithmic paper.

26. The vapor pressure P over a liquid may be related to temperature by $\log P = (a/T) + b$, where a and b are constants. Solve for P.

27. For an electric circuit containing a battery of voltage E, a resistance R, and an inductance L, the current as a function of time is given by

$$i = \frac{E}{R}(1 - e^{-Rt/L}).$$

Solve for t.

28. Table 4 in the Appendix is a short table of natural logarithms. Computations can be made by means of these logarithms, but such computations require adding or subtracting multiples of 2.3026 to locate the decimal point properly. We can see this in a case such as $N = P \cdot 10^k$. Then

$$\ln N = \ln P + k \ln 10 = \ln P + k(2.3026).$$

For example,

$$\ln 2.500 = 0.9163 \quad \text{and} \quad \ln 250.0 = 0.9163 + 2(2.3026) = 5.5215.$$

Find the natural logarithms of the following numbers: (a) 6.700   (b) 67.00 (c) 3400   (d) 0.3400

Calculate (6.700)(3400) by means of these values, rounding off the answer to the nearest number from the table.

29. The *hyperbolic sine* of u is defined as

$$\sinh u = \tfrac{1}{2}(e^u - e^{-u}),$$

and the *hyperbolic cosine* of u is defined as

$$\cosh u = \tfrac{1}{2}(e^u + e^{-u}).$$

These functions are called *hyperbolic* functions since, if $x = \cosh u$ and $y = \sinh u$, x and y satisfy the equation of the hyperbola $x^2 - y^2 = 1$. Verify this by substituting the appropriate exponential expressions into the equation of the hyperbola and simplifying.

7-2 Derivative of the logarithmic function

We shall first find the derivative of the logarithmic function. We can use the derivative of the logarithmic function to find the derivative of the exponential function, which we shall do in the next section. Again we utilize the Δ-process.

If we let $y = \log_b u$, where u is a function of x, we have

$$y + \Delta y = \log_b (u + \Delta u),$$

$$\Delta y = \log_b (u + \Delta u) - \log_b u = \log_b \left(\frac{u + \Delta u}{u} \right) = \log_b \left(1 + \frac{\Delta u}{u} \right),$$

$$\frac{\Delta y}{\Delta u} = \frac{\log_b (1 + \Delta u/u)}{\Delta u} = \frac{1}{u} \cdot \frac{u}{\Delta u} \log_b \left(1 + \frac{\Delta u}{u} \right) = \frac{1}{u} \log_b \left(1 + \frac{\Delta u}{u} \right)^{u/\Delta u}$$

(We multiply and divide by u for purposes of evaluating the limit, as we shall now show.) Before we can evaluate the $\lim_{\Delta u \to 0} \Delta y/\Delta u$ it is necessary to determine

$$\lim_{\Delta u \to 0} \left(1 + \frac{\Delta u}{u} \right)^{u/\Delta u}.$$

We can see that the exponent becomes unbounded, but the number being raised to this exponent approaches 1. Therefore we shall investigate this limiting value.

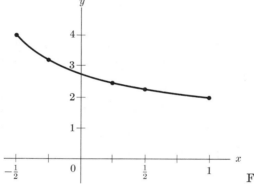

FIGURE 7–3

To find an approximate value, let us graph the function $y = (1 + x)^{1/x}$ (for purposes of graphing we let $\Delta u/u = x$). We construct a table of values and then graph the function (Fig. 7–3).

x	−0.5	−0.25	+0.25	+0.50	+1.00
y	4.00	3.16	2.44	2.25	2.00

Only these values are shown, since we are interested in the y-value corresponding to $x = 0$. We see from the graph that this value is approximately 2.7. Choosing very small values of x, we may obtain the following values:

x	0.1000	0.0100	0.0010	0.0001
y	2.594	2.705	2.717	2.718

By methods developed in Chapter 12, it can be shown that this value is about 2.71828. The limiting value is the irrational number e.

Returning to the derivative of the logarithmic function, we have

$$\lim_{\Delta u \to 0} \frac{\Delta y}{\Delta u} = \lim_{\Delta u \to 0} \left[\frac{1}{u} \log_b \left(1 + \frac{\Delta u}{u} \right)^{u/\Delta u} \right] = \frac{1}{u} \log_b e.$$

Therefore

$$\frac{dy}{du} = \frac{1}{u} \log_b e.$$

Combining this equation with Eq. (6–28), we have

$$\frac{d (\log_b u)}{dx} = \frac{1}{u} \log_b e \frac{du}{dx}. \tag{7–11}$$

At this point we see that if we choose e as the basis of a system of logarithms, the above formula becomes

$$\frac{d (\ln u)}{dx} = \frac{1}{u} \frac{du}{dx}. \tag{7–12}$$

The choice of e as the base b makes $\log_e e = 1$; thus this factor does not appear in Eq. (7–12). We can now see why the number e is chosen as the base for a system of logarithms.

Example A. Find the derivative of $y = \log 4x$.
We have

$$\frac{dy}{dx} = \frac{1}{4x} \log e \, (4) = \frac{1}{x} \log e \qquad (\log e = 0.434).$$

Example B. Find the derivative of $y = \ln 3x^4$.
We write

$$\frac{dy}{dx} = \frac{1}{3x^4} (12x^3) = \frac{4}{x}.$$

Example C. Find the derivative of $y = \ln \tan x$.
We write

$$\frac{dy}{dx} = \frac{1}{\tan x} \sec^2 x = \frac{\cos x}{\sin x} \frac{1}{\cos^2 x} = \csc x \sec x.$$

Example D. Find the derivative of $y = \ln [(x - 1)/(x + 1)]$.
In this example it is easier to write y in the form

$$y = \ln (x - 1) - \ln (x + 1).$$

(Often we can find a derivative more simply if we use the properties of logarithms to simplify the expression.) Hence

$$\frac{dy}{dx} = \frac{1}{x-1} - \frac{1}{x+1} = \frac{x+1-x+1}{(x-1)(x+1)} = \frac{2}{x^2-1}.$$

Example E. Find the derivative of $y = \ln (1-2x)^3$.
First we may rewrite the equation as $y = 3 \ln (1-2x)$. Then

$$\frac{dy}{dx} = 3 \left(\frac{1}{1-2x} \right) (-2) = \frac{-6}{1-2x}.$$

Care must be taken to distinguish this function from the function $y = [\ln (1-2x)]^3$. In this latter function it is the logarithm which is being cubed, whereas in the first function the quantity $(1-2x)$ is being cubed. The derivative in the latter case would be

$$\frac{dy}{dx} = 3 [\ln (1-2x)]^2 \left(\frac{1}{1-2x} \right) (-2) = - \frac{6 [\ln (1-2x)]^2}{1-2x}.$$

Exercises

In Exercises 1 through 18, find the derivatives of the given functions.

1. $y = \log x^2$

2. $y = \log_2 6x$

3. $y = \ln (1-3x)$

4. $y = \ln \sin x$

5. $y = \ln \sqrt{x}$

6. $y = \ln \sqrt{4x-3}$

7. $y = x \ln x$

8. $y = \dfrac{\ln x}{x}$

9. $y = \ln (\ln x)$

10. $y = \ln \cos x^2$

11. $y = \ln \dfrac{x}{1+x}$

12. $y = \ln (x\sqrt{x+1})$

13. $y = \sin \ln x$

14. $y = (\ln x)^3$

15. $y = \ln (x \tan x)$

16. $y = \ln (x + \sqrt{x^2-1})$

17. $y = \ln \dfrac{x^2}{x+2}$

18. $y = \sqrt{x^2+1} - \ln \dfrac{1+\sqrt{x^2+1}}{x}$

19. Find the slope of a tangent to the curve $y = \ln \cos x$ at $x = \pi/4$.

20. Find the second derivative of the function $y = x^2 \ln x$.

21. Find the derivative of $y = x^x$ by first taking logarithms of each side of the equation.

22. The temperature T from the inner surface of a certain steam pipe to the outer surface is given by

$$T = 100 - 40 \frac{\ln (r/5)}{\ln (6/5)},$$

where r is the distance from the center of the pipe. Determine the rate of change of temperature with respect to r. (This solution is valid only for $5 < r < 6$, since these are the inner and outer radii, respectively.)

7–3 Derivative of the exponential function

In order to obtain the derivative of the exponential function we let $y = b^u$, and then write the equation in logarithmic form:

$$u = \log_b y,$$

$$\frac{du}{dx} = \frac{1}{y} \log_b e \frac{dy}{dx},$$

$$\frac{dy}{dx} = \frac{1}{\log_b e} y \frac{du}{dx} = \frac{1}{\log_b e} b^u \left(\frac{du}{dx}\right).$$

Thus

$$\frac{d(b^u)}{dx} = \frac{1}{\log_b e} b^u \left(\frac{du}{dx}\right). \tag{7–13}$$

If we let $b = e$, Eq. (7–13) becomes

$$\frac{d(e^u)}{dx} = e^u \left(\frac{du}{dx}\right). \tag{7–14}$$

Example A. Find the derivative of $y = e^x$.
    We find that

$$\frac{dy}{dx} = e^x(1) = e^x.$$

We see that the derivative of the function e^x equals itself. This exponential function is widely used in applications of calculus.

Example B. Find the derivative of $y = 2^{4x}$.
    We write

$$\frac{dy}{dx} = \frac{1}{\log_2 e} 2^{4x}(4) = \frac{4}{\log_2 e} 2^{4x}.$$

Example C. Find the derivative of $y = \ln \cos e^{2x}$.
    This works out as

$$\frac{dy}{dx} = \frac{1}{\cos e^{2x}} (-\sin e^{2x})(e^{2x})(2) = -2e^{2x} \tan e^{2x}.$$

Example D. Find the derivative of $y = xe^{\tan x}$.
    Here we write

$$\frac{dy}{dx} = x(e^{\tan x}) \sec^2 x + e^{\tan x} = e^{\tan x} (x \sec^2 x + 1).$$

Example E. Find the derivative of $y = (e^{1/x})^2$.
   In this example,

$$\frac{dy}{dx} = 2(e^{1/x})(e^{1/x})(-1/x^2) = \frac{-2(e^{1/x})^2}{x^2} = \frac{-2e^{2/x}}{x^2}.$$

This problem could have also been solved by first writing the function as $y = e^{2/x}$, which is an equivalent form determined by the laws of exponents. When we use this form, the derivative becomes

$$\frac{dy}{dx} = e^{2/x}(-2/x^2) = \frac{-2e^{2/x}}{x^2}.$$

We can see that this change in form of the function simplifies the steps necessary for finding the derivative.

   The simplicity of Eq. (7–14) compared with Eq. (7–13) again shows the advantage of choosing e as the basis of natural logarithms. It is for this reason that e appears so often in applications of calculus.

Exercises

In Exercises 1 through 17, find the derivative of each of the given functions.

1. $y = e^{6x}$
2. $y = 4^{6x}$
3. $y = e^{\sqrt{x}}$
4. $y = 10^{x^2}$
5. $y = xe^x$
6. $y = e^x \sin x$
7. $y = e^{2x^4}$
8. $y = x^2 e^{2x}$
9. $y = e^{2x} - e^{-2x}$
10. $y = \dfrac{e^x}{x}$
11. $y = e^{-3x} \sin 4x$
12. $y = \tan e^{x+1}$
13. $y = \ln \sin 2e^{6x}$
14. $y = (\cos 2x)(e^{x^2-1})$
15. $y = 4e^{-(2/x)}$
16. $y = \text{Arctan } e^{3x}$
17. $y = xe^{\sin x}$

18. Show that $y = xe^{-x}$ satisfies the equation $(dy/dx) + y = e^{-x}$.
19. Show that $y = e^{-x} \sin x$ satisfies the equation

$$\frac{d^2y}{dx^2} + 2\frac{dy}{dx} + 2y = 0.$$

20. Find the derivative of the implicit function $xy^2 = x - e^{-y}$.
21. Show that the slope of the curve $y = e^x$ at $x = a$ equals the ordinate at $x = a$.
22. The Beer-Lambert law of light absorption may be expressed as

$$I = I_0 e^{-\alpha x},$$

where I/I_0 is that fraction of the incident light beam which is transmitted, α is a constant, and x is the distance the light travels through the medium. Find the rate of change of I with respect to x.

23. By using the definitions of the hyperbolic functions (see Exercise 29 of Section 7–1), show that

$$\frac{d}{dx} \sinh u = \cosh u \frac{du}{dx} \quad \text{and} \quad \frac{d}{dx} \cosh u = \sinh u \frac{du}{dx},$$

where u is a function of x.

7–4 Applications

The following examples show applications of the logarithmic and exponential functions to curve-tracing and time-rate-of-change problems. Certain other applications are indicated in the exercises.

Example A. Sketch the graph of the function $y = x \ln x$.

The only intercept is $(1, 0)$ (there is no intercept for $x = 0$ since $\log_b 0$ is not defined). Thus

$$\frac{dy}{dx} = x \left(\frac{1}{x} \right) + \ln x = 1 + \ln x, \qquad \frac{d^2y}{dx^2} = \frac{1}{x}.$$

The first derivative is zero if $\ln x = -1$, or $x = e^{-1}$. The second derivative is positive for this value of x. Thus there is a minimum point at $(1/e, -1/e)$. The only values of x which can be considered are positive values, since $\ln x$ is undefined for negative values. The second derivative indicates that the curve is always concave up. The graph is shown in Fig. 7–4.

FIGURE 7–4

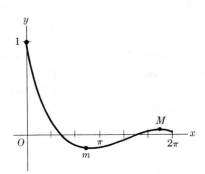

FIGURE 7–5

Example B. Sketch the graph of the function $y = e^{-x} \cos x$ $(0 \leq x \leq 2\pi)$.

This curve has intercepts for all values for which $\cos x$ is zero. Those values between 0 and 2π for which $\cos x = 0$ are $x = \pi/2$ and $x = 3\pi/2$. Also $(0, 1)$ is an intercept. We next write

$$\frac{dy}{dx} = -e^{-x} \sin x - e^{-x} \cos x = -e^{-x} (\sin x + \cos x).$$

Setting the first derivative equal to zero, we obtain $\sin x + \cos x = 0$, or $\tan x = -1$. There are maximum or minimum points for $x = 3\pi/4$ and $x = 7\pi/4$ (see Fig. 7–5). We then write

$$\frac{d^2y}{dx^2} = 2e^{-x} \sin x.$$

Thus d^2y/dx^2 is positive when $x = 3\pi/4$ and negative when $x = 7\pi/4$. Hence $(3\pi/4, -0.067)$ is a minimum and $(7\pi/4, 0.003)$ is a maximum. From the second derivative we find that points of inflection occur for $x = 0$, π, and 2π.

Example C. The population P, in terms of the population P_0 (at $t = 0$) and t, is given by $P = P_0 e^{kt}$. Show that the time-rate of change of population is proportional to the population present at time t.

By taking a derivative of P with respect to time, we have

$$\frac{dP}{dt} = kP_0 e^{kt} = kP.$$

Example D. A rocket moving vertically, assuming that the only force acting on it is that due to gravity and that its mass is decreasing at a constant rate r, has its velocity as a function of time given by

$$v = v_0 - gt - k \ln (1 - rt/m_0),$$

where v_0 is the initial velocity, m_0 is the initial mass, and k is a constant. Determine the expression for the acceleration.

Since the acceleration is the time-rate of change of the velocity, we must find dv/dt. Therefore

$$\frac{dv}{dt} = -g - k\,\frac{1}{1 - rt/m_0}\,(-r/m_0) = -g + \frac{km_0}{m_0 - rt}\left(\frac{r}{m_0}\right) = \frac{kr}{m_0 - rt} - g.$$

Exercises

In Exercises 1 through 10, sketch the graphs of the given functions.

1. $y = \ln \cos x$ 2. $y = xe^{-x}$ 3. $y = \dfrac{\ln x}{x}$ 4. $y = xe^x$

5. $y = \ln \dfrac{1}{x^2 + 1}$ 6. $y = x - e^x$ 7. $y = \ln x - x$ 8. $y = e^{-x} \sin x$

9. $y = \frac{1}{2}(e^x - e^{-x})$ (See Exercise 29 of Section 7–1.)

10. $y = \frac{1}{2}(e^x + e^{-x})$ (See Exercise 29 of Section 7–1.)

11. Find the equation of the line tangent to the curve $y = x^2 \ln x$ at the point $(1, 0)$.

12. The number N of atoms of radium at any time t is given in terms of the number at $t = 0$, N_0, by $N = N_0 e^{-kt}$. Show that the time-rate of change of N is proportional to N.

13. The velocity of an object moving through a resisting medium is found to obey the relation $v = 40(1 - e^{-0.05t})$. Find the acceleration when $t = 10$.

14. The charge on a capacitor in a circuit containing the capacitor C, a resistance R, and voltage source E is given by $q = CE(1 - e^{-t/RC})$. Show that this equation satisfies the equation

$$R\frac{dq}{dt} + \frac{q}{C} = E.$$

15. Assuming that force is proportional to acceleration, show that a particle moving along the x-axis, so that its displacement $x = ae^{kt} + be^{-kt}$, has a force acting on it which is proportional to its displacement.

16. The radius of curvature at any point on a curve is given by

$$R = \frac{[1 + (dy/dx)^2]^{3/2}}{d^2y/dx^2}.$$

Determine the radius of curvature of $y = \ln \sec x$ when $x = \pi/4$.

17. An object on the end of a spring is moving so that its displacement from the equilibrium position is given by $y = e^{-0.5t}(0.4 \cos 6t - 0.2 \sin 6t)$. Find the expression for the velocity of the object. What is the velocity when $t = \pi/12$ sec? The motion described by this equation is called "damped harmonic motion." The general shape of the curve of displacement as a function of time is that of the curve in Example B.

18. In an electronic tube, the maximum current density i_m of the filament as a function of the temperature T is given by $i_m = AT^2 e^{k/T}$, where A and k are constants. If the temperature is changing with time, find the expression for the time rate of change of i_m.

19. In developing the theory dealing with the friction between a pulley wheel and the pulley belt, the ratio of the tensions in the belt on either side of the wheel is given by

$$\frac{T_2}{T_1} = e^{k/\sin{(\theta/2)}},$$

where k is a constant and θ is the angle of the opening of the pulley wheel. Find the expression for a small change in the ratio of tensions for a small change in the angle θ.

Miscellaneous exercises for Chapter 7

In Exercises 1 through 12, find the derivative of each of the given functions.

1. $y = 3 \ln (x^2 + 1)$
2. $y = e^{\sin 2x}$
3. $y = (e^{x-3})^2$
4. $y = e^{\sqrt{1-x}}$
5. $y = \ln (\csc x^2)$
6. $y = \ln (3 + \sin x^2)$
7. $y = [\ln (3 + \sin x)]^2$
8. $y = \ln (3 + \sin x)^2$
9. $y = e^{-x} (\sec x)$
10. $y = e^{3x} \ln x$
11. $x^2 \ln y = y + x$
12. $y = x^2 (e^{\cos^2 x})^2$
13. Find the equation of the line tangent to the curve of $y = \ln \cos x$ where $x = \pi/6$.

14. Find the equation of the line normal to the curve of $y = e^{x^2}$ where $x = 1/2$.

15. For a circuit containing a capacitance C and a resistance R, the current as a function of time is given by $i = i_0 e^{-t/RC}$. If $i_0 = 10$ amps, $R = 2$ ohms, and $C = 50 \times 10^{-6}$ farad, find the approximate change in the current between 2.0×10^{-4} sec and 2.1×10^{-4} sec.

16. Under certain circumstances 2% of a substance changes chemically each minute. If there are originally 100 gm present, the amount at any time t which is present is $A = 100(0.98)^t$. What is the approximate change in the amount present during the fourth second?

17. Under certain conditions the work done by a gas in an expansion from a pressure P_1 to a pressure P_2 is given by $W = k \ln (P_1/P_2)$, where k is a constant depending on the gas. If P_2 varies with time at the rate of 0.01 atm/min, find the rate (in joules/min) at which the work changes when $P_2 = 3$ atm, if $k = 2400$ joules/mole-deg and $P_1 = 2$ atm.

18. Find the acceleration of an object whose x- and y-components of displacement are given by $x = e^{-t} \sin 2t$ and $y = e^{-t} \cos 2t$ when $t = \pi/4$.

19. An object is dropped from a weather balloon. The distance it falls, assuming a resisting force of the air on the object, is given by $y = 320(t + 10e^{-0.1t} - 10)$. Find the velocity after 10 sec.

20. The charge q on a certain capacitor as a function of time is given by

$$q = e^{-0.1t}(0.2 \sin 100t + \cos 100t).$$

The current i in the circuit is the time-rate of change of charge. Find the expression for i as a function of t.

21. Show, by graphical differentiation, that $de^x/dx = e^x$.

22. Show, by graphical differentiation, that $d \ln x/dx = 1/x$.

23. Find the area of the largest rectangle which can be inscribed under the curve of $y = e^{-x^2}$ in the first quadrant.

24. Sketch the graph of $y = \ln (1 + x)$.

25. Sketch the graph of $y = x (\ln x)^2$.

26. The curve formed by a uniform cable hanging from two points under its own weight is called the *catenary*. The equation of this curve is

$$y = \frac{H}{w} \cosh \frac{wx}{H},$$

where w and H are constants. Show that the equation of the catenary satisfies the equation

$$\frac{d^2y}{dx^2} = \frac{w}{H} \sqrt{1 + \left(\frac{dy}{dx}\right)^2}.$$

(See Exercise 29 of Section 7–1 and Exercise 23 of Section 7–3.)

8 Methods of integration

8-1 The general power formula

Having developed the derivatives of the basic transcendental functions, we can now expand considerably the functions which can be integrated. Even many algebraic functions which we were unable to integrate previously will now lend themselves to integration. The first integration formula to be discussed is the general power formula.

For reference, we repeat here the general power formula for integration, Eq. (4–5):

$$\int u^n \, du = \frac{u^{n+1}}{n+1} + C, \qquad n \neq -1. \tag{8–1}$$

This formula will now be applied to transcendental functions as well as algebraic functions. When we are applying the general power formula, it is essential that we properly recognize the quantities u, n, and du. This requires familiarity with the differential forms presented in Chapters 2, 6, and 7. The following examples illustrate the use of the general power formula.

Example A. Integrate: $\int \sin^3 x \cos x \, dx$; $n = 3$, $u = \sin x$; therefore $du = \cos x \, dx$. Thus

$$\int \sin^3 x \, (\cos x \, dx) = \frac{\sin^4 x}{4} + C.$$

Example B. Integrate: $\int \sqrt{1 + \tan x} \, \sec^2 x \, dx$; $n = \frac{1}{2}$, $u = 1 + \tan x$; therefore $du = \sec^2 x \, dx$. And so

$$\int \sqrt{1 + \tan x} \, (\sec^2 x \, dx) = \frac{2}{3} (1 + \tan x)^{3/2} + C.$$

218

Example C. Integrate: $\int \ln x \, (dx/x); n = 1, u = \ln x, du = dx/x$.
We write

$$\int \ln x \frac{dx}{x} = \frac{1}{2} (\ln x)^2 + C.$$

Example D. Integrate: $\int (2 + 3e^{2t})^3 e^{2t} \, dt; n = 3, u = 2 + 3e^{2t}, du = 6e^{2t} \, dt$.
Hence

$$\int (2 + 3e^{2t})^3 e^{2t} \, dt = \frac{1}{6} \int (2 + 3e^{2t})^3 (6e^{2t} \, dt)$$

$$= \frac{1}{6} \cdot \frac{1}{4} (2 + 3e^{2t})^4 + C$$

$$= \frac{1}{24} (2 + 3e^{2t})^4 + C.$$

Example E. Find the value of

$$\int_0^{0.5} \frac{\text{Arcsin } x}{\sqrt{1 - x^2}} \, dx; \qquad n = 1, \quad u = \text{Arcsin } x, \quad du = \frac{dx}{\sqrt{1 - x^2}}.$$

Therefore

$$\int_0^{0.5} \frac{\text{Arcsin } x}{\sqrt{1 - x^2}} \, dx = \left. \frac{(\text{Arcsin } x)^2}{2} \right|_0^{0.5} = \frac{(\pi/6)^2}{2} - 0 = \frac{\pi^2}{72}.$$

Exercises

In Exercises 1 through 16, integrate each of the given functions.

1. $\int \sin^4 x \cos x \, dx$

2. $\int \sqrt{\cos x} \sin x \, dx$

3. $\int \tan^2 x \sec^2 x \, dx$

4. $\int \sec^3 x \, (\sec x \tan x) \, dx$

5. $\int \cos 2x \sin 2x \, dx$

6. $\int e^{5x} (4 - e^{5x}) \, dx$

7. $\int \frac{\ln (2x + 3)}{2x + 3} \, dx$

8. $\int \frac{3 + \ln 2x}{x} \, dx$

9. $\int \sqrt{\cot x} \csc^2 x \, dx$

10. $\int \frac{\text{Arccos } 2x}{\sqrt{1 - 4x^2}} \, dx$

11. $\int \frac{\text{Arctan } 5x}{1 + 25x^2} \, dx$

12. $\int \sqrt{1 - e^{-x}} \, (e^{-x} \, dx)$

13. $\int (1 + \sec^2 x)^4 \, (\sec^2 x \tan x \, dx)$

14. $\int (e^x + e^{-x})^{1/4} (e^x - e^{-x}) \, dx$

15. $\int_0^{\pi/6} \frac{\tan x}{\cos^2 x} \, dx$

16. $\int_{\pi/3}^{\pi/2} \frac{\sin \theta \, d\theta}{\sqrt{1 + \cos \theta}}$

17. Find the area under the curve $y = \sin x \cos x$ from $x = 0$ to $x = \pi/2$.

18. In developing the expression for the total pressure P on a wall due to molecules with mass m and velocity v striking the wall, the following equation is found:

$$P = mnv^2 \int_0^{\pi/2} \sin \theta \cos^2 \theta \, d\theta.$$

The symbol n represents the number of molecules per unit volume and θ represents the angle between a perpendicular to the wall and the direction of the molecule. Find the final expression for P.

19. The general expression for the slope of a given curve is $(\ln x)^2/x$. If the curve passes through $(1, 2)$, find its equation.

20. Find the average value of the velocity of an object for the first two seconds if its velocity (in cm/sec), as a function of time, is given by $v = e^t/\sqrt{3 + e^t}$.

8–2 The basic logarithmic form

The general power formula for integration, Eq. (8–1), is valid for all values of n except $n = -1$. If n were set equal to -1 this would cause the result to be undefined. When we obtained the derivative of the logarithmic function, we found that

$$\frac{d (\ln u)}{dx} = \frac{1}{u} \frac{du}{dx},$$

which means that the differential of the logarithmic form is $d (\ln u) = du/u$. Reversing the process, we then determine that $\int du/u = \ln u + C$. In other words, when the exponent of the expression being integrated is -1, it is a logarithmic form.

Logarithms are only defined for positive numbers. Thus $\int du/u = \ln u + C$ is valid if $u > 0$. If $u < 0$, then $-u > 0$. In this case $d(-u) = -du$, or $\int(-du)/(-u) = \ln (-u) + C$. However, $\int du/u = \int(-du)/(-u)$. These results can be combined into the single form

$$\int \frac{du}{u} = \ln |u| + C. \qquad (8\text{–}2)$$

Example A. Integrate: $\int \dfrac{dx}{x + 1}$; $u = x + 1$, $du = dx$.

We have

$$\int \frac{dx}{x + 1} = \ln |x + 1| + C.$$

Example B. Integrate: $\int \dfrac{\cos x}{\sin x} dx$; $u = \sin x$, $du = \cos x \, dx$.

We write

$$\int \frac{\cos x}{\sin x} dx = \ln |\sin x| + C.$$

Example C. Integrate: $\displaystyle\int \frac{x\,dx}{4-x^2}\,;\qquad u = 4-x^2,\quad du = -2x\,dx.$

We write $\displaystyle\int \frac{x\,dx}{4-x^2} = -\frac{1}{2}\int \frac{-2x\,dx}{4-x^2} = -\frac{1}{2}\ln|4-x^2| + C.$

We should note that if the quantity $4-x^2$ were raised to any power other than that in the example, we would have to employ the general power formula for integration. For example,

$$\int \frac{x\,dx}{(4-x^2)^2} = -\frac{1}{2}\int \frac{-2x\,dx}{(4-x^2)^2} = -\frac{1}{2}\frac{(4-x^2)^{-1}}{-1} + C = \frac{1}{2(4-x^2)} + C.$$

Example D. Integrate: $\displaystyle\int \frac{e^{4x}\,dx}{1+3e^{4x}}\,;\qquad u = 1+3e^{4x},\quad du = 12e^{4x}\,dx.$

We write $\displaystyle\int \frac{e^{4x}\,dx}{1+3e^{4x}} = \frac{1}{12}\int \frac{12e^{4x}\,dx}{1+3e^{4x}} = \frac{1}{12}\ln|1+3e^{4x}| + C$

$$= \frac{1}{12}\ln(1+3e^{4x}) + C \quad (\text{since } 1+3e^{4x} > 0).$$

Example E. Evaluate:

$$\int_0^{\pi/8} \frac{\sec^2 2x}{1+\tan 2x}\,dx;\qquad u = 1+\tan 2x,\quad du = 2\sec^2 2x\,dx.$$

We write

$$\int_0^{\pi/8} \frac{\sec^2 2x}{1+\tan 2x}\,dx = \frac{1}{2}\int_0^{\pi/8} \frac{2\sec^2 2x\,dx}{1+\tan 2x}$$

$$= \frac{1}{2}\ln|1+\tan 2x|\Big|_0^{\pi/8} = \frac{1}{2}\ln|2| - \frac{1}{2}\ln|1|$$

$$= \frac{1}{2}\ln 2 - \frac{1}{2}\ln 1 = \frac{1}{2}\ln 2 - 0 = \frac{1}{2}\ln 2.$$

Exercises

In Exercises 1 through 15, integrate each of the given functions.

1. $\displaystyle\int \frac{dx}{1+4x}$

2. $\displaystyle\int \frac{dx}{1-4x}$

3. $\displaystyle\int \frac{x\,dx}{4-3x^2}$

4. $\displaystyle\int \frac{\sin x}{\cos x}\,dx$

5. $\displaystyle\int \frac{x^2\,dx}{1-x^3}$

6. $\displaystyle\int \frac{e^{-x}}{1-e^{-x}}\,dx$

7. $\displaystyle\int \frac{1+x}{4x+2x^2}\, dx$ 8. $\displaystyle\int \frac{\sin 2x}{1-\cos^2 x}\, dx$ 9. $\displaystyle\int \frac{\sec x \tan x\, dx}{1+4\sec x}$

10. $\displaystyle\int \frac{x+\cos 2x}{x^2+\sin 2x}\, dx$ 11. $\displaystyle\int \frac{dx}{x \ln x}$ 12. $\displaystyle\int \frac{dx}{x(1+2\ln x)}$

13. $\displaystyle\int_0^{\pi/12} \frac{\sec^2 3x}{4+\tan 3x}\, dx$ 14. $\displaystyle\int \frac{e^x - e^{-x}}{e^x + e^{-x}}\, dx$ 15. $\displaystyle\int_1^2 \frac{x^2+1}{x^3+3x}\, dx$

16. Find the area bounded by $xy = 1$, $x = 1$, $x = 2$, and $y = 0$.

17. Find the volume generated by rotating the area bounded by $y = 1/(x^2 + 1)$, $x = 0$, $x = 1$, $y = 0$ about the y-axis. (Use shells.)

18. Find the average value of the function $xy = 4$ from $x = 1$ to $x = 2$.

19. If the current (in amps), as a function of time, in a certain electric circuit is given by $i = t/(1 + 2t^2)$, find the total charge to pass a given point in the circuit in the first two seconds.

20. Under certain conditions an object is subject to a force, in lb, given by $F = 1/(1 + 3x)$. Find the work done on the object in moving it 5 ft from the origin.

21. Conditions are often such that a force proportional to the velocity tends to retard the motion of an object. Under such conditions, the acceleration of a certain object moving down an inclined plane is given by $20 - v$. This leads to the equation $dv/(20 - v) = dt$. If the object starts from rest, find the expression for the velocity as a function of time.

8-3 The exponential form

In deriving the derivative for the exponential function we obtained the result $de^u/dx = e^u\,(du/dx)$. This means that the differential of the exponential form is $d(e^u) = e^u\,du$. Reversing this form to find the proper form of the integral for the exponential function, we have

$$\int e^u\, du = e^u + C. \tag{8-3}$$

Example A. Integrate: $\int e^{5x}\, dx$; $u = 5x$, $du = 5\, dx$.
  We have
$$\int e^{5x}\, dx = \tfrac{1}{5}\int e^{5x}(5\, dx) = \tfrac{1}{5}e^{5x} + C.$$

Example B. Integrate: $\int xe^{x^2}\, dx$; $u = x^2$, $du = 2x\, dx$.
  We write
$$\int xe^{x^2}\, dx = \tfrac{1}{2}\int e^{x^2}(2x\, dx) = \tfrac{1}{2}e^{x^2} + C.$$

Example C. Integrate: $\displaystyle\int \frac{dx}{e^{3x}}$.

This integral can be put in proper form by writing it as $\int e^{-3x}\, dx$. In this form $u = -3x,\ du = -3\, dx.$ Thus

$$\int \frac{dx}{e^{3x}} = \int e^{-3x}\, dx = -\tfrac{1}{3}\int e^{-3x}(-3\, dx) = -\tfrac{1}{3}e^{-3x} + C.$$

Example D. Evaluate:

$$\int_{0}^{\pi/2} (\sin 2x)(e^{\cos 2x})\, dx; \qquad u = \cos 2x,\quad du = -2 \sin 2x\, dx.$$

We write

$$\int_{0}^{\pi/2} (\sin 2x)(e^{\cos 2x})\, dx = -\tfrac{1}{2}\int_{0}^{\pi/2} (e^{\cos 2x})(-2 \sin 2x\, dx)$$

$$= -\tfrac{1}{2}e^{\cos 2x}\Big|_{0}^{\pi/2} = -\tfrac{1}{2}\left(\frac{1}{e} - e\right) = 1.175.$$

Example E. Find the equation of the curve for which $dy/dx = e^{\sqrt{x+1}}/\sqrt{x+1}$ if the curve passes through $(0, 1)$.

The solution of this problem requires that we integrate the given function and then evaluate the constant of integration. Hence

$$dy = \frac{e^{\sqrt{x+1}}}{\sqrt{x+1}}\, dx, \qquad \int dy = \int \frac{e^{\sqrt{x+1}}}{\sqrt{x+1}}\, dx.$$

For purposes of integrating the right-hand side,

$$u = \sqrt{x+1} \qquad \text{and} \qquad du = \frac{1}{2\sqrt{x+1}}\, dx,$$

$$y = 2\int e^{\sqrt{x+1}}\left(\frac{1}{2\sqrt{x+1}}\, dx\right) = 2e^{\sqrt{x+1}} + C.$$

Letting $x = 0$ and $y = 1$, we have $1 = 2e + C$, or $C = 1 - 2e.$ This means that the equation is $y = 2e^{\sqrt{x+1}} + 1 - 2e.$

Exercises

In Exercises 1 through 13, integrate each of the given functions.

1. $\displaystyle\int e^{2x+5}\, dx$ 2. $\displaystyle\int e^{-4x}\, dx$ 3. $\displaystyle\int e^{x/2}\, dx$

4. $\displaystyle\int xe^{-x^2}\,dx$ 5. $\displaystyle\int \frac{e^{\sqrt{x}}}{\sqrt{x}}\,dx$ 6. $\displaystyle\int (\sec^2 x)e^{\tan x}\,dx$

7. $\displaystyle\int 4x^3 e^{2x^4}\,dx$ 8. $\displaystyle\int (e^x - e^{-x})^2\,dx$ 9. $\displaystyle\int \frac{(3 - e^x)\,dx}{e^{2x}}$

10. $\displaystyle\int_{-1}^{1} \frac{dx}{e^{2-3x}}$ 11. $\displaystyle\int \frac{e^{\text{Arctan }x}}{x^2 + 1}\,dx$ 12. $\displaystyle\int \frac{e^{2/x}\,dx}{x^2}$ 13. $\displaystyle\int_0^{\pi} (\sin 2x)\,(e^{\cos^2 x})\,(dx)$

14. Find the area bounded by $y = e^x$, $x = 0$, $y = 0$, and $x = 2$.

15. Find the volume generated by rotating the area bounded by $y = e^{x^2}$, $x = 1$, $y = 0$, and $x = 2$ about the y-axis.

16. Prove that the area bounded by $x = a$, $x = b$, $y = 0$, and $y = e^x$ equals the difference of the ordinates at $x = b$ and $x = a$.

17. Find the average value of the function $y = e^{2x}$ from $x = 0$ to $x = 4$.

18. Find the equation of the curve for which $dy/dx = \sqrt{e^{x+3}}$ if the curve passes through $(1, 0)$.

19. If the current in a certain electric circuit is given by $i = 2e^{-30t}$, find the expression for the voltage across a 250×10^{-6} farad capacitor as a function of time. The initial voltage across the capacitor is 60 volts.

20. Find the moment of inertia with respect to the y-axis of the first quadrant area bounded by $y = e^{x^3}$, $x = 1$, and the axes.

8–4 Basic trigonometric forms

In this section we shall discuss the integrals of the six trigonometric functions and the trigonometric integrals which arise directly from reversing the formulas for differentiation. Other trigonometric forms will be discussed in the following section.

By directly reversing the differentiation formulas, the following integral formulas are obtained:

$$\int \sin u\,du = -\cos u + C, \qquad (8\text{–}4)$$

$$\int \cos u\,du = \sin u + C, \qquad (8\text{–}5)$$

$$\int \sec^2 u\,du = \tan u + C, \qquad (8\text{–}6)$$

$$\int \csc^2 u\,du = -\cot u + C, \qquad (8\text{–}7)$$

$$\int \sec u \tan u\,du = \sec u + C, \qquad (8\text{–}8)$$

$$\int \csc u \cot u\,du = -\csc u + C. \qquad (8\text{–}9)$$

Example A. Integrate: $\int \sin 3x\, dx$; $u = 3x,\, du = 3\, dx$.
   We have

$$\int \sin 3x\, dx = \tfrac{1}{3}\int \sin 3x(3\, dx) = -\tfrac{1}{3}\cos 3x + C.$$

Example B. Integrate: $\int x \sec^2 (x^2)\, dx$; $u = x^2,\, du = 2x\, dx$.
   We write

$$\int x \sec^2 (x^2)\, dx = \tfrac{1}{2}\int \sec^2 (x^2) \cdot (2x\, dx) = \tfrac{1}{2}\tan (x^2) + C.$$

Example C. Integrate: $\displaystyle \int \frac{\tan 2x}{\cos 2x}\, dx.$

By using the basic identity $\sec \theta = 1/\cos \theta$, we can transform this integral to form $\int \sec 2x \tan 2x\, dx$. In this form $u = 2x,\, du = 2\, dx$. Therefore

$$\int \frac{\tan 2x}{\cos 2x}\, dx = \int \sec 2x \tan 2x\, dx = \tfrac{1}{2}\int \sec 2x \tan 2x(2\, dx) = \tfrac{1}{2}\sec 2x + C.$$

In order to find the integrals for the other trigonometric functions, we must change them to a form for which the integral can be determined by methods previously discussed. We can accomplish this by use of the basic trigonometric relations.

The formula for $\int \tan u\, du$ is found by expressing the integral in the form $\int [(\sin u)/(\cos u)]\, du$. We recognize this as being a logarithmic form, where the u of the logarithmic form is $\cos u$ in this integral. The differential of $\cos u$ is $-\sin u\, du$. Therefore we have

$$\int \tan u\, du = \int \frac{\sin u}{\cos u}\, du = -\int \frac{-\sin u\, du}{\cos u} = -\ln |\cos u| + C.$$

The formula for $\int \cot u\, du$ is found by writing it in the form

$$\int \frac{\cos u}{\sin u}\, du.$$

In this manner we obtain the following result:

$$\int \cot u\, du = \int \frac{\cos u}{\sin u}\, du = \int \frac{\cos u\, du}{\sin u} = \ln |\sin u| + C.$$

The formula for $\int \sec u\, du$ is found by writing it in the form

$$\int \frac{\sec u\, (\sec u + \tan u)}{\sec u + \tan u}\, du.$$

In this form we recognize this as being also a logarithmic form, since

$$d\, (\sec u + \tan u) = (\sec u \tan u + \sec^2 u)\, du.$$

The right side of this equation is the expression appearing in the numerator of the integral. Thus

$$\int \sec u \, du = \int \frac{\sec u \, (\sec u + \tan u) \, du}{\sec u + \tan u} = \int \frac{\sec u \tan u + \sec^2 u}{\sec u + \tan u} \, du$$

$$= \ln |\sec u + \tan u| + C.$$

To obtain the formula for $\int \csc u \, du$, we write it in the form

$$\int \frac{\csc u \, (\csc u - \cot u) \, du}{\csc u - \cot u} .$$

Thus we have

$$\int \csc u \, du = \int \frac{\csc u \, (\csc u - \cot u)}{\csc u - \cot u} \, du = \int \frac{(-\csc u \cot u + \csc^2 u) \, du}{\csc u - \cot u}$$

$$= \ln |\csc u - \cot u| + C.$$

Summarizing these results, we have the following integrals:

$$\int \tan u \, du = -\ln |\cos u| + C, \tag{8-10}$$

$$\int \cot u \, du = \ln |\sin u| + C, \tag{8-11}$$

$$\int \sec u \, du = \ln |\sec u + \tan u| + C, \tag{8-12}$$

$$\int \csc u \, du = \ln |\csc u - \cot u| + C. \tag{8-13}$$

Example D. Integrate: $\int \tan 4x \, dx$; $u = 4x, \quad du = 4 \, dx$.
   We write

$$\int \tan 4x \, dx = \tfrac{1}{4} \int \tan 4x \, (4 \, dx) = -\tfrac{1}{4} \ln |\cos 4x| + C.$$

Example E. Integrate: $\displaystyle \int \frac{\sec e^{-x} \, dx}{e^x}$; $u = e^{-x}, \quad du = -e^{-x} \, dx$.

   We have

$$\int \frac{\sec e^{-x} \, dx}{e^x} = -\int (\sec e^{-x} \, dx)(-e^{-x} \, dx)$$

$$= -\ln |\sec e^{-x} + \tan e^{-x}| + C.$$

Example F. Evaluate: $\displaystyle \int_{\pi/6}^{\pi/4} \frac{1 + \cos x}{\sin x} \, dx.$

We write

$$\int_{\pi/6}^{\pi/4} \frac{1 + \cos x}{\sin x}\, dx = \int_{\pi/6}^{\pi/4} \csc x\, dx + \int_{\pi/6}^{\pi/4} \cot x\, dx$$

$$= \ln |\csc x - \cot x|\Big|_{\pi/6}^{\pi/4} + \ln |\sin x|\Big|_{\pi/6}^{\pi/4}$$

$$= \ln |\sqrt{2} - 1| - \ln |2 - \sqrt{3}| + \ln |\sqrt{2}/2| - \ln |1/2|$$

$$= \ln \frac{(\sqrt{2}/2)(\sqrt{2} - 1)}{(\tfrac{1}{2})(2 - \sqrt{3})} = \ln \frac{2 - \sqrt{2}}{2 - \sqrt{3}} = \ln \frac{0.586}{0.268}$$

$$= \ln 2.19 = 0.784.$$

Exercises

In Exercises 1 through 15, integrate each of the given functions.

1. $\displaystyle\int \cos 2x\, dx$

2. $\displaystyle\int \tan \tfrac{1}{2}x\, dx$

3. $\displaystyle\int x \sec x^2\, dx$

4. $\displaystyle\int \csc 2x \cot 2x\, dx$

5. $\displaystyle\int e^x \csc^2 (e^x)\, dx$

6. $\displaystyle\int \cos (2 - x)\, dx$

7. $\displaystyle\int \frac{\sin (1/x)}{x^2}\, dx$

8. $\displaystyle\int_0^{\pi/6} \frac{dx}{\cos^2 2x}$

9. $\displaystyle\int \frac{dx}{\sin 4x}$

10. $\displaystyle\int_{\pi/4}^{\pi/3} (1 + \sec x)^2\, dx$

11. $\displaystyle\int \frac{\sec 5x}{\cot 5x}\, dx$

12. $\displaystyle\int (1 + \cot x)^2\, dx$

13. $\displaystyle\int \frac{1 + \sin 2x}{\tan 2x}\, dx$

14. $\displaystyle\int \frac{1 - \cot^2 x}{\cos^2 x}\, dx$

15. $\displaystyle\int \frac{1 - \sin x}{1 + \cos x}\, dx$

16. Find the area under the curve $y = \sin x$ from $x = 0$ to $x = \pi$.

17. Find the volume generated by rotating the area bounded by $y = \sec x$, $x = 0$, $x = \pi/3$, and $y = 0$ about the x-axis.

18. Find the volume generated by rotating the area bounded by $y = \cos x^2$, $x = 0$, $y = 0$, and $x = 1$ about the y-axis.

19. Under certain conditions the expression for the velocity as a function of time for a particle is $v = 4 \cos 3t$. Determine the distance as a function of the time, if $s = 0$ when $t = 0$.

20. If the current in a certain electric circuit is $i = 110 \cos 377t$, find the expression for the voltage across a 500×10^{-6} farad capacitor as a function of time. The initial voltage is zero. Show that the voltage across the capacitor is 90° out of phase with the current.

21. If the area bounded by $y = \sin(x^2)$, $y = 0$ and $x = 1$ is 0.3103 sq. units, find the x-coordinate of the centroid of this area.

22. A force, as a function of the distance from the origin, is given by

$$F = \frac{\sin x}{2 + \cos x}.$$

Express the work done by this force as a function of x, if $W = 0$ when $x = 0$.

8–5 Other trigonometric forms

The basic trigonometric relations developed in Chapter 6 provide the means by which many other integrals involving trigonometric functions may be integrated. By use of the square relations, Eqs. (6–7), (6–8), and (6–9), and the equation for the cosine of the double angle, Eq. (6–21), it is possible to transform integrals involving powers of the trigonometric functions into integrable form. We repeat these equations here for reference:

$$\cos^2 x + \sin^2 x = 1, \tag{8–14}$$

$$1 + \tan^2 x = \sec^2 x, \tag{8–15}$$

$$1 + \cot^2 x = \csc^2 x, \tag{8–16}$$

$$2\cos^2 x = 1 + \cos 2x, \tag{8–17}$$

$$2\sin^2 x = 1 - \cos 2x. \tag{8–18}$$

In order to integrate a product of powers of the sine and cosine, we use Eq. (8–14) if at least one of the powers is odd. The method is based on transforming the integral so that it is made up of powers of either the sine or cosine and the first power of the other. In this way this first power becomes a factor of du.

Example A. Integrate:

$$\int \sin^3 x \cos^2 x \, dx; \qquad \sin^3 x = \sin^2 x \sin x = (1 - \cos^2 x) \sin x.$$

Thus

$$\int \sin^3 x \cos^2 x \, dx = \int (1 - \cos^2 x)(\sin x)(\cos^2 x) \, dx$$

$$= \int (\cos^2 x - \cos^4 x)(\sin x \, dx)$$

$$= \int \cos^2 x (\sin x \, dx) - \int \cos^4 x (\sin x \, dx)$$

$$= -\int \cos^2 x (-\sin x \, dx) + \int \cos^4 x (-\sin x \, dx)$$

$$= -\tfrac{1}{3} \cos^3 x + \tfrac{1}{5} \cos^5 x + C.$$

Example B. Integrate: $\int \cos^5 2x \, dx$.
   We write

$$\int \cos^5 2x \, dx = \int (1 - \sin^2 2x)^2 \cos 2x \, dx$$

$$= \int (1 - 2 \sin^2 2x + \sin^4 2x) \cos 2x \, dx$$

$$= \int \cos 2x \, dx - \int 2 \sin^2 2x \cos 2x \, dx + \int \sin^4 2x \cos 2x \, dx$$

$$= \tfrac{1}{2} \int \cos 2x \, (2 \, dx) - \int \sin^2 2x (2 \cos 2x \, dx)$$

$$+ \tfrac{1}{2} \int \sin^4 2x (2 \cos 2x \, dx)$$

$$= \tfrac{1}{2} \sin 2x - \tfrac{1}{3} \sin^3 2x + \tfrac{1}{10} \sin^5 2x + C.$$

In integrating products of powers of the sine and cosine, if the powers are even, we use Eqs. (8–17) and (8–18) to transform the integral. Those most commonly met are $\int \cos^2 u \, du$ and $\int \sin^2 u \, du$.

Example C. Integrate: $\int \sin^2 2x \, dx$.
   We have

$$\int \sin^2 2x \, dx = \int [\tfrac{1}{2}(1 - \cos 4x)] \, dx = \tfrac{1}{2} \int dx - \tfrac{1}{8} \int \cos 4x (4 \, dx)$$

$$= \frac{x}{2} - \frac{1}{8} \sin 4x + C.$$

In order to integrate even powers of the secant, powers of the tangent or products of the secant and tangent, we use (8–15) to transform the integral. In transforming, the forms we look for are powers of the tangent with $\sec^2 x$, which becomes part of du, or powers of the secant along with $\sec x \tan x$, which becomes part of du in this case. Similar transformations are made when we integrate powers of the cotangent and cosecant, with the use of Eq. (8–16).

Example D. Integrate: $\int \tan^5 x \, dx$.

We write $\int \tan^5 x \, dx = \int \tan^3 x \, (\sec^2 x - 1) \, dx$

$$= \int \tan^3 x \, (\sec^2 x \, dx) - \int \tan^3 x \, dx$$

$$= \tfrac{1}{4} \tan^4 x - \int \tan x \, (\sec^2 x - 1) \, dx$$

$$= \tfrac{1}{4} \tan^4 x - \int \tan x \, (\sec^2 x \, dx) + \int \tan x \, dx$$

$$= \tfrac{1}{4} \tan^4 x - \tfrac{1}{2} \tan^2 x - \ln |\cos x| + C.$$

Example E. Integrate: $\int \sec^3 x \tan x \, dx$.

We have $\int \sec^3 x \tan x \, dx = \int (\sec^2 x)(\sec x \tan x \, dx) = \frac{1}{3} \sec^3 x + C$.

Example F. Integrate: $\int \csc^4 2x \, dx$.

We write $\int \csc^4 2x \, dx = \int \csc^2 2x(1 + \cot^2 2x) \, dx$

$$= \tfrac{1}{2} \int \csc^2 2x(2 \, dx) - \tfrac{1}{2} \int \cot^2 2x(-2 \csc^2 2x \, dx)$$

$$= -\tfrac{1}{2} \cot 2x - \tfrac{1}{6} \cot^3 2x + C.$$

Example G. Integrate: $\int_0^{\pi/4} \dfrac{\tan^3 x}{\sec^3 x} \, dx.$

We have $\int_0^{\pi/4} \dfrac{\tan^3 x}{\sec^3 x} \, dx$

$$= \int_0^{\pi/4} \frac{(\sec^2 x - 1) \tan x}{\sec^3 x} \, dx = \int_0^{\pi/4} \frac{\tan x}{\sec x} \, dx - \int_0^{\pi/4} \frac{\tan x \, dx}{\sec^3 x}$$

$$= \int_0^{\pi/4} \sin x \, dx - \int_0^{\pi/4} \frac{\sec x \tan x \, dx}{\sec^4 x} = -\cos x + \frac{1}{3} \cos^3 x \Big|_0^{\pi/4}$$

$$= -\frac{\sqrt{2}}{2} + \frac{1}{3}\left(\frac{\sqrt{2}}{2}\right)^3 - \left(-1 + \frac{1}{3}\right) = \frac{8 - 5\sqrt{2}}{12}.$$

Example H. The root-mean-square value of a function with respect to x is defined by

$$y_{\text{rms}} = \sqrt{\frac{1}{T} \int_0^T y^2 \, dx}. \tag{8–19}$$

Usually the value of T which is of importance is the period of the function. Find the root-mean-square value of the current in an electric circuit for one period, if $i = 3 \cos \pi t$.

The period of the current is $2\pi/\pi = 2$ sec. Therefore we must find the square root of the integral

$$\frac{1}{2} \int_0^2 (3\cos \pi t)^2 \, dt = \frac{9}{2} \int_0^2 \cos^2 \pi t \, dt.$$

Hence we have

$$\frac{9}{2} \int_0^2 \cos^2 \pi t \, dt = \frac{9}{4} \int_0^2 (1 + \cos 2\pi t) \, dt$$

after substituting $\frac{1}{2}(1 + \cos 2\pi t)$ for $\cos^2 \pi t$. Evaluating we have

$$\frac{9}{4} \int_0^2 (1 + \cos 2\pi t) \, dt = \frac{9}{4} t \Big|_0^2 + \frac{9}{8\pi} \int_0^2 \cos 2\pi t (2\pi \, dt)$$

$$= \frac{9}{2} + \frac{9}{8\pi} \sin 2\pi t \Big|_0^2 = \frac{9}{2}.$$

Thus, the root-mean-square current is

$$i_{\text{rms}} = \sqrt{\frac{9}{2}} = \frac{3\sqrt{2}}{2} = 2.12 \text{ amps.}$$

This value of the current, often referred to as the effective current, is the value of the direct current which would develop the same quantity of heat in the same time.

Exercises

In Exercises 1 through 24, integrate each of the given functions.

1. $\displaystyle\int \sin^2 x \cos x \, dx$

2. $\displaystyle\int \cos^3 x \, dx$

3. $\displaystyle\int \sin^2 x \cos^3 x \, dx$

4. $\displaystyle\int \sin^3 x \cos^6 x \, dx$

5. $\displaystyle\int \cos^2 2x \, dx$

6. $\displaystyle\int \sqrt{\cos x} \sin^3 x \, dx$

7. $\displaystyle\int \sin^5 x \, dx$

8. $\displaystyle\int \sin x \cos^5 x \, dx$

9. $\displaystyle\int \sin^2 x \, dx$

10. $\displaystyle\int \tan^3 x \, dx$

11. $\displaystyle\int \tan x \sec^4 x \, dx$

12. $\displaystyle\int \cot^3 x \, dx$

13. $\displaystyle\int \tan^4 2x \, dx$

14. $\displaystyle\int \cot 4x \csc^4 4x \, dx$

15. $\displaystyle\int \tan^3 3x \sec^3 3x \, dx$

16. $\displaystyle\int \sqrt{\tan x} \sec^4 x \, dx$

17. $\displaystyle\int (\sin x + \cos x)^2 \, dx$

18. $\displaystyle\int (\tan 2x + \cot 2x)^2 \, dx$

19. $\displaystyle\int \frac{1 - \cot x}{\sin^4 x} \, dx$

20. $\displaystyle\int \frac{1 + \sin x}{\cos^4 x} \, dx$

21. $\displaystyle\int_{\pi/6}^{\pi/4} \cot^5 x \, dx$

22. $\displaystyle\int_{\pi/6}^{\pi/3} \frac{dx}{1 + \sin x}$

23. $\displaystyle\int \sec^6 x \, dx$

24. $\displaystyle\int \tan^7 x \, dx$

25. Find the volume generated by rotating the area bounded by $y = \sin x$ and $y = 0$, from $x = 0$ to $x = \pi$, about the x-axis.

26. Find the volume generated by rotating the area bounded by $y = \tan^3 (x^2)$, $y = 0$, and $x = \pi/4$ about the y-axis.

27. In determining the rate of radiation by an accelerated charge, the following integral must be evaluated: $\int_0^\pi \sin^3 \theta \, d\theta$. Find the value of the integral.

28. Find the length of the curve $y = \ln \cos x$ from $x = 0$ to $x = \pi/3$. (See Exercise 13 of Section 5–6.)

29. Find the root-mean-square value of the current for one period if $i = 2 \sin t$.

30. Find the root-mean-square value of the voltage for one period if $V = 100 \sin 120\pi t$.

31. For a current $i = i_0 \sin \omega t$, show that the root-mean-square value of the current for one period is $i_0/\sqrt{2}$.

8–6 Inverse trigonometric forms

Referring to Eq. (6–37), we can find the differential of Arcsin (u/a), where a is a constant:

$$d\left(\text{Arcsin } \frac{u}{a}\right) = \frac{1}{\sqrt{1 - (u/a)^2}} \frac{du}{a} = \frac{a}{\sqrt{a^2 - u^2}} \frac{du}{a} = \frac{du}{\sqrt{a^2 - u^2}}.$$

Reversing this differentiation formula, we have the important integration formula:

$$\int \frac{du}{\sqrt{a^2 - u^2}} = \text{Arcsin } \frac{u}{a} + C. \tag{8–20}$$

By finding the differential of Arctan (u/a), and then reversing the equation, we derive another important integration formula:

$$d\left(\text{Arctan } \frac{u}{a}\right) = \frac{1}{1 + (u/a)^2} \frac{du}{a} = \frac{a^2}{a^2 + u^2} \frac{du}{a} = \frac{a \, du}{a^2 + u^2}.$$

Thus

$$\int \frac{du}{a^2 + u^2} = \frac{1}{a} \text{Arctan } \frac{u}{a} + C. \tag{8–21}$$

This shows one of the principal uses of the inverse trigonometric functions. That is, they provide a solution to the integration of important algebraic functions.

Example A. Integrate: $\displaystyle\int \frac{dx}{\sqrt{9 - x^2}}$; $u = x$, $du = dx$, $a = 3$.

We write $$\int \frac{dx}{\sqrt{9 - x^2}} = \text{Arcsin}\,\frac{x}{3} + C.$$

Example B. Integrate: $\int \dfrac{dx}{4x^2 + 25}$; $u = 2x,\quad du = 2\,dx,\quad a = 5.$

We have $$\int \frac{dx}{4x^2 + 25} = \frac{1}{2} \int \frac{2\,dx}{(2x)^2 + (5)^2}$$

$$= \frac{1}{2} \cdot \frac{1}{5}\,\text{Arctan}\,\frac{2x}{5} + C = \frac{1}{10}\,\text{Arctan}\,\frac{2x}{5} + C.$$

Example C. Integrate: $$\int_{-1}^{3} \frac{dx}{x^2 + 6x + 13}.$$

At first glance it does not appear that this integral fits any of the forms presented up to this point. However, by writing the denominator in the form $(x^2 + 6x + 9) + 4 = (x + 3)^2 + 2^2$, we recognize that $u = x + 3$, $du = dx$, and $a = 2$. Thus

$$\int_{-1}^{3} \frac{dx}{x^2 + 6x + 13} = \int_{-1}^{3} \frac{dx}{(x + 3)^2 + 2^2} = \frac{1}{2}\,\text{Arctan}\,\frac{x + 3}{2}\bigg|_{-1}^{3}$$

$$= \tfrac{1}{2}\,(\text{Arctan } 3 - \text{Arctan } 1) = \tfrac{1}{2}(1.25 - 0.79) = 0.23.$$

Now we can see the use of completing the square when we are transforming integrals into proper form. We also see the use of inverse trigonometric functions in evaluating integrals.

Example D. Integrate: $$\int \frac{2x + 5}{x^2 + 9}\,dx.$$

By writing this integral as the sum of two integrals, we may integrate each of these separately:

$$\int \frac{2x + 5}{x^2 + 9}\,dx = \int \frac{2x\,dx}{x^2 + 9} + \int \frac{5\,dx}{x^2 + 9}.$$

The first of these integrals is seen to be a logarithmic form, and the second the inverse tangent form. For the first, $u = x^2 + 9$, $du = 2x\,dx$. For the second, $u = x$, $du = dx$, $a = 3$. Thus

$$\int \frac{2x\,dx}{x^2 + 9} + 5\int \frac{dx}{x^2 + 9} = \ln|x^2 + 9| + \frac{5}{3}\,\text{Arctan}\,\frac{x}{3} + C.$$

Exercises

In Exercises 1 through 15, integrate the given functions.

1. $\displaystyle\int \frac{dx}{\sqrt{1-x^2}}$

2. $\displaystyle\int \frac{dx}{4+x^2}$

3. $\displaystyle\int \frac{dx}{9x^2+16}$

4. $\displaystyle\int \frac{dx}{\sqrt{9-4x^2}}$

5. $\displaystyle\int \frac{dx}{1+9x^2}$

6. $\displaystyle\int \frac{2\,dx}{\sqrt{4-36x^2}}$

7. $\displaystyle\int_1^2 \frac{dx}{5x^2+7}$

8. $\displaystyle\int \frac{4\,dx}{\sqrt{3-2x^2}}$

9. $\displaystyle\int_0^1 \frac{x\,dx}{1+x^4}$

10. $\displaystyle\int \frac{\sec^2 x\,dx}{\sqrt{1-\tan^2 x}}$

11. $\displaystyle\int \frac{dx}{x^2+2x+2}$

12. $\displaystyle\int_{\pi/6}^{\pi/2} \frac{\cos 2x}{1+\sin^2 2x}\,dx$

13. $\displaystyle\int \frac{dx}{\sqrt{2x-x^2}}$

14. $\displaystyle\int_{-4}^0 \frac{dx}{x^2+4x+5}$

15. $\displaystyle\int \frac{2-x}{\sqrt{4-x^2}}\,dx$

16. Integrate each of the following, being careful to properly recognize each form:

(a) $\displaystyle\int \frac{x\,dx}{\sqrt{1-x^2}}$
(b) $\displaystyle\int \frac{dx}{\sqrt{1-x^2}}$
(c) $\displaystyle\int \frac{x\,dx}{1+x^2}$
(d) $\displaystyle\int \frac{dx}{1+x^2}$

17. Find the area bounded by the curve $y(1+x^2)=1$, $x=0$, $y=0$, and $x=2$.

18. Find the area bounded by $y^2(4-x^2)=1$, $x=0$, $y=0$, and $x=1$.

19. In dealing with the theory for simple harmonic motion, it is necessary to solve the following equation:

$$\frac{dx}{\sqrt{A^2-x^2}} = \sqrt{k/m}\,dt, \qquad \text{with } k,\ m,\ \text{and } A \text{ as constants.}$$

Determine the solution to this equation if $x=x_0$ when $t=0$.

20. Determine the function of distance in terms of time if the velocity of an object is given by $v=1/(4+t^2)$ and $s=0$ when $t=0$.

21. Find the moment of inertia with respect to the y-axis for the area bounded by $y=1/(1+x^6)$, the x-axis, $x=1$, and $x=2$.

22. Find the length of arc along the curve $y=\sqrt{1-x^2}$ between $x=0$ and $x=1$. (See Exercise 13 of Section 5–6).

8–7 Integration by parts

There are many methods of transforming integrals into a form which can be integrated by one of the basic formulas. In the preceding section we saw that completing the square and trigonometric identities can be used for this purpose.

In this section and the following one, we shall develop two general methods. The method of integration by parts is discussed in this section.

Since the derivative of a product of functions is found by use of the formula

$$\frac{d(uv)}{dx} = u\frac{dv}{dx} + v\frac{du}{dx},$$

the differential of a product of functions is given by $d(uv) = u\,dv + v\,du$. Integrating both sides of this expression, we obtain $uv = \int u\,dv + \int v\,du$. Solving for $\int u\,dv$, we obtain

$$\int u\,dv = uv - \int v\,du. \tag{8–22}$$

Integration by use of Eq. (8–22) is called *integration by parts*.

Example A. Integrate: $\int x \sin x\,dx$.

This integral does not fit any of the previous forms which have been discussed, since neither x nor $\sin x$ can be made a factor of a proper du. However, by choosing $u = x$, and $dv = \sin x\,dx$, the above formula may be used. Thus

$$u = x, \qquad dv = \sin x\,dx,$$
$$du = dx, \qquad v = -\cos x.$$

(The constant of integration will be included in the final result.) Hence

$$\int (x)\,(\sin x\,dx) = -x\cos x - \int (-\cos x)\,dx = -x\cos x + \sin x + C.$$

Other choices of u and dv may be made in the above example, but they do not prove useful. If $u = \sin x$ and $dv = x\,dx$, v becomes $x^2/2$, which makes the integral $\int v\,du$ more complex than the original problem. The choice of $u = x \sin x$ makes the expression for du/dx more complex than u itself. There are no set rules which may be stated for the best choice of u and dv, but there are two guidelines which may be stated. (1) The quantity u is normally chosen such that du/dx is of simpler form than u. (2) The differential dv is normally chosen such that $\int dv$ is easily obtained. Working examples, and thereby gaining experience in methods of integrating, is the best way to determine when this method should be used and how to employ it.

Example B. Integrate:

$$\int_0^1 xe^{-x}\,dx; \qquad u = x, \quad dv = e^{-x}\,dx, \quad du = dx, \quad v = -e^{-x}.$$

We write $\displaystyle\int_0^1 xe^{-x}\,dx = -xe^{-x}\Big|_0^1 + \int_0^1 e^{-x}\,dx = -xe^{-x} - e^{-x}\Big|_0^1$

$$= -e^{-1} - e^{-1} + 1 = 1 - 2/e.$$

Example C. Integrate:

$$\int \text{Arcsin } x \, dx; \quad u = \text{Arcsin } x, \quad dv = dx, \quad du = \frac{dx}{\sqrt{1 - x^2}}, \quad v = x.$$

We obtain

$$\int \text{Arcsin } x \, dx = x \text{ Arcsin } x - \int \frac{x \, dx}{\sqrt{1 - x^2}} = x \text{ Arcsin } x + \frac{1}{2} \int \frac{-2x \, dx}{\sqrt{1 - x^2}}$$

$$= x \text{ Arcsin } x + \sqrt{1 - x^2} + C.$$

Example D. Integrate:

$$\int \sqrt{x} \ln x \, dx; \quad u = \ln x, \quad dv = x^{1/2} \, dx, \quad du = \frac{1}{x} \, dx, \quad v = \frac{2}{3} x^{3/2}.$$

We write

$$\int \sqrt{x} \ln x \, dx = \tfrac{2}{3} x^{3/2} \ln x - \tfrac{2}{3} \int x^{1/2} \, dx = \tfrac{2}{3} x^{3/2} \ln x - \tfrac{4}{9} x^{3/2} + C.$$

Example E. Integrate:

$$\int e^x \sin x \, dx; \quad u = \sin x, \quad dv = e^x \, dx, \quad du = \cos x \, dx, \quad v = e^x.$$

We write $\qquad \int e^x \sin x \, dx = e^x \sin x - \int e^x \cos x \, dx.$

At first glance it appears that we have made no progress in applying the method of integration by parts. We note, however, that when we integrated $\int e^x \sin x \, dx$, part of the result was a term of $\int e^x \cos x \, dx$. This implies that if $\int e^x \cos x \, dx$ were integrated, a term of $\int e^x \sin x \, dx$ might result. Thus the method of integration by parts is now applied to the integral $\int e^x \cos x \, dx$:

$$u = \cos x, \qquad dv = e^x \, dx, \qquad du = -\sin x \, dx, \qquad v = e^x.$$

And so $\int e^x \cos x \, dx = e^x \cos x + \int e^x \sin x \, dx$. Substituting this expression into the expression for $\int e^x \sin x \, dx$, we obtain

$$\int e^x \sin x \, dx = e^x \sin x - \left(e^x \cos x + \int e^x \sin x \, dx \right)$$

$$= e^x \sin x - e^x \cos x - \int e^x \sin x \, dx;$$

$$2 \int e^x \sin x \, dx = e^x (\sin x - \cos x) + 2C$$

$$\int e^x \sin x \, dx = \frac{e^x}{2} (\sin x - \cos x) + C.$$

Thus, by combining integrals of like form, we obtain the desired result.

Exercises

In Exercises 1 through 12, integrate each of the given functions.

1. $\int x \cos x \, dx$ 2. $\int x e^x \, dx$ 3. $\int x \sec^2 x \, dx$

4. $\int \ln x \, dx$ 5. $\int_0^1 \text{Arctan } x \, dx$ 6. $\int x \sqrt{x+1} \, dx$

7. $\int x \sec x \tan x \, dx$ 8. $\int x^2 \ln 4x \, dx$ 9. $\int x^2 \sin 2x \, dx$

10. $\int x^2 e^{2x} \, dx$ 11. $\int_0^{\pi/2} e^x \cos x \, dx$ 12. $\int e^{-x} \sin 2x \, dx$

13. Find the area bounded by $y = xe^{-x}$, $y = 0$, and $x = 2$.
14. Find the volume generated by rotating the area bounded by $y = \sin x$ and $y = 0$ (from $x = 0$ to $x = \pi$) about the y-axis.
15. Find the x-coordinate of the centroid of the area bounded by $y = \cos x$ and $y = 0$ for $0 \le x \le \pi/2$.
16. Find the moment of inertia with respect to its axis of the volume generated by rotating the area bounded by $y = e^x$, $x = 1$, and the coordinate axes about the y-axis.
17. Find the root-mean-square value of the function $y = \ln x$ between $x = 1$ and $x = 2$. (See Example H of Section 8–5.)
18. The general expression for the slope of a curve is $dy/dx = x^3 \sqrt{1 + x^2}$. Find the equation of the curve if it passes through the origin.
19. The current in a given circuit is given by $i = e^{-2t} \cos t$. Find an expression for the amount of charge which passes a given point in the circuit as a function of the time, if $q_0 = 0$.

8–8 Integration by trigonometric substitution

Trigonometric relations not only provide a means of transforming trigonometric integrals, but they can also be used to transform algebraic integrals. Substitutions based on Eqs. (8–14), (8–15), and (8–16) prove to be particularly useful for integrals involving radicals. The method is illustrated in the following examples.

Example A. Integrate: $$\int \frac{dx}{x^2 \sqrt{1 - x^2}}.$$

If we let $x = \sin \theta$, the radical becomes $\sqrt{1 - \sin^2 \theta} = \cos \theta$. Therefore, by making this substitution, the integral can be transformed into a trigonometric integral. We must be careful to replace all factors of the integral by proper expressions in terms of θ; $x = \sin \theta$, $dx = \cos \theta \, d\theta$.

And so we obtain

$$\int \frac{dx}{x^2\sqrt{1-x^2}} = \int \frac{\cos\theta\, d\theta}{\sin^2\theta\sqrt{1-\sin^2\theta}}$$

$$= \int \frac{\cos\theta\, d\theta}{\sin^2\theta\cos\theta} = \int \csc^2\theta\, d\theta$$

$$= -\cot\theta + C.$$

FIGURE 8-1

We have now performed the integration, but the answer is expressed in terms of a variable different from the original integral. It is necessary to express the result in terms of x. Making a right triangle with an angle θ such that $\sin\theta = x/1$ (Fig. 8-1), we may express any of the trigonometric functions in terms of x. (This is the method used with inverse trigonometric functions.) Thus

$$\cot\theta = \sqrt{1-x^2}/x.$$

Therefore the result of the integration becomes

$$\int \frac{dx}{x^2\sqrt{1-x^2}} = -\cot\theta + C = -\frac{\sqrt{1-x^2}}{x} + C.$$

Example B. Integrate:

$$\int \frac{dx}{\sqrt{x^2+4}}\,;$$

let $x = 2\tan\theta$, $dx = 2\sec^2\theta\, d\theta$.

We write

$$\int \frac{dx}{\sqrt{x^2+4}} = \int \frac{2\sec^2\theta\, d\theta}{\sqrt{4\tan^2\theta+4}}$$

$$= \int \frac{2\sec^2\theta\, d\theta}{2\sqrt{\tan^2\theta+1}} = \int \frac{2\sec^2\theta\, d\theta}{2\sec\theta}$$

$$= \int \sec\theta\, d\theta = \ln|\sec\theta + \tan\theta| + C$$

$$= \ln\left|\frac{\sqrt{x^2+4}}{2} + \frac{x}{2}\right| + C$$

$$= \ln\left|\frac{\sqrt{x^2+4}+x}{2}\right| + C.$$

See Fig. 8-2. This answer is acceptable, but there is another form. By using the properties of logarithms, we have

$$\ln \left| \frac{\sqrt{x^2 + 4} + x}{2} \right| + C$$

FIGURE 8–2

$$= \ln |\sqrt{x^2 + 4} + x| + (C - \ln 2)$$

$$= \ln |\sqrt{x^2 + 4} + x| + C'.$$

Here C' is another arbitrary constant, which combines all constants of the previous expression. Combining constants in this manner is a common practice in integration problems.

Example C. Integrate:

$$\int \frac{dx}{x\sqrt{x^2 - 9}} \; ; \qquad \text{let } x = 3 \sec \theta, \quad dx = 3 \sec \theta \tan \theta \, d\theta.$$

We write

$$\int \frac{dx}{x\sqrt{x^2 - 9}} = \int \frac{3 \sec \theta \tan \theta \, d\theta}{3 \sec \theta \sqrt{9 \sec^2 \theta - 9}}$$

$$= \int \frac{\tan \theta \, d\theta}{3\sqrt{\sec^2 \theta - 1}} = \int \frac{\tan \theta \, d\theta}{3 \tan \theta}$$

$$= \frac{1}{3} \int d\theta = \frac{1}{3} \theta + C = \frac{1}{3} \text{Arcsec} \, \frac{x}{3} + C.$$

In this solution it is not necessary to refer to a triangle in order to express the integral in terms of x. This solution is found by solving $x = 3 \sec \theta$ for θ, as indicated.

From the above examples we can see that by making the proper substitution in terms of a trigonometric function, we can solve integrals of algebraic functions by means of simpler equivalent trigonometric forms, due to the properties of the square relations of the trigonometric functions. Summarizing these substitutions, for the indicated radical form the following trigonometric substitutions are used.

For $\quad \sqrt{a^2 - x^2} \quad$ use $\quad x = a \sin \theta.$

For $\quad \sqrt{a^2 + x^2} \quad$ use $\quad x = a \tan \theta.$

For $\quad \sqrt{x^2 - a^2} \quad$ use $\quad x = a \sec \theta.$

Example D. Evaluate $\qquad \displaystyle\int_1^4 \frac{\sqrt{9 + x^2}}{x} \, dx.$

Since we have the form $\sqrt{a^2 + x^2}$, where $a = 3$, we make the substitution $x = 3 \tan \theta$. This means that $dx = 3 \sec^2 \theta \, d\theta$. Thus

$$\int \frac{\sqrt{9 + x^2}}{x} dx = \int \frac{\sqrt{9 + 9 \tan^2 \theta}}{3 \tan \theta} (3 \sec^2 \theta \, d\theta)$$

$$= 3 \int \frac{\sqrt{1 + \tan^2 \theta}}{\tan \theta} \sec^2 \theta \, d\theta = 3 \int \frac{\sec^3 \theta}{\tan \theta} d\theta$$

$$= 3 \int \frac{1 + \tan^2 \theta}{\tan \theta} \sec \theta \, d\theta$$

$$= 3 \left(\int \frac{\sec \theta}{\tan \theta} d\theta + \int \tan \theta \sec \theta \, d\theta \right)$$

$$= 3 \left(\int \csc \theta \, d\theta + \int \tan \theta \sec \theta \, d\theta \right)$$

$$= 3 \left[\ln |\csc \theta - \cot \theta| + \sec \theta \right]$$

$$= 3 \left[\ln \left| \frac{\sqrt{x^2 + 9}}{x} - \frac{3}{x} \right| + \frac{\sqrt{x^2 + 9}}{3} \right]$$

$$= 3 \left[\ln \left| \frac{\sqrt{x^2 + 9} - 3}{x} \right| + \frac{\sqrt{x^2 + 9}}{3} \right].$$

Limits have not been included, due to the changes in variables. The actual evaluation may now be completed:

$$\int_1^4 \frac{\sqrt{9 + x^2}}{x} dx = 3 \left[\ln \left| \frac{\sqrt{x^2 + 9} - 3}{x} \right| + \frac{\sqrt{x^2 + 9}}{3} \right]_1^4$$

$$= 3 \left[\left(\ln \frac{1}{2} - \ln \frac{\sqrt{10} - 3}{1} \right) + \left(\frac{5}{3} - \frac{\sqrt{10}}{3} \right) \right]$$

$$= 3 \left[\ln \frac{1}{2(\sqrt{10} - 3)} + \frac{5 - \sqrt{10}}{3} \right]$$

$$= 3 \ln \frac{\sqrt{10} + 3}{2} + \frac{5 - \sqrt{10}}{1} = 5.21.$$

Exercises

In Exercises 1 through 14, integrate each of the given functions.

1. $\int \frac{\sqrt{1 - x^2}}{x^2} dx$

2. $\int_0^4 \frac{dx}{(x^2 + 9)^{3/2}}$

3. $\int \frac{dx}{\sqrt{x^2 - 4}}$

4. $\int \frac{\sqrt{x^2 - 25}}{x} dx$

5. $\int \frac{dx}{x^2\sqrt{x^2 + 9}}$

6. $\int \frac{dx}{x\sqrt{4 - x^2}}$

7. $\int \dfrac{dx}{(4 - x^2)^{3/2}}$　　　　8. $\int \dfrac{x^3\,dx}{\sqrt{9 + x^2}}$　　　　9. $\int_0^{0.5} \dfrac{x^3\,dx}{\sqrt{1 - x^2}}$

10. $\int \dfrac{\sqrt{x^2 - 16}}{x^2}\,dx$　　　11. $\int \dfrac{dx}{\sqrt{x^2 + 2x + 2}}$　　　12. $\int \dfrac{dx}{x\sqrt{4x^2 - 9}}$

13. $\int \dfrac{dx}{\sqrt{e^{2x} - 1}}$　　　14. $\int \sqrt{16 - x^2}\,dx$

15. Find the area of a circle of radius 1 by integration.

16. Find the area bounded by $y = 1/x^2\sqrt{x^2 - 1}$, $x = \sqrt{2}$, $x = \sqrt{5}$, and $y = 0$.

17. Find the moment of inertia with respect to the y-axis of the first-quadrant area under the circle $x^2 + y^2 = a^2$ in terms of its mass.

18. Find the moment of inertia of a sphere of radius a with respect to its axis in terms of its mass.

19. Find the volume generated by rotating the area bounded by $y = \sqrt{x^2 - 16}/x^2$, $y = 0$, and $x = 5$ about the y-axis,

20. Find the length of arc along the curve of $y = \ln x$ from $x = 1$ to $x = 3$. (See Exercise 13 of Section 5–6).

8–9 Integration by use of tables

In this chapter we have introduced certain basic integrals, and have also brought in some methods of reducing other integrals to these basic forms. Often this transformation and integration require a number of steps to be performed, and therefore integrals are tabulated for reference. The integrals found in tables have been derived by using the methods introduced thus far, as well as many other methods which can be used. Therefore, an understanding of the basic forms and some of the basic methods is very useful in finding integrals from tables. Such an understanding forms a basis for proper recognition of the forms which are used in the tables, as well as the types of results which may be expected. Therefore, the use of the tables depends on the proper recognition of the form, and the variables and constants of the integral. The following examples illustrate the use of the table of integrals found in Table 6 in the Appendix.

Example A. Integrate: 　　　　$\displaystyle \int \dfrac{x\,dx}{\sqrt{2 + 3x}}$.

We first note that this integral fits the form of formula 6 of Table 6, with $u = x$, $a = 2$ and $b = 3$. Therefore

$$\int \frac{x\,dx}{\sqrt{2 + 3x}} = -\frac{2(4 - 3x)\sqrt{2 + 3x}}{27} + C.$$

Example B. Integrate: $\qquad \int \dfrac{\sqrt{4 - 9x^2}}{x}\, dx.$

This fits the form of formula 18, with proper identification of constants; $u = 3x$, $du = 3\, dx$, $a = 2$. Hence

$$\int \frac{\sqrt{4 - 9x^2}}{x}\, dx = \int \frac{\sqrt{4 - 9x^2}}{3x}\, 3\, dx$$

$$= \sqrt{4 - 9x^2} - 2 \ln \left(\frac{2 + \sqrt{4 - 9x^2}}{3x} \right) + C.$$

Example C. Integrate: $\int \sec^3 2x\, dx$.

This fits the form of formula 37; $n = 3$, $u = 2x$, $du = 2\, dx$. And so

$$\int \sec^3 2x\, dx = \frac{1}{2} \int \sec^3 2x (2\, dx) = \frac{1}{2} \frac{\sec 2x \tan 2x}{2} + \frac{1}{2} \cdot \frac{1}{2} \int \sec 2x (2\, dx).$$

[To complete this integral, we must use the basic form of Eq. (8–12).] Thus we complete it by

$$\int \sec^3 2x\, dx = \frac{\sec 2x \tan 2x}{4} + \frac{1}{4} \ln |\sec 2x + \tan 2x| + C.$$

Example D. Evaluate $\int_1^e x^2 \ln 2x\, dx$.

This integral fits the form of formula 46 if $u = 2x$. Thus we have

$$\frac{1}{8} \int_1^e (2x)^2 \ln 2x (2\, dx) = \frac{1}{8} (2x)^3 \left[\frac{\ln 2x}{3} - \frac{1}{9} \right]_1^e$$

$$= e^3 \left(\frac{\ln 2e}{3} - \frac{1}{9} \right) - \left(\frac{\ln 2}{3} - \frac{1}{9} \right)$$

$$= e^3 \left(\frac{\ln 2}{3} + \frac{\ln e}{3} - \frac{1}{9} \right) - \left(\frac{\ln 2}{3} - \frac{1}{9} \right)$$

$$= \frac{\ln 2}{3} (e^3 - 1) + \frac{1}{9} (2e^3 + 1) = 8.99.$$

Exercises

In Exercises 1 through 30, integrate each function by use of Table 6 in the Appendix.

1. $\displaystyle\int \frac{3x\, dx}{2 + 5x}$

2. $\displaystyle\int \frac{4x\, dx}{(1 + x)^2}$

3. $\displaystyle\int 5x\sqrt{2 + 3x}\, dx$

4. $\displaystyle\int \frac{dx}{x^2 - 4}$

5. $\displaystyle\int \sqrt{4 - x^2}\, dx$

6. $\displaystyle\int_0^{\pi/3} \sin^3 x\, dx$

7. $\displaystyle\int \sin 2x \sin 3x \, dx$

8. $\displaystyle\int \text{Arcsin } 3x \, dx$

9. $\displaystyle\int \frac{\sqrt{4x^2 - 9}}{x} \, dx$

10. $\displaystyle\int \frac{(9x^2 + 16)^{3/2}}{x} \, dx$

11. $\displaystyle\int \cos^5 4x \, dx$

12. $\displaystyle\int \tan^2 x \, dx$

13. $\displaystyle\int \text{Arctan } x^2 (x \, dx)$

14. $\displaystyle\int xe^{4x} \, dx$

15. $\displaystyle\int_1^2 (4 - x^2)^{3/2} \, dx$

16. $\displaystyle\int \frac{dx}{9 - 16x^2}$

17. $\displaystyle\int \frac{dx}{x\sqrt{4x^2 + 1}}$

18. $\displaystyle\int \frac{\sqrt{4 + x^2}}{x} \, dx$

19. $\displaystyle\int \frac{dx}{x\sqrt{1 - 4x^2}}$

20. $\displaystyle\int \frac{dx}{x(1 + 4x)^2}$

21. $\displaystyle\int \sin x \cos 5x \, dx$

22. $\displaystyle\int_0^2 x^2 e^{3x} \, dx$

23. $\displaystyle\int x^5 \cos x^3 \, dx$

24. $\displaystyle\int \sin^3 x \cos^2 x \, dx$

25. $\displaystyle\int \frac{x \, dx}{(1 - x^4)^{3/2}}$

26. $\displaystyle\int \frac{dx}{x(1 - 4x)}$

27. $\displaystyle\int x^3 \ln x^2 \, dx$

28. $\displaystyle\int \frac{x \, dx}{x^2 \sqrt{x^4 - 9}}$

29. $\displaystyle\int \frac{x^2 \, dx}{(x^6 - 1)^{3/2}}$

30. $\displaystyle\int x^7 \sqrt{x^4 + 4} \, dx$

31. Find the length of arc of the curve $y = x^2$ from $x = 0$ to $x = 1$. (See Exercise 13 of Section 5–6.)

32. Find the moment of inertia with respect to its axis of the volume generated by rotating the area bounded by $y = \ln x$, $x = e$, and the x-axis about the y-axis.

33. Find the force on the area bounded by $x = 1/\sqrt{1 + y}$, $y = 0$, $y = 3$, and the y-axis, if the surface of the water is at the upper edge of the area. (See Exercise 15 of Section 5–6.)

34. Under certain conditions the velocity as a function of time for a particle is given by $v = t/\sqrt{1 + 2t}$. Determine the distance as a function of time if $s = 6$ when $t = 0$.

35. Find the volume of the solid generated by rotating the area bounded by $y = e^x \sin x$ and the x-axis between $x = 0$ and $x = \pi$ about the x-axis.

Miscellaneous exercises for Chapter 8

In Exercises 1 through 20, integrate each of the given functions.

1. $\displaystyle\int e^{-2x} \, dx$

2. $\displaystyle\int x^{1/3} \sqrt{x^{4/3} + 1} \, dx$

3. $\displaystyle\int \frac{\cos x \, dx}{1 + \sin x}$

4. $\displaystyle\int \frac{\sec^2 x \, dx}{2 + \tan x}$

5. $\displaystyle\int_0^{\pi/2} \cos^3 2x \, dx$

6. $\displaystyle\int \frac{dx}{\sqrt{1 - 4x^2}}$

7. $\displaystyle\int_0^2 \frac{x\,dx}{4 + x^2}$

8. $\displaystyle\int \frac{\sin^3 x\,dx}{\sqrt{\cos x}}$

9. $\displaystyle\int \sec^4 3x \tan 3x\,dx$

10. $\displaystyle\int \frac{e^{2x}\,dx}{\sqrt{e^{2x} + 1}}$

11. $\displaystyle\int_1^e \frac{\ln x^2\,dx}{x}$

12. $\displaystyle\int \sin^2 3x\,dx$

13. $\displaystyle\int \frac{dx}{\sqrt{4x^2 - 9}}$

14. $\displaystyle\int x \operatorname{Arctan} x\,dx$

15. $\displaystyle\int \frac{x^2\,dx}{\sqrt{9 - x^2}}$

16. $\displaystyle\int \frac{\sin^2 2x\,dx}{1 + \cos 2x}$

17. $\displaystyle\int \frac{dx}{x\,(\ln 2x)^2}$

18. $\displaystyle\int_1^3 \frac{dx}{x^2 - 2x + 5}$

19. $\displaystyle\int \frac{x^2 - 1}{x + 2}\,dx$

20. $\displaystyle\int [\cos(\ln x)]\frac{dx}{x}$

21. The change in the thermodynamic entity of entropy ΔS may be expressed as $\Delta S = \int (c_v/T)\,dT$, where c_v is the heat capacity at constant volume and T is the temperature. For increased accuracy, c_v is often given by the equation $c_v = a + bT + cT^2$, where a, b, and c are constants. Express ΔS as a function of temperature.

22. A second-order chemical reaction leads to the equation

$$dt = \frac{k_1\,dx}{a - x} + \frac{k_2\,dx}{b - x},$$

where k_1 and k_2 are constants, a and b are initial concentrations, t is the time and x is the decrease in concentration. Solve for t as a function of x.

23. Assuming a resisting force, the velocity (in ft/sec) of a falling object in terms of time (in sec) is given by

$$\frac{dv}{32 - 0.1\,v} = dt.$$

If $v = 0$ when $t = 0$, find v as a function of t.

24. Find the area bounded by $y = x/(1 + x)^2$, the x-axis, and the line $x = 4$.

25. Find the equation of the curve for which $dy/dx = \sec^4 x$, if the curve passes through the origin.

26. Find the distance from the origin after $\frac{1}{2}$ second of the particle for which the velocity as a function of time is given by $v = 4 \cos 3t$. (That is, integrate the function with limits of 0 and $\frac{1}{2}$, or substitute into the function derived in Exercise 19 of Section 8–4. Compare the results of these two methods.)

27. Find the area inside the circle $x^2 + y^2 = 25$ and to the right of the line $x = 3$.

28. Find the volume generated by rotating about the y-axis the area bounded by $y = x + \sqrt{x + 1}$, $x = 3$, and the axes.

29. Find the centroid of the area bounded by $y = \ln x$, $x = 2$, and the x-axis.

30. The power delivered to an electric circuit is given by $P = ei$, where e and i are, respectively, the instantaneous voltage and the instantaneous current in the circuit. The mean power, averaged over a period $2\pi/\omega$, is given by

$$P_{\text{av}} = \frac{\omega}{2\pi} \int_0^{2\pi/\omega} ei\, dt.$$

If $e = 20\cos 2t$ and $i = 3\sin 2t$, find the average power over a period of $\pi/4$.

9 Introduction to partial derivatives and double integrals

9–1 Functions of two variables

To this point we have been dealing with functions which have a single independent variable. There are, however, numerous situations in science, engineering, and technology in which functions with more than one independent variable are used. Although some of these applications involve three or more independent variables, many involve only two, and we shall concern ourselves primarily with these. Therefore, in this section we shall establish the significance of a function of two variables, and in the following sections of the chapter show how the methods of the earlier chapters may be used with them.

Example A. The total surface area of a right circular cylinder is a function of the radius and the height of the cylinder. That is, the area will change if either or both of these change. The formula for the total surface area is

$$A = 2\pi r^2 + 2\pi rh.$$

We say that A is a function of r and h.

We define a function of two variables as follows. *If z is uniquely determined for given values of x and y, then z is a single-valued function of x and y.* Notation similar to that which is used for one independent variable is employed in this case. This notation is $z = f(x, y)$, where both x and y are independent variables. This is the meaning of a function of two variables.

Similar to the case with one independent variable, $f(a, b)$ means "the value of the function when $x = a$ and $y = b$."

Example B. If $f(x, y) = 3x^2 + 2xy - y^3$, find $f(-1, 2)$. Substituting, we have

$$f(-1, 2) = 3(-1)^2 + 2(-1)(2) - (2)^3 = 3 - 4 - 8 = -9.$$

Restricting values of the function to real numbers means that certain restrictions may be placed on the independent variables. Values of either x or y or both which lead to division by zero or to imaginary values for z are not permissible. The following example illustrates this point.

Example C. If

$$f(x, y) = \frac{3xy}{(x - y)(x + 3)},$$

all values of x and y are permissible, except those for which $x = y$ and $x = -3$. Each of these would indicate division by zero.

If $f(x, y) = \sqrt{4 - x^2 - y^2}$, neither x nor y may be more than 2 in absolute value, and the sum of their squares may not exceed 4. Otherwise, imaginary values of the function would result.

One of the primary difficulties students have with functions is setting them up from stated conditions. Although many examples of this have been encountered in our previous work, an example of setting up a function of two variables should prove helpful. Although no general rules can be given for this procedure, a careful analysis of the statement should lead to the desired function. The following example illustrates setting up such a function.

Example D. An open rectangular metal box is to be constructed such that it will contain 2 ft^3. The cost of sheet metal is c cents per square foot. Express the cost of this material as a function of the length and width of the box.

The cost in question depends on the surface area of the sides of the box. An "open" box is one which has no top. Thus, the surface area of the box is

$$S = lw + 2lh + 2hw,$$

where l is the length, w the width, and h the height of the box. However, this expression contains three independent variables. Using the condition that the volume of the box is 2 ft^3, we have $lwh = 2$. Since we wish to have only l and w, we solve this expression for h, and find that $h = 2/lw$. Substituting this in the expression for the surface area we have

$$S = lw + 2l\left(\frac{2}{lw}\right) + 2\left(\frac{2}{lw}\right)w$$

$$= lw + \frac{4}{w} + \frac{4}{l}.$$

Since the cost C is given by $C = cS$, we have the expression for the cost as

$$C = c\left(lw + \frac{4}{w} + \frac{4}{l}\right).$$

Exercises

1. Express the volume of a right circular cylinder as a function of the radius and height.

2. Express the volume of a right circular cone as a function of the radius of the base and the height.

3. Express the area of a triangle as a function of the base and the altitude.

4. Express the length of a diagonal of a rectangle as a function of the length and width.

In Exercises 5 through 14, evaluate the given functions for the given values of the independent variables.

5. $f(x, y) = 2x - 6y$, find $f(0, -4)$.

6. $F(x, y) = x^2 - 5y + y^2$, find $F(2, -2)$.

7. $g(r, s) = r - 2rs - r^2s$, find $g(-2, 1)$.

8. $\varphi(x, t) = 2x^3 - x^2t - 2t^2$, find $\varphi(-3, -1)$.

9. $Y(y, t) = \dfrac{2 - 3y}{t - 1} + 2y^2t$, find $Y(y, 2)$.

10. $f(r, t) = r^3 - 3r^2t + 3rt^2 - t^3$, find $f(3, t)$.

11. $X(x, t) = -6xt + xt^2 - t^3$, find $X(x, -t)$.

12. $H(p, q) = p - \dfrac{p - 2q^2 - 5q}{p + q}$, find $H(p, q + k)$.

13. $f(x, y) = x^2 - 2xy - 4x$, find $f(x + h, y + k) - f(x, y)$.

14. $\varphi(x, y) = \dfrac{3 - x}{y - x} - xy - xy^2$, find $\varphi(x + h, -1)$.

15. The voltage v across a resistor R in an electric circuit is given by $v = iR$, where i is the current. What is the voltage if the current is 3 amps and the resistance is 6 ohms?

16. The centripetal acceleration of an object moving in a circular path is $a = v^2/R$, where v is the velocity of the object and R is the radius of the circle. What is the centripetal acceleration of an object moving at 6 ft/sec in a circular path whose radius is 4 ft?

17. The pressure of a gas as a function of its volume and temperature is given by $p = nRT/V$, where n and R are constants. If $n = 3$ moles, $R = 0.082$ liter · atm/mole · °K, find the pressure (in atm) for $T = 300°$K and $V = 50$ liters.

18. The power supplied to a resistance R in an electric circuit by a current i is given by $P = i^2R$. Find the power (in watts) supplied by a current of 4 amps to a resistance of 2.4 ohms.

19. The reciprocal of the image distance from a lens as a function of the object distance p and the focal length f of the lens is given by

$$\frac{1}{q} = \frac{1}{f} - \frac{1}{p}.$$

Find the image distance of an object 20 cm from a lens whose focal length is 5 cm.

20. The pressure exerted by a force on an area is given by $p = F/A$. If a given force is doubled on an area which is $\frac{2}{3}$ a given area, what is the ratio of the first pressure to the second?

21. The crushing load of a pillar varies as the fourth power of its radius and inversely as the square of its length. Express L as a function of r and l for a pillar 20 ft tall and 1 ft in diameter which is crushed by a load of 20 tons.

22. The resonant frequency of an electric circuit containing an inductance L and capacitance C is inversely proportional to the square root of the product of the inductance and capacitance. If the resonant frequency of a circuit containing a 4-henry capacitor and a 64×10^{-6} farad capacitor is 10 cycles/sec, express f as a function of L and C,

23. What, if any, are the restrictions on the independent variables of the function $f(x, y) = \sqrt{x^2 + y^2 - x^2 y - y^3}$?

24. What, if any, are the restrictions on the independent variables of the function

$$f(x, y) = \frac{x^2 - 4y^2}{x^2 + 9} ?$$

25. The angle between two sides a and b of a triangle is 30°. Express the area of the triangle as a function of these sides.

26. A cylindrical can is to be made to contain a volume V. Express the total surface area of the can as a function of V and the radius of the can.

27. A right circular cylinder is to be inscribed in a sphere of radius r. Express the volume of the cylinder as a function of the height h of the cylinder and r.

9–2 Curves and surfaces in three dimensions

We will now undertake a brief description of the graphical representation of a function of two variables. We shall show first a method of representation in the rectangular coordinate system in two dimensions. The following example illustrates the method.

Example A. To represent $z = 2x^2 + y^2$, we will assume various values of z, and sketch the resulting equation in the xy-plane. For example, if $z = 2$ we have

$$2x^2 + y^2 = 2.$$

This we recognize as an ellipse with its major axis along the y-axis and vertices at $(0, \sqrt{2})$ and $(0, -\sqrt{2})$. The ends of the minor axis are $(1, 0)$ and $(-1, 0)$. (See Fig. 9–1.) However, the ellipse $2x^2 + y^2 = 2$ represents the function $z = 2x^2 + y^2$, only if $z = 2$. If $z = 4$, we have $2x^2 + y^2 = 4$, which is another ellipse. In fact, for all positive values of z, an ellipse results. Negative values for z are not possible, since neither

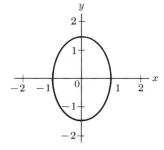

FIGURE 9–1

x^2 nor y^2 may be negative. Figure 9–2 shows the ellipses obtained by using the indicated values of z.

The method of representation illustrated in Example A is useful if only a few certain values of z are to be used, or at least if the various curves do not intersect such that they cannot be distinguished. If a general representation of z as a function of x and y is desired, it is necessary to use three coordinate axes, one each for x, y, and z. The most widely applicable system of this kind is to place a third coordinate axis at right angles to each of the x- and y-axes. In this way we employ three dimensions for the representation.

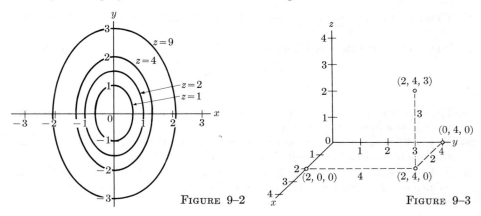

FIGURE 9–2   FIGURE 9–3

The three mutually perpendicular axes, the x-axis, the y-axis, and the z-axis, are the basis of the *rectangular coordinate system in three dimensions*. Together they form three mutually perpendicular planes in space, the xy-plane, the yz-plane, and the xz-plane. To every point in the space of the coordinate systems is associated the set of numbers (x, y, z). The point at which the axes meet is the origin. The positive directions of the axes are indicated in Fig. 9–3. That part of space in which all the values are positive is called the first *octant*. Numbers are not assigned to the other octants.

Example B. Represent the point $(2, 4, 3)$ in rectangular coordinates.

It is first noted that a certain distortion is necessary to reasonably represent values of x, since the x-axis "comes out" of the plane of the page. Units $\sqrt{2}/2$ ($=0.7$) as long as those used on the other axes give a good representation. With this in mind, we draw a line 4 units long from the point $(2, 0, 0)$ on the x-axis in the xy-plane. This locates the point $(2, 4, 0)$. From this point a line 3 units long is drawn vertically upward. This locates the desired point $(2, 4, 3)$. The point may be located by starting from $(0, 4, 0)$, proceeding two units *parallel* to the x-axis to $(2, 4, 0)$ and then vertically three units to $(2, 4, 3)$. It may also be located by starting from $(0, 0, 3)$. See Fig. 9–3.

The remainder of this section is devoted to showing certain basic techniques by which three-dimensional figures may be drawn. We start by showing the general equation of a plane.

In Chapter 1 we showed that the graph of the equation $Ax + By + C = 0$ in two dimensions is a straight line. By the following example, we will verify that the graph of the equation

$$Ax + By + Cz + D = 0 \qquad (9\text{--}1)$$

is a plane in three dimensions.

Example C. Show that the graph of the equation $2x + 3y + z - 6 = 0$ in three dimensions is a plane.

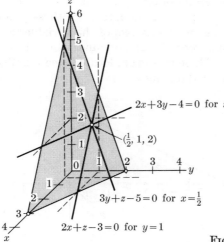

FIGURE 9–4

If we let any of the three variables take on a specific value, we obtain a linear equation in the other two variables. For example, the point $(\frac{1}{2}, 1, 2)$ satisfies the equation, and therefore lies on the graph of the equation. For $x = \frac{1}{2}$, we have

$$3y + z - 5 = 0$$

which is the equation of a straight line. This means that all pairs of values of y and z which satisfy this equation, along with $x = \frac{1}{2}$, satisfy the given equation. Thus, for $x = \frac{1}{2}$, the straight line $3y + z - 5 = 0$ lies on the graph of the equation.

For $z = 2$, we have

$$2x + 3y - 4 = 0$$

which is also a straight line. By similar reasoning this line lies on the graph of the equation. Since two lines through a point define a plane, these lines through $(\frac{1}{2}, 1, 2)$ define a plane. This plane is the graph of the equation. See Fig. 9–4.

To complete the verification, it can be seen that for any point on the graph, there is a straight line parallel to one of the coordinate planes which lies on the graph. Thus, regardless of the point chosen, intersecting straight lines through the point which lie on the graph exist. Thus, the graph is a plane. Also, a similar analysis could be made for any equation of the same form.

Since we know that the graph of an equation of the form of Eq. (9–1) is a plane, its graph can be found by determining its three intercepts, and the plane can then be represented by drawing in the lines between these intercepts. If the plane passes through the origin, by letting two of the variables in turn be zero, two straight lines which define the plane are found.

Example D. Sketch the graph of $3x - y + 2z - 4 = 0$.

The intercepts of the graph of an equation are those points where it crosses the respective axes. Thus, by letting two of the variables equal zero at a time, we obtain the intercepts. For the given equation the intercepts are $(\frac{4}{3}, 0, 0)$, $(0, -4, 0)$ and $(0, 0, 2)$. These points are located (see Fig. 9–5) and lines drawn between them to represent the plane.

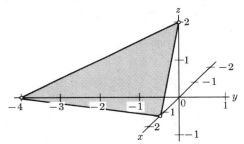

FIGURE 9–5

In general the graph of an equation in three variables, which is essentially equivalent to a function with two independent variables, is a *surface* in space. This is seen in the case of the plane, and will be verified for other cases in the examples which follow.

The intersection of two surfaces is a curve in space. This has been seen in Examples C and D, since the intersection of the given planes and the coordinate planes are lines (which in the general sense are curves). We define the *traces* of a surface to be the curves of intersection of the surface and the coordinate planes. The traces of a plane are those lines drawn between the intercepts to represent the plane. Many surfaces may be sketched by finding its traces and intercepts.

Example E. Find the intercepts and traces and sketch the graph of the equation $z = 4 - x^2 - y^2$.

The intercepts of the graph of the equation are $(2, 0, 0)$, $(-2, 0,0)$, $(0, 2, 0)$, $(0, -2, 0)$, and $(0, 0, 4)$.

Since the traces of a surface lie within the coordinate planes, for each trace one of the variables is zero. Thus, by letting each variable in turn be zero, we find the trace of the surface in the plane of the other two variables. Therefore, the traces of this surface are

in the yz-plane: $z = 4 - y^2$ (a parabola),
in the xz-plane: $z = 4 - x^2$ (a parabola),
in the xy-plane: $x^2 + y^2 = 4$ (a circle).

Using the intercepts and sketching the traces (see Fig. 9–6), we obtain the surface of the equation. This figure is called a *circular paraboloid*.

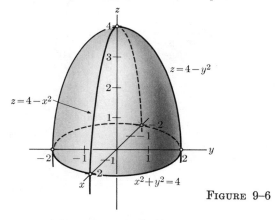

FIGURE 9–6

There are numerous techniques in analyzing the equation of a surface in order to obtain its graph. Another which we shall discuss here, which is closely associated to a trace, is that of a *section*. By assuming a specific value of one of the variables, we obtain an equation in two variables, the graph of which lies in a plane parallel to the coordinate plane of the two variables. The following example illustrates sketching a surface by use of intercepts, traces, and sections.

Example F. Sketch the graph of $4x^2 + y^2 - z^2 = 4$.

The intercepts are $(1, 0, 0)$, $(-1, 0, 0)$, $(0, 2, 0)$, and $(0, -2, 0)$. It is noted that there are no intercepts on the z-axis, for this would necessitate $z^2 = -4$.

The traces are

in the yz-plane: $y^2 - z^2 = 4$ (a hyperbola),
in the xz-plane: $4x^2 - z^2 = 4$ (a hyperbola),
in the xy-plane: $4x^2 + y^2 = 4$ (an ellipse).

The surface is reasonably defined by these curves, but, by assuming suitable values of z, we may indicate its shape better. For example, if $z = 3$, we have $4x^2 + y^2 = 13$, which is an ellipse. In using it we must remember that it is valid for $z = 3$ and therefore should be drawn 3 units above the xy-plane. If $z = -2$, we have $4x^2 + y^2 = 8$, which is also an ellipse. Thus, we have the sections

$$\text{for } z = 3: 4x^2 + y^2 = 13 \text{ (an ellipse)},$$
$$\text{for } z = -2: 4x^2 + y^2 = 8 \text{ (an ellipse)}.$$

Other sections could be found, but these are sufficient to obtain a good sketch of the graph. See Fig. 9–7. The figure is called an *elliptic hyperboloid*.

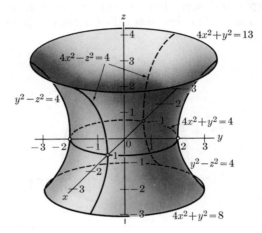

FIGURE 9–7

An equation with only two variables may represent a surface in space. Since only two variables are included in the equation, the surface is independent of the other variable. Another interpretation is that all sections, for all values of the variable not included, are the same. That is, all sections parallel to the coordinate plane of the included variables are the same as the trace in that plane. The following example illustrates this type of *cylindrical surface*.

FIGURE 9–8

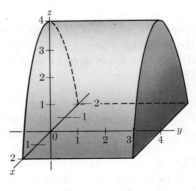

FIGURE 9–9

Example G. The graph of the equation $x^2 + 4y^2 = 4$ in three dimensions is a cylindrical surface, whose sections, for all values of z, are given by the ellipse $x^2 + 4y^2 = 4$. See Fig. 9–8.

The graph of the equation $z = 4 - x^2$ in three dimensions is a cylindrical surface, whose sections, for all values of y, are given by the parabola $z = 4 - x^2$. See Fig. 9–9.

It must be realized that most of the figures shown extend beyond the range indicated by the traces and sections. However, these are convenient for representing and visualizing the surfaces.

Exercises

In Exercises 1 through 4, use the method of Example A, and draw the graphs of the indicated equations for the given values of z.

1. $z = x^2 + y^2, z = 1, z = 4, z = 9$ 2. $z = x - 2y, z = -2, z = 2, z = 5$
3. $z = y - x^2, z = 0, z = 2, z = 4$ 4. $z = x^2 - 4y^2, z = -4, z = 1, z = 4$

Sketch the graphs of the equations given in Exercises 5 through 22 in the rectangular coordinate system in three dimensions.

5. $x + y + 2z - 4 = 0$ 6. $2x - y - z + 6 = 0$
7. $4x - 2y + z - 8 = 0$ 8. $3x + 3y - 2z - 6 = 0$
9. $z = y - 2x - 2$ 10. $z = x - 4y$
11. $x^2 + y^2 + z^2 = 4$ 12. $2x^2 + 2y^2 + z^2 = 8$
13. $z = 4 - 4x^2 - y^2$ 14. $z = x^2 + y^2$
15. $z = 2x^2 + y^2 + 2$ 16. $x^2 + y^2 - 4z^2 = 4$
17. $x^2 - y^2 - z^2 = 9$ 18. $z^2 = 9x^2 + 4y^2$
19. $x^2 + y^2 = 16$ 20. $4z = x^2$ 21. $y^2 + 9z^2 = 9$ 22. $xy = 2$

23. Sketch the line in space defined by the intersection of the planes

$$x + 2y + 3z - 6 = 0 \quad \text{and} \quad 2x + y + z - 4 = 0.$$

24. Sketch the curve in space defined by the intersection of the surfaces

$$x^2 + (z - 1)^2 = 1 \quad \text{and} \quad z = 4 - x^2 - y^2.$$

25. An electric charge is so distributed that the electric potential at all points on an imaginary surface is the same. Such a surface is called an *equipotential surface.* Sketch the graph of the equipotential surface whose equation is $2x^2 + 2y^2 + 3z^2 = 6$.

26. For a certain gas, the pressure, volume, and temperature are related by the equation $p = T/2V$, where p is measured in atmospheres, T in °K, and V in liters. Sketch the p-V-T surface, by using the z-axis for p, the x-axis for V, and the y-axis for T. Use units of 100°K for T, 10 atm for p, and 10 liters for V. Sections must be used to sketch this surface, a *thermodynamic surface,* since none of the variables may equal zero.

9–3 Partial derivatives

When we developed the concept of the derivative in Chapter 2, we showed that we were dealing with the rate of change of one variable with respect to another. However, only one independent variable was involved. In order to extend the derivative and its applications to functions of two (or more) variables, we find the derivative of the function with respect to one of the independent variables, while the other is held constant. If $z = f(x, y)$, this is equivalent to saying, for example, that for a specified value of y, we have the derivative of z with respect to x.

Therefore, if $z = f(x, y)$, and y is kept constant, z becomes a function of x alone. The derivative of this function with respect to x is termed *the partial derivative of z with respect to x*. Similarly, if $z = f(x, y)$ and x is kept constant, the derivative of the resulting function with respect to y is the *partial derivative of z with respect to y*.

The notation $\partial z/\partial x$ is the most common notation to denote "the partial derivative of z with respect to x," although z_x and $f_x(x, y)$ are also used. Similarly, $\partial z/\partial y$ denotes "the partial derivative of z with respect to y." Often in speaking, this is shortened to "the partial of z with respect to y."

Example A. If $z = 4x^2 + xy - y^2$, find $\partial z/\partial x$ and $\partial z/\partial y$.

$$\frac{\partial z}{\partial x} = 8x + y \qquad \text{and} \qquad \frac{\partial z}{\partial y} = x - 2y.$$

Example B. If $y = e^x \cos t - e^{-x} \sin t$, find $\partial y/\partial x$ and $\partial y/\partial t$.

$$\frac{\partial y}{\partial x} = e^x \cos t + e^{-x} \sin t \qquad \text{and} \qquad \frac{\partial y}{\partial t} = -e^x \sin t - e^{-x} \cos t.$$

To determine the geometric interpretation of a partial derivative, assume that $z = f(x, y)$ is the surface shown in Fig. 9–10. Choosing a point P on the surface, we then draw a plane through P parallel to the xz-plane. On this plane through P, the value of y is constant. The intersection of this plane and the surface is the curve as indicated. The partial derivative of z with respect to x represents the slope of a line tangent to this curve. When the values of the coordinates of point P are substituted into the expression which is the partial derivative, it gives the slope of the tangent line at that point. In the same way, the partial

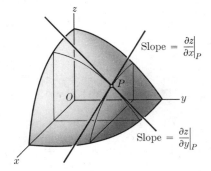

FIGURE 9–10

derivative of z with respect to y, evaluated at P, gives the slope of the line tangent to the curve which is found from the intersection of the surface and the plane parallel to the yz-plane through P.

Example C. Find the slope of a line tangent to the surface $2z = x^2 + 2y^2$ and parallel to the xz-plane at the point $(2, 1, 3)$. Also find the slope of a line tangent to this surface and parallel to the yz-plane at the same point.

Finding the partial derivative of z with respect to x we have

$$2\frac{\partial z}{\partial x} = 2x \qquad \text{or} \qquad \frac{\partial z}{\partial x} = x.$$

This derivative, evaluated at the point $(2, 1, 3)$ will give us the slope of the line tangent which is also parallel to the xz-plane. Thus, the first required slope is

$$\left.\frac{\partial z}{\partial x}\right|_{(2,1,3)} = 2.$$

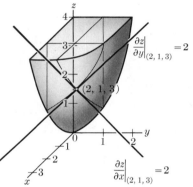

The partial derivative of z with respect to y, evaluated at $(2, 1, 3)$ will give us the second required slope. Thus,

$$\frac{\partial z}{\partial y} = 2y, \qquad \left.\frac{\partial z}{\partial y}\right|_{(2,1,3)} = 2.$$

Therefore, both slopes are 2. See Fig. 9–11.

FIGURE 9–11

Applications of partial derivatives are found in various fields of technology. Vacuum tube and transistor characteristics are defined in terms of partial derivatives, as are numerous quantities in thermodynamics. We present here an application from electronics, while others are found in the exercises.

Example D. A triode is an electronic vacuum tube, which consists essentially of a cathode, from which electrons are emitted, a plate, to which the electrons travel, and a grid, a controlling device located between the cathode and plate. The plate current is a function of the plate voltage and the grid voltage. Certain tube characteristics are defined as partial derivatives of one of these with respect to another. One of these tube characteristics is the mutual conductance g_m, measured in mhos (reciprocal ohms), which is defined as

$$g_m = \frac{\partial i_b}{\partial e_c},$$

where i_b is the plate current and e_c is the grid voltage. For a certain triode, an approximate relation between these and the plate voltage e_b is

$$i_b = 50(e_b + 5e_c)^{1.5} \times 10^{-6} \text{ amp.}$$

If the tube is operated such that $e_b = 200$ volts and $e_c = -20$ volts, find g_m.

By finding the indicated partial derivative, and then evaluating it we may determine the value of g_m:

$$g_m = \frac{\partial i_b}{\partial e_c} = 50(1.5)(e_b + 5e_c)^{0.5}(5) \times 10^{-6}$$

$$= 375(e_b + 5e_c)^{0.5} \times 10^{-6}.$$

Evaluating for the given values of e_b and e_c we have

$$g_m = 375(200 - 100)^{0.5} \times 10^{-6}$$

$$= 3750 \times 10^{-6} = 3.75 \times 10^{-3} \text{ mhos.}$$

Exercises

In Exercises 1 through 12, find the partial derivative of the dependent variable or function with respect to each of the independent variables.

1. $z = 5x + 4x^2y$

2. $z = \dfrac{x^2}{y} - 2xy$

3. $\varphi = r\sqrt{1 + 2rs}$

4. $f(x, y) = \dfrac{x + y}{x - y}$

5. $z = (x^2 + xy^3)^4$

6. $u = e^{x+2y}$

7. $z = \sin xy$

8. $y = \text{Arctan}\left(\dfrac{x}{t}\right)$

9. $y = \ln(r^2 + s)$

10. $z = \sin x + \cos xy - \cos y$

11. $f(x, y) = e^x \cos xy + e^{-2x} \tan y$

12. $u = \ln\dfrac{y^2}{x - y} + e^{-x}(\sin y - \cos 2y)$

In Exercises 13 through 16, evaluate the indicated partial derivatives at the given points.

13. $z = 3xy - x^2 + y$, $\dfrac{\partial z}{\partial x}\bigg|_{(1,-2,-9)}$

14. $z = x\sqrt{x^2 - y^2}$, $\dfrac{\partial z}{\partial x}\bigg|_{(5,3,20)}$

15. $z = e^y \ln xy$, $\dfrac{\partial z}{\partial y}\bigg|_{(e,1,e)}$

16. $F(r, \varphi) = r^2 \sin 4\varphi$, $F_\varphi\left(2, \dfrac{\pi}{4}\right)$

17. Find the slope of a line, tangent to the surface $z = 9 - x^2 - y^2$, parallel to the yz-plane, which passes through $(1, 2, 4)$. Repeat the instructions for the line through $(2, 2, 1)$. Draw an appropriate figure.

18. Find $\partial z/\partial y$ for the function $z = 4x^2 - 8$. Explain your result. Draw an appropriate figure.

19. Two resistors R_1 and R_2, placed in parallel, have a combined resistance R_T given by

$$\frac{1}{R_T} = \frac{1}{R_1} + \frac{1}{R_2}.$$

Find $\partial R_T/\partial R_1$.

20. For a gas, the isothermal bulk modulus B, a measure of compressibility, is given by

$$B = -V \left(\frac{\partial P}{\partial V}\right).$$

If the pressure, volume, and temperature are related by van der Waals equation

$$\left(P + \frac{a}{V^2}\right) (V - b) = RT,$$

where a, b, and R are constants, find the expression for B.

21. The plate resistance r_p, measured in ohms, another of the triode characteristics, is defined as

$$r_p = \frac{\partial e_b}{\partial i_b}.$$

For the triode described in Example D, find r_p.

22. The amplification factor μ, a third triode characteristic, is defined as

$$\mu = -\frac{\partial e_b}{\partial e_c}.$$

For the triode described in Example D, find μ.

23. The coefficient of linear expansion α of a wire whose length is a function of the tension and temperature is given by

$$\alpha = \frac{1}{L} \left(\frac{\partial L}{\partial T}\right),$$

where L is the length and T is the temperature. If L is a function of T and the tension F given by the relation

$$L = L_0 + k_1 F + k_2 T + k_3 F T^2,$$

where k_1, k_2, k_3, and L_0 are constants, find the expression for α.

24. An isothermal process is one during which the temperature does not change. If the pressure, volume, and temperature of an ideal gas are related by the equation

$$pV = nRT,$$

where n and R are constants, find the expression for $\partial p/\partial V$, which would be the rate of change of pressure with respect to volume for an isothermal process.

25. The fundamental frequency of vibration of a string varies directly as the square root of the tension T and inversely as the length L. If a string 60 cm long is under a tension of 6.5×10^6 dynes and has a fundamental frequency of 30 cycles/sec, find the partial derivative of f with respect to T, and evaluate it for the given values.

9–4 Certain applications of partial derivatives

We noted some important areas of application of partial derivatives in the last section. However, as we found that we can apply the derivative to problems such as related rates, applied maximum and minimum problems, and error calculations by the use of differentials, we can also solve similar problems by the use of partial derivatives. In this section we shall show how to calculate the differential of a function of two variables and apply it to certain applied situations. Then we will discuss applied maximum and minimum problems for functions of two variables.

In Section 4–1 we defined the differential of a function of one variable as

$$dy = f'(x) \, dx.$$

In a similar manner, we define the *total differential* of a function $z = f(x, y)$ to be

$$dz = \frac{\partial z}{\partial x} \, dx + \frac{\partial z}{\partial y} \, dy. \tag{9–2}$$

It will be noted that this definition is consistent with our original definition of the differential, in that if y is constant, $dz = (\partial z/\partial x) \, dx$. Also, if x is constant, $dz = (\partial z/\partial y) \, dy$. Therefore, each term measures the differential of z, with respect to one of the independent variables, assuming the other is constant.

Example A. Find the expression for the total differential of the function $z = x^3y + x^2y^2 - 3xy^3$:

$$\frac{\partial z}{\partial x} = 3x^2y + 2xy^2 - 3y^3,$$

$$\frac{\partial z}{\partial y} = x^3 + 2x^2y - 9xy^2.$$

Therefore,

$$dz = (3x^2y + 2xy^2 - 3y^3) \, dx + (x^3 + 2x^2y - 9xy^2) \, dy.$$

We found that we could apply the differential of a function of one variable to finding changes in the value of the function for small changes in the independent variable. This led to applied problems in error calculations. We may also apply the total differential of a function of two variables in the same manner. The following examples illustrate the method.

Example B. The power delivered to a resistor in an electric circuit is given by $P = i^2R$. Find the approximate change in power if the current changes from 4.0 to 4.1 amps, and the resistance from 22.0 to 22.4 ohms.

By finding dP and evaluating the expression for $i = 4.0$, $di = 0.1$, $R = 22.0$, and $dR = 0.4$, we will have the desired result:

$$dP = \frac{\partial P}{\partial i}\, di + \frac{\partial P}{\partial R}\, dR$$

$$= (2iR)di + (i^2)dR.$$

Evaluating we have

$$dP = [2(4.0)(22.0)](0.1) + (4.0)^2(0.4)$$

$$= 17.6 + 6.4 = 24 \text{ watts.}$$

Therefore, the approximate change in the power is 24 watts.

Example C. A conical funnel, with a very small opening, was to be constructed such that the diameter across the top was 10 cm and the depth 6 cm. However, in the construction, the diameter was made only 9.8 cm and the depth 5.8 cm. What percentage error in the volume of liquid which the funnel will hold resulted?

The volume of a cone as a function of its radius and height is

$$V = \tfrac{1}{3}\pi r^2 h.$$

Finding dV, we have

$$dV = (\tfrac{2}{3}\pi rh)\, dr + (\tfrac{1}{3}\pi r^2)\, dh.$$

Using the values $r = 5.0$ cm, $dr = 0.1$ cm, $h = 6.0$ cm, and $dh = 0.2$ cm, we have

$$dV = \tfrac{2}{3}\pi(5.0)(6.0)(0.1) + \tfrac{1}{3}\pi(25)(0.2)$$

$$= 2\pi + \frac{5\pi}{3} = 11.5 \text{ cm}^3.$$

Calculating the intended volume V, we have

$$V = \tfrac{1}{3}\pi(25)(6) = 50\pi = 157 \text{ cm}^3.$$

The percentage error in the volume is

$$100\left(\frac{dV}{V}\right) = 100\left(\frac{11.5}{157}\right) = 7.3\%.$$

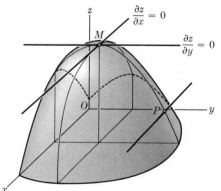

FIGURE 9–12

We will now consider the problem of finding the maximum value or the minimum value of a function of two variables. Considering the geometric interpretation of the maximum value of a function of two variables, we note the surface indicated in Fig. 9–12.

At the maximum point M, a line tangent to the surface, *in any direction*, must be horizontal. This means that

$$\frac{\partial z}{\partial x} = 0 \quad \text{and} \quad \frac{\partial z}{\partial y} = 0. \tag{9-3}$$

That just either of these partial derivatives be zero is not sufficient. Observe point P where $\partial z / \partial x = 0$ also. Actually, a complete analysis requires more than that shown in Eqs. (9–3), but this is beyond that which we can develop here. We shall consider only functions for which Eqs. (9–3) are sufficient to find the maximum and minimum points.

Of course, Eqs. (9–3) will hold for a minimum point as well as a maximum point. By using the first derivative test in one of the sections of the surface containing the point, the determination of whether the point is a maximum or a minimum can be made. The following example illustrates the use of Eqs. (9–3).

Example D. Examine the function $z = x^2 + 2xy + 2y^2 - 4x$ for maximum and minimum points.

First, finding the partial derivatives, we have

$$\frac{\partial z}{\partial x} = 2x + 2y - 4 \quad \text{and} \quad \frac{\partial z}{\partial y} = 2x + 4y.$$

Setting these expressions equal to zero, we obtain the equations

$$2x + 2y - 4 = 0,$$

$$2x + 4y = 0.$$

Since these equations must hold at the same point, we solve them simultaneously. This gives us $x = 4$ and $y = -2$. Testing the section where $y = -2$, we find

$$\frac{\partial z}{\partial x} = 2x - 8.$$

Thus, when $x < 4$, $\partial z / \partial x < 0$, and when $x > 4$, $\partial z / \partial x > 0$. This means that the point $(4, -2, -8)$ is a minimum point, since, as x increases, $\partial z / \partial x$ changes from negative to positive.

We shall now show an example of an applied maximum and minimum problem involving a function of two variables.

Example E. A rectangular box is to be made of material such that the base costs twice as much per square inch as the sides and top. Find the dimensions of the box if it is to hold 324 in^3.

Assuming the length, width, and height of the box to be l, w, and h, respectively, we may write the equations for the volume and cost in terms of these quantities. The equation for the volume is

$$324 = lwh. \tag{1}$$

Since the cost per square inch was not actually given, let us assume the cost for the sides and top is a cents/in^2, which means that of the base is $2a$ cents/in^2. Thus, the expression for the cost is

$$C = 2a(lw) + a(lw + 2wh + 2lh)$$
$$= a(3lw + 2wh + 2lh). \tag{2}$$

Solving Eq. (1) for h, and substituting this into Eq. (2), we may express C as a function of l and w:

$$C = a\left(3lw + \frac{648}{l} + \frac{648}{w}\right). \tag{3}$$

Taking partial derivatives of C with respect to l and w, we may find the values of l and w which give the minimum cost. From these values we then can find h:

$$\frac{\partial C}{\partial w} = a\left(3l - \frac{648}{w^2}\right),$$

$$\frac{\partial C}{\partial l} = a\left(3w - \frac{648}{l^2}\right). \tag{4}$$

Setting each of these expressions equal to zero, we obtain the following equations:

$$l = \frac{216}{w^2}, \qquad w = \frac{216}{l^2}.$$

Substituting the expression for l into the solution for w we have

$$w = \frac{216}{\left(\dfrac{216}{w^2}\right)^2} = \frac{w^4}{216},$$

$$w^3 = 216, \qquad w = 6 \text{ in.}$$

Substituting, we find $l = 6$ in. and $h = 9$ in. Equation (3) shows that the maximum cost is unbounded, because of the l and w in the denominators, which means the solution we obtained must represent a minimum. Also, the first derivative test used on either of Eqs. (4) will demonstrate that the solution is a minimum.

Exercises

In Exercises 1 through 6, find the total differential of the given functions.

1. $z = 2x^2 - y^2 + 3x$
2. $z = xy - 3yx^2 + y^3$
3. $z = \sin xy - y \cos x$

4. $z = \dfrac{\sec x^2}{x - y}$
5. $z = y \operatorname{Arctan} \dfrac{y}{x^2}$
6. $z = e^{2xy} \ln (x^2 + y^2)$

In Exercises 7 through 10, examine the given functions for maximum and minimum points.

7. $z = x^2 + y^2 - 2x - 6y + 10$
8. $z = x^2 + xy + y^2 + 3x - 3y + 1$

9. $z = x^2 + xy + y^2 - 3y + 2$
10. $z = x^4 - 4x + y^2$

11. The centripetal acceleration of an object moving in a circular path is given by $a = r\omega^2$, where r is the radius of the circle and ω is the angular velocity. Find the approximate change in the centripetal acceleration if the radius changes from 10.0 cm to 10.3 cm, and the angular velocity changes from 400 to 406 rad/min.

12. The current i through a resistor R which has a voltage V across it is $i = V/R$. Find the approximate change in current, in amps, if the voltage changes from 220 to 225 volts and the resistance changes from 20 to 21 ohms.

13. The index of refraction of a medium is defined as $n = \sin i/\sin r$, where i is the angle of incidence of light on the surface of the medium and r is the angle of refraction. In a particular experiment, n was calculated from values of $i = 45°$ and $r = 30°$. Then, an error was discovered and each angle was 1° too high. What was the approximate percentage error in the calculated value of n?

14. The electric current in a circuit containing a variable resistor R and an inductance of 10 henrys is a function of R and the time t given by $i = 10(1 - e^{-(Rt/10)})$. Find the approximate percentage change in current as R changes from 2.00 ohms to 2.04 ohms between $t = 10$ sec and $t = 11$ sec.

15. Two sides and the included angle of a triangular machine part were measured to be 2.30 cm, 2.10 cm, and 90°, respectively. The length of the third side was calculated from these values. It was then discovered that an error of 0.10 cm was made in each of the sides. What was the percentage error in the calculation of the third side?

16. If the radius and height of a right circular cylindrical container were measured to be 3.00 ft and 5.00 ft, and then the radius was found to be 3.10 ft and the height 5.20 ft, what was the error in the original value of the volume?

17. Find three positive numbers, whose sum is 120, such that their product is a maximum.

18. A flat plate is heated such that the temperature T at any point (x, y) is
$$T = x^2 + 2y^2 - x.$$
Find the temperature at the coldest point.

19. An open rectangular box is to be made to contain 500 in³. What dimensions will require the least material in building it?

20. A long metal strip 9 in. wide is to be made into a trough by bending up equal edges, making equal angles with the bottom. Find the width of the bottom and the angle between the bottom and the edges if the volume of the trough is a maximum.

21. If x, y, and z are functions of the time t, and we divide each term of Eq. (9–2) by the differential of t, dt, we obtain an equation for the *total derivative* of z with respect to t. Thus, the total derivative is

$$\frac{dz}{dt} = \frac{\partial z}{\partial x}\frac{dx}{dt} + \frac{\partial z}{\partial y}\frac{dy}{dt}. \tag{9–4}$$

If the radius and height of a right circular cylinder are increasing at the rate of 0.05 ft/sec and 0.20 ft/sec, respectively, find the rate at which the volume is increasing when $r = 6.00$ ft and $h = 3.00$ ft, by use of Eq. (9–4).

9–5 Double integrals

We now turn our attention to integration in the case of a function of two variables. The analysis has similarities to that of partial differentiation, in that an operation is performed while holding one of the independent variables constant.

If $z = f(x, y)$ and we wish to integrate with respect to x and y, we first consider either x or y constant, and integrate with respect to the other. After this integral is evaluated, we then integrate with respect to the variable first held constant. We shall now define this type of integral, and then give an appropriate geometric interpretation.

If $z = f(x, y)$, the *double integral* of the function over x and y is defined as

$$\int_a^b \left[\int_{g(x)}^{G(x)} f(x, y)\, dy \right] dx.$$

It will be noted that the limits on the inner integral are *functions* of x and those on the outer integral are explicit values of x. In performing the integration, x is held constant while the inner integral is found and evaluated. This results in a function of x only. This function is then integrated and evaluated.

It is customary not to include the brackets in stating a double integral. Therefore we write

$$\int_a^b \left[\int_{g(x)}^{G(x)} f(x, y)\, dy \right] dx = \int_a^b \int_{g(x)}^{G(x)} f(x, y)\, dy\, dx. \tag{9–5}$$

Example A. Evaluate $\int_0^1 \int_{x^2}^{x} xy\, dy\, dx$.

Integrating and evaluating the inner integral, we have

$$\int_{x^2}^{x} xy\, dy = \left. \left(x\frac{y^2}{2} \right) \right|_{x^2}^{x} = x\left(\frac{x^2}{2} - \frac{x^4}{2} \right)$$

$$= \tfrac{1}{2}(x^3 - x^5).$$

This means

$$\int_0^1 \int_{x^2}^x xy\, dy\, dx = \int_0^1 \frac{1}{2}(x^3 - x^5)\, dx = \frac{1}{2}\left(\frac{x^4}{4} - \frac{x^6}{6}\right)\Big|_0^1$$

$$= \frac{1}{2}\left(\frac{1}{4} - \frac{1}{6}\right) - \frac{1}{2}(0) = \frac{1}{24}.$$

It is also common to have an integral which is integrated over x first and then over y. The following example illustrates such a case.

Example B. Evaluate $\qquad \displaystyle\int_1^4 \int_0^{4y} \sqrt{2x + y}\, dx\, dy.$

Integrating and evaluating, we have

$$\int_1^4 \int_0^{4y} \sqrt{2x + y}\, dx\, dy = \int_1^4 \left[\frac{1}{2}\int_0^{4y} (2x + y)^{1/2} 2\, dx\right] dy$$

$$= \int_1^4 \left[\tfrac{1}{3}(2x + y)^{3/2}\right]_0^{4y} dy$$

$$= \frac{1}{3}\int_1^4 [(9y)^{3/2} - (y)^{3/2}]\, dy$$

$$= \frac{1}{3}\int_1^4 (27y^{3/2} - y^{3/2})\, dy = \frac{26}{3}\int_1^4 y^{3/2}\, dy$$

$$= \frac{26}{3}\cdot\frac{2}{5} y^{5/2}\Big|_1^4 = \frac{52}{15}(32 - 1) = \frac{1612}{15}.$$

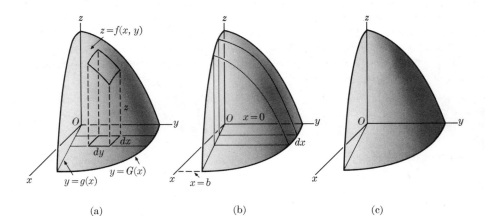

(a)   (b)   (c)

FIGURE 9–13

To understand the geometric interpretation of a double integral, consider the surface shown in Fig. 9–13(a). Now consider an *element of volume* (as shown), of dimensions dx, dy, and z, which extends from the xy plane to the surface. We now make x a constant and sum (integrate) these elements of volume from the left boundary, $y = g(x)$, to the right boundary, $y = G(x)$. In this way we have the volume of the vertical slice as shown in Fig. 9–13(b). Now, by summing (integrating) the volumes of these slices from $x = a$ ($x = 0$ in the figure) to $x = b$, we have the complete volume as shown in Fig. 9–13(c).

Therefore, we may interpret a double integral as the *volume under a surface*, in the same way as the integral was interpreted as the area of a plane figure. It will be noted that this is not necessarily a volume of revolution, as discussed in Section 5–3. This means we may find the volume of a more general figure than previously possible. The following examples illustrate finding volumes by use of double integrals.

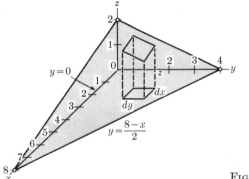

FIGURE 9–14

Example C. Find the volume in the first octant under the plane

$$x + 2y + 4z - 8 = 0.$$

See Fig. 9–14.

This figure is a tetrahedron, for which $V = \frac{1}{3}Bh$. Assuming the base is in the xy-plane, $B = \frac{1}{2}(4)(8) = 16$, and $h = 2$. Therefore, $V = \frac{1}{3}(16)(2) = \frac{32}{3}$ cubic units. We shall use this value to check that which we find by double integration.

To find $z = f(x, y)$, we solve the given equation for z. Thus

$$z = \frac{8 - x - 2y}{4}.$$

Next, we must find the limits on y and x. Choosing to integrate over y first, we see that y goes from $y = 0$ to $y = (8 - x)/2$. This last limit is the trace of the surface in the xy-plane. Next we note that x goes from $x = 0$ to $x = 8$.

Therefore, we set up and evaluate the integral:

$$V = \int_0^8 \int_0^{(8-x)/2} \left(\frac{8-x-2y}{4}\right) dy\, dx$$

$$= \int_0^8 \left[\tfrac{1}{4}\left(8y - xy - y^2\right)\Big|_0^{(8-x)/2}\right] dx$$

$$= \frac{1}{4}\int_0^8 \left[8\left(\frac{8-x}{2}\right) - x\left(\frac{8-x}{2}\right) - \left(\frac{8-x}{2}\right)^2\right] dx$$

$$= \frac{1}{4}\int_0^8 \left(32 - 4x - 4x + \frac{x^2}{2} - 16 + 4x - \frac{x^2}{4}\right) dx$$

$$= \frac{1}{4}\int_0^8 \left(16 - 4x + \frac{x^2}{4}\right) dx = \frac{1}{4}\left(16x - 2x^2 + \frac{x^3}{12}\right)\Big|_0^8$$

$$= \tfrac{1}{4}(128 - 128 + \tfrac{512}{12}) = \tfrac{1}{4}(\tfrac{128}{3}) = \tfrac{32}{3} \text{ cubic units.}$$

We see that the values by the two different methods agree.

Example D. Find the volume above the xy-plane, below the surface $z = xy$, and enclosed by the cylinder $y = x^2$ and the plane $y = x$.

Constructing the figure, shown in Fig. 9–15, we now note that $z = xy$ is the desired function of x and y. Integrating over y first, the limits on y are $y = x^2$ to $y = x$. The corresponding limits on x are $x = 0$ to $x = 1$. Thus, the integral is

$$V = \int_0^1 \int_{x^2}^x xy\, dy\, dx.$$

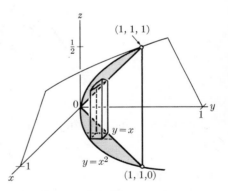

FIGURE 9–15

The evaluation of this integral has already been performed in Example A of this section. Therefore, we see the geometric interpretation of that integral. This means that the required volume is $\frac{1}{24}$ cubic unit.

Example E. Find the volume in the first octant under the surface

$$z = 4 - x^2 - y^2,$$

and between the cylinder $x^2 = 3y$ and the plane $y = 1$. See Fig. 9–16.

Setting up the integration such that we integrate over x first, we have

$$V = \int_0^1 \int_0^{\sqrt{3y}} (4 - x^2 - y^2)\, dx\, dy$$

$$= \int_0^1 \left[4x - \frac{x^3}{3} - y^2 x \right]_0^{\sqrt{3y}} dy$$

$$= \int_0^1 (4\sqrt{3y} - \sqrt{3}y^{3/2} - \sqrt{3}y^{5/2})\, dy$$

$$= \sqrt{3}[4(\tfrac{2}{3})y^{3/2} - \tfrac{2}{5}y^{5/2} - \tfrac{2}{7}y^{7/2}]|_0^1$$

$$= \sqrt{3}\left(\frac{8}{3} - \frac{2}{5} - \frac{2}{7} \right) = \frac{208\sqrt{3}}{105} \text{ cubic units.}$$

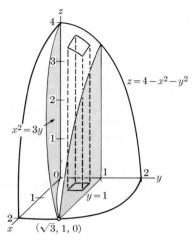

FIGURE 9–16

If we had integrated over y first, the integral would be

$$V = \int_0^{\sqrt{3}} \int_{x^2/3}^1 (4 - x^2 - y^2)\, dy\, dx.$$

Integrating and evaluating this integral, we arrive at the same result,

$$V = \frac{208\sqrt{3}}{105} \text{ cubic units.}$$

Exercises

In Exercises 1 through 10, evaluate the given double integrals.

1. $\displaystyle\int_0^1 \int_0^x 2y\, dy\, dx$

2. $\displaystyle\int_0^2 \int_1^x 2x\, dy\, dx$

3. $\displaystyle\int_1^2 \int_0^{y^2} xy^2\, dx\, dy$

4. $\displaystyle\int_0^4 \int_1^{\sqrt{y}} (x - y)\, dx\, dy$

5. $\displaystyle\int_0^1 \int_0^{\sqrt{1-x^2}} y\, dy\, dx$

6. $\displaystyle\int_4^9 \int_0^x \sqrt{x - y}\, dy\, dx$

7. $\displaystyle\int_0^{\pi/6} \int_{\pi/3}^y \sin x\, dx\, dy$

8. $\displaystyle\int_0^{\sqrt{3}} \int_{x^2/3}^1 (4 - x^2 - y^2)\, dy\, dx$

9. $$\int_0^{\ln 3} \int_0^x e^{2x+3y} \, dy \, dx$$ 10. $$\int_0^{1/2} \int_y^{y^2} \frac{dx \, dy}{\sqrt{y^2 - x^2}}$$

In Exercises 11–18, find the indicated volumes by double integration.

11. The first octant volume under the plane $x + y + z - 4 = 0$.

12. The first octant volume under the surface $z = y^2$ and bounded by the planes $x = 2$ and $y = 3$.

13. The volume above the xy-plane and under the surface $z = 4 - x^2 - y^2$.

14. The volume above the xy-plane, below the surface $z = x^2 + y^2$, and inside the cylinder $x^2 + y^2 = 4$.

15. The first octant volume bounded by the xy-plane, the planes $x = y$, $y = 2$, and $z = 2 + x^2 + y^2$.

16. The volume bounded by the planes $x = 0$, $z = 0$, $2x = y$, and $x + 3y + 2z - 6 = 0$.

17. The first octant volume under the plane $z = x + y$ and inside the cylinder $x^2 + y^2 = 9$.

18. The volume above the xy-plane and bounded by the cylinders $x = y^2$, $y = 8x^2$, and $z = x^2 + 1$. Integrate over y first and then check by integrating over x first.

19. Draw an appropriate figure indicating a volume which is found from the integral

$$\int_0^{1/2} \int_{x^2}^1 (4 - x - 2y) \, dy \, dx.$$

20. Repeat Exercise 19 for the integral

$$\int_1^2 \int_0^{2-y} \sqrt{1 + x^2 + y^2} \, dx \, dy.$$

9–6 Centroids and moments of inertia by double integration

Among the important applications of double integration are those of finding centroids and moments of inertia of plane areas. In this section we shall show how double integration is applied in these cases.

Considering the area shown in Fig. 9–17, we see that we may determine the value of this area from the double integral

$$A = \int_a^b \int_{g(x)}^{G(x)} dy \, dx \qquad (9\text{--}6)$$

This is the case, since, by summing (integrating) the elements of area $dy \, dx$ over y

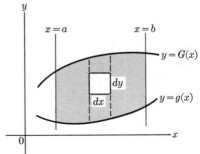

FIGURE 9–17

while holding x constant, we find the area of the vertical strip. Then by summing (integrating) from $x = a$ to $x = b$ we find the total area.

In Section 5–4, we showed that the moment of an area with respect to the y-axis is $kx\,dA$, where k is the mass per unit area, x is the moment arm, and dA is the element of area. Recalling that the x-coordinate of the centroid is the moment with respect to the y-axis, divided by the area, we have

$$\bar{x} = \frac{\int_a^b \int_{g(x)}^{G(x)} x \, dy \, dx}{A} \tag{9–7}$$

as the equation by which we may find the x-coordinate of the centroid by double integration.

Also, since the moment of the area with respect to the x-axis is $ky\,dA$, the y coordinate of the centroid is found from

$$\bar{y} = \frac{\int_a^b \int_{g(x)}^{G(x)} y \, dy \, dx}{A}. \tag{9–8}$$

For many problems, use of Eqs. (9–7) and (9–8) is more convenient than the equivalent method in Section 5–4. One advantage is that the integration is often simplified. The following example illustrates the use of Eqs. (9–7) and (9–8).

Example A. Find the centroid of the area bounded by the lines $y = 2x$, $y = 3 - x$, and $x = 0$. See Fig. 9–18.

$$A = \int_0^1 \int_{2x}^{3-x} dy \, dx = \int_0^1 y \Big|_{2x}^{3-x} dx$$

$$= \int_0^1 (3 - 3x) \, dx = 3x - \frac{3x^2}{2} \Big|_0^1 = \frac{3}{2},$$

$$A\bar{x} = \int_0^1 \int_{2x}^{3-x} x \, dy \, dx = \int_0^1 y \Big|_{2x}^{3-x} x \, dx$$

$$= \int_0^1 (3x - 3x^2) \, dx = \frac{3x^2}{2} - x^3 \Big|_0^1 = \frac{1}{2},$$

$$A\bar{y} = \int_0^1 \int_{2x}^{3-x} y \, dy \, dx = \int_0^1 \frac{y^2}{2} \Big|_{2x}^{3-x} dx$$

$$= \frac{1}{2} \int_0^1 (9 - 6x - 3x^2) \, dx = \frac{1}{2} (9x - 3x^2 - x^3) \Big|_0^1 = \frac{5}{2}.$$

Therefore, $\bar{x} = \frac{1}{2} \cdot \frac{2}{3} = \frac{1}{3}$ and $\bar{y} = \frac{5}{2} \cdot \frac{2}{3} = \frac{5}{3}$.

FIGURE 9–18

In many problems, integrating over x first is definitely preferable. The following example illustrates this type of problem.

Example B.   Find the centroid of the area bounded by $x = 2y - y^2$ and the y-axis. See Fig. 9–19.

$$A = \int_0^2 \int_0^{2y-y^2} dx\, dy = \int_0^2 (2y - y^2)\, dy$$

$$= \left[y^2 - \frac{y^3}{3} \right]\Big|_0^2 = \frac{4}{3},$$

$$A\bar{x} = \int_0^2 \int_0^{2y-y^2} x\, dx\, dy = \int_0^2 \frac{x^2}{2}\Big|_0^{2y-y^2}$$

$$= \frac{1}{2} \int_0^2 (4y^2 - 4y^3 + y^4)\, dy$$

$$= \frac{1}{2} \left(\frac{4}{3} y^3 - y^4 + \frac{y^5}{5} \right)\Big|_0^2 = \frac{8}{15},$$

FIGURE 9–19

$$A\bar{y} = \int_0^2 \int_0^{2y-y^2} y\, dx\, dy = \int_0^2 (2y^2 - y^3)\, dy = \left(\frac{2}{3} y^3 - \frac{1}{4} y^4 \right)\Big|_0^2 = \frac{4}{3}.$$

Therefore, $\bar{x} = \frac{8}{15} \cdot \frac{3}{4} = \frac{2}{5}$ and $\bar{y} = \frac{4}{3} \cdot \frac{3}{4} = 1$.

From Section 5–5, we recall that the moment of inertia of an element of area with respect to the y-axis is $I_y = kx^2\, dA$. Therefore, using double integrals to find the moments of inertia of the area indicated in Fig. 9–17, we have (assuming $k = 1$)

$$I_y = \int_a^b \int_{g(x)}^{G(x)} x^2\, dy\, dx \tag{9–9}$$

and

$$I_x = \int_a^b \int_{g(x)}^{G(x)} y^2\, dy\, dx. \tag{9–10}$$

Also, from Section 5–5, the radius of gyration of the area with respect to an axis was defined by $R^2 = I/A$. The following examples illustrate the use of double integrals to find the moment of inertia and radius of gyration of an area.

Example C.   Find I_y and I_x for the area bounded by $y = 2x$ and $y = x^2$. See Fig. 9–20.

FIGURE 9–20

FIGURE 9–21

Setting up the integrals for integration over y first, we solve for I_y and I_x:

$$I_y = \int_0^2 \int_{x^2}^{2x} x^2 \, dy \, dx = \int_0^2 y \Big|_{x^2}^{2x} x^2 \, dx$$

$$= \int_0^2 (2x^3 - x^4) \, dx = \frac{x^4}{2} - \frac{x^5}{5} \Big|_0^2 = \frac{8}{5},$$

$$I_x = \int_0^2 \int_{x^2}^{2x} y^2 \, dy \, dx = \int_0^2 \frac{y^3}{3} \Big|_{x^2}^{2x} dx$$

$$= \frac{1}{3} \int_0^2 (8x^3 - x^6) \, dx = \frac{1}{3} \left(2x^4 - \frac{x^7}{7} \right) \Big|_0^2 = \frac{32}{7}.$$

Example D. Find the radius of gyration with respect to the y-axis for the area bounded by $y = x^3$, $x = 2$, and $y = 0$. See Fig. 9–21.

Since integration is more convenient over y first than over x first, we set up our integrals in this way:

$$A = \int_0^2 \int_0^{x^3} dy \, dx = \int_0^2 y \Big|_0^{x^3} dx = \int_0^2 x^3 \, dx = \frac{x^4}{4} \Big|_0^2 = 4,$$

$$I_y = \int_0^2 \int_0^{x^3} x^2 \, dy \, dx = \int_0^2 y \Big|_0^{x^3} x^2 \, dx = \int_0^2 x^5 \, dx = \frac{x^6}{6} \Big|_0^2 = \frac{32}{3},$$

$$R_y^2 = \frac{32}{3} \cdot \frac{1}{4} = \frac{8}{3}, \quad R_y = \frac{2}{3} \sqrt{6} = 1.63.$$

Exercises

All exercises are to be solved by the use of double integrals. In Exercises 1 through 4, find the coordinates of the centroid of the area bounded by the given curves.

1. $y = 2 - x$, $y = 0$, $x = 0$ 2. $y = x^2$, $y = 4$, $x = 0$

3. $y = 9 - x^2$, $y = 0$, $x = 0$ 4. $y = 2x$, $x = 1$, $x = 2$

5. Find I_y and I_x for the area of Exercise 1.

6. Find I_y and I_x for the area of Exercise 2.

7. Find R_y for the area of Exercise 3.   8. Find R_x for the area of Exercise 4.

9. Find the coordinates of the centroid and R_y for the area bounded by $y = 1 - x^2$, $x = 1$, and $y = 1$.

10. Find R_y for the area bounded by $y = 3 - x$ and $y = 3 + 2x - x^2$.

11. Find the coordinates of the centroid of a right triangle with legs a and b.

12. Find the coordinates of the centroid of a quarter circle of radius a.

13. Find the moment of inertia of a rectangular area with sides a and b with respect to side a. Express the result in terms of the mass of the area.

14. Find the moment of inertia of an isosceles right triangle with respect to one of the legs a. Express the result in terms of the mass of the area.

15. Find the radius of gyration of a rhombus of side 2, if the angle between two adjacent sides is 45°, with respect to one of the sides.

Miscellaneous exercises for Chapter 9

In Exercises 1 through 6, find the partial derivatives of the given functions with respect to each of the independent variables.

1. $z = 5x^3y^2 - 2xy^4$ 2. $u = \dfrac{r}{(r - 3s)^2}$ 3. $z = \sqrt{x^2 - 3y^2}$

4. $q = p \ln (r + 1) - \dfrac{rp}{r + 1}$ 5. $z = \text{Arcsin} \sqrt{x + y}$ 6. $z = ye^{xy} \sin (2x - y)$

In Exercises 7 through 10, evaluate each of the given double integrals.

7. $\displaystyle\int_0^3 \int_1^x (x + 2y) \, dy \, dx$ 8. $\displaystyle\int_1^2 \int_0^{\pi/4} r \sec^2 \theta \, d\theta \, dr$

9. $\displaystyle\int_0^1 \int_0^{2x} x^2 e^{xy} \, dy \, dx$ 10. $\displaystyle\int_{\pi/4}^{\pi/2} \int_1^{\sqrt{\cos \theta}} r \sin \theta \, dr \, d\theta$

In Exercises 11 through 13 use the function $z = \sqrt{x^2 + 4y^2}$.

11. Sketch the surface representing the function.

12. Find the equation of a line tangent to the surface of the function at $(2, 1, 2\sqrt{2})$ which is parallel to the yz-plane.

13. Find the approximate change in the function as x changes from 2.00 to 2.04 and y changes from 1.00 to 1.06.

In Exercises 14 through 17 use the function $z = e^{x+y}$.

14. Sketch the surface representing the function.

15. Find the equation of the line tangent to the surface of the function at $(1, 1, e^2)$ which is parallel to the xz-plane.

16. Find the approximate change in the function as x changes from 1.00 to 1.01 and y changes from 1.00 to 1.02.

17. Find the volume in the first octant under the surface of the function, and inside the planes $x = 1$ and $y = x$.

18. For a gas, the volume expansivity is defined as

$$\beta = \frac{1}{V} \frac{\partial V}{\partial T},$$

where V is the volume and T the temperature of the gas. If V is a function of T and the pressure p given by

$$V = a + \frac{bT}{p} - \frac{c}{T^2},$$

where a, b and c are constants, find β.

19. In the theory dealing with transistors, the current gain α of a transistor is defined as

$$\alpha = \frac{\partial i_c}{\partial i_e},$$

where i_c is the collector current and i_e is the emitter current. If i_c is a function of i_e and the collector voltage v_c given by

$$i_c = i_e(1 - e^{-2v_c}),$$

find α if v_c is 2 volts.

20. Young's modulus, which measures the ratio of the stress to strain in a stretched wire, is defined as

$$Y = \frac{L}{A} \frac{\partial F}{\partial L},$$

where L is the length of the wire, A is its cross-sectional area and F is the tension on the wire. Find Y, in dynes/cm^2, if

$$F = -\frac{10^7 T}{L^2},$$

for $L = 110$ cm, $T = 300°$K and $A = 10^{-2}$cm^2.

21. The image distance q from a lens as a function of the object distance p and the focal length f of the lens is given by

$$q = \frac{pf}{p - f}.$$

Find the approximate change in q, if f changes from 20 to 21 cm, and if p changes from 100 to 105 cm.

22. The impedance Z for an alternating current circuit is given by

$$Z = \sqrt{R^2 + X^2},$$

where R is the resistance and X is the reactance. If R is measured to be 6 ohms and X to be 8 ohms, and each has a maximum possible error of 2%, what is the maximum possible error in the impedance?

23. A flat plate 5 inches square is heated such that the temperature as a function of distances x and y from intersecting edges is

$$T = 2xy - y^2 - 2x^2 + 3y + 2.$$

Find the hottest point.

24. A closed rectangular box is made to contain 1000 in³. What dimensions should it have such that its surface area is a minimum?

25. Find the volume in the first octant below the plane $x + y + z - 6 = 0$ and inside the cylinder $y = 4 - x^2$.

26. Find the volume in the first octant below the surface $z = 4 - y^2$ and inside the plane $x + y = 2$.

27. Find, by double integration, the coordinates of the centroid of the area bounded by $y = 2$, $x + y = 4$, $x = 0$, and $y = 0$.

28. Find, by double integration, the coordinates of the centroid of the area bounded by $y = x$ and $y = 4x - x^2$.

29. Find, by double integration, R_y for the area of Exercise 27.

30. Find, by double integration, R_x for the area of Exercise 28.

31. The power delivered to an electric resistor is given by $P = V^2/R$, where V is the voltage across the resistor R. If V is increasing at the rate of 1 volt/min and R is increasing at the rate of 2 ohms/min, find the time rate of change of power, in watts/min, when $V = 60$ volts and $R = 20$ ohms. See Exercise 21 of Section 9-4.

10 Polar coordinates

10–1 Polar coordinates

Thus far we have graphed all plane curves in one coordinate system. This system, which is the rectangular coordinate system, is probably the most useful and widely applicable system. However, for certain types of curves, other coordinate systems prove to be better adapted. These coordinate systems are widely used, especially when certain applications of higher mathematics are involved. We shall discuss one of these systems here.

Instead of designating a point by its x- and y-coordinates, we can specify its location by its radius vector, and by the angle which the radius vector makes with the x-axis. Thus the r and θ that are used in the definitions of the trigonometric functions can also be used as the coordinates of points in the plane. The important aspect of choosing coordinates is that, for each set of values, there must be only one point which corresponds to this set. We can see that this condition is satisfied by the use of r and θ as coordinates. In polar coordinates the origin is called the *pole*, and the positive x-axis is called the *polar axis*. See Fig. 10–1.

Example A. If $r = 2$ and $\theta = \pi/6$, we have the point indicated in Fig. 10–2. The coordinates of this point are written as $(2, \pi/6)$ when polar coordinates are used. This point corresponds to $(\sqrt{3}, 1)$ in rectangular coordinates.

FIGURE 10–1

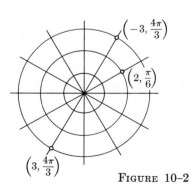

FIGURE 10–2

One difference between rectangular coordinates and polar coordinates is that, for each point in the plane, there are limitless possibilities for the polar coordinates of that point. For example, the point $(4, \pi/6)$ can also be represented by $(4, 13\pi/6)$ since the angles $\pi/6$ and $13\pi/6$ are coterminal. We also remove one restriction on r that we imposed in the definitions of the trigonometric functions. That is, r is allowed to take on positive and negative values. If r is considered negative, then the point is found on the opposite side of the pole from that on which it is positive.

Example B. The coordinates $(3, 4\pi/3)$ and $(3, -2\pi/3)$ represent the same point. However, the point $(-3, 4\pi/3)$ is on the opposite side of the pole, three units from the pole. Another possible set of coordinates for $(-3, 4\pi/3)$ is $(3, \pi/3)$. See Fig. 10–2.

The relationships between the polar coordinates of a point and the rectangular coordinates of the same point come directly from the definitions of the trigonometric functions. Those most commonly used are

$$x = r \cos \theta, \qquad y = r \sin \theta \tag{10–1}$$

and

$$\tan \theta = \frac{y}{x}, \qquad r = \sqrt{x^2 + y^2}. \tag{10–2}$$

Equations (10–1) are used when a relation in x and y is transformed into r and θ, and they are often used for the reverse process along with the second of Eqs. (10–2). Equations (10–2) are normally used for changing values of particular sets of coordinates.

Example C. Using Eq. (10–1), we can transform the polar coordinates of $(4, \pi/4)$ into the rectangular coordinates $(2\sqrt{2}, 2\sqrt{2})$, since

$$x = 4 \cos \pi/4 = 4(\sqrt{2}/2) = 2\sqrt{2}$$

and

$$y = 4 \sin \pi/4 = 4(\sqrt{2}/2) = 2\sqrt{2}.$$

Example D. If the rectangular coordinates of a point are $(3, -5)$, we can find the polar coordinates of the same point by $\tan \theta = -\frac{5}{3}$. This means that $\theta = 5.25$ (or -1.03). Also, $r = \sqrt{9 + 25} = 5.83$. Therefore the point $(3, -5)$ in rectangular coordinates is the point $(5.83, 5.25)$ in polar coordinates.

Example E. Find the polar equation of the circle $x^2 + y^2 = 2x$.
  Since $r^2 = x^2 + y^2$ and $x = r \cos \theta$, we have $r^2 = 2r \cos \theta$, or $r = 2 \cos \theta$. This is the polar equation; that is, the equation of the curve expressed in the variables r and θ.

Example F. Find the rectangular equation of the "rose" $r = 4 \sin 2\theta$.

Using the relation $2 \sin \theta \cos \theta = \sin 2\theta$, we have $r = 8 \sin \theta \cos \theta$. Then, using Eqs. (10–1) and (10–2), we have

$$\sqrt{x^2 + y^2} = 8 \left(\frac{y}{r}\right)\left(\frac{x}{r}\right)$$

$$= \frac{8xy}{r^2} = \frac{8xy}{x^2 + y^2}.$$

Squaring both sides, we obtain

$$x^2 + y^2 = \frac{64x^2y^2}{(x^2 + y^2)^2}$$

or

$$(x^2 + y^2)^3 = 64x^2y^2.$$

From this example we can see that plotting the graph from the rectangular coordinates would be complicated.

Exercises

In Exercises 1 through 10, plot the given points on polar coordinate paper.

1. $(3, \pi/6)$ 2. $(2, \pi)$ 3. $(4, 7\pi/6)$ 4. $(5, -\pi/3)$ 5. $(\frac{5}{2}, -8\pi/3)$
6. $(-5, \pi/4)$ 7. $(3, -5\pi)$ 8. $(4, 2\pi/5)$ 9. $(-4, -5\pi/3)$ 10. $(-1, -1)$

In Exercises 11 through 14, find a set of polar coordinates for each of the given points expressed in rectangular coordinates.

11. $(1, \sqrt{3})$ 12. $(-1, -1)$ 13. $(-\sqrt{3}/2, -\frac{1}{2})$ 14. $(-5, 4)$

In Exercises 15 through 18, find the rectangular coordinates corresponding to the points for which the polar coordinates are given.

15. $(8, 4\pi/3)$ 16. $(-4, -\pi)$ 17. $(3, -\pi/8)$ 18. $(-1, -1)$

In Exercises 19 through 23, find the polar equation of each of the given equations.

19. $x^2 + y^2 = a^2$ 20. $x^2 - y^2 = a^2$ 21. $x^2 + 4y^2 = 4$
22. $x = 3$ 23. $y = x^2$

In Exercises 24 through 27, find the rectangular equation of each of the given equations.

24. $r = \sin \theta$ 25. $r \cos \theta = 4$ 26. $r = 2(1 + \cos \theta)$ 27. $r^2 = 16 \cos 2\theta$
28. If we refer back to Eqs. (6–24) and (6–25), we see that the length along the arc of a circle and the area within a circular sector vary with two variables. These variables are those which we refer to as the polar coordinates. Express the arc length s and the area A in terms of rectangular coordinates.

29. Under certain conditions, the x- and y-components of a magnetic field B are given by the equations

$$B_x = \frac{-ky}{x^2 + y^2} \quad \text{and} \quad B_y = \frac{kx}{x^2 + y^2}.$$

Write these equations in terms of polar coordinates.

30. Express the equation of the cable (see Exercise 22 of Section 1–7) in polar coordinates.

31. The x- and y-coordinates of the position of a certain moving object as functions of time are given by $x = 2t$ and $y = \sqrt{8t^2 + 1}$. Find the polar equation of the path of the object.

32. The polar equation of an artificial satellite of the earth is

$$r = \frac{4800}{1 + 0.14 \cos \theta},$$

where r is measured in miles. Find the rectangular equation of this satellite. The path is an ellipse, with the earth at one of the foci.

10–2 Curves in polar coordinates

The basic method for finding a curve in polar coordinates is the same as it is in rectangular coordinates. We assume values of θ and then find the corresponding values of r. These points are plotted and joined, thus forming the curve which represents the function. The following examples illustrate the method.

Example A. Plot the graph of $r = 3$.

Since $r = 3$ for all values of θ, the graph must be a circle of radius 3, with center at the pole (Fig. 10–3). It is not actually necessary to find specific points. (In the same way we can show that $\theta = \pi/6$ is a straight line through the pole. It represents all points for which $\theta = \pi/6$, regardless of the value of r, positive or negative.)

FIGURE 10–3

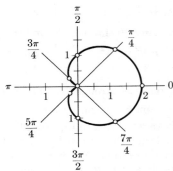

FIGURE 10–4

Example B. Plot the graph of $r = 1 + \cos \theta$.

We find the following table of values of r corresponding to the assumed values of θ.

θ	0	$\dfrac{\pi}{4}$	$\dfrac{\pi}{2}$	$\dfrac{3\pi}{4}$	π	$\dfrac{5\pi}{4}$	$\dfrac{3\pi}{2}$	$\dfrac{7\pi}{4}$	2π
r	2	1.7	1	0.3	0	0.3	1	1.7	2

We now see that the points on the curve start repeating, and it is unnecessary to find additional points. This curve is called a cardioid (Fig. 10–4).

Example C. Plot the graph of $r = 1 - 2 \sin \theta$.

θ	0	$\dfrac{\pi}{4}$	$\dfrac{\pi}{2}$	$\dfrac{3\pi}{4}$	π	$\dfrac{5\pi}{4}$	$\dfrac{3\pi}{2}$	$\dfrac{7\pi}{4}$	2π
r	1	-0.4	-1	-0.4	1	2.4	3	2.4	1

This curve is known as a limaçon (Fig. 10–5).

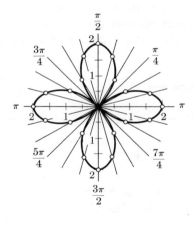

FIGURE 10–5   FIGURE 10–6

Example D. Plot the graph of $r = 2 \cos 2\theta$.

θ	0	$\dfrac{\pi}{12}$	$\dfrac{\pi}{6}$	$\dfrac{\pi}{4}$	$\dfrac{\pi}{3}$	$\dfrac{5\pi}{12}$	$\dfrac{\pi}{2}$	$\dfrac{7\pi}{12}$	$\dfrac{2\pi}{3}$	$\dfrac{3\pi}{4}$	$\dfrac{5\pi}{6}$	$\dfrac{11\pi}{12}$	π
r	2	1.7	1	0	-1	-1.7	-2	-1.7	-1	0	1	1.7	2

For the values of θ from π to 2π, the values of r repeat. We have a four-leaf rose (Fig. 10–6).

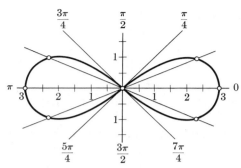

FIGURE 10-7

Example E. Plot the graph of $r^2 = 9 \cos 2\theta$.

θ	0	$\dfrac{\pi}{8}$	$\dfrac{\pi}{4}$	$\cdots$	$\dfrac{3\pi}{4}$	$\dfrac{7\pi}{8}$	π
r	± 3	± 2.5	0		0	± 2.5	± 3

There are no values of r corresponding to values of θ in the range $\pi/4 < \theta < 3\pi/4$, since twice these angles are in the second and third quadrants, and the cosine is negative for such angles. The value of r^2 cannot be negative. Also, the values of r repeat for $\theta > \pi$. The figure is called a lemniscate (Fig. 10-7).

Exercises

In Exercises 1 through 18, plot the given curves in polar coordinates.

1. $r = 4$

2. $r = 2 \sin \theta$

3. $\theta = 5\pi/3$

4. $r = 4 \sec \theta$

5. $r \sin \theta = 4$

6. $r = 1 - \cos \theta$ (cardioid)

7. $r = 2 - \cos \theta$ (limaçon)

8. $r^2 = 4 \sin 2\theta$ (lemniscate)

9. $r = 4 \sin 2\theta$ (rose)

10. $r = 2 \sin 3\theta$ (rose)

11. $r = \sin \theta - 1$ (cardioid)

12. $r = \dfrac{1}{1 - \cos \theta}$ (parabola)

13. $r = -4 \sin 4\theta$ (rose)

14. $r = 2 + 3 \sin \theta$ (limaçon)

15. $r = \dfrac{1}{2 - \cos \theta}$ (ellipse)

16. $r = 10^\theta$ (spiral)

17. $r = 3 - \sin 3\theta$

18. $r = 4 \tan \theta$

19. Considering the equation for the length of arc of a circle, if s has a constant value of 4, plot the resulting curve of r as a function of θ. What are the meaningful values of θ in reference to finding the length of a circular arc? What are the meaningful values of θ in reference to discussing the total distance an object travels in a circular path?

20. Plot the graph of $r = 2a \sin \theta$. The charged particle (see Exercise 19 of Section 1–6) is originally traveling along the line $\theta = \pi$ toward the pole. When it reaches the pole it enters the magnetic field. Determine the equation of its path in polar coordinates.

21. A cam is shaped such that the equation of the edge of the upper "half" is given by $r = 2 + \cos \theta$, and the equation of the edge of the lower "half" by $r = 3/(2 - \cos \theta)$. Plot the curve which represents the shape of the cam.

22. A satellite at a height proper to make one revolution per day around the earth will have for an excellent approximation of its projection on the earth of its path the curve

$$r^2 = R^2 \cos 2 \left(\theta + \frac{\pi}{2} \right),$$

where R is the radius of the earth. Sketch the path of the projection.

23. Sketch the graph of the rectangular equation

$$4(x^6 + 3x^4y^2 + 3x^2y^4 + y^6 - x^4 - 2x^2y^2 - y^4) + y^2 = 0.$$

[*Hint:* The equation can be written as

$$4(x^2 + y^2)^3 - 4(x^2 + y^2)^2 + y^2 = 0.$$

Transform to polar coordinates, and then sketch the curve.]

10–3 Applications of differentiation and integration in polar coordinates

Polar coordinates are used extensively in applications and theoretical discussions in advanced mechanics, electricity, and certain other fields. However, a number of applications of differentiation and integration which we have previously discussed may be solved in polar coordinates. In this section we shall discuss an application of differentiation and one of integration. Certain other applications are in the exercises.

The application of differentiation we shall discuss is of velocity. In Section 3–2 we were able to determine the resultant velocity of an object if we knew its x- and y-components. Here we shall consider the components of velocity in the direction of increasing r and increasing θ. These components are denoted by v_r and v_θ.

The *radial component* of velocity v_r and the *transverse component* of velocity v_θ are given by

$$v_r = \frac{dr}{dt} \quad \text{and} \quad v_\theta = r\frac{d\theta}{dt}. \tag{10–3}$$

See Fig. 10–8. To show that these are proper relations we recall that $x = r \cos \theta$ and $y = r \sin \theta$. Taking derivatives with respect to time, treating both r and

θ as functions of time, we have

$$\frac{dx}{dt} = \cos\theta\,\frac{dr}{dt} - r\sin\theta\,\frac{d\theta}{dt},$$

$$\frac{dy}{dt} = \sin\theta\,\frac{dr}{dt} + r\cos\theta\,\frac{d\theta}{dt}.$$

Since $dx/dt = v_x$ and $dy/dt = v_y$, and using Eqs. (10–3), we have

$$v_x = v_r\cos\theta - v_\theta\sin\theta,$$

$$v_y = v_r\sin\theta + v_\theta\cos\theta.$$

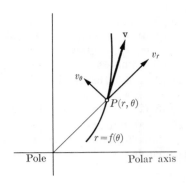

FIGURE 10–8

Squaring each of the sides of each of these equations and adding we have

$$v_x^2 = v_r^2\cos^2\theta - 2v_r v_\theta\cos\theta\sin\theta + v_\theta^2\sin^2\theta,$$

$$v_y^2 = v_r^2\sin^2\theta + 2v_r v_\theta\cos\theta\sin\theta + v_\theta^2\cos^2\theta,$$

$$v_x^2 + v_y^2 = v_r^2 + v_\theta^2 = v^2. \tag{10–4}$$

This analysis, along with the fact that dr/dt is the velocity in the r-direction, for constant θ, and $r(d\theta/dt)$ is the velocity in the θ-direction, for constant r, verifies that these are the correct relations. The following examples illustrate the use of Eqs. (10–3) and (10–4).

Example A. Find the radial and transverse components of velocity of an object moving such that $r = t^2 - 2$ and $\theta = \frac{1}{4}t^2$, when $t = 2$. From these values calculate the magnitude of the velocity of v when $t = 2$.

$$v_r = \frac{dr}{dt} = 2t, \qquad v_\theta = r\frac{d\theta}{dt} = (t^2 - 2)\left(\frac{t}{2}\right) = \tfrac{1}{2}(t^3 - 2t).$$

Evaluating for $t = 2$, we have

$$v_r\big|_{t=2} = 4,$$

$$v_\theta\big|_{t=2} = \tfrac{1}{2}(8 - 4) = 2.$$

Thus,

$$v = \sqrt{16 + 4} = \sqrt{20} = 4.47.$$

Example B. A particle is moving along the curve $r = 3 + 2\sin\theta$ with a constant angular velocity, $\omega = d\theta/dt = 2$ rad/sec. (See Fig. 10–9.) Find the magnitude of the speed when $\theta = \pi/3$.

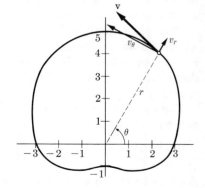

FIGURE 10–9

Taking derivatives of $r = 3 + 2 \sin \theta$ with respect to t, we have

$$\frac{dr}{dt} = 2 \cos \theta \frac{d\theta}{dt}.$$

Therefore,

$$v_r = \frac{dr}{dt} = 2 \cos \theta \frac{d\theta}{dt},$$

$$v_\theta = r \frac{d\theta}{dt} = (3 + 2 \sin \theta) \frac{d\theta}{dt}.$$

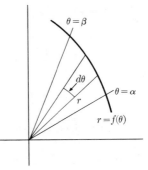

FIGURE 10–10

Evaluating, we have

$$v_r|_{\theta = \pi/3} = 2 \left(\cos \frac{\pi}{3} \right) (2) = 4(\tfrac{1}{2}) = 2.00,$$

$$v_\theta|_{\theta = \pi/3} = \left[3 + 2 \left(\frac{\sqrt{3}}{2} \right) \right] (2) = 2(3 + \sqrt{3}) = 9.46,$$

$$v = \sqrt{4.00 + 89.5} = \sqrt{93.5} = 9.67 \text{ units/sec.}$$

The application of integration in polar coordinates which we shall consider is the area bounded by polar curves. We recall Eq. (6–25) which states that the area of a circular sector is $A = \tfrac{1}{2}r^2\theta$. In Fig. 10–10, consider the element of area, with radius r and central angle $d\theta$, as shown. If these elements are summed (integrated) from $\theta = \alpha$ to $\theta = \beta$, the sum will represent the area shown. Thus, the area is found by

$$A = \tfrac{1}{2} \int_\alpha^\beta r^2 \, d\theta. \tag{10–5}$$

The following examples illustrate the use of Eq. (10–5).

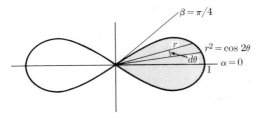

FIGURE 10–11

Example C. Find the area enclosed by one loop of the lemniscate $r^2 = \cos 2\theta$.

Employing Eq. (10–5) we substitute $r^2 = \cos 2\theta$. To determine the limits α and β, we note the symmetry of the curve (see Fig. 10–11). By choosing $\alpha = 0$ and β to be the value where r is first zero, we will find the area of the upper half of the loop. Doubling this will give the desired area. Thus, by setting

$r^2 = \cos 2\theta = 0$, we find $2\theta = \pi/2$ or $\theta = \pi/4$. This means $\beta = \pi/4$. Therefore, the integral for the area is

$$A = 2\left[\tfrac{1}{2}\int_0^{\pi/4} \cos 2\theta \, d\theta\right]$$

$$= \tfrac{1}{2}\int_0^{\pi/4} \cos 2\theta(2 \, d\theta) = \tfrac{1}{2}\sin 2\theta\big|_0^{\pi/4} = \tfrac{1}{2}(1 - 0) = \tfrac{1}{2}.$$

Thus, the area is $\tfrac{1}{2}$ sq. unit.

Example D. Find the area outside the cardioid $r = 1 + \sin \theta$ and inside the circle $r = 3 \sin \theta$.

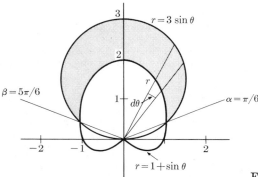

FIGURE 10–12

    Drawing the figure, we see that the desired area is the shaded portion of Fig. 10–12. By substituting $r = 3 \sin \theta$ into the equation of the cardioid, we have

$$3 \sin \theta = 1 + \sin \theta,$$

$$\sin \theta = \tfrac{1}{2},$$

or

$$\theta = \frac{\pi}{6}, \ \frac{5\pi}{6}.$$

This means the points $(3/2, \pi/6)$ and $(3/2, 5\pi/6)$ are common to each curve.
    Therefore, the area inside the circle between $\theta = \pi/6$ and $\theta = 5\pi/6$ is

$$A_1 = \tfrac{1}{2}\int_{\pi/6}^{5\pi/6} (3 \sin \theta)^2 \, d\theta.$$

The area inside the cardioid between $\theta = \pi/6$ and $\theta = 5\pi/6$ is

$$A_2 = \tfrac{1}{2}\int_{\pi/6}^{5\pi/6} (1 + \sin \theta)^2 \, d\theta.$$

The desired area is the difference of A_1 and A_2. Thus,

$$A = \tfrac{1}{2} \int_{\pi/6}^{5\pi/6} [(3 \sin \theta)^2 - (1 + \sin \theta)^2] \, d\theta$$

$$= \tfrac{1}{2} \int_{\pi/6}^{5\pi/6} (8 \sin^2 \theta - 2 \sin \theta - 1) \, d\theta$$

$$= \tfrac{1}{2} \int_{\pi/6}^{5\pi/6} (4 - 4 \cos 2\theta - 2 \sin \theta - 1) \, d\theta$$

$$= \tfrac{1}{2}(3\theta - 2 \sin 2\theta + 2 \cos \theta)|_{\pi/6}^{5\pi/6}$$

$$= \tfrac{1}{2}\left[3\left(\frac{5\pi}{6} - \frac{\pi}{6}\right) - 2\left(\sin \frac{5\pi}{3} - \sin \frac{\pi}{3}\right) + 2\left(\cos \frac{5\pi}{6} - \cos \frac{\pi}{6}\right)\right]$$

$$= \tfrac{1}{2}\left[2\pi - 2\left(-\frac{\sqrt{3}}{2} - \frac{\sqrt{3}}{2}\right) + 2\left(-\frac{\sqrt{3}}{2} - \frac{\sqrt{3}}{2}\right)\right] = \pi.$$

Advantage could have been taken of the symmetry by integrating from $\pi/6$ to $\pi/2$ and doubling the result.

Exercises

1. A particle moves such that $r = 3t$ and $\theta = t^3$, where t is the time. By finding v_r and v_θ when $t = 1$, find the magnitude of the velocity of the particle when $t = 1$.

2. A particle moves such that

$$r = \sin \frac{\pi t}{6} \quad \text{and} \quad \theta = \frac{1}{2t + 1},$$

where t is the time. Repeat the instructions given in Exercise 1 for $t = 2$.

In Exercises 3 through 8, find the magnitude of the velocity of an object moving along the given curves with a constant angular velocity $\omega = 2$ rad/sec for the indicated values of θ, if r is measured in ft.

3. $r = 2, \theta = \pi/3$

4. $r = 4\theta, \theta = 2$

5. $r = 4 - \cos \theta, \theta = \pi/2$

6. $r = 5 + 2 \sin 2\theta, \theta = \pi/6$

7. $r = \dfrac{1}{2 - \sin \theta}, \theta = \pi/6$

8. $r = 1 + \cos^2 \theta, \theta = \pi/4$

In Exercises 9 through 16, find the area bounded by the given curves.

9. $\theta = 0, \theta = \pi/4, r = \sec \theta$

10. $\theta = \pi/6, \theta = \pi/2, r \sin \theta = 2$

11. $r = 2 \cos \theta$

12. $r = 4 \sin \theta, \theta = 0, \theta = \pi/3$

13. One loop of $r^2 = 4 \sin 2\theta$

14. $r = 1 - \cos \theta$

15. $r = 2 \sin \theta, r = 2 \cos \theta$ (common area)

16. $r = 2 + \cos\theta, r = 5\cos\theta$ (outside of $2 + \cos\theta$)

17. A particle moves in a counterclockwise direction on the circle $r = 2\sin\theta$. When $\theta = \pi/3, v = 10$ ft/sec. Find v_r and v_θ.

18. Change $(x^2 + y^2)^2 - (x^2 + y^2) = 2xy$ into polar coordinates and find the area bounded by $\theta = 0, \theta = \pi/4$, and the curve.

19. Using $x = r\cos\theta$ and $y = r\sin\theta$, take derivatives of each with respect to θ and treat r as a function of θ. From these results show that

$$\frac{dy}{dx} = \frac{r'\tan\theta + r}{r' - r\tan\theta} \tag{10--6}$$

represents the slope of a line tangent to a polar curve. Here, $r' = dr/d\theta$.

20. Use Eq. (10--6) to find the slope of a line tangent to $r = \cos\theta$ at $\theta = \pi/6$.

21. The length of arc along a polar curve is given by

$$s = \int_\alpha^\beta \sqrt{r^2 + (r')^2}\, d\theta \tag{10--7}$$

where $r' = dr/d\theta$. Using this equation find the total perimeter of $r = \cos^2(\theta/2)$.

22. Using Eq. (10--7) find the circumference of the circle $r = \sin\theta + \cos\theta$.

Miscellaneous exercises for Chapter 10

In Exercises 1 through 4 find the polar equation of each of the given rectangular equations.

1. $y = 2x$

2. $y = 4$

3. $x^2 + y^2 = 7 - 6y$

4. $\dfrac{x^2}{a^2} + \dfrac{y^2}{b^2} = 1$

In Exercises 5 through 8 find the rectangular equation of each of the given polar equations.

5. $r = 2\sin 2\theta$

6. $r = \csc\theta$

7. $r = \dfrac{2}{1 - \sin\theta}$

8. $r = \cos\left(\dfrac{\theta}{2}\right)$

In Exercises 9 through 16, sketch each of the given polar curves.

9. $r = 4(1 + \sin\theta)$

10. $r = 1 + 2\cos\theta$

11. $r = \cot\theta$

12. $r = \dfrac{1}{2(\sin\theta - 1)}$

13. $r = 2\sin\left(\dfrac{\theta}{2}\right)$

14. $r = \theta$

15. $r = 2 + \cos 3\theta$

16. $r = 3 - \cos 2\theta$

17. A particle moves such that $r = t^3 - 6t$ and $\theta = t/(t + 1)$, where t is the time. Find the magnitude of the velocity of the particle when $t = 1$.

18. Find the magnitude of the velocity (in ft/sec) of an object moving on the curve $r = 2 + 3 \cos 2\theta$ with a constant angular velocity $\omega = 3$ rad/sec for $\theta = \pi/12$.

19. Find the area enclosed by $r = 2 - \cos \theta$.

20. Find the area of the smaller loop of the curve $r = 1 - 2 \cos \theta$.

21. Under certain circumstances, the path that an electron follows when passing through a magnetic field is closely approximated by the parabola $x^2 = ky$, where k is a constant. Express the equation of the path in polar coordinates.

22. Under certain conditions the electric potential is given by

$$V = \left(\frac{a}{r^2} - br \right) \cos \theta,$$

where a and b are constants. The polar components of the electric field are given by

$$E_r = - \frac{\partial V}{\partial r} \quad \text{and} \quad E_\theta = - \frac{1}{r} \frac{\partial V}{\partial \theta}.$$

Find the expressions for E_r and E_θ in terms of r and θ.

23. In the theory dealing with an object moving through a liquid, a quantity called the velocity potential is introduced. Find v_r and v_θ if the velocity potential is given by

$$P = \frac{k \cos \theta}{r^2},$$

where k is a constant, and

$$v_r = - \frac{\partial P}{\partial r} \quad \text{and} \quad v_\theta = - \frac{1}{r} \frac{\partial P}{\partial \theta}.$$

Express the result in terms of rectangular coordinates.

24. Under a force which varies inversely as the square of the distance from an attracting object (such as the force the sun exerts on the earth), it can be shown that the equation that an object follows is given in general by

$$\frac{1}{r} = a + b \cos \theta,$$

where a and b are constant for a particular path. By transforming this equation to rectangular coordinates, show that this equation represents one of the conic sections, the particular section depending on the values of a and b. It is through this kind of analysis that we know that the paths of the planets and comets are conic sections.

25. The approximate maximum velocity attained by the artificial satellite of Exercise 32 of Section 10–1 is 5 mi/sec. This velocity occurs when the satellite is closest to the earth. Calculate v_r and v_θ for this satellite at this point.

26. The angle φ between r and a tangent line to a curve is given by $\tan \varphi = r/(dr/d\theta)$. Find the angle between r and a tangent line to the curve $r = \sin (\theta/2)$ for $\theta = \pi/2$.

11   Empirical curve fitting

11-1 Frequency distributions and measures of central tendency

Much of that which we "know" is probable knowledge. In building any field of knowledge, we accept certain basic concepts as being true, without having complete proof. That situation exists in mathematics, as in all other fields of knowledge. For example, in mathematics the concepts of a point, of a line, of the whole being greater than any of its parts, and similar *axioms* or undefinable quantities are used as the basis for later conclusions. Those concepts accepted without proof in mathematics are normally those which cannot be conceived to be wrong (although there have been systems of mathematics in which certain axioms are not valid). Definitions are based on those properties which exhibit consistency within a given set of axioms. In other fields, it is possible to make only a limited number of observations, and to base predictions of future happenings on these results. This is well documented in the study of physics, for example. Throughout the history of physics, certain concepts believed true at one time have been shown to be wrong at a later date. However, in the course of developing a new theory, we learn a great deal more about the phenomena.

This chapter will deal briefly with methods of analyzing empirical data. A few basic concepts from elementary statistics will be introduced, with the primary aim of being able to derive an equation of a curve to "fit" given empirical data. Such an equation determines a basic relationship between the variables of the experiment, and from which it is possible to develop and better prepare later experimentation. We shall start with basic methods of tabulating and graphing data.

When a mathematician wishes to state the relation between the area of a circle and its radius, he writes $A = \pi r^2$, and he knows that this relation is true for all circles. When an engineer wishes to find the safe load which a particular cable is able to support, he cannot so simply write an equation for the relation, because the load which a cable may support depends on the diameter of the cable, the material of which it is made, the quality of material in the particular cable, any possible defects in its manufacture, and anything else which could make this cable different from all other cables. Thus, in order to determine the load which a cable can support, he may test many cables of particular specifications. He will find that most of the cables can support approximately the same load, but that there is some variation, and occasionally perhaps a great variation for some reason or other. Any conclusions he may draw will, by the nature of their source, yield probable knowledge of the cable.

In this section and in the remainder of this chapter, we are going to discuss the methods of tabulating and analyzing this kind of statistical information. The first thing to be done, after the information is collected, is to tabulate it in some convenient form.

Normally the number of measurements is sufficiently large that it is not feasible to attempt to tabulate the number of occurrences for a particular value. Values are therefore grouped within specified ranges of values, and the number of values within each range is then counted. This is then called a *frequency distribution;* that is, the association of a set of values with the number of times this set occurs.

Example A. A certain mathematics course had 80 students enrolled in it. After all the tests and exams were recorded, the instructors determined a numerical average (based on 100) for each student. The following is a list of the numerical grades, with the number of students receiving each.

22—1	61—1	74—5	86—3
37—1	63—4	75—4	87—2
40—2	65—2	77—7	88—1
44—1	66—1	78—4	90—2
47—1	67—5	79—1	92—1
53—1	68—2	81—2	93—2
55—3	70—2	82—4	95—1
56—1	71—4	84—1	97—1
60—3	72—3	85—1	

We can observe from this listing that it is difficult to see just how the grades were distributed. Therefore the instructors grouped the grades into intervals, which included five possible grades in each interval. This led to the following table.

Interval	20–24	25–29	30–34	35–39	40–44	45–49	50–54	55–59
Number in interval	1	0	0	1	3	1	1	4
Interval	60–64	65–69	70–74	75–79	80–84	85–89	90–94	94–99
Number in interval	8	10	14	16	7	7	5	2

We can see that the distribution of grades becomes much clearer in the above table. Finally, since the school graded students only with the letters A, B, C, D, and F, the instructors then grouped the grades in intervals below 60, from 60–69, from 70–79, from 80–89, and from 90–100, and assigned the appropriate letter grade to each numerical grade within each interval. This led to the following table.

Grade	A	B	C	D	F
Number receiving this grade	7	14	30	18	11

Thus we can see the distribution according to letter grades. We can also note that, if the number of intervals were reduced much further, it would be difficult to draw any reasonable conclusions regarding the distribution of grades.

Just as graphs are useful in representing algebraic functions, so also are they a very convenient method of representing frequency distributions. There are several useful methods of graphing such distributions, among which the most important are the *histogram* and the *frequency curve*. The following examples illustrate these graphical representations.

FIGURE 11–1

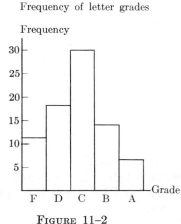

FIGURE 11–2

Example B. A histogram represents a particular set of data by use of rectangles. The width of each rectangle is the width of the interval being represented, and the height is the number of values within the interval. Also, it is common to use one number, the middle value, to represent the interval. The histograms in Figs. 11–1 and 11–2 represent the grouped data of Example A.

Example C. The frequency curve represents a set of data by plotting as abscissas (*x*-values) the representative value of the interval, and as ordinates (*y*-values)

FIGURE 11–3

FIGURE 11–4

the number of values in the interval (the frequency). If the resulting points are joined by straight-line segments, the figure is called a frequency polygon. If the points are joined by a smooth curve, the figure is called a frequency curve. Figures 11–3 and 11–4 represent a frequency polygon and a frequency curve illustrating the data of Example A.

Tables and graphical representations give a general description of data. However, it is often profitable and convenient to find representative values for the location of the center of distribution, and other numbers to give a measure of the deviation from this central value. In this way we can obtain an arithmetical description of the data. We shall now discuss the values commonly used to measure the location of the center of the distribution. These are referred to as "measures of central tendency."

The first of these measures of central tendency is the *median*. The median is the middle number, that number for which there are as many above it as below it in the distribution. If there is no middle number, the median is that number halfway between the two numbers nearest the middle of the distribution.

Example D. In the distribution of grades in Example A the median is 74. There are 80 grades in all, and if they are listed in numerical order we find that the 39th through the 43rd grade is 74. This means that the 40th and 41st grades are both 74. The number halfway between the 40th and 41st grades would be the median. The fact that both are 74 means that the median is also 74.

Example E. Given the numbers 5, 2, 6, 4, 7, 4, 7, 2, 8, 9, 4, 11, 9, 1, 3, we find that when they are arranged in numerical order, the median (the middle number) is 5.

Another, and more widely applied, measure of central tendency is the *arithmetic mean*. The mean is calculated by finding the sum of all the values and then dividing by the number of values. This calculation can be somewhat simplified if any of the numbers appear more than once. By multiplying each number by its frequency, adding these results, and then dividing by the total number of values considered, the mean can be calculated. Letting $\bar{x}$ (usually read as "x bar") stand for the mean of the values $x_1, x_2, \ldots, x_n$, which occur $f_1, f_2, \ldots, f_n$ times, respectively, we have

$$\bar{x} = \frac{x_1 f_1 + x_2 f_2 + \cdots + x_n f_n}{f_1 + f_2 + \cdots + f_n}. \tag{11-1}$$

(This notation can be simplified by letting

$$x_1 f_1 + x_2 f_2 + \cdots + x_n f_n = \sum_{i=1}^{n} x_i f_i,$$

the notation normally used to indicate a sum, where $\sum$ is the *summation sign*.) Compare this equation and its meaning with Eq. (5–24).

Example F. We find the arithmetic mean (average) of the grades in Example A by

$$\bar{x} = \frac{22(1) + (37)(1) + (40)(2) + \cdots + (67)(5) + \cdots + (97)(1)}{80}$$

$$= \frac{5733}{80} = 71.7.$$

Example G. We find the mean of the numbers in Example E by

$$\bar{x} = \frac{1(1) + 2(2) + 3(1) + 4(3) + 5(1) + 6(1) + 7(2) + 8(1) + 9(2) + 11(1)}{15}$$

$$= \frac{82}{15} = 5.5.$$

Exercises

In Exercises 1 through 9, given the sets of numbers

A: 36, 15, 22, 18, 35, 27, 43, 53, 26, 25, 30
B: 2, 5, 3, 8, 6, 7, 8, 3, 4, 1, 9, 7, 5, 2, 1, 7, 5
C: 11, 14, 17, 12, 15, 22, 23, 13, 14, 12, 17, 16, 14, 13, 20, 11, 22, 17, 14, 15, find:

1. The median of Set A   2. The median of Set B   3. The median of Set C
4. The mean of Set A   5. The mean of Set B   6. The mean of Set C
7. A frequency table with intervals 0–9, 10–19, etc., for Set A.
8. A frequency table with intervals 0–1, 2–3, etc., for Set B.
9. A frequency table with intervals 10–12, 13–15, etc., for Set C.

In Exercises 10 through 12, draw histograms for the data found in:

10. Exercise 7   11. Exercise 8   12. Exercise 9

In Exercises 13 through 15, draw a frequency curve for the data found in:

13. Exercise 7   14. Exercise 8   15. Exercise 9

16. The following table was compiled when a particular type of cable was being tested for its breaking load. Form a histogram for these data.

Load interval, pounds	830 –839	840 –849	850 –859	860 –869	870 –879	880 –889	890 –899
Number of cables breaking	4	14	48	531	85	22	2

17. Form a frequency polygon for the data given in Exercise 16.
18. A Geiger counter records the presence of high-energy nuclear particles. Even though no apparent radioactive source is present, a certain number of particles will be recorded. These are primarily cosmic rays, which are caused by very high-energy particles from outer space. In an experiment to measure the amount of cosmic radiation, the number of counts were recorded during 200 5-sec intervals. The following table gives the number of counts, and the number of 5-sec intervals having this number of counts. Draw a frequency curve for this data.

Counts	0	1	2	3	4	5	6	7	8	9	10
Intervals	3	10	25	45	29	39	26	11	7	2	3

19. Find the median number of counts per 5-sec interval from the data of Exercise 18.
20. Find the arithmetic mean of the counts per 5-sec interval from the data of Exercise 18.
21. A researcher, testing an electric circuit, found the following values for the current (in milliamperes) in the circuit on successive trials: 3.44, 3.46, 3.39, 3.44, 3.48, 3.40,

3.29, 3.46, 3.41, 3.37, 3.45, 3.47, 3.43, 3.38, 3.50, 3.41, 3.42, 3.47. Form a histogram for the intervals 3.25–3.29, 3.30–3.34, etc.

22. Form a histogram for the data given in Exercise 21 for the intervals 3.21–3.30, 3.31–3.40, etc.

23. Find the median of the data given in Exercise 21.

24. Find the mean of the data given in Exercise 21.

11-2 Standard deviation

As we mentioned in the preceding section, numbers which give a measure of the deviation from the measure of central tendency are of importance in analyzing statistical data. If there is a great deviation from the mean, this probably signifies that the data are less meaningful than if the deviation is relatively small. The measure of deviation presented in this section is called the *standard deviation*.

The standard deviation of a set of numbers is given by the equation

$$s = \sqrt{\overline{(x - \bar{x})^2}}. \qquad (11-2)$$

The definition of s indicates that the following steps are to be taken in computing its value. (1) Find the arithmetic mean $\bar{x}$ of the set of numbers. (2) Subtract the mean from each of the numbers of the set. (3) Square these differences. (4) Find the arithmetic mean of these squares. (Note that a bar over any quantity signifies the mean of the set of values of that quantity.) (5) Find the square root of this last arithmetic mean. Defined in this way, s must be a positive number, and thus indicates a deviation from the mean, regardless of whether or not individual numbers are greater or less than the mean.

Example A. Find the standard deviation of the numbers 1, 5, 4, 2, 6, 2, 1, 1, 5, 3. The most efficient method of finding s is to make a table in which Steps (1) to (4) are indicated.

x	$x - \bar{x}$	$(x - \bar{x})^2$
1	-2	4
5	2	4
4	1	1
2	-1	1
6	3	9
2	-1	1
1	-2	4
1	-2	4
5	2	4
3	0	0
30		32

$\bar{x} = \frac{30}{10} = 3,$

$\overline{(x - \bar{x})^2} = \frac{32}{10} = 3.2,$

$s = \sqrt{3.2} = 1.8.$

We can see from this example that if there had been a great many numbers, and if $\bar{x}$ had been a decimal of some form, the calculations would have been much more tedious to carry out. There is one way we can reduce the amount of work somewhat: by algebraic manipulation within the radical of the definition of s.

To find the mean of the sum of two sets of numbers, x_i and y_i, we can determine the mean of the x's and the mean of the y's and add the results. That is,

$$\overline{x + y} = \bar{x} + \bar{y}. \tag{11–3}$$

This is true by the meaning of the definition of the arithmetic mean.

$$\overline{x + y} = \frac{x_1 + x_2 + \cdots + x_n + y_1 + y_2 + \cdots + y_n}{n}$$

$$= \frac{x_1 + x_2 + \cdots + x_n}{n} + \frac{y_1 + y_2 + \cdots y_n}{n}$$

$$= \bar{x} + \bar{y}.$$

Also, when we find the arithmetic mean, if all the numbers contain a constant factor, this number can be factored before the mean is found. That is,

$$\overline{kx} = k\bar{x}. \tag{11–4}$$

If we multiply out the quantity under the radical in Eq. (11–2), and then apply Eq. (11–3), we obtain

$$\overline{x^2 - 2x\bar{x} + \bar{x}^2} = \overline{x^2} - \overline{2x\bar{x}} + \overline{\bar{x}^2}.$$

In this equation the number 2 and $\bar{x}$ are constants for any given problem. Thus, by using Eq. (11–4), we have

$$\overline{x^2} - \overline{2x\bar{x}} + \overline{\bar{x}^2} = \overline{x^2} - 2\bar{x}(\bar{x}) + \bar{x}^2(1) = \overline{x^2} - \bar{x}^2.$$

Substituting this last result into Eq. (11–2), we have

$$s = \sqrt{\overline{x^2} - \bar{x}^2}. \tag{11–5}$$

Equation (11–5) shows us that the standard deviation s may be found by finding the mean of the squares of the x's, subtracting the square of $\bar{x}$, and then finding the square root. This eliminates the step of subtracting $\bar{x}$ from each x, a step required by the original definition.

Example B. In an ammeter, two resistances are connected in parallel. Most of the current passing through the meter goes through the one called the shunt. In order to determine the accuracy of the resistance of shunts being made for ammeters, a manufacturer tested a sample of 100 shunts. The resistance of each, to the nearest one-hundredth of an ohm, is indicated in the following table. Calculate the standard deviation of the resistances of the shunts.

R, ohms	f	fR	fR^2
0.200	1	0.200	0.0400
0.210	3	0.630	0.1323
0.220	5	1.100	0.2420
0.230	10	2.300	0.5290
0.240	17	4.080	0.9792
0.250	40	10.000	2.5000
0.260	13	3.380	0.8788
0.270	6	1.620	0.4374
0.280	3	0.840	0.2352
0.290	2	0.580	0.1682
	100	24.730	6.1421

$$\overline{R} = \frac{\Sigma fR}{\Sigma f} = \frac{24.73}{100} = 0.2473, \quad \overline{R}^2 = 0.06116,$$

$$\overline{R^2} = \frac{\Sigma fR^2}{\Sigma f} = \frac{6.142}{100} = 0.06142, \quad \overline{R^2} - \overline{R}^2 = 0.00026,$$

$$s = \sqrt{0.00026} = 0.016.$$

The arithmetic mean of the resistances is 0.247 ohm, with a mean deviation of 0.016 ohm. In the calculations, one extra significant figure was carried.

Example C. By using Eq. (11–5), find s for the numbers in Example A. Again, a table is the most convenient form.

x	x^2
1	1
5	25
4	16
2	4
6	36
2	4
1	1
1	1
5	25
3	9
30	122

$$\overline{x} = \tfrac{30}{10} = 3, \quad \overline{x}^2 = 9,$$

$$\overline{x^2} = \tfrac{122}{10} = 12.2,$$

$$\overline{x^2} - \overline{x}^2 = 12.2 - 9 = 3.2,$$

$$s = \sqrt{3.2} = 1.8.$$

Example D. Find the standard deviation of the grades in Example A of Section 11–1. Use the frequency distribution as grouped in intervals 20–24, 25–29, and so forth, and then assume that each value in the interval is equal to the representative value (middle value) of the interval. (This method is not exact, but when a problem involves a large number of values, the method provides a very good approximation and eliminates a great deal of arithmetic work.)

x	f	fx	fx^2
22	1	22	484
27	0	0	0
32	0	0	0
37	1	37	1,370
42	3	126	5,290
47	1	47	2,210
52	1	52	2,700
57	4	228	13,000
62	8	496	30,800
67	10	670	44,900
72	14	1,008	72,600
77	16	1,232	94,900
82	7	574	47,100
87	7	609	53,000
92	5	460	42,300
97	2	194	18,800
	80	5,755	429,500

$$\bar{x} = \frac{\Sigma fx}{\Sigma f} = \frac{5,755}{80} = 71.9,$$

$$\bar{x}^2 = 5,170,$$

$$\overline{x^2} = \frac{\Sigma fx^2}{80} = \frac{429,500}{80} = 5,370,$$

$$\overline{x^2} - \bar{x}^2 = 200,$$

$$s = \sqrt{200} = 14.1.$$

(Three significant figures are used so that the slide rule may be employed for calculations. Actually s is good only to two significant figures, because 200 only has two.)

The normal probability curve

FIGURE 11–5

The significance of the standard deviation lies in the fact that, in practice, about 68% of the values are found within the limits of $\bar{x} - s$ to $\bar{x} + s$. This forms part of the basis of deriving what is known as the *normal probability curve* (see Fig. 11–5), which is a curve giving the theoretical distribution about the

arithmetic mean. In a more complete discussion of the normal probability
curve, it is shown that its theoretical equation is

$$y = \frac{1}{\sqrt{2\pi}} e^{-x^2/2}. \tag{11-6}$$

In Example D we find that 59 of the 80 values (74%) are from 58 to 86, which
is the range of $\bar{x} - s$ to $\bar{x} + s$. This means that there are more values near the
mean than there are in a theoretical normal distribution.

Exercises

In Exercises 1 through 6, by means of Eq. (11–2), find s for the indicated sets of numbers
from exercises of Section 11–1.

  1. Set A   2. Set B   3. Set C

  4. Exercise 16   5. Exercise 21   6. Exercise 18

In Exercises 7 through 12, by means of Eq. (11–5), find s for the indicated sets of
numbers from the exercises of Section 11–1.

  7. Set A   8. Set C   9. Exercise 9

10. Exercise 16   11. Exercise 21   12. Exercise 18

In Exercises 13 through 15, find the percentage of values in the range $\bar{x} - s$ to $\bar{x} + s$
for the indicated sets of numbers from the exercises of Section 11–1.

13. Set C   14. Exercise 21   15. Exercise 18

16. Sketch the graph of Eq. (11–6). See Section 7–4.

11–3 Fitting a straight line to a set of points

We have been discussing statistical methods for dealing with one variable.
Methods of tabulating, graphing, measuring the central tendency and the
deviations from this value have been discussed, up to now, for one variable.
We now shall discuss how to obtain a relationship between two variables, for
which a set of points is known.

In this section we shall show a method of "fitting" a straight line to a given
set of points. In the following section fitting suitable nonlinear curves to given
sets of points will be discussed. Some of the reasons for doing this are (1) to
have a concise relationship expressed between the variables, (2) to use the
equation for the purpose of predicting certain fundamental results, (3) to determine the reliability of certain sets of data, and (4) to use the data for testing
theoretical concepts.

We shall assume for the examples and exercises of the remainder of this
chapter that there is some relationship between the variables. Often when we

are analyzing statistics for variables between which we think a relationship might exist, the points are so scattered as to give no reasonable idea regarding the possible functional relationship. We shall assume here that such combinations of variables have been discarded in the analysis.

Example A. All the students enrolled in the mathematics course referred to in Example A of Section 11–1 took an entrance test in mathematics. To study the reliability of this test, an instructor tabulated the test scores of 10 students (selected at random), along with their course averages, and made a graph of these figures. (See table below, and Fig. 11–6.)

Student	Entrance test score, based on 40	Course average, based on 100
A	29	63
B	33	88
C	22	77
D	17	67
E	26	70
F	37	93
G	30	72
H	32	81
I	23	47
J	30	74

We now ask whether or not there is a functional relationship between the test scores and the course grades. Certainly no clear-cut relationship exists, but in general we see that the higher the test score, the higher the course grade. This leads to the possibility that there might be some straight line, from which none of the points would vary too significantly. If such a line could be found, then it could be the basis of predictions as to the possible success a student might have in the course, on the basis of his grade on the entrance test. Assuming that such a straight line exists, the problem is to find the equation of this line. Figure 11–7 shows two such possible lines.

FIGURE 11–6

FIGURE 11–7

There are various methods of determining the line which best fits the given points. We shall employ the one which is most widely used: the *method of least squares*. The basic principle of this method is that the sum of the squares of the deviation of all points from the best line (in accordance with this method) is the least it can be. By "deviation," we mean the difference between the y-value of the line and the y-value for the point (of original data) for a particular value of x.

Example B. In Fig. 11–7 the deviation of one point is indicated. The point $(67, 17)$ (student D of Example A) has a deviation of 8 from the indicated line of Fig. 11–7. Thus we square the value of this deviation to obtain 64. The method of least squares requires that the sum of all such squares be a minimum in order to determine the line which fits best.

Therefore, in applying this method, it is necessary to use the equation of a straight line and the coordinates of the points of the data. The deviation of these is indicated and squared. The problem then arises as to the method of determining the constants m and b in the equation of the line $y = mx + b$ for which these squares are a minimum. The following example indicates the method employed and forms a basis for determining the equations for finding m and b.

Example C. Given the points (x_1, y_1), (x_2, y_2), and (x_3, y_3), find m and b in the equation

$$y = mx + b$$

for which the sum of the squares of the deviations is a minimum.

The deviations are

$$d_1 = y_1 - (mx_1 + b),$$

$$d_2 = y_2 - (mx_2 + b),$$

and

$$d_3 = y_3 - (mx_3 + b).$$

Squaring each of these expressions and finding the sum of the squares, we have

$$S = y_1^2 + y_2^2 + y_3^2 + m^2(x_1^2 + x_2^2 + x_3^2)$$
$$+ 3b^2 - 2m(x_1y_1 + x_2y_2 + x_3y_3)$$
$$-2b(y_1 + y_2 + y_3) + 2mb(x_1 + x_2 + x_3).$$

We want S to be a minimum with respect to each of m and b. Therefore this is a maximum-minimum type of problem of Section 9–4. We shall find the partial derivatives of S with respect to m and with respect to b, set each of these equal to zero, and solve the resulting equations simultaneously:

$$\frac{\partial S}{\partial m} = 2m(x_1^2 + x_2^2 + x_3^2) - 2(x_1y_1 + x_2y_2 + x_3y_3) + 2b(x_1 + x_2 + x_3),$$

$$\frac{\partial S}{\partial b} = 6b - 2(y_1 + y_2 + y_3) + 2m(x_1 + x_2 + x_3).$$

Setting the second of these equations equal to zero, and solving for b, we have

$$b = \frac{(y_1 + y_2 + y_3) - m(x_1 + x_2 + x_3)}{3}.$$

Observation of this equation shows it may be written as

$$b = \bar{y} - m\bar{x}, \tag{1}$$

where $\bar{y}$ and $\bar{x}$ are the arithmetic means of the coordinates of the given points.

Setting $\partial S/\partial m = 0$, we may obtain

$$m(x_1^2 + x_2^2 + x_3^2) = (x_1y_1 + x_2y_2 + x_3y_3) - b(x_1 + x_2 + x_3).$$

Dividing this equation through by 3, we note it may be written as

$$m\overline{x^2} = \overline{xy} - b\bar{x}, \tag{2}$$

where $\overline{x^2}$ and $\overline{xy}$ are the respective arithmetic means of the coordinates of the given points.

Substituting the expression for b from Eq. (1) in Eq. (2) we have

$$m\overline{x^2} = \overline{xy} - (\bar{y} - m\bar{x})\bar{x},$$

which may be written as

$$m = \frac{\overline{xy} - \bar{x}\,\bar{y}}{\overline{x^2} - \bar{x}^2}. \tag{3}$$

Evaluating the appropriate arithmetic means, m and b may be determined for the least-squares line when actual numerical values are given.

Generalizing on Example C, and using Eq. (11–5), we have the general equations for m and b for the least-squares straight line as

$$m = \frac{\overline{xy} - \bar{x}\bar{y}}{s_x^2} \tag{11–7}$$

and

$$b = \bar{y} - m\bar{x}, \tag{11–8}$$

where s_x is the standard deviation of the x-values. Evaluating m and b for a given set of points and substituting them into the equation of a straight line

$$y = mx + b, \qquad (11-9)$$

we have the equation of the *least-squares line*.

Example D. Find the least-squares line of the data of Example A.

Here the y-values will be the entrance-test scores, and the x-values the course averages. The results are best obtained by tabulating the necessary quantities, as we do in the table below.

x	y	xy	x^2
63	29	1,830	3,970
88	33	2,900	7,740
77	22	1,690	5,930
67	17	1,140	4,490
70	26	1,820	4,900
93	37	3,440	8,650
72	30	2,160	5,180
81	32	2,590	6,560
47	23	1,080	2,210
74	30	2,220	5,480
732	279	20,870	55,110

$$\bar{x} = \frac{732}{10} = 73.2, \qquad \bar{x}^2 = 5358,$$

$$\bar{y} = \frac{279}{10} = 27.9, \qquad \bar{x}\,\bar{y} = 2040,$$

$$\overline{xy} = \frac{20,870}{10} = 2087, \qquad \overline{x^2} = \frac{55,110}{10} = 5511,$$

$$s_x^2 = \overline{x^2} - \bar{x}^2 = 153$$

$$m = \frac{\overline{xy} - \bar{x}\,\bar{y}}{s_x^2} = \frac{2087 - 2040}{153}$$

$$= \frac{47}{153} = 0.307,$$

$$b = \bar{y} - m\bar{x} = 27.9 - (0.307)(73.2) = 27.9 - 22.5 = 5.4;$$

$$y = 0.307x + 5.4.$$

Thus the equation of the line is $y = 0.307x + 5.4$. This is the line indicated in Fig. 11–8.

Remark 1: For ease of computation, and to keep the graph within the same limits as the original points, we can reduce all x-values by 40 and all y-values by 10. The origin of these values would be at the intersection of the light lines in Fig. 11–8.

FIGURE 11–8

Remark 2: When we are plotting the least-squares line, we know two points on it. These are $(0, b)$ and $(\bar{x}, \bar{y})$. We can see that $(\bar{x}, \bar{y})$ satisfies the equation from the solution for b [Eq. (11–8)].

Example E. In an experiment to determine the relation between the load on a spring and the length of the spring, the following data were found.

Load (lb)	0.0	1.0	2.0	3.0	4.0	5.0
Length (in.)	10.0	11.2	12.3	13.4	14.6	15.9

Find the least-squares line for this data which expresses the length as a function of the load.

x	y	xy	x^2
0.0	10.0	0.0	0.0
1.0	11.2	11.2	1.0
2.0	12.3	24.6	4.0
3.0	13.4	40.2	9.0
4.0	14.6	58.4	16.0
5.0	15.9	79.5	25.0
15.0	77.4	213.9	55.0

$$\bar{x} = \frac{15.0}{6} = 2.50, \quad \bar{x}^2 = 6.25,$$

$$\bar{y} = \frac{77.4}{6} = 12.9, \quad \bar{x}\,\bar{y} = 32.25,$$

$$\overline{xy} = \frac{213.9}{6} = 35.65, \quad \overline{x^2} = \frac{55.0}{6} = 9.17,$$

$$s_x^2 = \overline{x^2} - \bar{x}^2 = 9.17 - 6.25 = 2.92,$$

$$m = \frac{35.65 - 32.25}{2.92} = 1.16, \quad b = 12.9 - (1.16)(2.50) = 10.0.$$

Therefore, the least-squares line in this case is

$$y = 1.16x + 10.0,$$

where y is the length of the spring and x is the load. In Fig. 11–9, the line shown is the least-squares line, and the points are the experimental data points.

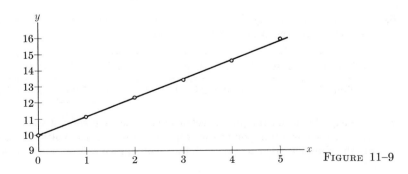

FIGURE 11–9

Exercises

In Exercises 1 through 8, find the equation of the least-squares line for the given data. In each case graph the line and the data points on the same graph.

1. The points in the following table:

x	4	6	8	10	12
y	1	4	5	8	9

2. The points in the following table:

x	1	2	3	4	5	6	7
y	10	17	28	37	49	56	72

3. The points in the following table:

x	20	26	30	38	48	60
y	160	145	135	120	100	90

4. The points in the following table:

x	1	3	6	5	8	10	4	7	3	8
y	15	12	10	8	9	2	11	9	11	7

5. In an electrical experiment, the following data were found for the values of current and voltage for a particular element of the circuit. Find the voltage as a function of the current.

Voltage (volts)	3.00	4.10	5.60	8.00	10.50
Current (milliamperes)	15.0	10.8	9.30	3.55	4.60

6. The velocity of a falling object was found each second by use of an electrical device as shown. Find the velocity as a function of time.

Velocity (cm/sec)	970	1950	2950	3940	4920	5890	6860
Time (sec)	1.00	2.00	3.00	4.00	5.00	6.00	7.00

7. In an experiment on the photoelectric effect, the frequency of the light being used was measured as a function of the stopping potential (the voltage just sufficient to stop the photoelectric current) with the results given below. Find the least-squares

line for V as a function of f. The frequency for $V = 0$ is known as the *threshold frequency*. From the graph, determine the threshold frequency.

V (volts)	0.35	0.60	0.85	1.10	1.45	1.80
f ($\times$ 10^{14} 1/sec)	5.50	6.05	6.60	7.35	8.05	8.80

8. If a gas is cooled under conditions of constant volume, it is noted that the pressure falls nearly proportionally as the temperature. If this were to happen until there was no pressure, the theoretical temperature for this case is referred to as *absolute zero*. In an elementary experiment, the following data were found for pressure and temperature for a gas under constant volume.

P (cm of Hg)	100	107	115	121	129	137
T (°C)	0.0	20	40	50	80	100

Find the least-squares line for P as a function of T, and, from the graph, determine the value of absolute zero found in this experiment.

The linear coefficient of correlation, a measure of the relatedness of two variables, is defined by

$$r = m \frac{s_x}{s_y}.$$

Due to its definition, the values of r lie in the range $-1 \le r \le 1$. If r is near 1, the correlation is considered good. For values of r between $-\frac{1}{2}$ and $+\frac{1}{2}$, the correlation is poor. If r is near -1, the variables are said to be negatively correlated; that is, one increases while the other decreases.

In Exercises 9 through 12 compute r for the given sets of data.

  9. Exercise 1   10. Exercise 2   11. Exercise 4   12. Example A

11–4 Fitting nonlinear curves to data

If the experimental points do not appear to be on a straight line, but we recognize them as being approximately on some other type of curve, the method of least squares can be extended to use on these other curves. For example, if the points are apparently on a parabola, we could use the function $y = a + bx^2$. To use the above method, we shall extend the least-squares line to

$$y = m[f(x)] + b. \qquad (11\text{–}10)$$

Here, $f(x)$ must be calculated first, and then the problem can be treated as a least-squares line to find the values of m and b. Some of the functions $f(x)$ which may be considered for use are x^2, $1/x$, and 10^x.

Example A. Find the least-squares curve $y = mx^2 + b$ for the points in the following table.

y	1	5	12	24	53	76
x	0	1	2	3	4	5

The necessary quantities are tabulated for purposes of calculation.

x	y	$f(x) = x^2$	yx^2	$(x^2)^2$
0	1	0	0	0
1	5	1	5	1
2	12	4	48	16
3	24	9	216	81
4	53	16	848	256
5	76	25	1900	625
	171	55	3017	979

$$\overline{x^2} = \frac{55}{6} = 9.17, \ \overline{x^2}^2 = 84.1,$$

$$\bar{y} = \frac{171}{6} = 28.5, \ \overline{x^2 y} = 261,$$

$$\overline{yx^2} = \frac{3017}{6} = 503, \ \overline{(x^2)^2} = \frac{979}{6} = 163.2,$$

$$s_{(x^2)}^2 = 163.2 - 84.1 = 79.1,$$

$$m = \frac{503 - 261}{79.1} = \frac{242}{79.1} = 3.06, \ b = 28.5 - (3.06)(9.17) = 0.40.$$

Therefore the desired equation is $y = 3.06x^2 + 0.40$. The graph of this equation and the data points are shown in Fig. 11–10.

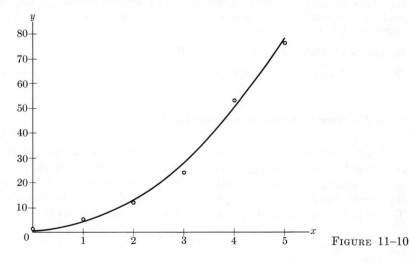

FIGURE 11–10

Example B. In a physics experiment, designed to measure the pressure and volume of a gas at constant temperature, the following data were found. When the points were plotted, they were seen to approximate the hyperbola $y = c/x$.

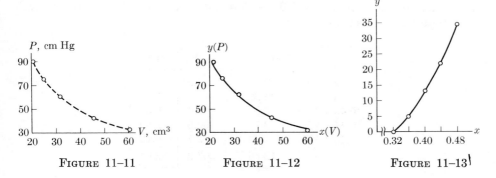

FIGURE 11–11   FIGURE 11–12   FIGURE 11–13

Find the least-squares approximation to this hyperbola $[y = m(1/x) + b]$. See Fig. 11–11.

P, cm Hg	V, cm^3		$x(=V)$	$y(=P)$	$f(x) = 1/x$	$y(1/x)$	$(1/x)^2$
90.0	21.0		21.0	90.0	0.0476	4.29	0.00227
74.4	25.0		25.0	74.4	0.0400	2.98	0.00160
61.0	31.8		31.8	61.0	0.0314	1.92	0.00100
45.5	41.1		41.1	45.5	0.0243	1.11	0.00059
32.0	60.1		60.1	32.0	0.0166	0.53	0.00028
				302.9	0.1599	10.83	0.00574

$$\overline{\frac{1}{x}} = 0.0320, \quad \overline{\left(\frac{1}{x}\right)}^2 = 0.00102, \quad \overline{y} = 60.6, \quad \overline{\frac{1}{x}\,\overline{y}} = 1.94,$$

$$\overline{y\left(\frac{1}{x}\right)} = 2.17, \quad \overline{\left(\frac{1}{x}\right)^2} = 0.00115, \quad s^2_{(1/x)} = 0.00115 - 0.00102$$

$$= 0.00013,$$

$$m = \frac{2.17 - 1.94}{0.00013} = 1770, \quad b = 60.6 - 1770(0.032) = 4.0.$$

Thus the equation of the hyperbola $y = m(1/x) + b$ is $y = 1770/x + 4$. The graph of this hyperbola and the points representing the data are shown in Fig. 11–12.

Example C. It has been found experimentally that the tensile strength of brass (a copper-zinc alloy) increases (within certain limits) with the percentage of zinc. The following table indicates the values which have been found. (Also see Fig. 11–13.)

Tensile strength (10^5 lb/in^2)	0.32	0.36	0.40	0.44	0.48
Percentage of zinc	0	5	13	22	34

Fit a curve of the form $y = m(10^x) + b$ to the data. Let $x =$ tensile strength ($\times 10^5$) and $y =$ percentage of zinc.

x	y	$f(x) = 10^x$	$y(10^x)$	$(10^x)^2$
0.32	0	2.09	0.0	4.37
0.36	5	2.29	11.4	5.25
0.40	13	2.51	32.6	6.31
0.44	22	2.75	60.5	7.59
0.48	34	3.02	102.7	9.12
	74	12.66	207.2	32.64

To find $f(x) = 10^x$, we use logarithms. When $x = 0.32$, $10^{0.32}$ may be found by looking up the number for which 0.32 is the logarithm. This is due to the definition of a logarithm. Values of $(10^x)^2$ are found in the same manner. When $x = 0.32$, $(10^{0.32})^2 = (10)^{0.64}$, and the antilogarithm of 0.64 is required.

$$\overline{10^x} = 2.53, \quad \overline{10^{x^2}} = 6.40,$$

$$\bar{y} = 14.8,$$

$$\overline{10^x}\,\bar{y} = 37.4,$$

$$\overline{y(10^x)} = 41.4, \quad \overline{(10^x)^2} = 6.53,$$

$$s^2_{(10^x)} = 6.53 - 6.40 = 0.13,$$

$$m = \frac{41.4 - 37.4}{0.13} = 31,$$

$$b = 14.8 - 31(2.53) = -64.$$

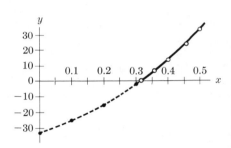

FIGURE 11–14

The equation of the curve is $y = 31(10^x) - 64$. It must be remembered that for practical purposes y must be positive. The graph of the equation is shown in Fig. 11–14, with the solid portion denoting the meaningful part of the curve. The points of the data are also shown.

Exercises

In each of the following exercises, find the indicated least-squares curve. Sketch the curve and plot the data points on the same graph.

1. For the points in the following table, find the least-squares curve $y = mx^2 + b$.

x	2	4	6	8	10
y	12	38	72	135	200

2. For the points in the following table, find the least-squares curve $y = m\sqrt{x} + b$.

x	0	4	8	12	16
y	1	9	11	14	15

3. For the points in the following table, find the least-squares curve $y = m(1/x) + b$.

x	1.10	2.45	4.04	5.86	6.90	8.54
y	9.85	4.50	2.90	1.75	1.48	1.30

4. For the points in the following table, find the least-squares curve $y = m(10^x) + b$.

x	0.00	0.200	0.500	0.950	1.325
y	6.00	6.60	8.20	14.0	26.0

5. The following data was found for the distance y that an object rolled down an inclined plane in time t. Determine the least-squares curve $y = mt^2 + b$.

y (cm)	6.0	23	55	98	148
t (sec)	1.0	2.0	3.0	4.0	5.0

6. The increase in length of a certain metallic rod was measured in relation to particular increases in temperature. If y represents the increase in length for the corresponding increase in temperature x, find the least-squares curve $y = m(x^2) + b$ for these data.

x (°C)	50.0	100	150	200	250
y (cm)	1.00	4.40	9.40	16.4	24.0

7. Use the data of Exercise 6 and determine the least-squares curve $y = m(10^z) + b$ where $z = x/1000$.

8. Measurements were made of the current in an electric circuit as a function of time. The circuit contained a resistance of 5 ohms and an inductance of 10 henries. The following data was found.

i (amps)	0.00	2.52	3.45	3.80	3.92
t (sec)	0.00	2.00	4.00	6.00	8.00

Find the least-squares curve $i = m(e^{-0.5t}) + b$ for this data. Use natural logarithms. From the equation, determine the value the current approaches as t approaches infinity.

9. The resonant frequency of an electric circuit containing a 4×10^{-6} farad capacitor was measured as a function of an inductance in the circuit. The following data was found.

f (1/sec)	490	360	250	200	170
L (henries)	1	2	4	6	9

Find the least-squares curve $f = m(1/\sqrt{L}) + b$.

10. The displacement of a pendulum bob from its equilibrium position as a function of time gave the following results.

Displacement (cm)	0.00	7.80	10.0	8.10	0.00
Time (sec)	0.00	0.90	1.60	2.20	3.15

Find the least-squares curve of the form $y = m(\sin x) + b$, expressing the displacement as y and the time as x.

Miscellaneous exercises for Chapter 11

In Exercises 1 through 3 use the following set of numbers. 2.3, 2.6, 4.2, 3.6, 3.5, 4.1, 4.8, 2.5, 3.0, 4.1, 3.8.

1. Determine the median of the set of numbers.
2. Determine the arithmetic mean of the given set of numbers.
3. Determine the standard deviation of the given set of numbers.

An important property of oil is its coefficient of viscosity, which gives a measure of how well it flows. In order to determine the viscosity of a certain motor oil, a refinery took samples from 12 different storage tanks and tested them at 130°F (a standard reference temperature). The results (in centipoise units) were 240, 280, 290, 260, 270, 260, 250, 270, 280, 260, 260, 250. In Exercises 4 through 8, for these data:

4. Determine the median.
5. Determine the arithmetic mean.
6. Make a histogram.
7. Make a frequency polygon.
8. Determine the standard deviation.

Two machine parts are considered satisfactorily assembled if their total thickness (to the nearest one-hundredth of an inch) is between or equal to 0.92 and 0.94 in. One hundred sample assemblies are tested, and the thicknesses, to the nearest one-hundredth of an inch, are given in the following table:

Total thickness	0.90	0.91	0.92	0.93	0.94	0.95	0.96
Number	3	9	31	38	12	5	2

In Exercises 9 through 13, for these data:

9. Determine the median total thickness.
10. Determine the arithmetic mean of the total thickness.
11. Make a histogram.
12. Make a frequency polygon.
13. Determine the standard deviation.
14. In a certain experiment, the resistance of a certain resistor was measured as a function of the temperature. The data found was as follows:

R (ohms)	25.0	26.8	28.9	31.2	32.8	34.7
T (°C)	0	20	40	60	80	100

Find the least-squares line for this data, expressing R as a function of T. Sketch the line and data points on the same graph.

15. The solubility of sodium chloride (table salt) (in grams per 100 cm^3 of water) as a function of temperature (°C) is measured as follows:

Solubility	35.7	36.0	36.6	37.3	38.4
Temperature	0	20	40	60	80

Find the least-squares straight line for these data.

16. The coefficient of friction of an object sliding down an inclined plane was measured as a function of the angle of incline of the plane. The following results were obtained.

Coefficient of friction	0.16	0.34	0.55	0.85	1.24	1.82	2.80
Angle (deg)	10	20	30	40	50	60	70

Find the least-squares curve of the form $y = m(\tan x) + b$, expressing the coefficient of friction as y and the angle as x.

17. An electrical device recorded the total distance (in cm) which an object fell at 0.1 sec intervals. Following are the data which were found.

Distance	4.90	19.5	44.0	78.1	122.0
Time	0.10	0.20	0.30	0.40	0.50

Find the least-squares curve of the form $y = mx^2 + b$, using y to represent distance and x to represent the time.

18. The period of a pendulum as a function of its length was measured, giving the following results.

Period (sec)	1.10	1.90	2.50	2.90	3.30
Length (ft)	1.00	3.00	5.00	7.00	9.00

Find the least-squares curve of the form $y = m\sqrt{x} + b$, which expresses the period as a function of the length.

19. In an elementary experiment which measured the wavelength of sound as a function of the frequency, the following results were obtained.

Wavelength (cm)	140	107	81	70	60
Frequency (1/sec)	240	320	400	480	560

Find the least-squares curve of the form $y = m(1/x) + b$ for this data, expressing wavelength as y and frequency as x.

12 Expansion of functions in series

12–1 Maclaurin series

The values of the trigonometric functions can be determined exactly only for a few certain angles. The value of e can only be approximated in decimal form. The question arises as to how these values may be determined, particularly if a specified degree of accuracy is necessary. In this chapter we shall show how a given function may be expressed in terms of a polynomial. Once the polynomial which approximates a given function has been found, we will be able to evaluate the function to any desired accuracy. Also, a number of other uses of this polynomial form will be shown.

Example A. By using long division, we have

$$\frac{2}{2 - x} = 1 + \tfrac{1}{2}x + \tfrac{1}{4}x^2 + \cdots + (\tfrac{1}{2}x)^{n-1} + \cdots, \qquad (1)$$

where n is the number of the term of the expression on the right. Since x represents a number, the right-hand side of Eq. (1) becomes a geometric progression of infinitely many terms.

From algebra, we know that the sum of a geometric progression of infinitely many terms is

$$S = \frac{a}{1 - r}, \qquad (2)$$

where a is the first term and r is the common ratio of successive terms.

If $x = 1$, the right-hand side of Eq. (1) is

$$1 + \tfrac{1}{2} + \tfrac{1}{4} + \cdots + (\tfrac{1}{2})^{n-1}.$$

For this progression, $r = \frac{1}{2}$ and $a = 1$, which means $S = 2$. If $x = 3$, the right-hand side of Eq. (1) is

$$1 + \tfrac{3}{2} + \tfrac{9}{4} + \cdots + (\tfrac{3}{2})^{n-1} + \cdots,$$

and this we know does not have a defined value, since $r > 1$. Referring back to the left side of Eq. (1), we see that it also equals 2, when $x = 1$. If $x = 3$, the left side is -2. Thus, we see that the two sides agree for $x = 1$, and do not give consistent results for $x = 3$. In fact, as long as $|x| < 2$, the values will agree. From this we can conclude that the expression on the right-hand side properly represents that on the left side, as long as $|x| < 2$.

From the above example, we see that an algebraic function may be properly represented by a function of the form

$$f(x) = a_0 + a_1 x + a_2 x^2 + \cdots + a_n x^n + \cdots. \tag{12-1}$$

Equation (12-1) is known as a *power-series expansion* of the function $f(x)$. The problem now arises as to whether or not functions in general may be represented in this form. If such a representation were possible, it would provide a means of evaluating the transcendental functions for the purpose of making tables of values. Also, since a power-series expansion is in the form of a polynomial, it makes algebraic operations much simpler, due to the properties of polynomials. A further study of calculus shows many other uses of power series.

At this point we shall assume that, unless otherwise noted, the functions with which we shall be dealing may be properly represented by a power-series expansion (it takes more advanced methods to prove that this is generally possible), for specified ranges of values of x. We shall find that the methods of calculus are very useful in developing the method of general representation. Thus, writing a general power series, along with the first few derivatives, we have

$$f(x) \;\; = a_0 + a_1 x + a_2 x^2 + a_3 x^3 + a_4 x^4 + a_5 x^5 + \cdots + a_n x^n + \cdots,$$

$$f'(x) \;\; = a_1 + 2a_2 x + 3a_3 x^2 + 4a_4 x^3 + 5a_5 x^4 + \cdots + na_n x^{n-1} + \cdots,$$

$$f''(x) \;\; = 2a_2 + 2 \cdot 3a_3 x + 3 \cdot 4a_4 x^2 + 4 \cdot 5a_5 x^3 + \cdots$$
$$\qquad\qquad + (n-1)na_n x^{n-2} + \cdots,$$

$$f'''(x) = 2 \cdot 3a_3 + 2 \cdot 3 \cdot 4a_4 x + 3 \cdot 4 \cdot 5a_5 x^2 + \cdots$$
$$\qquad\qquad + (n-2)(n-1)na_n x^{n-3} + \cdots,$$

$$f^{iv}(x) = 2 \cdot 3 \cdot 4a_4 + 2 \cdot 3 \cdot 4 \cdot 5a_5 x + \cdots$$
$$\qquad\qquad + (n-3)(n-2)(n-1)na_n x^{n-4} + \cdots.$$

Regardless of the values of the constants a_n for any power series, if $x = 0$, the left and right sides must be equal, and all the terms on the right are zero except the first. Thus, setting $x = 0$ in each of the above equations, we have

$$f(0) = a_0, \qquad f'(0) = a_1, \qquad f''(0) = 2a_2, \qquad f'''(0) = 2 \cdot 3a_3,$$

$$f^{\text{iv}}(0) = 2 \cdot 3 \cdot 4a_4.$$

Solving each of these for the constants a_n, we have

$$a_0 = f(0), \qquad a_1 = f'(0), \qquad a_2 = \frac{f''(0)}{2!}, \qquad a_3 = \frac{f'''(0)}{3!}, \qquad a_4 = \frac{f^{\text{iv}}(0)}{4!}.$$

Substituting these back into the expression for $f(x)$, we have

$$f(x) = f(0) + f'(0)x + \frac{f''(0)x^2}{2!} + \frac{f'''(0)x^3}{3!} + \cdots + \frac{f^{(n)}(0)x^n}{n!} + \cdots . \qquad (12\text{–}2)$$

Equation (12–2) is known as the *Maclaurin series expansion* of a function. For a function to be represented by a Maclaurin expansion, the function and all its derivatives must exist at $x = 0$.

In developing the Maclaurin series, we introduced the *factorial notation*, $n!$. By definition,

$$n! = n(n - 1)(n - 2)(\cdots)(1). \qquad (12\text{–}3)$$

For example, $4! = 4 \cdot 3 \cdot 2 \cdot 1 = 24$. As we can see, this notation is convenient for use in power-series expansions. It is also used in other fields of mathematics.

Example B. Find the first four terms of the Maclaurin series expansion of $f(x) = 2/(2 - x)$.

This is written as

$$f(x) \quad = \frac{2}{2 - x}, \qquad f(0) \quad = 1,$$

$$f'(x) \quad = \frac{2}{(2 - x)^2}, \quad f'(0) \quad = \frac{1}{2},$$

$$f''(x) \quad = \frac{4}{(2 - x)^3}, \quad f''(0) \quad = \frac{1}{2},$$

$$f'''(x) = \frac{12}{(2 - x)^4}, \quad f'''(0) = \frac{3}{4},$$

$$f(x) \quad = 1 + \frac{1}{2}x + \frac{1}{2}\left(\frac{x^2}{2!}\right) + \frac{3}{4}\left(\frac{x^3}{3!}\right) + \cdots$$

or

$$\frac{2}{2 - x} = 1 + \frac{1}{2}x + \frac{1}{4}x^2 + \frac{1}{8}x^3 + \cdots .$$

We see that this result agrees with that obtained by direct division.

Example C. Find the first four terms of the Maclaurin series expansion of $f(x) = e^{-x}$.

We write

$$f(x) \quad = e^{-x}, \quad f(0) \quad = 1,$$
$$f'(x) \quad = -e^{-x}, \quad f'(0) \quad = -1,$$
$$f''(x) \quad = e^{-x}, \quad f''(0) = 1,$$
$$f'''(x) = -e^{-x}, \quad f'''(0) = -1,$$
$$f(x) \quad = 1 + (-1)x + 1\left(\frac{x^2}{2!}\right) + (-1)\left(\frac{x^3}{3!}\right) + \cdots$$

or

$$e^{-x} = 1 - x + \frac{x^2}{2!} - \frac{x^3}{3!} + \cdots.$$

Example D. Find the first three nonzero terms of the Maclaurin series expansion of $f(x) = \sin 2x$.

We have

$$f(x) \quad = \quad \sin 2x, \quad f(0) \quad = 0, \quad f'(x) \quad = \quad 2\cos 2x, \quad f'(0) \quad = \quad 2,$$
$$f''(x) = -4\sin 2x, \quad f''(0) = 0, \quad f'''(x) = -8\cos 2x, \quad f'''(0) = -8,$$
$$f^{iv}(x) = \quad 16\sin 2x, \quad f^{iv}(0) = 0, \quad f^{v}(x) \quad = \quad 32\cos 2x, \quad f^{v}(0) \quad = \quad 32,$$
$$f(x) \quad = 0 + 2x + 0 + (-8)\frac{x^3}{3!} + 0 + 32\frac{x^5}{5!} + \cdots$$

or

$$\sin 2x = 2x - \frac{4}{3}x^3 + \frac{4}{15}x^5 - \cdots.$$

This series is called an *alternating series*, since every other term is negative.

Example E. Find the first three nonzero terms of the Maclaurin expansion of the function $f(x) = xe^{2x}$.

$$f(x) \quad = xe^{2x}, \quad f(0) \quad = 0,$$
$$f'(x) \quad = e^{2x}(1 + 2x), \quad f'(0) = 1,$$
$$f''(x) \quad = e^{2x}(4 + 4x), \quad f''(0) = 4,$$
$$f'''(x) = e^{2x}(12 + 8x), \quad f'''(0) = 12,$$
$$f(x) \quad = 0 + x + 4\left(\frac{x^2}{2!}\right) + 12\left(\frac{x^3}{3!}\right) + \cdots$$

or

$$xe^{2x} = x + 2x^2 + 2x^3 + \cdots.$$

Exercises

In Exercises 1 through 10, find in each case the first three nonzero terms of the Maclaurin expansion of the given functions.

1. $f(x) = e^x$ 2. $f(x) = \sin x$ 3. $f(x) = \cos x$

4. $f(x) = \ln (1 + x)$ 5. $f(x) = \sqrt{1 + x}$ 6. $f(x) = \frac{1}{2}(e^x + e^{-x})$

7. $f(x) = \cos 4x$ 8. $f(x) = \dfrac{1}{(1 + x)^2}$ 9. $f(x) = \dfrac{1}{1 - x}$

10. $f(x) = e^x \sin x$

In Exercises 11 through 16, find the first two nonzero terms of the Maclaurin expansion of the given functions.

11. $f(x) = \text{Arctan } x$ 12. $f(x) = \tan x$ 13. $f(x) = \ln \cos x$

14. $f(x) = \sec x$ 15. $f(x) = \cos x^2$ 16. $f(x) = xe^{\sin x}$

17. Why is it not possible to find a Maclaurin expansion of the following functions?

 (a) $f(x) = \csc x$, (b) $f(x) = \sqrt{x}$, (c) $f(x) = \ln x$.

12–2 Certain operations with series

The series found in the first four exercises of Section 12–1 are of particular importance. They are used to find values of exponential functions, trigonometric functions, and logarithms. Also they may be used to develop other series. We shall give them here for reference:

$$e^x = 1 + x + \frac{x^2}{2!} + \frac{x^3}{3!} + \cdots, \qquad (12\text{–}4)$$

$$\sin x = x - \frac{x^3}{3!} + \frac{x^5}{5!} - \cdots, \qquad (12\text{–}5)$$

$$\cos x = 1 - \frac{x^2}{2!} + \frac{x^4}{4!} - \cdots, \qquad (12\text{–}6)$$

$$\ln (1 + x) = x - \frac{x^2}{2} + \frac{x^3}{3} - \frac{x^4}{4} + \cdots. \qquad (12\text{–}7)$$

In the next section we shall see how we make use of these series in the development of tables. In this section we shall not only see how new series may be developed by using the above basic series, but also we shall see certain other uses of series.

When we discussed functions in Chapter 2, we made brief mention of functions such as $f(2x)$, $f(x^2)$, and $f(-x)$. By using this functional notation and the above series, we can find the series expansions of a great many other series without the use of direct expansion. This can often save a great deal of time in finding a desired series. The examples given here illustrate the use of series for this purpose.

Example A. Find the Maclaurin expansion of e^{2x}.
  From Eq. (12–4), we know the expansion of e^x. Hence

$$f(x) = 1 + x + \frac{x^2}{2!} + \frac{x^3}{3!} + \cdots .$$

Since $e^{2x} = f(2x)$, we have

$$f(2x) = 1 + (2x) + \frac{(2x)^2}{2!} + \frac{(2x)^3}{3!} + \cdots$$

or

$$e^{2x} = 1 + 2x + 2x^2 + \frac{4x^3}{3} + \cdots .$$

Example B. Find the Maclaurin expansion of $\sin x^2$.
  From Eq. (12–5), we know the expansion of $\sin x$. Therefore

$$f(x) = x - \frac{x^3}{3!} + \frac{x^5}{5!} - \cdots .$$

Since $\sin x^2 = f(x^2)$, we have

$$f(x^2) = (x^2) - \frac{(x^2)^3}{3!} + \frac{(x^2)^5}{5!} - \cdots$$

or

$$\sin x^2 = x^2 - \frac{x^6}{3!} + \frac{x^{10}}{5!} - \cdots .$$

Direct expansion of this series is quite lengthy.

A result very important in the development of complex numbers in mathematics and in electrical theory is now demonstrated. Assuming that the Maclaurin expansions for e^x, $\sin x$, and $\cos x$ are valid for complex numbers, we have ($j = \sqrt{-1}$)

$$e^{j\theta} = 1 + j\theta + \frac{(j\theta)^2}{2!} + \frac{(j\theta)^3}{3!} + \cdots = 1 + j\theta - \frac{\theta^2}{2!} - j\frac{\theta^3}{3!} + \cdots , \quad (12\text{–}8)$$

$$j \sin \theta = j\theta - j\frac{\theta^3}{3!} + \cdots , \quad (12\text{–}9)$$

$$\cos \theta = 1 - \frac{\theta^2}{2!} + \cdots . \quad (12\text{–}10)$$

When we add the terms of Eq. (12–9) to those of Eq. (12–10), the result is the series given in Eq. (12–8). Thus

$$e^{j\theta} = \cos \theta + j \sin \theta. \quad (12\text{–}11)$$

The *rectangular form* of a complex number is $a + bj$. The *polar* (or trigonometric) *form* is $r(\cos \theta + j \sin \theta)$, and the *exponential form* is $re^{j\theta}$, where $r = \sqrt{a^2 + b^2}$. Thus, by these definitions and Eq. (12–11), we have

$$a + bj = r(\cos \theta + j \sin \theta) = re^{j\theta}, \tag{12–12}$$

where

$$r = \sqrt{a^2 + b^2}. \tag{12–13}$$

The following example illustrates the use of Eq. (12–12), and certain applications are found in the exercises.

Example C. Express $2e^{4.80j}$ in rectangular form.
  Using Eq. (12–12), we have

$$2e^{4.80j} = 2(\cos 4.80 + j \sin 4.80).$$

Since $4.80 = 275°$, we find

$$2e^{4.80j} = 2(\cos 275° + j \sin 275°)$$

$$= 2(0.0872 - j\, 0.9962)$$

$$= 0.1744 - 1.9924j.$$

An additional use of power series is now shown. Many integrals which occur in practice cannot be integrated by methods given in the preceding chapters. However, power series can be very useful in giving excellent approximations to some definite integrals.

Example D. Evaluate: $\displaystyle\int_0^1 \frac{\sin x}{x}\, dx.$

By using the series expansion of $\sin x$, and dividing each term by x, we have

$$\int_0^1 \frac{\sin x}{x}\, dx = \int_0^1 \left(1 - \frac{x^2}{3!} + \frac{x^4}{5!} - \cdots\right) dx = \left(x - \frac{x^3}{3(3!)} + \frac{x^5}{5(5!)} - \cdots\right)\Big|_0^1$$

$$= 1 - \frac{1}{3(6)} + \frac{1}{5(120)} - \cdots.$$

Combining the values indicated, we have $1 - 0.05556 + 0.00166 = 0.9461$. We can see that each of the terms omitted was very small. The correct answer, to 4 decimal places, is 0.9461, which is precisely the value found by using only three terms of the expansion for $\sin x$.

Example E. Evaluate: $\displaystyle\int_0^{0.1} e^{-x^2}\, dx.$

We write
$$e^{-x^2} = 1 + (-x^2) + \frac{(-x^2)^2}{2!} + \cdots.$$

Thus
$$\int_0^{0.1} e^{-x^2}\, dx = \int_0^{0.1} \left(1 - x^2 + \frac{x^4}{2} - \cdots\right) dx$$

$$= \left(x - \frac{x^3}{3} + \frac{x^5}{10} - \cdots\right)\Bigg|_0^{0.1}$$

$$= 0.1 - \frac{0.001}{3} + \frac{0.00001}{10} = 0.09967.$$

This answer is correct to the indicated accuracy.

The question of accuracy now arises. The integrals just evaluated indicate that the more terms used, the greater the accuracy of the result. As an indication of the accuracy involved, Fig. 12–1 shows the graphs of $y = \sin x$ and the graphs of

$$y = x, \qquad y = x - \frac{x^3}{3!} \qquad \text{and} \qquad y = x - \frac{x^3}{3!} + \frac{x^5}{5!},$$

which are the first three approximations. We can see that each term added gives a better fit to the $\sin x$. Also, a graphical representation of the meaning of series expansions is indicated.

We have just shown that the more terms included, the more accurate the result. For small values of x, a Maclaurin series can give good accuracy with a very few terms. When this happens, we say that the series *converges* rapidly. For this reason a Maclaurin series is of particular use if small values of x are being considered. If larger values of x are being considered, usually a function is expanded in a Taylor series (see Section 12–4). Of course, when we omit the later terms in any series, a certain error is inherent in the calculation.

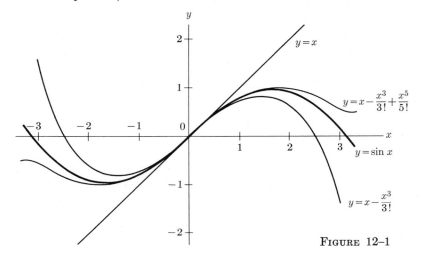

FIGURE 12–1

Exercises

In Exercises 1 through 8, find in each case the first four nonzero terms of the Maclaurin expansions of the given functions by using Eqs. (12–4) to (12–7).

1. $f(x) = \cos 4x$ 2. $f(x) = \ln (1 - x)$

3. $f(x) = \sin (x + \pi/6)$ [leave in powers of $(x + \pi/6)$]

4. $f(x) = e^{-2x}$ 5. $f(x) = \cos 2x^3$

6. $f(x) = \frac{1}{2}(e^x + e^{-x})$ (add terms of the proper series)

7. $f(x) = \ln (1 + x^2)$ 8. $f(x) = \sin x^4$

In Exercises 9 through 12, change the given complex numbers to the form indicated.

9. $3e^{0.5j}$ (rectangular)   10. $2(\cos 230° + j \sin 230°)$ (exponential)

11. $6 + j$ (polar)   12. $-3 + 2j$ (exponential)

In Exercises 13 through 16, evaluate the given integrals by use of three terms of the appropriate series.

13. $\displaystyle\int_0^1 \sin x^2 \, dx$ 14. $\displaystyle\int_0^{0.1} \frac{e^x - 1}{x} \, dx$

15. $\displaystyle\int_0^{0.2} \cos \sqrt{x} \, dx$ 16. $\displaystyle\int_0^1 \frac{\cos x - 1}{x} \, dx$

17. Show that by differentiating the expansion term by term for $\sin x$, the result is the expansion for $\cos x$.

18. Find the first three terms of the expansion for $e^x \sin x$ by multiplying the proper expansions together, term by term.

19. Find the approximate value of the area bounded by $y = x^2 e^x$, $x = 0.2$, and the x-axis, by use of three terms of the appropriate Maclaurin series.

20. Show, by use of Eq. (12–12) and the laws of exponents, that

$$(a + bj)^{1/n} = r^{1/n} \left(\cos \frac{\theta}{n} + j \sin \frac{\theta}{n} \right).$$

21. By use of the equation in Exercise 20, find the cube roots of 1. [*Hint:* Note that $1 = \cos 0° + j \sin 0° = \cos 360° + j \sin 360° = \cos 720° + j \sin 720°$.]

22. The impedance Z of an alternating current circuit, containing a resistance R, inductance L, and capacitance C, may be defined as $Z = R + j(X_L - X_C)$, where X_L and X_C are known as the inductive reactance and the capacitive reactance, respectively. Show, by use of Eq. (12–12) that the angle between Z and R is given by

$$\tan \theta = \frac{X_L - X_C}{R}.$$

23. Find the magnitude of the impedance of a circuit if $R = 8$ ohms, $X_L = 7$ ohms and $X_C = 13$ ohms. (Finding the magnitude of Z is equivalent to finding r for a complex number.)

12–3 Computations by use of series expansions

As mentioned previously, power-series expansions can be used to compute numerical values of transcendental functions. Also, by including a sufficient number of terms, we can calculate the values to any desired degree of accuracy. It is through such calculations that tables of values are made, and values of such numbers as e and π can be found.

Example A. Calculate the value of $e^{0.1}$;

$$e^x = 1 + x + \frac{x^2}{2!} + \cdots.$$

Let $x = 0.1$. Thus

$$e^{0.1} = 1 + 0.1 + \frac{(0.1)^2}{2} + \cdots = 1.105 \quad \text{(using 3 terms)}.$$

To 5 significant figures, $e^{0.1} = 1.1052$, which indicates that our answer is valid to four significant figures.

Example B. Calculate the value of $\sin 2°$;

$$\sin x = x - \frac{x^3}{3!} + \cdots.$$

Let $x = (\pi/90)$ (converting to radians). Hence

$$\sin 2° = \left(\frac{\pi}{90}\right) - \frac{(\pi/90)^3}{6} + \cdots = 0.034907 - 0.000007 = 0.034900.$$

This result is accurate to the number of figures shown.

Example C. Calculate the value of $\ln (1.2)$;

$$\ln (1 + x) = x - \frac{x^2}{2} + \frac{x^3}{3} - \cdots.$$

Let $x = 0.2$. Therefore

$$\ln (1 + 0.2) = 0.2 - \frac{(0.2)^2}{2} + \frac{(0.2)^3}{3} - \cdots = 0.183.$$

To 4 significant figures, $\ln (1.2) = 0.1823$. One more term is required to obtain this accuracy.

Series approximations can also be used to determine errors in calculated values due to errors in measured values. We have already discussed this topic as an application of differentials. A series solution of this kind of problem allows as close a calculation of the error as needed. With differentials, only one term can be found. Of course, for many purposes this is sufficient. The following example illustrates the use of series in error calculations.

Example D. The velocity v attained by an object that has fallen h ft is given by $v = 8\sqrt{h}$. Find the approximate error in the velocity of an object which has been found to drop 100 ft, with a possible error of 2 ft.

If we let $v = 8\sqrt{100 + x}$, where x is the error in h, we may express v as a Maclaurin series in x.

$$f(x) = 8(100 + x)^{1/2}, \qquad f(0) = 80,$$

$$f'(x) = 4(100 + x)^{-1/2}, \qquad f'(0) = 0.4,$$

$$f''(x) = -2(100 + x)^{-3/2}, \qquad f''(0) = -0.002.$$

Therefore,

$$v = 8\sqrt{100 + x} = 80 + 0.4x - 0.001x^2 - \cdots.$$

Since the actual calculated value of v, for $x = 0$, is 80, the error e in the value of v is

$$e = 0.4x - 0.001x^2 - \cdots.$$

Calculating the error for $x = 2$ is

$$e = 0.4(2) - 0.001(4) = 0.800 - 0.004 = 0.796 \text{ ft/sec.}$$

The value 0.8 is the same as that which would be found by use of differentials. The additional terms are corrections to this term. The one additional term in this case indicates that the first term is a good approximation to the error. Although this problem could be done numerically, a series solution, once set up, allows us to easily calculate the error for a given value of x.

Example E. Assuming that the earth is a perfect sphere 4000 mi in radius, find how far the end of a tangent line 2 mi long is from the surface.

From Fig. 12–2 we see that

$$x = 4000 \sec \theta - 4000.$$

Finding the series for $\sec \theta$, we have

$$f(\theta) = \sec \theta, \qquad f(0) = 1,$$

$$f'(\theta) = \sec \theta \tan \theta, \qquad f'(0) = 0,$$

$$f''(\theta) = \sec^3 \theta + \sec \theta \tan^2 \theta, \qquad f''(0) = 1.$$

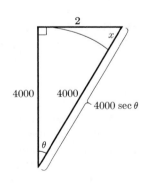

FIGURE 12–2

Thus the first two nonzero terms are sec $\theta = 1 + (\theta^2/2)$. Thus

$$x = 4000(\sec \theta - 1) = 4000 \left(1 + \frac{\theta^2}{2} - 1\right) = 2000\theta^2.$$

The first two terms of the expansion for tan θ are $\theta + \theta^3/3$, which means that if θ is small, which it is in this case, then $\theta = \tan \theta$. From Fig. 12–2, $\tan \theta = 2/4000$. Therefore, $\theta = 1/2000$. Substituting this value into the expression for x, we have

$$x = 2000 \left(\frac{1}{2000}\right)^2 = \frac{1}{2000} = 0.0005 \text{ mi.}$$

This means that the end of a two-mile line drawn tangent to the earth would only be about 2.6 ft from the surface!

Exercises

In Exercises 1 through 15, calculate the value of each of the given functions. Use the indicated number of terms of the appropriate series.

1. $e^{0.2}$ (3)
2. $e^{-0.5}$ (3)
3. sin (0.1) (2)
4. sin 4° (2)
5. e (7)
6. $\sqrt{e}$ (5)
7. cos 3° (2)
8. cos (0.5°) (2)
9. ln (1.4) (4)
10. ln (0.95) (4)
11. sin 1 (4)
12. ln (0.5) (5)
13. $\sqrt{1.1}$ (3) (use the expansion for $\sqrt{1 + x}$)
14. $\sqrt{0.8}$ (3)
15. $\sqrt[3]{1.1}$ (3)

If a series is alternating (if every other term is negative) the maximum possible error in the calculated value is the value of the first term omitted. Using this fact, calculate the maximum error of the values indicated in Exercises 16 through 18.

16. The value found in Exercise 2.
17. The value found in Exercise 3.
18. The value found in Exercise 9.
19. The electric current in a circuit containing a resistance R, and inductance L and a battery whose voltage is E is given by

$$i = \frac{E}{R} (1 - e^{-Rt/L}).$$

Approximate this expression by using the first three terms of the appropriate exponential series. Under what conditions will this approximation be valid?

20. The image distance q from a certain lens as a function of the object distance p is given by $q = 20p/(p - 20)$. Find the first three nonzero terms of the expansion of the right side. From this expression calculate q for $p = 2$ cm and compare with the value found by substituting 2 in the original expression.

21. From what height can a person see a point 10 mi distant along the earth's surface?

22. The efficiency (in percent) of an internal combustion engine in terms of its compression ratio c is given approximately by $E = 100(1 - c^{-0.4})$. Determine the possible approximate error in the efficiency for a compression ratio measured to be 6.00 with a possible error of 0.50. [*Hint:* Set up a series for $(6 + x)^{-0.4}$.]

12–4 Taylor's series

If values of certain functions are determined for values of x which are not close to zero, it is usually necessary to use many terms of a Maclaurin expansion to obtain accurate values. Therefore, another type of series, called a *Taylor's series*, is used for this purpose. Also, functions for which a Maclaurin series may not be found may have a Taylor's series. Actually, a Taylor's series is a more general expansion than a Maclaurin expansion.

The basic assumption in formulating a Taylor's expansion is that a function may be expanded in a polynomial of the form

$$f(x) = c_0 + c_1(x - a) + c_2(x - a)^2 + \cdots. \qquad (12\text{–}14)$$

By following precisely the same line of reasoning that we did in deriving the general Maclaurin expansion, we may find the constants c_0, c_1, c_2, and so forth. That is, derivatives of Eq. (12–14) are taken, and the function and its derivatives are evaluated for $x = a$. This leads to

$$f(x) = f(a) + f'(a)(x - a) + \frac{f''(a)(x - a)^2}{2!} + \cdots. \qquad (12\text{–}15)$$

The following examples illustrate the derivation of Taylor's series.

Example A. Expand $f(x) = e^x$ in a Taylor's series with $a = 1$.

$$f(x) = e^x, \qquad f(1) = e,$$
$$f'(x) = e^x, \qquad f'(1) = e,$$
$$f''(x) = e^x, \qquad f''(1) = e,$$
$$f'''(x) = e^x, \qquad f'''(1) = e, \text{ etc.,}$$

$$f(x) = e + e(x - 1) + e\frac{(x - 1)^2}{2!} + e\frac{(x - 1)^3}{3!} + \cdots,$$

$$e^x = e\left[1 + (x - 1) + \frac{(x - 1)^2}{2} + \frac{(x - 1)^3}{6} + \cdots\right].$$

This series is of particular use in evaluating e^x for values of x near 1.

Example B. Expand $f(x) = \sqrt{x}$ in powers of $(x - 4)$.

Another way of stating this is to find the Taylor's series for $f(x) = \sqrt{x}$, with $a = 4$. Thus,

$$f(x) = x^{1/2}, \qquad f(4) = 2,$$

$$f'(x) = \frac{1}{2x^{1/2}}, \qquad f'(4) = \frac{1}{4},$$

$$f''(x) = -\frac{1}{4x^{3/2}}, \quad f''(4) = -\frac{1}{32},$$

$$f'''(x) = \frac{3}{8x^{5/2}}, \qquad f'''(4) = \frac{3}{256}, \text{ etc.,}$$

$$f(x) = 2 + \tfrac{1}{4}(x - 4) - \frac{1}{32}\frac{(x - 4)^2}{2!} + \frac{3}{256}\frac{(x - 4)^3}{3!} - \cdots,$$

$$\sqrt{x} = 2 + \frac{(x - 4)}{4} - \frac{(x - 4)^2}{64} + \frac{(x - 4)^3}{512} - \cdots.$$

This series would be used to evaluate square roots of numbers near 4.

In the last section we evaluated functions by the use of Maclaurin series. In the following examples we shall use Taylor's series to determine certain values of functions.

Example C. By use of a Taylor series, evaluate $\sqrt{4.5}$.

Using the four terms of the series found in Example B, we have

$$\sqrt{4.5} = 2 + \frac{(4.5 - 4)}{4} - \frac{(4.5 - 4)^2}{64} + \frac{(4.5 - 4)^3}{512}$$

$$= 2 + \frac{(0.5)}{4} - \frac{(0.5)^2}{64} + \frac{(0.5)^3}{512}$$

$$= 2.0000 + 0.1250 - 0.0039 + 0.0002$$

$$= 2.1213.$$

The result is accurate to the number of places shown.

Example D. Calculate the approximate value of $\sin 29°$ by means of the appropriate Taylor expansion.

Since the value of $\sin 30°$ is known to be $\frac{1}{2}$, if we let $a = \pi/6$ (remember, we must use values expressed in radians), when we evaluate the expansion for $x = 29°$ (when expressed in radians) the quantity $(x - a)$ is $-\pi/180$ (equivalent to $-1°$). This means that its numerical values are small, and become smaller when it is raised to higher powers.

Therefore

$$f(x) \;=\; \sin x, \qquad f(\pi/6) \;=\; 1/2,$$
$$f'(x) \;=\; \cos x, \qquad f'(\pi/6) = \sqrt{3}/2,$$
$$f''(x) = -\sin x, \qquad f''(\pi/6) = -1/2,$$
$$f(x) \;=\; \frac{1}{2} + \frac{\sqrt{3}}{2}(x - \pi/6) - \frac{1}{4}(x - \pi/6)^2 - \cdots,$$

or

$$\sin x \;=\; \frac{1}{2} + \frac{\sqrt{3}}{2}(x - \pi/6) - \frac{1}{4}(x - \pi/6)^2 - \cdots;$$

$$\sin 29^\circ = \sin(\pi/6 - \pi/180)$$

$$= \frac{1}{2} + \frac{\sqrt{3}}{2}(\pi/6 - \pi/180 - \pi/6) - \frac{1}{4}(\pi/6 - \pi/180 - \pi/6)^2 - \cdots$$

$$= \frac{1}{2} + \frac{\sqrt{3}}{2}(-\pi/180) - \frac{1}{4}(-\pi/180)^2 - \cdots$$

$$= 0.500000 - (0.86603)(0.017453) - (0.25000)(0.017453)^2$$

$$= 0.500000 - 0.015115 - 0.000076 = 0.48481.$$

This result is accurate to the number of places shown.

Exercises

In Exercises 1 through 6, evaluate the given functions by use of the series developed in the examples of this section.

1. $e^{1.2}$ (use $e = 2.718$)   2. $e^{0.7}$
3. $\sqrt{4.2}$ 4. $\sqrt{3.5}$ 5. $\sin 31^\circ$ 6. $\sin 28^\circ$

In Exercises 7 through 14, find the first three nonzero terms of the Taylor expansion for the given function and given value of a.

7. e^{-x} $(a = 2)$ 8. $\cos x$ $(a = \pi/4)$ 9. $\sin x$ $(a = \pi/3)$

10. $\ln x$ $(a = 3)$ 11. $\sqrt[3]{x}$ $(a = 8)$ 12. $\dfrac{1}{x}$ $(a = 2)$

13. $\tan x$ $(a = \pi/4)$ 14. $\ln \sin x$ $(a = \pi/2)$

In Exercises 15 through 20, evaluate the given functions by use of three terms of the appropriate Taylor series.

15. $e^{-2.2}$ (use $e^{-2} = 0.1353$)   16. $\ln(3.1)$ (use $\ln 3 = 1.0986$)
17. $\sqrt[3]{8.3}$ 18. $\tan 46^\circ$ 19. $\sin 61^\circ$ 20. $\cos 42^\circ$

21. By completing the steps indicated before Eq. (12–15) in the text, complete the derivation of Eq. (12–15).

12–5 Fourier series

In expanding functions by use of Maclaurin and Taylor series, we have seen that it is possible to get excellent approximations near a specific value, but for values farther from this value the approximation requires many more terms. Often we need a good approximation over a greater range. For this purpose we use a series made of terms of sines and cosines. This also allows us to represent complicated functions in terms of the simpler sines and cosines.

We shall now assume that a function $f(x)$ may be represented by the series of sines and cosines as indicated:

$$f(x) = a_0 + a_1 \cos x + a_2 \cos 2x + \cdots + a_n \cos nx + \cdots$$
$$+ b_1 \sin x + b_2 \sin 2x + \cdots + b_n \sin nx + \cdots . \quad (12\text{–}16)$$

Since all the sines and cosines indicated in this expansion have a period of 2π (the period of any given term may be less than 2π, but all do repeat every 2π units—e.g., $\sin 2x$ has a period of π, but it also repeats every 2π), the series expansion indicated in Eq. (12–16) will also have a period of 2π. This series is called a *Fourier series*.

The principal problem to be solved is that of finding the coefficients a_n and b_n. Derivatives proved to be useful in finding the coefficients for a Maclaurin expansion. We use the properties of certain integrals to find the coefficients of a Fourier series. To utilize these properties, we multiply all terms of Eq. (12–16) by $\cos mx$, and then evaluate from $-\pi$ to π (in this way we take advantage of the period 2π). Thus we have

$$\int_{-\pi}^{\pi} f(x) \cos mx \, dx = \int_{-\pi}^{\pi} (a_0 + a_1 \cos x + a_2 \cos 2x + \cdots)(\cos mx) \, dx$$

$$+ \int_{-\pi}^{\pi} (b_1 \sin x + b_2 \sin 2x + \cdots)(\cos mx) \, dx. \quad (12\text{–}17)$$

Using the methods of integration of Chapter 8, we have the following:

$$\int_{-\pi}^{\pi} a_0 \cos mx \, dx = \frac{a_0}{m} \sin mx \Big|_{-\pi}^{\pi} = \frac{a_0}{m}(0 - 0) = 0; \quad (12\text{–}18)$$

$$\int_{-\pi}^{\pi} a_n \cos nx \cos mx \, dx = a_n \left(\frac{\sin(n-m)x}{2(n-m)} + \frac{\sin(n+m)x}{2(n+m)} \right) \Big|_{-\pi}^{\pi} = 0$$

(since the sine of any multiple of π is zero), $\quad n \neq m; \quad (12\text{–}19)$

$$\int_{-\pi}^{\pi} a_n \cos nx \cos nx \, dx = \int_{-\pi}^{\pi} a_n \cos^2 nx \, dx = \left(\frac{a_n x}{2} + \frac{1}{2n} \sin nx \cos nx \right) \Big|_{-\pi}^{\pi}$$

$$= \frac{a_n x}{2} \Big|_{-\pi}^{\pi} = \pi a_n; \quad (12\text{–}20)$$

as well as

$$\int_{-\pi}^{\pi} b_n \sin nx \cos mx \, dx = b_n \left(-\frac{\cos (n - m)x}{2(n - m)} - \frac{\cos (n + m)x}{2(n + m)} \right) \Big|_{-\pi}^{\pi}$$

$$= b_n \left(-\frac{\cos (n - m)\pi}{2(n - m)} - \frac{\cos (n + m)\pi}{2(n + m)} \right.$$

$$\left. + \frac{\cos (n - m)(-\pi)}{2(n - m)} + \frac{\cos (n + m)(-\pi)}{2(n + m)} \right)$$

$$= 0 \quad [\text{since } \cos \theta = \cos (-\theta)], \qquad n \neq m; \qquad (12\text{–}21)$$

$$\int_{-\pi}^{\pi} b_n \sin nx \cos nx \, dx = \frac{b_n}{2n} \sin^2 nx \Big|_{-\pi}^{\pi} = 0. \qquad (12\text{–}22)$$

These integrals are seen to be zero, except for the case of $\int_{-\pi}^{\pi} a_n \cos nx \cos mx \, dx$ when $n = m$, for which the result is indicated in Eq. (12–20). Using these results in Eq. (12–17), we have

$$\int_{-\pi}^{\pi} f(x) \cos nx \, dx = a_n \int_{-\pi}^{\pi} \cos^2 nx \, dx = \pi a_n$$

or

$$a_n = \frac{1}{\pi} \int_{-\pi}^{\pi} f(x) \cos nx \, dx. \qquad (12\text{–}23)$$

This equation allows us to find the coefficients a_n, except a_0. We find the term a_0 by direct integration of Eq. (12–16) from $-\pi$ to π. When we perform this integration, all the sine and cosine terms integrate to zero, thereby giving the result

$$\int_{-\pi}^{\pi} f(x) \, dx = \int_{-\pi}^{\pi} a_0 \, dx = a_0 x \Big|_{-\pi}^{\pi} = 2\pi a_0$$

or

$$a_0 = \frac{1}{2\pi} \int_{-\pi}^{\pi} f(x) \, dx. \qquad (12\text{–}24)$$

By multiplying all terms of Eq. (12–16) by $\sin mx$ and then integrating from $-\pi$ to π, we find the coefficients b_n. We obtain the result

$$b_n = \frac{1}{\pi} \int_{-\pi}^{\pi} f(x) \sin nx \, dx. \qquad (12\text{–}25)$$

Summarizing these results, we restate our equations for the Fourier series of a function $f(x)$:

$$f(x) = a_0 + a_1 \cos x + a_2 \cos 2x + \cdots + a_n \cos nx + \cdots$$

$$+ b_1 \sin x + b_2 \sin 2x + \cdots + b_n \sin nx + \cdots, \qquad (12\text{–}16)$$

where the coefficients are found by

$$a_0 = \frac{1}{2\pi} \int_{-\pi}^{\pi} f(x) \, dx, \tag{12-24}$$

$$a_n = \frac{1}{\pi} \int_{-\pi}^{\pi} f(x) \cos nx \, dx \tag{12-23}$$

and

$$b_n = \frac{1}{\pi} \int_{-\pi}^{\pi} f(x) \sin nx \, dx. \tag{12-25}$$

Example A. Find the Fourier series for the square wave function

$$f(x) = 0 \quad (\text{for } -\pi < x < 0),$$

$$f(x) = 1 \quad (\text{for } 0 \le x \le \pi).$$

(Many of the functions which we shall expand in Fourier series are discontinuous functions like this one. That is, there is a break in the curve in going from one portion to another.)

Since $f(x)$ is defined differently for the ranges of x indicated, it requires two integrals for each coefficient:

$$a_0 = \frac{1}{2\pi} \int_{-\pi}^{0} 0 \, dx + \frac{1}{2\pi} \int_{0}^{\pi} (1) \, dx = \frac{1}{2},$$

$$a_n = \frac{1}{\pi} \int_{-\pi}^{0} 0 \, dx + \frac{1}{\pi} \int_{0}^{\pi} (1) \cos nx \, dx = \frac{1}{n\pi} (\sin nx) \Big|_{0}^{\pi} = 0$$

for all values of n, since $\sin n\pi = 0$;

$$b_1 = \frac{1}{\pi} \int_{-\pi}^{0} 0 \, dx + \frac{1}{\pi} \int_{0}^{\pi} \sin x \, dx = -\frac{1}{\pi} (\cos x) \Big|_{0}^{\pi}$$

$$= -\frac{1}{\pi} (-1 - 1) = \frac{2}{\pi};$$

$$b_2 = \frac{1}{\pi} \int_{-\pi}^{0} 0 \, dx + \frac{1}{\pi} \int_{0}^{\pi} \sin 2x \, dx = -\frac{1}{2\pi} (\cos 2x) \Big|_{0}^{\pi}$$

$$= -\frac{1}{2\pi} (1 - 1) = 0;$$

$$b_3 = \frac{1}{\pi} \int_{-\pi}^{0} 0 \, dx + \frac{1}{\pi} \int_{0}^{\pi} \sin 3x \, dx = -\frac{1}{3\pi} (\cos 3x) \Big|_{0}^{\pi}$$

$$= -\frac{1}{3\pi} (-1 - 1) = \frac{2}{3\pi}.$$

In general we can see that if n is even, $b_n = 0$, and if n is odd, then $b_n = 2/n\pi$.

FIGURE 12–3

FIGURE 12–4

Thus we have

$$f(x) = \frac{1}{2} + \frac{2}{\pi} \sin x + \frac{2}{3\pi} \sin 3x + \cdots .$$

A graph of the function as defined, and the curve found by using the first three terms of the Fourier series, is shown in Fig. 12–3.

Since functions found by Fourier series have a period of 2π, they can represent functions with this period. If the function $f(x)$ were defined to be periodic with period 2π, with the same definitions as originally indicated, we would graph the function as shown in Fig. 12–4. The Fourier series representation would follow it as in Fig. 12–3. If more terms were used, the fit would be closer.

Example B. Find the Fourier series for the function

$$f(x) = 1 \quad (\text{for } -\pi \le x < 0), \qquad f(x) = x \quad (\text{for } 0 \le x < \pi).$$

For the periodic function, let $f(x + 2\pi) = f(x)$ for all x.

FIGURE 12–5

A graph of three periods of this function is shown in Fig. 12–5. The coefficients are

$$a_0 = \frac{1}{2\pi} \int_{-\pi}^{0} dx + \frac{1}{2\pi} \int_{0}^{\pi} x\, dx = \frac{x}{2\pi}\Big|_{-\pi}^{0} + \frac{x^2}{4\pi}\Big|_{0}^{\pi} = \frac{1}{2} + \frac{\pi}{4} = \frac{2 + \pi}{4},$$

$$a_1 = \frac{1}{\pi} \int_{-\pi}^{0} \cos x\, dx + \frac{1}{\pi} \int_{0}^{\pi} x \cos x\, dx = \frac{1}{\pi} \sin x\Big|_{-\pi}^{0}$$
$$+ \frac{1}{\pi} (\cos x + x \sin x)\Big|_{0}^{\pi} = -\frac{2}{\pi},$$

$$a_2 = \frac{1}{\pi} \int_{-\pi}^{0} \cos 2x\, dx + \frac{1}{\pi} \int_{0}^{\pi} x \cos 2x\, dx = \frac{1}{2\pi} \sin 2x\Big|_{-\pi}^{0}$$
$$+ \frac{1}{4\pi} (\cos 2x + 2x \sin 2x)\Big|_{0}^{\pi} = 0,$$

$$a_3 = \frac{1}{\pi} \int_{-\pi}^{0} \cos 3x\, dx + \frac{1}{\pi} \int_{0}^{\pi} x \cos 3x\, dx = \frac{1}{3\pi} \sin 3x\Big|_{-\pi}^{0}$$
$$+ \frac{1}{9\pi} (\cos 3x + 3x \sin 3x)\Big|_{0}^{\pi} = -\frac{2}{9\pi},$$

$$b_1 = \frac{1}{\pi} \int_{-\pi}^{0} \sin x\, dx + \frac{1}{\pi} \int_{0}^{\pi} x \sin x\, dx = -\frac{1}{\pi} \cos x\Big|_{-\pi}^{0}$$
$$+ \frac{1}{\pi} (\sin x - x \cos x)\Big|_{0}^{\pi} = \frac{\pi - 2}{\pi},$$

$$b_2 = \frac{1}{\pi} \int_{-\pi}^{0} \sin 2x\, dx + \frac{1}{\pi} \int_{0}^{\pi} x \sin 2x\, dx = -\frac{\cos 2x}{2\pi}\Big|_{-\pi}^{0}$$
$$+ \frac{\sin 2x - 2x \cos 2x}{4\pi}\Big|_{0}^{\pi} = -\frac{1}{2}.$$

Thus

$$f(x) = \frac{2 + \pi}{4} - \frac{2}{\pi} \cos x - \frac{2}{9\pi} \cos 3x - \cdots$$
$$+ \left(\frac{\pi - 2}{\pi}\right) \sin x - \frac{1}{2} \sin 2x + \cdots.$$

Example C. Certain electronic devices allow an electric current to pass through in only one direction. The result is that when an alternating current is applied, the current exists for only half the cycle. Figure 12–6 is a representation for such a current as a function of time. A device which causes this effect is called a half-wave rectifier. Derive the Fourier series for the half of the rectified wave for which $f(t) = \sin t$ $(0 \leq t \leq \pi)$, and $f(t) = 0$ for the other half of the

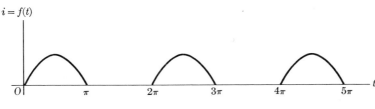

$i = f(t)$

FIGURE 12–6

cycle. We write

$$a_0 = \frac{1}{2\pi} \int_0^\pi \sin t \, dt = \frac{1}{2\pi} (-\cos t) \Big|_0^\pi = \frac{1}{2\pi} (1 + 1) = \frac{1}{\pi}.$$

In the previous example we evaluated each of the coefficients individually. Here we shall show how to set up a general expression for a_n and another for b_n. Once we have determined these, we can substitute values of n in the formula to obtain the individual coefficients:

$$a_n = \frac{1}{\pi} \int_0^\pi \sin t \cos nt \, dt = -\frac{1}{2\pi} \left[\frac{\cos (1 - n)t}{1 - n} + \frac{\cos (1 + n)t}{1 + n} \right]_0^\pi$$

$$= -\frac{1}{2\pi} \left[\frac{\cos (1 - n)\pi}{1 - n} + \frac{\cos (1 + n)\pi}{1 + n} - \frac{1}{1 - n} - \frac{1}{1 + n} \right].$$

See formula 40 of Table 6 in the Appendix. This formula is valid for all values of n except $n = 1$. Now we write

$$a_1 = \frac{1}{\pi} \int_0^\pi \sin t \cos t \, dt = \frac{1}{2\pi} \sin^2 t \Big|_0^\pi = 0,$$

$$a_2 = -\frac{1}{2\pi} \left(\frac{-1}{-1} + \frac{-1}{3} - \frac{1}{-1} - \frac{1}{3} \right) = -\frac{2}{3\pi},$$

$$a_3 = -\frac{1}{2\pi} \left(\frac{1}{-2} + \frac{1}{4} - \frac{1}{-2} - \frac{1}{4} \right) = 0,$$

$$a_4 = -\frac{1}{2\pi} \left(\frac{-1}{-3} + \frac{-1}{5} - \frac{1}{-3} - \frac{1}{5} \right) = -\frac{2}{15\pi},$$

$$b_n = \frac{1}{\pi} \int_0^\pi \sin t \sin nt \, dt = \frac{1}{2\pi} \left[\frac{\sin (1 - n)t}{1 - n} - \frac{\sin (1 + n)t}{1 + n} \right]_0^\pi$$

$$= \frac{1}{2\pi} \left[\frac{\sin (1 - n)\pi}{1 - n} - \frac{\sin (1 + n)\pi}{1 + n} \right].$$

See formula 39 of Table 6 in the Appendix. This formula is valid for all values of

n except $n = 1$. Thus

$$b_1 = \frac{1}{\pi} \int_0^\pi \sin t \sin t \, dt = \frac{1}{\pi} \int_0^\pi \sin^2 t \, dt = \frac{1}{2\pi} (t - \sin t \cos t) \Big|_0^\pi = \frac{1}{2}.$$

We see that $b_n = 0$ if $n > 1$, since each is evaluated in terms of the sine of a multiple of π.

Therefore the Fourier series for the rectified wave is

$$f(t) = \frac{1}{\pi} + \frac{1}{2} \sin t - \frac{2}{\pi} \left(\frac{1}{3} \cos 2t + \frac{1}{15} \cos 4t + \cdots \right).$$

All the types of periodic functions included in this section (as well as many others) may actually be seen on an oscilloscope when the proper signal is sent into it. In this way the oscilloscope may be used to analyze the periodic nature of such phenomena as sound waves and electrical currents.

Exercises

In Exercises 1 through 10, find a few terms of the Fourier series for the given functions, and sketch at least three periods of the function $f(x + 2\pi) = f(x)$.

1. $f(x) = \begin{cases} 1, & -\pi \le x < 0 \\ 0, & 0 \le x < \pi \end{cases}$ 2. $f(x) = \begin{cases} -1, & -\pi \le x < 0 \\ 1, & 0 \le x < \pi \end{cases}$

3. $f(x) = \begin{cases} 1, & -\pi \le x < 0 \\ 2, & 0 \le x < \pi \end{cases}$ 4. $f(x) = \begin{cases} 0, & -\pi \le x < 0, \pi/2 < x < \pi \\ 1, & 0 \le x \le \pi/2 \end{cases}$

5. $f(x) = \begin{cases} 0, & -\pi \le x < 0 \\ x, & 0 \le x < \pi \end{cases}$ 6. $f(x) = x, \quad -\pi \le x < \pi$

7. $f(x) = \begin{cases} -1, & -\pi \le x < 0 \\ 0, & 0 \le x < \pi/2 \\ 1, & \pi/2 \le x < \pi \end{cases}$ 8. $f(x) = x^2, \quad -\pi \le x < \pi$

9. $f(x) = \begin{cases} -x, & -\pi \le x < 0 \\ x, & 0 \le x < \pi \end{cases}$ 10. $f(x) = \begin{cases} 0, & -\pi \le x < 0 \\ x^2, & 0 \le x < \pi \end{cases}$

11. Find the Fourier expansion of a full-wave rectifier. This is found by using as the function for the current $f(t) = -\sin t$ for $-\pi \le t \le 0$ and $f(t) = \sin t$ for

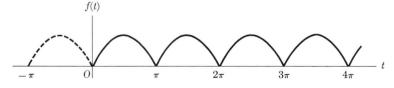

FIGURE 12–7

$0 < t < \pi$. (See Fig. 12–7.) The portion of the line to the left of the $f(t)$-axis is dashed, since from a physical point of view we can give no significance to this part of the wave, although mathematically we can derive the proper form of the expansion by using it.

Miscellaneous exercises for Chapter 12

In Exercises 1 through 8, find the first three nonzero terms of the Maclaurin expansion of the given functions.

1. $f(x) = \dfrac{1}{1 + e^x}$ 2. $f(x) = \frac{1}{2}(e^x - e^{-x})$ 3. $f(x) = \sin 2x^2$

4. $f(x) = \dfrac{1}{(1 - x)^2}$ 5. $f(x) = (x + 1)^{1/3}$ 6. $f(x) = \dfrac{2}{2 - x^2}$

7. $f(x) = \text{Arcsin } x$ 8. $f(x) = \ln \cos x$

In Exercises 9 and 10, evaluate the given integrals by using three terms of the appropriate series.

9. $\displaystyle\int_{0.1}^{0.2} \frac{\cos x}{\sqrt{x}}\, dx$ 10. $\displaystyle\int_{0}^{0.1} \sqrt[3]{1 + x^2}\, dx$

In Exercises 11 through 16, calculate the value of each of the given functions. Use three terms of the appropriate series.

11. $e^{-0.2}$ 12. $\ln (1.10)$ 13. $\sqrt[3]{1.3}$

14. $\sin 58°$ 15. $\tan 43°$ 16. $\sqrt[4]{260}$

In Exercises 17 and 18, find a few terms of the Fourier series for the given functions. Sketch three periods of the function $f(x + 2\pi) = f(x)$.

17. $f(x) = \begin{cases} 0, & -\pi \le x < -\pi/2 \quad \text{and} \quad \pi/2 < x < \pi \\ 1, & -\pi/2 \le x \le \pi/2 \end{cases}$

18. $f(x) = \begin{cases} -x, & -\pi \le x < 0 \\ 0, & 0 \le x < \pi \end{cases}$

19. On the same diagram plot $y = e^x$, $y = 1$, $y = 1 + x$ and $y = 1 + x + (x^2/2)$.

20. Find the approximate area between the curve $y = (x - \sin x)/x^2$ and the x-axis between $x = 0$ and $x = 0.1$.

21. Find the approximate value of the moment of inertia with respect to its axis of the volume generated by rotating the area bounded by $y = \sin x$, $x = 0.3$, and the x-axis about the y-axis. Use two terms of the appropriate series.

22. A certain electric current is pulsating so that the current as a function of time is given by $f(t) = 0$ if $-\pi \le t < 0$ and $\pi/2 < t < \pi$. If $0 < t < \pi/2, f(t) = \sin t$. Find the Fourier expansion for this pulsating current, and plot three periods.

23. By use of series, find the greatest distance that a great circle arc 200 miles long on the earth is from its chord.

13 First-order differential equations

13-1 Solutions of differential equations

A great many physical laws give rise to equations involving the rate of change of one variable with respect to another. This type of relationship requires that the rate of change be expressed as a derivative. Any equation which contains derivatives, or differentials, is called a *differential equation*. This leads us to one of the most powerful methods of solving applied problems—the solution of differential equations.

It is necessary that we define certain terms used in discussing differential equations. The *order* of a differential equation is that of the highest derivative in the equation. The *degree* of a differential equation is the highest power of that derivative.

Example A. The equation $(dy/dx) + x = y$ is a differential equation of the first order and first degree. (This means that there is no higher derivative than the first, and it appears only to the first power.)

Example B. The equation

$$\frac{d^2y}{dx^2} + \left(\frac{dy}{dx}\right)^4 - y = 6$$

is a differential equation of the second order and the first degree. That is, the highest derivative which appears is the second, and it is raised to the first power. Since the second derivative appears, the fourth power of the first derivative does not affect the degree.

In our discussion of differential equations, we shall restrict our attention to equations of the first degree.

A *solution* of a differential equation is a relation between the variables which satisfies the differential equation. That is, when this relation is substituted into the differential equation, an algebraic identity results. A solution containing a number of independent arbitrary constants equal to the order of the differential equation is called the *general solution* of the equation. When specific values are given to at least one of these constants, the solution is called a *particular solution*.

Example C. Any coefficients which are not specified numerically, after like terms have been combined, are independent arbitrary constants. The expression $c_1 x + c_2 + c_3 x$ has only two independent constants, in that the two x terms may be combined with one arbitrary constant; $c_2 + c_4 x$ is an equivalent expression with $c_4 = c_1 + c_3$.

Example D. The equation $y = c_1 e^{-x} + c_2 e^{2x}$ is the general solution of the differential equation

$$\frac{d^2 y}{dx^2} - \frac{dy}{dx} = 2y.$$

The order of this differential equation is two, and there are two independent arbitrary constants in the equation representing the solution. The equation $y = 4e^{-x}$ is a particular solution. This particular solution can be derived from the general solution by letting $c_1 = 4$ and $c_2 = 0$. Each of these solutions can be shown to satisfy the differential equation by taking two derivatives and substituting.

In order to solve a differential equation, we have to find some method of transforming the equation so that the terms may be integrated. This will be the topic of principal concern after this section. The purpose here is to show that a given equation is a solution of a differential equation by taking the required derivatives, and to show that an algebraic identity results after substitution.

Example E. Show that $y = c_1 \sin x + c_2 \cos x$ is the general solution of the differential equation $(d^2 y/dx^2) + y = 0$.

The function and its first two derivatives are

$$y = c_1 \sin x + c_2 \cos x, \qquad y' = c_1 \cos x - c_2 \sin x,$$

and

$$y'' = -c_1 \sin x - c_2 \cos x.$$

Substituting these into the differential equation, we have

$$(-c_1 \sin x - c_2 \cos x) + (c_1 \sin x + c_2 \cos x) = 0, \qquad \text{or} \qquad 0 = 0.$$

We know that this must be the general solution, since there are two independent arbitrary constants, and the order of the differential equation is two.

Example F. Show that $y = cx + x^2$ is a solution of the differential equation $xy' - y = x^2$.

Taking one derivative, $y' = c + 2x$, and substituting, we have

$$x(c + 2x) - (cx + x^2) = x^2, \quad \text{or} \quad x^2 = x^2.$$

Exercises

In Exercises 1 through 16, show that each equation is a solution of the indicated differential equation.

1. $\dfrac{dy}{dx} = 1, \quad y = x + 3$

2. $\dfrac{dy}{dx} - 3 = 2x, \quad y = x^2 + 3x$

3. $xy' = 2y, \quad y = cx^2$

4. $\dfrac{d^2y}{dx^2} + 4y = 0, \quad y = 3 \cos 2x$

5. $y'' - 4y' + 4y = e^{2x}, \quad y = e^{2x}\left(c_1 + c_2 x + \dfrac{x^2}{2}\right)$

6. $\dfrac{d^3y}{dx^3} = \dfrac{d^2y}{dx^2}, \quad y = c_1 + c_2 x + c_3 e^x$

7. $x\dfrac{d^2y}{dx^2} + \dfrac{dy}{dx} = 0, \quad y = c_1 \ln x + c_2$

8. $y'' + 9y = 4 \cos x, \quad 2y = \cos x$

9. $x^2 y' + y^2 = 0, \quad xy = cx + cy$

10. $xy' - 3y = x^2, \quad y = cx^3 - x^2$

11. $\dfrac{d^3y}{dx^3} + 4\dfrac{d^2y}{dx^2} + 4\dfrac{dy}{dx} = 0, \quad y = c_1 + c_2 e^{-2x} + xe^{-2x}$

12. $(x + y) - xy' = 0, \quad y = x \ln x - cx$

13. $y' + y = 2 \cos x, \quad y = \sin x + \cos x - e^{-x}$

14. $xy''' + 2y'' = 0, \quad y = c_1 x + c_2 \ln x$

15. $y'' + y' = 6 \sin 2x, \quad y = e^{-x} - \tfrac{3}{5}\cos 2x - \tfrac{6}{5}\sin 2x$

16. $2xyy' + x^2 = y^2, \quad x^2 + y^2 = cx$

13–2 Separation of variables

The first type of differential equation we shall solve is one of the first order and first degree. There are many methods for solving such equations, a few of which are presented in this and the following two sections. The first of these is the method of *separation of variables*.

By the definitions of order and degree, a differential equation of the first order and first degree contains the first derivative to the first power. That is, it may be written as $dy/dx = f(x, y)$. This type of equation is more commonly expressed in its differential form

$$M(x, y)\, dx + N(x, y)\, dy = 0, \tag{13–1}$$

where $M(x, y)$ and $N(x, y)$ may represent constants, functions of either x or y, or functions of x and y.

In order to find the solution of an equation of the form (13–1), it is necessary to integrate. However, if $M(x, y)$ is a function of x and y, we cannot integrate this term. It is integrable only if $M(x, y)$ is a function of x only. For the same reason, the second term is integrable only if $N(x, y)$ is a function of y only. If it is possible, by some algebraic means, to rewrite Eq. (13–1) in the form

$$A(x)\, dx + B(y)\, dy = 0, \tag{13–2}$$

where $A(x)$ is a function of x alone and $B(y)$ is a function of y alone, then we may find the solution by integrating each term and adding the constant of integration. (If division is involved, we must remember that the solution is not valid for values which make the divisor zero.) Many elementary differential equations lend themselves to this type of solution.

Example A. Solve the differential equation $dx - 4xy^3\, dy = 0$; $M(x, y) = 1$ (a function of neither x nor y), $N(x, y) = -4xy^3$ (a function of both x and y).

We have to remove the x from the coefficient of dy, without introducing any factor of y in the coefficient of dx. This can be done by dividing each term of the equation by x, which results in the equation $(dx/x) - 4y^3\, dy = 0$. It is now possible to integrate each term separately. Performing this integration, we have $\ln x - y^4 = c$, which is the desired solution. The c is the constant of integration, which becomes the arbitrary constant of the solution.

Example B. Solve the differential equation $xy\, dx + (x^2 + 1)\, dy = 0$.

In order to integrate each term, it is necessary to divide each term by $y(x^2 + 1)$. When this is done, we have

$$\frac{x\, dx}{x^2 + 1} + \frac{dy}{y} = 0.$$

Integrating, we have $\frac{1}{2} \ln (x^2 + 1) + \ln y = c$, which is the desired solution. It is possible to make use of the properties of logarithms to make the form of this solution much neater. If we write the constant of integration as $\ln c_1$, rather than c, we have $\frac{1}{2} \ln (x^2 + 1) + \ln y = \ln c_1$. Multiplying through by 2, and using the property of logarithms given by Eq. (7–9), we have $\ln (x^2 + 1) + \ln y^2 = \ln c_1^2$. Next, using the property of logarithms given by Eq. (7–7), we have $\ln (x^2 + 1)y^2 = \ln c_1^2$, which means $(x^2 + 1)y^2 = c_1^2$. This form of the solution is much more compact, and would be generally preferred. However, it must be pointed out that any expression representing a constant may be chosen as the constant of integration and leads to a proper result. In checking answers, we must remember that a different choice of constant will lead to a different form of the answer. Thus two different-appearing answers may both be correct. It often happens that there is more than one reasonable choice of a constant, and different forms of the answer may be expected.

Example C. Solve the differential equation

$$\frac{dy}{dx} = \frac{y}{x^2 + 4} \cdot$$

The variables are separated by writing the equation in the form

$$\frac{dy}{y} = \frac{dx}{x^2 + 4} \cdot$$

Integrating, we have

$$\ln y = \frac{1}{2} \text{Arctan} \frac{x}{2} + \frac{c}{2}, \qquad \text{or} \qquad 2 \ln y = \text{Arctan} \frac{x}{2} + c.$$

The choice of $\ln c$ as the constant of integration (on the left) is also reasonable. It would lead to the result $2 \ln cy = \text{Arctan}(x/2)$.

Example D. Solve the differential equation $3x^2y^2 \, dx + y^2 \, dx + dy = 0$, subject to the condition that $x = 2$ when $y = 1$.

Dividing through by y^2 and combining terms, we have $(3x^2 + 1) \, dx + (dy/y^2) = 0$. Integrating, the result is $x^3 + x - (1/y) = c$. Since a specified set of values is given, we can evaluate the constant of integration. Using these values, we have $8 + 2 - 1 = c$, or $c = 9$. Thus, the solution may be written as

$$x^3 + x - \frac{1}{y} = 9, \qquad \text{or} \qquad yx^3 + yx = 1 + 9y.$$

Example E. If the function in Example B is subject to the condition that $x = 0$ when $y = e$, we have

$$\tfrac{1}{2} \ln (0 + 1) + \ln e = c, \qquad \tfrac{1}{2} \ln 1 + 1 = c, \qquad \text{or} \quad c = 1.$$

The solution is then

$$\tfrac{1}{2} \ln (x^2 + 1) + \ln y = 1, \qquad \ln (x^2 + 1) + 2 \ln y = 2,$$

$$\ln y^2(x^2 + 1) = 2, \qquad \text{or} \qquad y^2(x^2 + 1) = e^2.$$

If we use the solution with c_1, we have $(0 + 1)e^2 = c_1^2$, or $c_1^2 = e^2$. The solution is then $y^2(x^2 + 1) = e^2$. We see, therefore, that the choice of the constant does not affect the final result, and therefore is truly arbitrary.

Exercises

In Exercises 1 through 12, solve the given differential equations.

1. $y^2 \, dx + dy = 0$

2. $(x^3 + x^2) \, dx + (x + 1)y \, dy = 0$

3. $x^2 \, dx + (x^3 + 5) \, dy = 0$

4. $y \, dx + x \, dy = 0$

5. $e^{x+y} \, dx + dy = 0$

6. $\sin x \sec y \, dx - dy = 0$

7. $yx^2 \, dx - y \, dx = x^2 \, dy$

8. $2y(x^3 + 1) \, dy + 3x^2(y^2 - 1) \, dx = 0$

9. $y\sqrt{1 - x^2} \, dy + 2 \, dx = 0$

10. $e^{\sin x} \, dx + \sec x \, dy = 0$

11. $\sqrt{1 + 4x^2} \, dy - y^3 x \, dx = 0$

12. $y^2 \, dx - x^2 \, dy = 0$

In Exercises 13 through 16, in each case find the particular solution of the given differential equations for the indicated conditions.

13. $\dfrac{dy}{dx} + yx^2 = 0,$ $x = 0$ when $y = 1$

14. $y' = \sec y,$ $x = 0$ when $y = 0$

15. $y' = (1 - y) \cos x,$ $x = \pi/6$ when $y = 0$

16. $2y \cos y \, dy - \sin y \, dy = y \sin y \, dx,$ $x = 0$ when $y = \pi/2$

13–3 Integrable combinations

Many differential equations cannot be solved by the method of separation of variables. Many other methods have been developed for solving such equations. One of these methods is based on the fact that certain combinations of basic differentials can be integrated together as a unit. The following differentials suggest some of these combinations which may occur:

$$d(xy) = x \, dy + y \, dx, \tag{13–3}$$

$$d(x^2 + y^2) = 2(x \, dx + y \, dy), \tag{13–4}$$

$$d\left(\frac{y}{x}\right) = \frac{x \, dy - y \, dx}{x^2}, \tag{13–5}$$

$$d\left(\frac{x}{y}\right) = \frac{y \, dx - x \, dy}{y^2}. \tag{13–6}$$

Equation (13–3) suggests that, if the combination of $x \, dy + y \, dx$ occurs in a differential equation, we look for functions of xy. Equation (13–4) suggests that, if the combination $x \, dx + y \, dy$ occurs, we look for functions of $x^2 + y^2$. Equations (13–5) and (13–6) suggest that, if the combination $x \, dy - y \, dx$ occurs, we look for functions of y/x or x/y. The following examples illustrate the use of these combinations.

Example A. Solve the differential equation $x \, dy + y \, dx + xy \, dy = 0$.

By dividing through by xy, we have

$$\frac{x \, dy + y \, dx}{xy} + dy = 0.$$

The left term is the differential of xy divided by xy. This means it integrates to $\ln xy$. Thus we have

$$\ln xy + y = c.$$

Example B. Solve the differential equation $y \, dx - x \, dy + x \, dx = 0$.

The combination of $y \, dx - x \, dy$ suggests that this equation might make use of either Eq. (13–5) or (13–6). This would require dividing through by x^2 or y^2. If we divide by y^2, the last term cannot be integrated, but division by x^2 still allows integration of the last term. Performing this division, we obtain

$$\frac{y \, dx - x \, dy}{x^2} + \frac{dx}{x} = 0.$$

This left combination is the negative of Eq. (13–5). The result then becomes

$$-(y/x) + \ln x = c.$$

Example C. Solve the differential equation $(x^2 + y^2 + x) \, dx + y \, dy = 0$. Regrouping the terms of this equation, we have

$$(x^2 + y^2) \, dx + (x \, dx + y \, dy) = 0.$$

By dividing through by $x^2 + y^2$, we have

$$dx + \frac{x \, dx + y \, dy}{x^2 + y^2} = 0.$$

The right term now can be made into the form of du/u (with $u = x^2 + y^2$) by multiplying each of the terms of the numerator by 2. The result then becomes

$$x + \frac{1}{2} \ln (x^2 + y^2) = \frac{c}{2}, \qquad \text{or} \qquad 2x + \ln (x^2 + y^2) = c.$$

Example D. Find the particular solution of the differential equation

$$(x^3 + xy^2 + 2y) \, dx + (y^3 + x^2y + 2x) \, dy = 0$$

which satisfies the condition that $x = 1$ when $y = 0$.

Regrouping the terms of the equation, we have

$$x(x^2 + y^2) \, dx + y(x^2 + y^2) \, dy + 2(y \, dx + x \, dy) = 0.$$

Factoring $x^2 + y^2$ from each of the first two terms gives

$$(x^2 + y^2)(x \, dx + y \, dy) + 2(y \, dx + x \, dy) = 0.$$

The first term can be integrated by multiplying the $x\,dx + y\,dy$ factor by 2. The result is

$$\frac{1}{2}\cdot\frac{1}{2}\,(x^2 + y^2)^2 + 2xy + \frac{c}{4} = 0, \qquad \text{or} \qquad (x^2 + y^2)^2 + 8xy + c = 0.$$

Using the given condition gives $(1 + 0)^2 + 0 + c = 0$, or $c = -1$. The particular solution is then

$$(x^2 + y^2)^2 + 8xy = 1.$$

The use of these integrable combinations depends on proper recognition of the forms. At times it may take two or three arrangements to arrive at the combination which leads to the result. Of course, many problems cannot be so arranged as to give integrable combinations in all terms.

Exercises

In Exercises 1 through 10, solve the given differential equations.

1. $x\,dy + y\,dx + x\,dx = 0$
2. $x\,dy - y\,dx + y^2\,dx = 0$
3. $y\,dx - x\,dy + x^3\,dx = 2\,dx$
4. $x\,dx + (x^2 + y^2 + y)\,dy = 0$
5. $y\,dy - x\,dx + (y^2 - x^2)\,dx = 0$
6. $x\,dy + y\,dx + 4xy^3\,dy = 0$
7. $x^3\,dy + x^2 y\,dx + y\,dx - x\,dy = 0$
8. $x^3 y^4 (x\,dy + y\,dx) = dy$
9. $\sqrt{x^2 + y^2}\,dx - 2y\,dy = 2x\,dx$
10. $\sec(xy)\,dx + (x\,dy + y\,dx) = 0$

In Exercises 11 and 12, find the particular solution to the given differential equations which satisfy the given conditions.

11. $y\,dx - x\,dy = y^3\,dx + y^2 x\,dy$, $\quad x = 2$ when $y = 4$
12. $e^{x/y}(x\,dy - y\,dx) = y^4\,dy$, $\qquad x = 0$ when $y = 2$

13–4 The linear differential equation of the first order

There is one type of differential equation of the first order and first degree for which an integrable combination can always be determined. It is the linear differential equation of the first order and is of the form

$$dy + Py\,dx = Q\,dx, \tag{13–7}$$

where P and Q are functions of x only. We shall find that this type of equation occurs widely in applications.

If each side of Eq. (13–7) is multiplied by $e^{\int P\,dx}$ it becomes integrable, since the left side becomes of the form du with $u = ye^{\int P\,dx}$, and the right side is a function of x only. This is shown by finding the differential of $ye^{\int P\,dx}$. Thus

$$d(ye^{\int P\,dx}) = e^{\int P\,dx}\,(dy + Py\,dx).$$

(In finding the differential of $\int P\,dx$ we use the fact that, by definition, these are reverse processes. Thus $d(\int P\,dx) = P\,dx$.) Therefore, if each side is multiplied by $e^{\int P\,dx}$, the left side may be immediately integrated to $ye^{\int P\,dx}$, and the right-side integration may be indicated. The solution becomes

$$ye^{\int P\,dx} = \int Qe^{\int P\,dx}\,dx + c. \tag{13-8}$$

Example A. Solve the differential equation $dy + (2/x)y\,dx = 4x\,dx$. Here we note that $P = 2/x$ and $Q = 4x$.

The first expression to find is $e^{\int P\,dx}$. In this case this is $e^{\int (2/x)\,dx} = e^{2\ln x} = e^{\ln x^2} = x^2$ (see below). This means that the left side integrates to yx^2, while the right side becomes $\int 4x(x^2)\,dx$. Thus

$$yx^2 = \int 4x^3\,dx + c, \quad\text{or}\quad yx^2 = x^4 + c.$$

In finding solutions to this type of differential equation, we often have need of certain basic properties of logarithms and exponential functions. In finding the factor $e^{\int P\,dx}$, we often obtain an expression of the form $e^{\ln u}$. It is easily shown that this equals u.

Let $y = e^{\ln u}$. Writing this in logarithmic form, we have $\ln y = \ln u$. Thus $y = u$ or $u = e^{\ln u}$.

Example B. Solve the differential equation $x\,dy - 3y\,dx = x^3\,dx$.

This equation can be put in the form of Eq. (13-7) by dividing through by x. This gives $dy - (3/x)y\,dx = x^2\,dx$. The factor $e^{\int P\,dx}$ becomes

$$e^{\int (-3/x)\,dx} = e^{-3\ln x} = e^{\ln x^{-3}} = x^{-3}.$$

The original equation can now be written as

$$yx^{-3} = \int x^2(x^{-3})\,dx = \int x^{-1}\,dx = \ln x + c.$$

A better form of the answer is $y = x^3(\ln x + c)$.

Example C. Solve the differential equation $dy + y\,dx = x\,dx$; $e^{\int P\,dx} = e^{\int (1)\,dx} = e^x$. Therefore

$$ye^x = \int xe^x\,dx + c = e^x(x - 1) + c, \quad\text{or}\quad y = x - 1 + ce^{-x}.$$

Example D. Solve the differential equation $x^2\,dy + 2xy\,dx = \sin x\,dx$.

This equation is first written in the form of Eq. (13-7). This gives us

$$dy + \left(\frac{2}{x}\right)y\,dx = \frac{1}{x^2}\sin x\,dx; \quad\text{thus}\quad e^{\int P\,dx} = e^{\int (2/x)\,dx} = x^2.$$

The solution to the equation then becomes

$$yx^2 = \int \sin x \, dx + c = -\cos x + c, \qquad \text{or} \qquad yx^2 + \cos x = c.$$

Exercises

In Exercises 1 through 10, solve the given differential equations.

1. $dy + y \, dx = e^{-x} \, dx$

2. $x \, dy + 3y \, dx = dx$

3. $dy + y \, dx = e^{-x} \cos x \, dx$

4. $\dfrac{dy}{dx} + 2xy = x$

5. $\dfrac{dy}{dx} = xe^{4x} + 4y$

6. $dy + y \tan x \, dx + \sin x \, dx = 0$

7. $y' + y = 3$

8. $y' = x^2 y + 3x^2$

9. $x\dfrac{dy}{dx} = y + (x^2 - 1)^2$

10. $(1 + x^2) \, dy + xy \, dx = x \, dx$

In Exercises 11 and 12, find the particular solution of the given differential equations which satisfy the given conditions.

11. $\dfrac{dy}{dx} + 2y = e^{-x}, \quad x = 0$ when $y = 1$

12. $(\sin x)y' + y = \tan x, \quad x = \pi/4$ when $y = 0$

13–5 Applications

The differential equations of the first order and first degree which we have discussed thus far have a number of applications in geometry and the various fields of technology. In this section we shall illustrate some of these applications, both through the examples and the exercises.

Example A. A curve which intersects all the members of a family of curves at right angles is called an *orthogonal trajectory* of the family. By a family of curves is meant a specified set of curves which satisfy given conditions. Find the equations of the orthogonal trajectories of the parabolas $x^2 = cy$.

Finding the derivative of the given equation, we have $dy/dx = 2x/c$. This equation contains the constant c which depends on the point (x, y) on the parabola. Eliminating this constant between the equations of the parabola and its derivative, we have $dy/dx = 2y/x$. This expression gives us a general expression for the slope of any of the members of the family. For a curve to be perpendicular, its slope must equal the negative reciprocal of this expression, or the slope of the orthogonal trajectories must be given by

$$\frac{dy}{dx}\Big|_{OT} = -\frac{x}{2y}.$$

Solving this differential equation gives the family of orthogonal trajectories:

$$2y\,dy = -x\,dx, \qquad y^2 = -\frac{x^2}{2} + \frac{c}{2}, \qquad \text{or} \qquad 2y^2 + x^2 = c.$$

Thus the orthogonal trajectories are a family of ellipses. Note in Fig. 13–1 that each parabola intersects each ellipse at right angles.

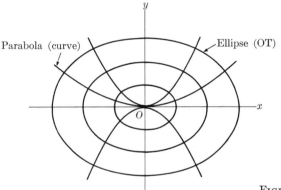

Parabola (curve)   Ellipse (OT)

FIGURE 13–1

Example B. Radioactive elements decay at rates proportional to the amount present. A certain isotope of uranium decays so that half of the original amount disappears in 20 days. Determine the equation relating the amount present with the time.

Let N_0 be the original amount and N the amount present at any time t (in days). Then

$$\frac{dN}{dt} = kN, \qquad \frac{dN}{N} = k\,dt, \qquad \ln N = kt + \ln c.$$

Evaluating the constant, we have $\ln N_0 = \ln c$, or $c = N_0$. Thus we obtain the following:

$$\ln N - \ln N_0 = kt, \qquad \ln (N/N_0) = kt, \qquad \text{or} \quad N = N_0 e^{kt}.$$

Now, using the condition that half of this isotope decays in 20 days, we have $N = N_0/2$ when $t = 20$. This gives

$$\frac{N_0}{2} = N_0 e^{20k}, \qquad \text{or} \quad \frac{1}{2} = (e^k)^{20}, \qquad \text{or} \quad e^k = \left(\frac{1}{2}\right)^{1/20}.$$

The solution is $N = N_0(\frac{1}{2})^{t/20}$.

Example C. The general equation relating the current i, voltage E, inductance L, capacitance C, and resistance R of a simple electric circuit (Fig. 13–2) is given by

$$L\frac{di}{dt} + Ri + \frac{q}{C} = E,$$

where q is the charge on the capacitor. Find the general expression for the current in a circuit containing an inductance, resistance, and voltage source if $i = 0$ when $t = 0$.

The differential equation for this circuit is

$$L\frac{di}{dt} + Ri = E. \qquad (13\text{–}9)$$

FIGURE 13–2

Using the method of the linear differential equation of the first order, we have

$$di + \frac{R}{L}i\,dt = \frac{E}{L}\,dt.$$

The factor $e^{\int P\,dt}$ is $e^{\int (R/L)\,dt} = e^{(R/L)t}$. This gives

$$ie^{(R/L)t} = \frac{E}{L}\int e^{(R/L)t}\,dt = \frac{E}{R}e^{(R/L)t} + c.$$

Letting the current be zero for $t = 0$, we have $c = -E/R$. The result is

$$ie^{(R/L)t} = \frac{E}{R}e^{(R/L)t} - \frac{E}{R}$$

or

$$i = \frac{E}{R}\left(1 - e^{-(R/L)t}\right).$$

(We can see that $i \to E/R$ as $t \to \infty$. In practice the exponential term becomes negligible very quickly.)

Example D. Fifty gallons of brine originally containing 20 lb of salt are in a tank into which 2 gal of water run each minute with the same amount of mixture running out each minute. How much salt remains in the tank after 10 min?

Let $x =$ the number of pounds of salt in the tank at time t. Each gallon of brine contains $x/50$ lb of salt, and in time dt, $2\,dt$ gal of mixture leave the tank with $(x/50)(2\,dt)$ lb of salt. The amount of salt which is leaving may also be written as $-dx$ (the minus sign is included to show that x is decreasing). This means

$$-dx = \frac{2x\,dt}{50} \qquad \text{or} \qquad \frac{dx}{x} = -\frac{dt}{25}.$$

This leads to $\ln x = -(t/25) + \ln c$. Using the fact that $x = 20$ when $t = 0$, we have $\ln 20 = \ln c$, or $c = 20$. Therefore

$$x = 20e^{-t/25}$$

is the general expression for the amount of salt in the tank at time t. When $t = 10$ we have

$$x = 20e^{-10/25} = 20e^{-0.4} = 20(0.670) = 13.4.$$

There are 13.4 lb of salt in the tank after 10 min.

Example E. An object moving through (or across) a resisting medium often experiences a retarding force approximately proportional to the velocity. Applying Newton's laws of motion to this leads to the equation

$$m\frac{dv}{dt} = F - kv, \tag{13-10}$$

where m is the mass of the object, v is the velocity, t is the time, F is the force causing the motion, and k is a constant ($k > 0$). The quantity kv is the retarding force.

We assume these conditions hold for a certain falling object whose mass is 1 slug (this is the unit of mass when force is expressed in pounds) and which experiences a force (its weight) of 32 lb, if the object starts from rest and the retarding force is numerically equal to 0.2 times the velocity.

Substituting in Eq. (13-10), we have

$$\frac{dv}{dt} = 32 - 0.2\,v.$$

Separating variables, we have

$$\frac{dv}{32 - 0.2\,v} = dt.$$

Integrating, we find

$$-5\ln(32 - 0.2\,v) = t - 5\ln c.$$

Solving for v, we obtain

$$\ln(32 - 0.2\,v) = -\frac{t}{5} + \ln c,$$

$$32 - 0.2\,v = ce^{-t/5},$$

$$v = 5(32 - ce^{-t/5}).$$

Since the object started from rest, $v = 0$ when $t = 0$. Thus,

$$0 = 5(32 - c) \qquad \text{or} \qquad c = 32.$$

Therefore the expression giving the velocity as a function of time is

$$v = 160(1 - e^{-t/5}).$$

Evaluating v for $t = 5$, we have

$$v = 160(1 - e^{-1}) = 160(1 - 0.368) = 101 \text{ ft/sec}.$$

Exercises

1. Find the equation of the curve for which the slope is given by $2x/y$ and which passes through $(2, 3)$.
2. Find the equation of the curve for which the slope is given by $-y/(x + y)$ and which passes through $(-1, 3)$.
3. Find the equation of the curve for which the slope is given by $y + x$ and which passes through $(0, 1)$.
4. Find the equation of the orthogonal trajectories of the exponential curves $y = ce^x$.
5. Find the equation of the orthogonal trajectories of the cubic curves $y = cx^3$.
6. Find the equation of the orthogonal trajectories of the curves $y = c(\sec x + \tan x)$.
7. Find the equation of the orthogonal trajectories of the family of circles, all with centers at the origin.
8. An object falling under the influence of gravity has a variable acceleration given by $32 - v$, where v represents the velocity. If the object starts from rest, find an expression for the velocity in terms of the time. Also find the limiting value of the velocity (find $\lim_{t \to \infty} v$).
9. The rate of change of air pressure with respect to height is approximately proportional to the pressure. If the pressure is 15 lb/in^2 when $h = 0$, and $p = 10 \text{ lb/in}^2$ when $h = 10{,}000$ ft, find the expression relating pressure and height.
10. A certain isotope decays in such a way that half the original amount disappears in 2 hr. Find the proportion remaining after 3 hr, by first finding the relation between the amount present and the time.
11. When a gas undergoes an adiabatic change (no gain or loss of heat), the rate of change of pressure with respect to volume is directly proportional to the pressure and inversely proportional to the volume. Express the pressure in terms of the volume.
12. A particle moves on the parabola $y = x^2 + x$, such that $dx/dt = 4t + 1$. Express x and y in terms of t, if both x and y are zero when $t = 0$.
13. If the current in an RL circuit with a voltage source E is zero when $t = 0$ (see Example C), show that $\lim_{t \to \infty} i = E/R$.
14. If a circuit contains only an inductance and a resistance, find the expression for the current in terms of the time, if $i = i_0$ when $t = 0$.
15. If a circuit contains only a resistance and a capacitance, find the expression relating the charge on the capacitor in terms of the time, if $i = dq/dt$ and $q = q_0$ when $t = 0$.

16. For the circuit in Example C, find the current after 10^{-3} sec, if $R = 10$ ohms, $L = 0.1$ henry, and $E = 100$ volts.

17. For the circuit in Exercise 14, what is the value of the current after 10^{-3} sec, if $R = 10$ ohms, $L = 0.1$ henry, and $i_0 = 2$ amps?

18. One hundred gallons of brine originally containing 30 lb of salt are in a tank into which 5 gal of water run each minute. The same amount of mixture from the tank leaves each minute. How much salt is in the tank after 20 min?

19. Repeat Exercise 18 with the change that the water entering the tank contains 1 lb of salt per gal.

20. Under certain conditions, the rate of change of temperature of an object is proportional to the difference in temperature between it and the surrounding medium. (Remember, the temperature decreases with time.) Find the temperature after an hour of an object originally 100°C, if it cools to 90° in 5 min in air which is at 20°C.

21. A mass of 2 slugs (weight is 64 lb) is falling under the influence of gravity. Find its velocity after 5 sec if it starts from rest and experiences a retarding force numerically equal to 0.1 times the velocity.

22. A boat with a mass of 10 slugs is being towed at 8 mi/hr. The tow rope is then cut and a motor, which exerts a force of 20 lb, on the boat is started. If the water exerts a retarding force which numerically equals twice the velocity, what is the velocity of the boat 3 minutes later?

23. A parachutist is falling at the rate of 200 ft/sec when his parachute opens. If the air resists the fall with a force equal to $0.5v^2$, find the velocity as a function of time. The man and his equipment have a mass of 5 slugs (weight is 160 lb).

24. The lines of equal potential in a field of force are all at right angles to the lines of force. In an electric field of force caused by charged particles, the lines of force are given by

$$x^2 + y^2 = cx.$$

Find the equation of the lines of equal potential. Sketch a few members of the lines of force and those of equal potential.

Miscellaneous exercises for Chapter 13

In Exercises 1 through 12, find the general solution of each given differential equation.

1. $4xy^3 \, dx + (x^2 + 1) \, dy = 0$

2. $\dfrac{dy}{dx} = e^{x-y}$

3. $\dfrac{dy}{dx} + 2y = e^{-2x}$

4. $x \, dy + y \, dx = y \, dy$

5. $(x + y) \, dx + (x + y^3) \, dy = 0$

6. $y \ln x \, dx = x \, dy$

7. $x \dfrac{dy}{dx} - 3y = x^2$

8. $dy - 2y \, dx = (x - 2)e^x \, dx$

9. $dy = 2y \, dx + y^2 \, dx$

10. $x^2y \, dy = (1 + x) \csc y \, dx$

11. $\sin x \dfrac{dy}{dx} + y \cos x + x = 0$ 12. $y\,dy = (x^2 + y^2 - x)\,dx$

In Exercises 13 through 16, find the particular solution of each of the given differential equations.

13. $y' = 2y \cot x, \qquad x = \pi/2$ when $y = 2$

14. $x\,dy - y\,dx = y^3\,dy, \qquad x = 1$ when $y = 3$

15. $y' = 4x - 2y, \ x = 0$ when $y = -2$

16. $xy^2\,dx + e^x\,dy = 0, \ x = 0$ when $y = 2$

17. The time rate of change of volume of an evaporating substance is proportional to the surface area. Express the radius of the sphere as a function of time. [*Hint:* Express both V and A in terms of the radius r.]

18. An insulated tank is filled with a solution containing radioactive cobalt. Due to the radioactivity, energy is released and the temperature T (in °F) of the solution rises with the time t (in hours). The following differential equation expresses the relation between temperature and time for a specific case:

$$56{,}600 = 262(T - 70) + 20{,}200\,\dfrac{dT}{dt}.$$

If the initial temperature is 70°F, what is the temperature 24 hr later?

19. An object with a mass of 1000 gm slides down a long inclined plane. The effective force of gravity is 4×10^5 dynes, and the motion is retarded by a force numerically equal to the velocity. If the object starts from rest, what is its velocity (in cm/sec) 4 sec later?

20. Find the orthogonal trajectories of the family of curves $y = cx^5$.

21. If a circuit contains a resistance R, capacitance C, and a source of voltage E, express the charge q on the capacitor as a function of time.

22. Find the equation of the curves such that their normals at all points are in the direction with the lines connecting the points and the origin.

23. The angle φ between the radius vector and a curve $r = f(\theta)$ at (r, θ) is given by

$$\dfrac{dr}{d\theta} = \dfrac{r}{\tan \varphi}.$$

Find the polar equation of the orthogonal trajectories of the circles

$$r = a \sin \theta.$$

24. A differential equation of the form

$$M(x, y)\,dx + N(x, y)\,dy = 0$$

is termed *exact* if

$$\dfrac{\partial M}{\partial y} = \dfrac{\partial N}{\partial x}.$$

Determine whether or not the equation

$$3x^2 \cos^2 y\,dx - x^3 \sin 2y\,dy = 0$$

is exact.

14 Second-order differential equations

14-1 Linear differential equations of higher order

Until now we have restricted our attention to differential equations of the first order and first degree. Another important type of differential equation is the linear differential equation of the second order with constant coefficients. Before restricting our attention to this specific type, we shall briefly describe the general higher-order equation, and the notation we shall use with this type of equation.

The general linear differential equation of the nth order is of the form

$$a_0 \frac{d^n y}{dx^n} + a_1 \frac{d^{n-1} y}{dx^{n-1}} + \cdots + a_{n-1} \frac{dy}{dx} + a_n y = b, \qquad (14\text{--}1)$$

where the a's and b are either functions of x or are constants.

For convenience of notation, the nth derivative with respect to x will be denoted by D^n. The other derivatives are denoted in a similar manner. In this notation, the general linear differential equation becomes

$$a_0 D^n y + a_1 D^{n-1} y + \cdots + a_{n-1} Dy + a_n y = b. \qquad (14\text{--}2)$$

If $b = 0$ the general linear equation is called *homogeneous*, and if $b \neq 0$ it is called *nonhomogeneous*. Both these types have important applications.

Although the a's may be functions of x, we shall restrict our attention to the case where they are all constants. We shall, however, consider both homogeneous and nonhomogeneous equations. Since second-order equations occur widely in applied problems, the remainder of the chapter will be devoted to this type of equation. The methods developed, however, may be applied to equations of higher order.

354

14–2 Second-order homogeneous equations with constant coefficients

In accordance with the notation and terminology introduced in Section (14–1), a second-order, linear, homogeneous differential equation with constant coefficients is one of the form

$$a_0 D^2 y + a_1 Dy + a_2 y = 0, \tag{14–3}$$

where the a's are now constants. The following example will indicate the kind of solution we should expect for this type of equation.

Example A. Solve the differential equation $D^2 y - Dy - 2y = 0$.

First we put this equation in the form $(D^2 - D - 2)y = 0$. This is another way of saying that we are to take the second derivative of y, subtract the first derivative, and finally subtract twice the function. This may now be factored as $(D - 2)(D + 1)y = 0$. (We shall not develop the algebra of the operator D. However, most such algebraic operations can be shown to be valid.) This formula tells us to find the first derivative of the function and add this to the function. Then twice this result is to be subtracted from the derivative of this result. If we let $z = (D + 1)y$, which is valid since $(D + 1)y$ is a function of x, we have $(D - 2)z = 0$. This equation is easily solved by separation of variables. Thus

$$\frac{dz}{dx} - 2z = 0, \qquad \frac{dz}{z} - 2\, dx = 0, \qquad \ln z - 2x = \ln c_1,$$

$$\ln \frac{z}{c_1} = 2x, \qquad \text{or} \qquad z = c_1 e^{2x}.$$

Replacing z by $(D + 1)y$, we have

$$(D + 1)y = c_1 e^{2x}.$$

This is a linear equation of the first order. Then

$$dy + y\, dx = c_1 e^{2x}\, dx.$$

The factor $e^{\int P\, dx}$ is $e^{\int dx} = e^x$. And so

$$ye^x = \int c_1 e^{3x}\, dx = \frac{c_1}{3} e^{3x} + c_2$$

or

$$y = c_1' e^{2x} + c_2 e^{-x},$$

where $c_1' = c_1/3$. This example indicates that solutions of the form e^{mx} result for this equation.

Basing our reasoning on the result of this example, let us assume that an equation of the form (14–3) has a particular solution e^{mx}. Substituting this into Eq. (14–3) gives

$$a_0 m^2 e^{mx} + a_1 m e^{mx} + a_2 e^{mx} = 0.$$

The exponential function e^{mx} is never zero, which means that the polynomial in m is zero, or

$$a_0 m^2 + a_1 m + a_2 = 0. \tag{14–4}$$

Equation (14–4) is called the *auxiliary equation* of Eq. (14–3). Note that it may be formed directly by inspection from Eq. (14–3).

There are two roots of the auxiliary Eq. (14–4) and there are two arbitrary constants in the solution of Eq. (14–3). These factors lead us to the general solution of Eq. (14–3), which is

$$y = c_1 e^{m_1 x} + c_2 e^{m_2 x}, \tag{14–5}$$

where m_1 and m_2 are the solutions of Eq. (14–4). This is seen to be in agreement with the results of Example A.

Example B. Solve the differential equation $D^2 y - 5Dy + 6y = 0$. The auxiliary equation is $m^2 - 5m + 6 = 0$.

Factoring this equation, we have $(m - 3)(m - 2) = 0$, which gives the roots $m_1 = 3$ and $m_2 = 2$. Thus the solution is

$$y = c_1 e^{3x} + c_2 e^{2x}.$$

Obviously it makes no difference which constant is written with each exponential function.

Example C. Solve the differential equation $D^2 y - 6Dy = 0$. Here

$$m^2 - 6m = 0,$$
$$m(m - 6) = 0,$$

or

$$m_1 = 0 \quad \text{and} \quad m_2 = 6.$$

The solution is $y = c_1 e^{0x} + c_2 e^{6x}$. Since $e^{0x} = 1$, we have $y = c_1 + c_2 e^{6x}$.

Example D. Solve the differential equation $2D^2 y + 7Dy - 4y = 0$. In this case

$$2m^2 + 7m - 4 = 0, \qquad (2m - 1)(m + 4) = 0,$$

or

$$m_1 = \tfrac{1}{2} \quad \text{and} \quad m_2 = -4.$$

The solution is

$$y = c_1 e^{x/2} + c_2 e^{-4x}.$$

Example E. Find the particular solution of the differential equation $D^2y - 2Dy - 15y = 0$, which satisfies the conditions that $Dy = 2$, $y = -1$ when $x = 0$. (It is necessary to give two conditions since there are two constants to evaluate.)

We have

$$m^2 - 2m - 15 = 0, \qquad (m - 5)(m + 3) = 0,$$

or

$$m_1 = 5 \quad \text{and} \quad m_2 = -3; \quad y = c_1e^{5x} + c_2e^{-3x}.$$

This equation is the general solution. In order to evaluate the constants c_1 and c_2, we use the given conditions to find two simultaneous equations in c_1 and c_2. These are then solved to determine the particular solution. Thus

$$y' = 5c_1e^{5x} - 3c_2e^{-3x}.$$

Using the given conditions in the general solution and its derivative, we have

$$c_1 + c_2 = -1, \qquad 5c_1 - 3c_2 = 2.$$

The solution to this system of equations is $c_1 = -\frac{1}{8}$ and $c_2 = -\frac{7}{8}$. The particular solution becomes

$$y = -\tfrac{1}{8}e^{5x} - \tfrac{7}{8}e^{-3x}$$

or

$$8y + e^{5x} + 7e^{-3x} = 0.$$

In order to solve the auxiliary equation for differential equations of higher order, we use methods developed in the theory of equations. With these roots, we form the solutions in the same way as we do those for second-order equations.

Exercises

In Exercises 1 through 14, solve the given differential equations.

1. $\dfrac{d^2y}{dx^2} - \dfrac{dy}{dx} - 6y = 0$ 2. $\dfrac{d^2y}{dx^2} + \dfrac{dy}{dx} = 0$ 3. $\dfrac{d^2y}{dx^2} + 4\dfrac{dy}{dx} + 3y = 0$

4. $\dfrac{d^2y}{dx^2} - 2\dfrac{dy}{dx} - 8y = 0$ 5. $D^2y - Dy = 0$ 6. $D^2y + 7Dy + 6y = 0$

7. $3y'' + 8y' - 3y = 0$ 8. $8y'' + 6y' - 9y = 0$

9. $3D^2y + 2Dy - y = 0$ 10. $2D^2y - 7Dy + 6y = 0$

11. $2D^2y - 4Dy + y = 0$ 12. $\dfrac{d^2y}{dx^2} + \dfrac{dy}{dx} - 5y = 0$

13. $y'' = 3y' + y$ 14. $5y'' - y' = 4y$

In Exercises 15 through 17, find the particular solution of each of the differential equations which satisfy the given conditions.

15. $D^2y - 4Dy - 21y = 0$, $Dy = 0$ and $y = 2$ when $x = 0$
16. $D^2y - 4Dy = 0$, $Dy = 2$ and $y = 4$ when $x = 0$
17. $D^2y - Dy - 12y = 0$, $y = 0$ when $x = 0$ and $y = 1$ when $x = 1$
18. Solve $y''' - 2y'' - 3y' = 0$. (The auxiliary equation is $m^3 - 2m^2 - 3m = 0$ and the solution will have 3 arbitrary constants.)
19. Solve $y''' - 2y'' - y' + 2y = 0$.

14–3 Auxiliary equation with repeated or complex roots

The way to solve a second-order homogeneous linear differential equation was shown in the last section. However, we purposely avoided repeated and complex roots of the auxiliary equation. In this section we shall develop the solutions for such equations. The following example indicates the type of solution which results from the case of repeated roots.

Example A. Solve the differential equation $D^2y - 4Dy + 4y = 0$.

Using the method of Example A of the previous section, we have the following steps:

$$(D^2 - 4D + 4)y = 0, \qquad (D - 2)(D - 2)y = 0, \qquad (D - 2)z = 0,$$

where $z = (D - 2)y$. The solution to $(D - 2)z = 0$ is found by separation of variables. And so

$$\frac{dz}{dx} - 2z = 0, \qquad \frac{dz}{z} - 2\,dx = 0, \qquad \ln z - 2x = \ln c_1, \qquad \text{or} \quad z = c_1e^{2x}.$$

Substituting back, we have $(D - 2)y = c_1e^{2x}$, which is a linear equation of the first order. Then

$$dy - 2y\,dx = c_1e^{2x}\,dx, \qquad e^{\int -2\,dx} = e^{-2x}.$$

This leads to

$$ye^{-2x} = c_1\int dx = c_1x + c_2, \qquad \text{or} \qquad y = c_1xe^{2x} + c_2e^{2x}.$$

This example indicates the type of solution which results when the auxiliary equation has repeated roots. If the method of the previous section were to be used, the solution of the above example would be $y = c_1e^{2x} + c_2e^{2x}$. This would not be the general solution, since both terms are similar, which means that there is only one independent constant. The constants can be combined to give a solution of the form $y = ce^{2x}$, where $c = c_1 + c_2$. This solution would contain only one constant for a second-order equation.

Based on the above example, the solution to Eq. (14–3) when the auxiliary Eq. (14–4) has repeated roots is

$$y = e^{mx}(c_1 + c_2 x), \tag{14–6}$$

where m is the double root. (In the above example, this double root is 2.)

Example B. Solve the differential equation $(D + 2)^2 y = 0$. Here $(m + 2)^2 = 0$, $m = -2, -2$.
    The solution is

$$y = e^{-2x}(c_1 + c_2 x).$$

Example C. Solve the differential equation $(D - 5)^2 y = 0$. In this case $(m - 5)^2 = 0$, $m = 5, 5$.
    We therefore have

$$y = e^{5x}(c_1 + c_2 x).$$

The case when the auxiliary equation has complex roots can be solved by the method developed in the preceding section. However, the solution can be put in a special, more useful form. Let us assume that the quadratic formula is used to find the roots of the auxiliary equation, and that these roots are complex of the form $m = \alpha \pm j\beta$. This means that the solution is of the form

$$y = c_1 e^{(\alpha+j\beta)x} + c_2 e^{(\alpha-j\beta)x} = e^{\alpha x}(c_1 e^{j\beta x} + c_2 e^{-j\beta x}).$$

Using the exponential form of a complex number, Eq. (12–12), we have

$$
\begin{aligned}
y &= e^{\alpha x}[c_1 \cos \beta x + jc_1 \sin \beta x + c_2 \cos(-\beta x) + jc_2 \sin(-\beta x)] \\
&= e^{\alpha x}(c_1 \cos \beta x + c_2 \cos \beta x + jc_1 \sin \beta x - jc_2 \sin \beta x) \\
&= e^{\alpha x}(c_3 \cos \beta x + c_4 \sin \beta x),
\end{aligned}
$$

where $c_3 = c_1 + c_2$ and $c_4 = jc_1 - jc_2$.
    Summarizing these results, we see that if the auxiliary equation has complex roots of the form $\alpha \pm j\beta$, the solution to Eq. (14–3) is

$$y = e^{\alpha x}(c_1 \sin \beta x + c_2 \cos \beta x). \tag{14–7}$$

The c_1 and c_2 here are not the same as those above. They are simply the two arbitrary constants of the solution.

Example D. Solve the differential equation $D^2 y - Dy + y = 0$. Thus

$$m^2 - m + 1 = 0, \quad \text{or} \quad m = \frac{1 \pm \sqrt{3}\, j}{2}, \quad \alpha = \frac{1}{2} \quad \text{and} \quad \beta = \frac{\sqrt{3}}{2}.$$

    We have

$$y = e^{x/2}\left(c_1 \sin \frac{\sqrt{3}}{2} x + c_2 \cos \frac{\sqrt{3}}{2} x\right).$$

Example E.   Solve the differential equation $D^2y + 4y = 0$. In this case we have $m^2 + 4 = 0$, $m_1 = 2j$, and $m_2 = -2j$; $\alpha = 0$ and $\beta = 2$.

The solution is

$$y = e^{0x}(c_1 \sin 2x + c_2 \cos 2x), \quad \text{or} \quad y = c_1 \sin 2x + c_2 \cos 2x.$$

Exercises

In Exercises 1 through 15, solve the given differential equations.

1. $\dfrac{d^2y}{dx^2} - 2\dfrac{dy}{dx} + y = 0$ 2. $\dfrac{d^2y}{dx^2} + y = 0$ 3. $D^2y - 6Dy + 9y = 0$

4. $D^2y + 8Dy + 16y = 0$ 5. $4D^2y - 12Dy + 9y = 0$

6. $D^2y - 2Dy + 4y = 0$ 7. $D^2y = 0$

8. $9D^2y - 24Dy + 16y = 0$ 9. $4D^2y + y = 0$

10. $2D^2y - 3Dy - y = 0$ 11. $3D^2y - 12Dy + 12y = 0$

12. $D^2y - 5Dy - 4y = 0$ 13. $25y'' + 2y = 0$

14. $9y'' + 0.6y' + 0.01y = 0$ 15. $3y'' + 12y' = 2y$

In Exercises 16 through 18, find the particular solution of the given differential equations which satisfy the stated conditions.

16. $D^2y + 16y = 0$, $Dy = 0$ and $y = 2$ when $x = \pi/2$

17. $D^2y - 8Dy + 16y = 0$, $Dy = 2$ and $y = 4$ when $x = 0$

18. $4y'' + 20y' + 25y = 0$, $y = 0$ when $x = 0$ and $y = e$ when $x = -2/5$

14–4 Solutions of nonhomogeneous equations

In order to solve a nonhomogeneous linear equation of the form

$$a_0 D^2y + a_1 Dy + a_2 y = b, \tag{14–8}$$

where b is a function of x or is a constant, the solution must be such that if we substitute it into the left side, we obtain the right side. Solutions obtained from the methods of Sections (14–2) and (14–3) give zero when substituted into the left side, but they do contain the arbitrary constants necessary in the solution. If we could find some particular solution, which when substituted into the left side produced the expression of the right, it could be added to the solution containing the arbitrary constants. Thus the solution is of the form

$$y = y_c + y_p, \tag{14–9}$$

where y_c, called the *complementary solution*, is obtained by solving the corresponding homogeneous equation, and y_p is the particular solution necessary to produce the expression b of Eq. (14–8).

Example A. The differential equation $D^2y - Dy - 6y = e^x$ has the solution $y = c_1e^{3x} + c_2e^{-2x} - \frac{1}{6}e^x$, with $y_c = c_1e^{3x} + c_2e^{-2x}$ and $y_p = -\frac{1}{6}e^x$. The complementary solution y_c is obtained by solving the corresponding homogeneous equation $D^2y - Dy - 6y = 0$, and we shall discuss below the method of finding y_p. We can see that y_p alone will satisfy the differential equation, but since it has no arbitrary constants, it cannot be the general solution.

By inspection of the form of the expression b on the right side of the equation, we can determine the form which the particular solution must have. Since a combination of the derivatives and the function itself must form the function b, we assume an expression which contains *all possible forms of b and its derivatives* will form y_p. The method used to find the exact form of this expression is called the *method of undetermined coefficients.*

Example B. If the function on the right of (14–8), b, is $4x + e^{2x}$, we would assume the particular solution is of the form $y_p = A + Bx + Ce^{2x}$. The Bx term is included to account for the presence of the $4x$. The A term is included to account for any derivatives of the Bx term which may occur. The Ce^{2x} is included to account for the presence of the e^{2x} term. Since all the derivatives of Ce^{2x} are of this same form, it is not necessary to include any other terms for the e^{2x}.

Example C. If the expression b is of the form $x^2 + e^{-x}$, we would assume y_p to be of the form $y_p = A + Bx + Cx^2 + Ee^{-x}$.

If b is of the form $xe^x - 5$, we would assume y_p to be of the form $y_p = Ae^x + Bxe^x + C$.

If b is of the form $x \sin x$, we would assume y_p to be of the form $A \sin x + B \cos x + Cx \sin x + Ex \cos x$. All of these terms occur in the derivatives of $x \sin x$.

Once we have determined the form of the particular solution, we have to find the numerical values of the coefficients $A, B, \ldots$. This is done by substituting the form into the differential equation, and equating coefficients of like terms.

Example D. Solve the differential equation $D^2y - Dy - 6y = e^x$. Therefore, in this case we have $m^2 - m - 6 = 0$, $m_1 = 3$, and $m_2 = -2$. Thus $y_c = c_1e^{3x} + c_2e^{-2x}$. The proper form of y_p is $y_p = Ae^x$.

Substituting y_p and its derivatives into the differential equation, we have $Ae^x - Ae^x - 6Ae^x = e^x$. To produce equality, the coefficients of e^x must be the same on each side of the equation. Thus $-6A = 1$, or $A = -\frac{1}{6}$. This gives the complete solution $y = y_c + y_p = c_1e^{3x} + c_2e^{-2x} - \frac{1}{6}e^x$. See Example A.

Example E. Solve the differential equation $D^2y + 4y = x - 4e^{-x}$. Thus, this means that $m^2 + 4 = 0$, $m_1 = 2j$, and $m_2 = -2j$; $y_c = c_1 \sin 2x + c_2 \cos 2x$.

The proper form of the particular solution is $y_p = A + Bx + Ce^{-x}$. Finding two derivatives and then substituting gives the following result:

$$y_p' = B - Ce^{-x}, \qquad y_p'' = Ce^{-x};$$

$$(Ce^{-x}) + 4(A + Bx + Ce^{-x}) = x - 4e^{-x},$$

$$Ce^{-x} + 4A + 4Bx + 4Ce^{-x} = x - 4e^{-x},$$

$$(4A) + (4Bx) + (5Ce^{-x}) = 0 + (1)x + (-4e^{-x}).$$

Equating the coefficients of the constants, x and e^{-x}, gives $4A = 0$, $4B = 1$, and $5C = -4$. Thus $A = 0$, $B = \frac{1}{4}$, and $C = -\frac{4}{5}$. This means that the particular solution is $y_p = \frac{1}{4}x - \frac{4}{5}e^{-x}$. In turn this tells us that the complete solution is

$$y = c_1 \sin 2x + c_2 \cos 2x + \tfrac{1}{4}x - \tfrac{4}{5}e^{-x}.$$

Example F. Solve the differential equation $D^2y - 3Dy + 2y = 2 \sin x$. Thus,

$$m^2 - 3m + 2 = 0, \qquad (m - 1)(m - 2) = 0, \qquad m_1 = 1 \quad \text{and} \quad m_2 = 2.$$

We write $y_c = c_1e^x + c_2e^{2x}$. Then

$$y_p = A \sin x + B \cos x,$$

$$Dy_p = A \cos x - B \sin x,$$

$$D^2y = -A \sin x - B \cos x;$$

$$(-A \sin x - B \cos x) - 3(A \cos x - B \sin x)$$

$$+ 2(A \sin x + B \cos x) = 2 \sin x,$$

$$(A + 3B) \sin x + (B - 3A) \cos x = 2 \sin x,$$

$$A + 3B = 2, \qquad -3A + B = 0.$$

The solution of this system is $A = \frac{1}{5}$ and $B = \frac{3}{5}$. Thus $y_p = \frac{1}{5} \sin x + \frac{3}{5} \cos x$. Therefore

$$y = c_1e^x + c_2e^{2x} + \tfrac{1}{5} \sin x + \tfrac{3}{5} \cos x.$$

Exercises

In Exercises 1 through 16, solve the given differential equations.

1. $D^2y - Dy - 2y = 4$ (Let $y_p = A$.)
2. $D^2y - Dy - 6y = 4x$ (Let $y_p = A + Bx$.)
3. $D^2y + y = x^2$ (Let $y_p = A + Bx + Cx^2$.)
4. $D^2y + Dy + y = e^{2x}$ 5. $D^2y + 4Dy + 3y = 2 + e^x$
6. $D^2y - y = \sin x$ 7. $D^2y - Dy - 20y = 8 + e^{2x}$

8. $D^2y + 4y = \sin x + 4$ 9. $D^2y - 4y = \sin x + 2\cos x$

10. $2D^2y + 5Dy - 3y = e^x + 4e^{2x}$ 11. $D^2y + y = 4 + \sin 2x$

12. $D^2y - Dy + y = x + \sin x$ 13. $D^2y + 5Dy + 4y = xe^x + 4$

14. $3D^2y + Dy - 2y = 4 + 2x + e^x$ 15. $y'' + 6y' + 9y = e^{2x} - e^{-2x}$

16. $y'' + 8y' - y = x^2 + 4e^{-2x}$

In Exercises 17 through 20, find the particular solution of each differential equation for the given conditions.

17. $D^2y - Dy - 6y = 5 - e^x,$ $Dy = 4$ and $y = 2$ when $x = 0$.

18. $3y'' - 10y' + 3y = xe^{-2x},$ $Dy = 0$ and $y = -1$ when $x = 0$.

19. $y'' + y = x + \sin 2x,$ $Dy = 1$ and $y = 0$ when $x = \pi$.

20. $D^2y - 2Dy + y = xe^{2x} - e^{2x},$ $Dy = 4$ and $y = -2$ when $x = 0$.

14–5 Applications

Linear differential equations of the second order have many important applications. We shall restrict our attention to two of these. In this section, we shall apply second-order differential equations to solving problems in simple harmonic motion and simple electric circuits.

Example A. Simple harmonic motion may be defined as motion in a straight line for which the acceleration is proportional to the displacement, and in the opposite direction. Examples of this type of motion are a weight on a spring, a simple pendulum and an object bobbing in water. If x represents the displacement, d^2x/dt^2 is the acceleration.

Using the definition of simple harmonic motion, we have

$$\frac{d^2x}{dt^2} = -k^2x.$$

(We chose k^2 for convenience of notation in the solution.) Writing this equation in the form

$$D^2x + k^2x = 0 \qquad \left(\text{here } D = \frac{d}{dt}\right),$$

we find that its solution is $x = c_1 \sin kt + c_2 \cos kt$. This solution indicates an oscillating motion, which is known to be the case. If, for example, $k = 4$ and we know that $x = 2$ and $Dx = 0$ (which means the velocity is zero) for $t = 0$, we have

$$Dx = 4c_1 \cos 4t - 4c_2 \sin 4t,$$

or (substituting into the expression for x and that for Dx)

$$2 = c_1(0) + c_2(1) \qquad \text{and} \qquad 0 = 4c_1(1) - 4c_2(0),$$

which gives $c_1 = 0$ and $c_2 = 2$. Therefore

$$x = 2 \cos 4t$$

is the equation relating the displacement and time; Dx is the velocity and D^2x is the acceleration.

Example B. In practice an object will in time cease to move due to unavoidable frictional forces. It is found that a "freely" oscillating object has a force retarding it which is approximately proportional to the velocity. The differential equation for this case is $D^2x = -k^2x - bDx$, which results from applying (from physics) Newton's second law of motion, which states that the net force acting on an object equals its mass times its acceleration. The term D^2x represents the acceleration, the term $-k^2x$ is a measure of the restoring force (of the spring, for example) and the term $-bDx$ is the term which represents the retarding (damping) force. This equation can be written as

$$D^2x + bDx + k^2x = 0.$$

The auxiliary equation is $m^2 + bm + k^2 = 0$, for which the roots are

$$m = \frac{-b \pm \sqrt{b^2 - 4k^2}}{2}.$$

If $k = 3$ and $b = 4$, $m = -2 \pm \sqrt{5}j$, which means the solution is

$$x = e^{-2t}(c_1 \sin \sqrt{5}t + c_2 \cos \sqrt{5}t). \tag{1}$$

Here, $4k^2 > b^2$, and this case is called *underdamped*.

If $k = 2$ and $b = 5$, $m = -1, -4$, which means the solution is

$$x = c_1 e^{-t} + c_2 e^{-4t}. \tag{2}$$

Here $4k^2 < b^2$, and the case is called *overdamped*. It will be noted that the motion is not oscillatory, since no sine or cosine terms appear.

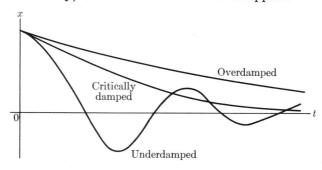

FIGURE 14–1

If $k = 2$ and $b = 4$, $m = -2, -2$, which means the solution is

$$x = e^{-2t}(c_1 + c_2 t). \tag{3}$$

Here $4k^2 = b^2$, and the case is called *critically damped*. Again the motion is not oscillatory. See Fig. 14–1 in which Eqs. (1), (2), and (3) are represented in general. Of course, the actual values depend upon c_1 and c_2, which in turn depend upon the conditions imposed on the motion.

Example C. A basic relation for electric circuits is that the impressed voltage of a circuit equals the sums of the voltages across the components of the circuit. When this principle is applied to a circuit containing a resistance, inductance, capacitance, and a voltage source (Fig. 14–2), the differential equation is

$$L\frac{d^2q}{dt^2} + R\frac{dq}{dt} + \frac{q}{C} = E. \tag{14-10}$$

E or $E_0 \sin \omega t$

FIGURE 14–2

By definition q represents the electric charge, $dq/dt = i$ is the current and d^2q/dt^2 is the time rate of change of current. This equation may be written as $LD^2q + RDq + q/C = E$. The auxiliary equation is $Lm^2 + Rm + 1/C = 0$. The roots are

$$m = \frac{-R \pm \sqrt{R^2 - 4L/C}}{2L} = -\frac{R}{2L} \pm \sqrt{\frac{R^2}{4L^2} - \frac{1}{LC}}.$$

If we let $a = R/2L$ and $\omega = \sqrt{1/LC - R^2/4L^2}$, we have (assuming complex roots, which corresponds to realistic values of R, L, and C)

$$q_c = e^{-at}(c_1 \sin \omega t + c_2 \cos \omega t).$$

This indicates an oscillating charge, or an alternating current. However, the exponential term usually is such that the current dies out rapidly unless there is a source of voltage in the circuit.

If there is no source of voltage in the circuit of Example C, we have a homogeneous differential equation to solve. If we have a constant voltage source, the particular solution is of the form $q_p = A$. If there is an alternating voltage source, the particular solution is of the form $q_p = A \sin \omega_1 t + B \cos \omega_1 t$, where ω_1 is the angular velocity of the source. After a very short time, the exponential factor in the complementary solution makes it negligible. For this reason it is referred to as the *transient* term, and the particular solution is the *steady-state* solution. Therefore, to find the steady-state solution, we need find only the particular solution.

Example D. Find the steady-state solution for the current in a circuit containing the following elements: $C = 4 \times 10^{-4}$ farad, $L = 1$ henry, $R = 10$ ohms, and a voltage source of $500 \sin 100t$.

This means the differential equation to be solved is

$$\frac{d^2q}{dt^2} + 10 \frac{dq}{dt} + \frac{10^4}{4} q = 500 \sin 100t.$$

Since we wish to find the steady-state solution, we must find q_p from which we may find i_p by finding a derivative. Thus,

$$q_p = A \sin 100t + B \cos 100t,$$

$$\frac{dq_p}{dt} = 100A \cos 100t - 100B \sin 100t,$$

$$\frac{d^2q_p}{dt^2} = -10^4 A \sin 100t - 10^4 B \cos 100t.$$

Substituting into the differential equation, we have

$$-10^4 A \sin 100t - 10^4 B \cos 100t + 10^3 A \cos 100t - 10^3 B \sin 100t$$

$$+ \frac{10^4}{4} A \sin 100t + \frac{10^4}{4} B \cos 100t = 500 \sin 100t.$$

This means

$$(-0.75 \times 10^4 A - 10^3 B) \sin 100t + (-0.75 \times 10^4 B + 10^3 A) \cos 100t$$
$$= 500 \sin 100t$$

or

$$-7.5 \times 10^3 A - 10^3 B = 500, \qquad 10^3 A - 7.5 \times 10^3 B = 0.$$

Solving these equations, we obtain $B = -8.73 \times 10^{-3}$ and $A = -65.5 \times 10^{-3}$. Therefore,

$$q_p = -65.5 \times 10^{-3} \sin 100t - 8.73 \times 10^{-3} \cos 100t$$

and

$$i_p = \frac{dq_p}{dt} = -6.55 \cos 100t + 0.87 \sin 100t,$$

which is the desired solution.

It should be noted that the complimentary solutions of the mechanical and electrical cases are of the same identical form. There is also an equivalent mechanical case to that of an impressed sinusoidal voltage source in the electrical case. This arises when an external force affecting the vibrations is applied to the system. Such cases are called *forced vibrations.*

Exercises

1. An object moves with simple harmonic motion according to the equation $D^2x + 100x = 0$; $D = d/dt$. Find the displacement x as a function of the time, subject to the conditions that $x = 4$ and $Dx = 0$ when $t = 0$. Sketch the resulting curve.

2. Solve Exercise 1 if the motion is in accordance with the equation $D^2x + 0.2Dx + 100x = 0$. Sketch the curve.

3. What must be the value of b so that the motion given by the equation $D^2x + bDx + 100x = 0$ is critically damped?

4. What is the displacement of an object which moves according to the equation $D^2x + 4Dx + 6x = 0$ (if $x = 6$ and $Dx = 0$ when $t = 0$) after 2 sec?

5. For a certain spring a 4-lb weight stretches it 1/8 ft. With this weight attached, the spring is pulled three inches longer than its equilibrium length and released. Find the equation of the resulting motion, assuming no damping.

6. Find the solution for the spring of Exercise 5 if a damping force numerically equal to the velocity is present.

7. Find the solution for the spring of Exercise 5 if no damping is present, but an external force of $4 \sin 2t$ is acting on the spring.

8. Find the solution for the spring of Exercise 5 if the damping force of Exercise 6 and the impressed force of Exercise 7 are both acting.

9. For a given circuit, $L = 0.1$ henry, $R = 0$, $C = 10^{-4}$ farad and $E = 100$ volts. Find the equation relating the charge and time if $q = 0$ and $i = 0$ when $t = 0$.

10. Find the relation between the current and time for the circuit of Exercise 9.

11. For a given circuit, $L = 0.5$ henry, $R = 10$ ohms, $C = 2 \times 10^{-4}$ farad, and $E = 100 \sin 200t$. Find the expression relating charge and time.

12. Find the relation between current and time for the circuit of Exercise 11.

13. Find the steady-state current for the circuit of Exercise 11.

14. Find the steady-state current for a circuit with $L = 1$ henry, $R = 5$ ohms, $C = 1.5 \times 10^{-4}$ farad, and $E = 120 \sin 100t$ volts.

15. Find the steady-state solution for the charge of the circuit of Exercise 14 if the voltage source is changed to $100 \sin 400t$.

Miscellaneous exercises for Chapter 14

In Exercises 1 through 12, find the general solution of each of the given differential equations.

1. $2D^2y + Dy = 0$

2. $2D^2y - 5Dy + 2y = 0$

3. $y'' + 2y' + y = 0$

4. $y'' + 2y' + 2y = 0$

5. $2\dfrac{d^2y}{dx^2} + \dfrac{dy}{dx} - 3y = 6$

6. $\dfrac{d^2y}{dx^2} + 6\dfrac{dy}{dx} + 9y = 3x$

7. $9D^2y - 18Dy + 8y = 16 + 4x$

8. $D^2y + 9y = xe^x$

9. $y'' + y' - y = 2e^x$ 10. $y'' + y = 4 \cos 2x$

11. $D^2y + 9y = \sin x$ 12. $y'' + y' = e^x + \cos 2x$

In Exercises 13 through 16, find the indicated particular solutions of the given differential equations.

13. $\dfrac{d^2y}{dx^2} + \dfrac{dy}{dx} + 4y = 0$, $Dy = \sqrt{15}$, $y = 0$ when $x = 0$.

14. $5y'' + 7y' - 6y = 0$, $y' = 10$, $y = 2$ when $x = 0$.

15. $(D^2 + 4D + 4)y = 4 \cos x$, $Dy = 1$, $y = 0$ when $x = 0$.

16. $y'' - 2y' + y = e^{2x} + x$, $Dy = 0$, $y = 2$ when $x = 0$.

17. A certain spring stretches 2 ft by a 64-lb weight. With this weight suspended on it, the spring is stretched 2 ft beyond the equilibrium position and released. Find the equation of the resulting motion if the medium in which the weight is suspended retards the motion with a force equal to 16 times the velocity. Classify the motion as underdamped, critically damped, or overdamped.

18. What is the expression for the steady-state displacement x of an object which moves according to the relation $D^2x - 2Dx - 8x = 5 \sin 2t$?

19. The approximate differential equation relating the displacement y of a beam at a horizontal distance x from one end is

$$EI \frac{d^2y}{dx^2} = M,$$

where E is the modulus of elasticity, I is the moment of inertia of the cross section of the beam perpendicular to its axis, and M is the bending moment at the cross section. If $M = 2000x - 40x^2$ for a particular beam of length L for which $y = 0$ when $x = 0$ and when $x = L$, express y in terms of x. Consider E and I as constants.

20. Find the general expression for the charge on the capacitor in a circuit having a resistance of 20 ohms, an inductor of 4 henries and a capacitor of 10^{-4} farad if the initial charge on the capacitor is 0.01 coul and the current is zero when $t = 0$.

21. Find the solution for the current for the circuit of Exercise 20, if a battery of 100 volts is placed in the circuit.

22. If a circuit contains an inductor L, capacitor C, and a sinusoidal source of voltage $E_0 \sin \omega t$, express the charge q on the capacitor as a function of the time. Assume $q = 0$, $i = 0$ when $t = 0$.

23. When a circular disk of mass m and radius r is suspended by a wire at the center on one of its flat faces and the disk is twisted through an angle θ, torsion in the wire tends to turn the disk back in the opposite direction. The differential equation for this case is

$$\tfrac{1}{2}mr^2 \frac{d^2\theta}{dt^2} = -k\theta,$$

where k is a constant. Find the equation of motion if $\theta = \theta_0$ and $d\theta/dt = \omega_0$ when $t = 0$.

15 Other methods of solving differential equations

15–1 Numerical solutions—the increment method

In the last two chapters we presented methods of solving certain types of differential equations. Other types of differential equations, many of which do not have exact solutions, have important applications. Numerous methods and techniques have been developed for these equations. In this chapter three of these methods are introduced. The first of these is the *increment method,* a numerical method of solution.

Numerical methods of solving differential equations often require a great deal of time and computation to arrive at the desired solution. For this reason they lend themselves very well to the use of modern computers, by which these calculations may be done very rapidly. Also, due to the increasing importance of computers, these numerical methods are of increasing importance in industry. The increment method, which illustrates the basic numerical technique, can be used with nearly any method of computation.

In order to find an approximate solution to a differential equation of the form $dy/dx = f(x, y)$ which passes through a known point (x_1, y_1), we approximate the increment of y, Δy, by the differential of y, dy. From Section 4–1 we recall that this approximation is good if Δx is small. The use of this approximation is illustrated in the following examples.

Example A. Find an approximate solution to the differential equation $dy/dx = x + y$ by the increment method. The curve passes through the point $(0, 1)$.

The differential equation can be written as

$$dy = (x + y)\,\Delta x$$

(since $\Delta x = dx$). We know that $y = 1$ for $x = 0$. Let us choose $\Delta x = 0.1$. With these values we can find a good approximation for dy. Thus,

$$dy = (0 + 1)(0.1) = 0.1.$$

This tells us that the curve passes (or nearly passes) through the point (0.1, 1.1). This is seen by adding 0.1 to the original value of x, 0, and then adding 0.1 to the original value of y, 1.0. Assuming this point is correct we use the values $x = 0.1$, $y = 1.1$, and $\Delta x = 0.1$ to find the next approximate point. This time

$$dy = (0.1 + 1.1)(0.1) = 0.12,$$

which means that the curve passes through (0.2, 1.22). Continuing this process we find a set of points which would approximately satisfy the function which is the solution of the differential equation. Tabulating the results obtained in this manner, we have the following table.

x	y	$x + y$	dy	(correct value of y)
0.0	1.00	1.00	0.10	1.00
0.1	1.10	1.20	0.12	1.11
0.2	1.22	1.42	0.14	1.24
0.3	1.36	1.66	0.17	1.40
0.4	1.53	1.93	0.19	1.58
0.5	1.72	2.22	0.22	1.80
0.6	1.94	2.54	0.25	2.04

In this case we are able to find correct values since the differential equation can be expressed as $dy/dx - y = x$, of which the solution is $y = 2e^x - x - 1$.

In order to show that better values are obtained by using smaller values of Δx, the following table is presented in which $\Delta x = 0.05$ is also used in solving the differential equation.

x	$y(\Delta x = 0.1)$	$y(\Delta x = 0.05)$	y(correct)
0.00	1.00	1.00	1.00
0.05		1.05	1.05
0.10	1.10	1.11	1.11
0.15		1.17	1.17
0.20	1.22	1.24	1.24
0.25		1.31	1.32
0.30	1.36	1.39	1.40
0.35		1.47	1.49
0.40	1.53	1.56	1.58
0.45		1.66	1.69
0.50	1.72	1.77	1.80
0.55		1.88	1.92
0.60	1.94	2.00	2.04

See Fig. 15–1 for the graphs of the curves using these values.

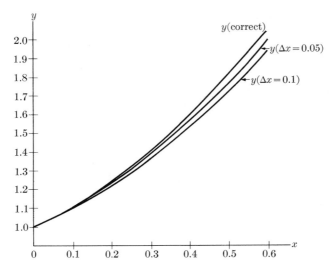

FIGURE 15–1

Example B. By the increment method, solve the differential equation $dy/dx = 2x^2 - y^2$ if the curve passes through the point $(1, 2)$. Use $\Delta x = 0.1$.

By following the method as outlined in Example A, the values in the following table are found.

x	y	$2x^2$	y^2	$2x^2 - y^2$	dy
1.00	2.00	2.00	4.00	−2.00	−0.20
1.10	1.80	2.42	3.24	−0.82	−0.08
1.20	1.72	2.88	2.96	−0.08	−0.01
1.30	1.71	3.38	2.92	0.46	0.05
1.40	1.76	3.92	3.10	0.82	0.08
1.50	1.84	4.50	3.39	1.11	0.11
1.60	1.95	5.12	3.80	1.32	0.13

See Fig. 15–2 for the graph of this solution.

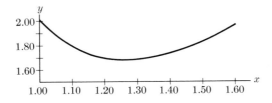

FIGURE 15–2

Example C. By the increment method, solve the differential equation $dy/dx = \cos x + \sin y$ if the curve passes through the point $(0, 0)$. Use $\Delta x = 0.1$ and construct the graph for $0 \leq x \leq 0.80$.

By following the method as outlined in Example A, the values in the following table are found.

x	y	$\cos x$	$\sin y$	$\cos x + \sin y$	dy
0.00	0.00	1.00	0.00	1.00	0.10
0.10	0.10	1.00	0.10	1.10	0.11
0.20	0.21	0.98	0.21	1.19	0.12
0.30	0.33	0.96	0.32	1.28	0.13
0.40	0.46	0.92	0.44	1.36	0.14
0.50	0.60	0.88	0.56	1.44	0.14
0.60	0.74	0.83	0.67	1.50	0.15
0.70	0.89	0.76	0.78	1.54	0.15
0.80	1.04	0.70	0.86	1.56	0.16

See Fig. 15–3 for the graph of this solution.

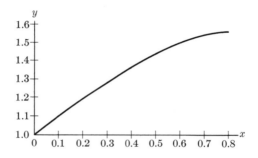

FIGURE 15–3

This method is actually limited in its usefulness. The values obtained are not particularly accurate if Δx is very large. Also, it is seen from Example A that the values vary more and more from the true values the farther the values of x are from that of the original given point. However, it is very useful in demonstrating the method of solving a differential equation numerically by successive approximations. Most such methods follow a similar technique.

Exercises

In Exercises 1 through 4 solve the given differential equations by the increment method for the specified values of x and Δx. Check the results against known values by solving the differential equations exactly. Plot the graphs of the solutions.

1. $\dfrac{dy}{dx} = x + 1$, $y = 1$ when $x = 0$, $0 \leq x \leq 1$, $\Delta x = 0.2$

2. Solve the differential equation of Exercise 1 if $\Delta x = 0.1$.

3. $\dfrac{dy}{dx} = y + e^x$, $y = 0$ when $x = 0$, $0 \le x \le 0.5$, $\Delta x = 0.1$

4. Solve the differential equation of Exercise 3 if $\Delta x = 0.05$.

In Exercises 5 through 10 solve the given differential equations by the increment method for the specified values of x and Δx. Plot the graphs of the solutions.

5. $\dfrac{dy}{dx} = xy + 1$, $y = 0$ when $x = 0$, $0 \le x \le 1$, $\Delta x = 0.1$

6. $\dfrac{dy}{dx} = x^2 + y^2$, $y = 1$ when $x = 0$, $0 \le x \le 0.8$, $\Delta x = 0.1$

7. $\dfrac{dy}{dx} = e^{xy}$, $y = 0$ when $x = 0$, $0 \le x \le 1.2$, $\Delta x = 0.2$

8. $\dfrac{dy}{dx} = \sqrt{1 + xy}$, $y = 1$ when $x = 0$, $0 \le x \le 0.5$, $\Delta x = 0.05$

9. $\dfrac{dy}{dx} = \cos(x + y)$, $y = \pi/2$ when $x = 0$, $0 \le x \le 1$, $\Delta x = 0.1$

10. $\dfrac{dy}{dx} = y + \sin x$, $y = 0$ when $x = 0.5$, $0.5 \le x \le 1.5$, $\Delta x = 0.1$

11. Evaluate the solution of the differential equation $y' = \ln(xy)$ for $x = 1.7$ if the solution passes through $(1, 1)$. Use $\Delta x = 0.1$.

12. A 3-slug object moves through a resisting medium. A constant force of 10 lb caused the motion, and a retarding force of $2v^{3/2}$ is present, where v is the velocity. The resulting differential equation is

$$3 \frac{dv}{dt} = 10 - 2v^{3/2}.$$

By the increment method graph the solution for v as a function of t for $0 \le t \le 2$ sec, using $\Delta t = 0.2$ sec, if the object starts from rest. The velocity is in ft/sec.

13. An electric circuit contains a 1-henry inductor, a 2-ohm resistor and a voltage source of $\sin t$. The resulting differential equation relating current and time is

$$\frac{di}{dt} + 2i = \sin t.$$

Find i after 0.5 sec by the increment method if the initial current is zero. Solve the equation exactly and compare the values.

14. An object is being heated such that the rate of change of temperature with respect to time is

$$\frac{dT}{dt} = \sqrt[3]{1 + t^3}.$$

Find the temperature T (°C) for $t = 5$ min by using the increment method with $\Delta t = 1.0$ min, if the initial temperature is 0°C.

15-2 A method of successive approximations

The second method of solving a differential equation to be discussed in this chapter is one based on successive approximations. In the previous section we saw how to develop a numerical solution based essentially on successive approximations. In this section we shall demonstrate a method that leads to a function which approximates the solution.

The method generally applies to a differential equation of the form $y' = f(x, y)$. If one point on the solution curve is known, the value of y is substituted into the right side, thereby giving a function of x alone. This equation can then be integrated, yielding y as a function of x, this solution being referred to as the first approximation. By substituting this expression into the right side for y, integrating again, a second approximation may be obtained. This process may be repeated as often as required, each time the solution for y being a better approximation than the last. The following example illustrates the method.

Example A. Obtain the first three approximations to the solution of the differential equation $dy = (x + y)\, dx$, if the solution curve passes through $(0, 1)$.

By substituting $y = 1$ in the right side of the differential equation, we have

$$dy = (x + 1)\, dx.$$

Integrating, we obtain the first approximation

$$y_1 = \frac{x^2}{2} + x + 1,$$

where the constant of integration has been evaluated as being 1 from the fact that the curve passes through $(0, 1)$. Substituting the expression for y_1 in the differential equation, we have

$$dy = \left(x + \frac{x^2}{2} + x + 1\right) dx = \left(\frac{x^2}{2} + 2x + 1\right) dx,$$

$$y_2 = \frac{x^3}{6} + x^2 + x + 1,$$

where the constant of integration again was evaluated to be 1, and y_2 is the second approximation. Substituting the expression for y_2 in the differential equation, we have

$$dy = \left(x + \frac{x^3}{6} + x^2 + x + 1\right) dx = \left(\frac{x^3}{6} + x^2 + 2x + 1\right) dx,$$

$$y_3 = \frac{x^4}{24} + \frac{x^3}{3} + x^2 + x + 1,$$

where, again, the constant of integration is 1 and y_3 is the third approximation.

We note that this differential equation is the same as that of the previous section. Therefore, the exact solution is

$$y = 2e^x - x - 1.$$

Figure 15–4 shows the graph of the exact solution and each of the three approximations. The accuracy of these approximations can be seen on the graph.

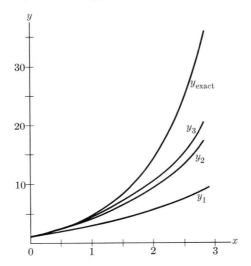

FIGURE 15–4

Example B. Find the first two approximations of the solution of the differential equation $y' = 2 - xy^2$ if the solution curve passes through $(0, 1)$.

Writing the equation in differential form and substituting 1 for y, we have

$$dy = (2 - x)\, dx,$$

which when integrated (the constant of integration is 1) gives

$$y_1 = 1 + 2x - \frac{x^2}{2}.$$

Substituting this expression for y in the differential equation, we have

$$dy = \left[2 - x\left(1 + 2x - \frac{x^2}{2}\right)^2\right] dx,$$

$$= \left(2 - x - 4x^2 - 3x^3 + 2x^4 - \frac{x^5}{4}\right) dx,$$

$$y_2 = 1 + 2x - \frac{x^2}{2} - \frac{4x^3}{3} - \frac{3x^4}{4} + \frac{2x^5}{5} - \frac{x^6}{24},$$

where the constant of integration is 1 and y_2 is the desired approximation.

Example C. Find the third approximation to the solution of the differential equation $y' = y + \sin x$, if the solution curve passes through $(0, \frac{1}{2})$. Evaluate the function for $x = 1$.

Following the method as previously illustrated we have the following steps:

$$dy = (\tfrac{1}{2} + \sin x)\, dx,$$

$$y_1 = \frac{x}{2} - \cos x + C_1.$$

Since the curve passes through $(0, \frac{1}{2})$ we have

$$\tfrac{1}{2} = 0 - 1 + C_1 \quad \text{or} \quad C_1 = \tfrac{3}{2}.$$

Thus

$$y_1 = \frac{3}{2} + \frac{x}{2} - \cos x,$$

$$dy = \left(\frac{3}{2} + \frac{x}{2} - \cos x + \sin x \right) dx,$$

$$y_2 = \frac{3x}{2} + \frac{x^2}{4} - \sin x - \cos x + C_2.$$

Here $C_2 = \frac{3}{2}$, which means

$$y_2 = \frac{3}{2} + \frac{3x}{2} + \frac{x^2}{4} - \sin x - \cos x,$$

$$dy = \left(\frac{3}{2} + \frac{3x}{2} + \frac{x^2}{4} - \cos x \right) dx,$$

$$y_3 = \frac{3x}{2} + \frac{3x^2}{4} + \frac{x^3}{12} - \sin x + C_3.$$

Here $C_3 = \frac{1}{2}$, which means

$$y_3 = \frac{1}{2} + \frac{3x}{2} + \frac{3x^2}{4} + \frac{x^3}{12} - \sin x.$$

Evaluating y_3 for $x = 1$, we have

$$y_3 = \frac{1}{2} + \frac{3}{2} + \frac{3}{4} + \frac{1}{12} - 0.84 = 1.99.$$

This function can be integrated exactly by methods developed in Chapter 13. The value found from the exact solution for $x = 1$ is 2.03. Also it should be noted that the constant of integration was not the same for each of the approximations.

The method of this section has the disadvantage that it can be applied only if the resulting differentials can be integrated. This naturally limits the equations which can be solved in this manner. However, for those to which it is applicable, it often provides a quicker and more accurate value for the solution for a specified value of x than the method of the previous section.

Exercises

In Exercises 1 through 4 find the indicated approximation of the solution of each of the given differential equations for which the solution curve passes through the given point. Solve each exactly and evaluate the solutions for the indicated value of x.

1. $y' = y^2, y_2, (0, 1), \quad x = 0.1.$
2. $y' = x - y, y_2, (0, 1), \quad x = 1/2.$
3. $y' = 2x(1 + y), y_3, (0, 0), \quad x = 1.$
4. $y' = y + e^x, y_3, (0, 0), \quad x = 0.2.$

In Exercises 5 through 8 find the indicated approximation of the solution of each of the given differential equations for which the solution curve passes through the given point.

5. $y' = x + y^2, y_3, (0, 0).$
6. $y' = 1 + xy^2, y_2, (0, 0).$
7. $y' = y - \cos 2x, y_2, (0, 1).$
8. $y' = x + y \cos x, y_2, (0, 1).$
9. Substitute the first few terms of the Maclaurin series for e^x in the expression $2e^x - x - 1$ and compare the results with the solution for Example A.
10. Evaluate i for $t = 0.5$ sec for the differential equation in Exercise 13 of Section (15–1) by finding i_2. Compare the results with those found in the indicated exercise.
11. A 1-slug object moves through a resisting medium such that the motion is resisted by a force numerically equal to the cube of the velocity. If a 2-lb force causes the motion, the resulting differential equation is

$$\frac{dv}{dt} = 2 - v^3.$$

Find the velocity when $t = 0.3$ sec if the object starts from rest. Use the second approximation of the solution.

15–3 Laplace transforms

The final method of solving differential equations which we shall discuss is by means of *Laplace transforms*. As we shall see, Laplace transforms provide an algebraic method of obtaining a *particular* solution of a differential equation from stated initial conditions. Since this is often what is desired in practice, Laplace transforms are often preferred for the solution of differential equations in engineering and electronics. In this section we shall discuss the meaning of the transform and its operations. These methods will be applied to solving differential equations in the following section. The treatment in this text is intended only as an introduction to the topic of Laplace transforms.

The Laplace transform of a function $f(t)$ is defined as the function $F(s)$ by the equation

$$F(s) = \int_0^\infty e^{-st} f(t)\, dt. \tag{15–1}$$

By writing the transform as $F(s)$ we show that the result of integrating and evaluating is a function of s. To denote that we are dealing with "the Laplace transform of the function $f(t)$" the notation $\mathcal{L}(f)$ is used. Thus,

$$F(s) = \mathcal{L}(f) = \int_0^\infty e^{-st} f(t)\, dt. \tag{15–2}$$

We will see that both notations are quite useful.

Example A. Find the Laplace transform of the function $f(t) = t,\ t > 0$.
   By the definition of the Laplace transform

$$\mathcal{L}(f) = \mathcal{L}(t) = \int_0^\infty e^{-st} t\, dt.$$

This may be integrated by parts or by formula (44) of Table 6 in the Appendix. Using the formula we have

$$\mathcal{L}(t) = \int_0^\infty t e^{-st}\, dt = \left. \frac{e^{-st}(-st - 1)}{s^2} \right|_0^\infty.$$

In evaluating the function for the upper limit it is necessary to consider the limit as $t \to \infty$. In this case $e^{-st} \to 0$ as $t \to \infty$ and the value for the upper limit is zero. Thus,

$$\mathcal{L}(t) = \frac{1}{s^2}.$$

Example B. Find the Laplace transform of the function $f(t) = \cos at$.
   By definition

$$\mathcal{L}(f) = \mathcal{L}(\cos at) = \int_0^\infty e^{-st} \cos at\, dt.$$

Using formula (50) of Table 6 we have

$$\mathcal{L}(\cos at) = \int_0^\infty e^{-st} \cos at\, dt = \left. \frac{e^{-st}(-s \cos at + a \sin at)}{s^2 + a^2} \right|_0^\infty$$

$$= 0 - \left(-\frac{s}{s^2 + a^2} \right) = \frac{s}{s^2 + a^2}.$$

Therefore the Laplace transform of the function cos at is

$$\mathcal{L}(\cos at) = \frac{s}{s^2 + a^2}.$$

It is noted that in both examples the resulting transform was an algebraic function of s.

An important property of Laplace transforms is the *linearity property*

$$\mathcal{L}[af(t) + bg(t)] = a\mathcal{L}(f) + b\mathcal{L}(g). \tag{15–3}$$

We state this property here since it determines that the transform of a sum of functions is the sum of the transforms. This is of definite importance when dealing with a sum of functions. This property is a direct result of the definition of the Laplace transform.

We now present a short table of Laplace transforms. The transforms given here are sufficient for our remaining work in this chapter. Much more complete tables are available in many standard reference sources.

TABLE OF LAPLACE TRANSFORMS

	$f(t) = \mathcal{L}^{-1}(F)$	$\mathcal{L}(f) = F(s)$
1.	1	$\dfrac{1}{s}$
2.	$\dfrac{t^{n-1}}{(n-1)!}$	$\dfrac{1}{s^n}$ $(n = 1, 2, 3, \ldots)$
3.	e^{-at}	$\dfrac{1}{s + a}$
4.	$1 - e^{-at}$	$\dfrac{a}{s(s + a)}$
5.	$\cos at$	$\dfrac{s}{s^2 + a^2}$
6.	$\sin at$	$\dfrac{a}{s^2 + a^2}$
7.	$1 - \cos at$	$\dfrac{a^2}{s(s^2 + a^2)}$
8.	$at - \sin at$	$\dfrac{a^3}{s^2(s^2 + a^2)}$
9.	$e^{-at} - e^{-bt}$	$\dfrac{b - a}{(s + a)(s + b)}$

(continued)

TABLE OF LAPLACE TRANSFORMS (*continued*)

	$f(t) = \mathcal{L}^{-1}\ (F)$	$\mathcal{L}(f) = F(s)$
10.	$ae^{-at} - be^{-bt}$	$\dfrac{s(a - b)}{(s + a)(s + b)}$
11.	te^{-at}	$\dfrac{1}{(s + a)^2}$
12.	$t^{n-1}e^{-at}$	$\dfrac{(n - 1)!}{(s + a)^n}$
13.	$e^{-at}(1 - at)$	$\dfrac{s}{(s + a)^2}$
14.	$[(b - a)t + 1]e^{-at}$	$\dfrac{s + b}{(s + a)^2}$
15.	$\sin at - at \cos at$	$\dfrac{2a^3}{(s^2 + a^2)^2}$
16.	$t \sin at$	$\dfrac{2as}{(s^2 + a^2)^2}$
17.	$\sin at + at \cos at$	$\dfrac{2as^2}{(s^2 + a^2)^2}$
18.	$t \cos at$	$\dfrac{s^2 - a^2}{(s^2 + a^2)^2}$
19.	$e^{-at} \sin bt$	$\dfrac{b}{(s + a)^2 + b^2}$
20.	$e^{-at} \cos bt$	$\dfrac{s + a}{(s + a)^2 + b^2}$

Another Laplace transform important to the solution of a differential equation is the transform of the derivative of a function. Let us first find the Laplace transform of the first derivative of a function.

By definition

$$\mathcal{L}(f') = \int_0^\infty e^{-st}f'(t)\ dt.$$

Integrating by parts, where $u = e^{-st}$ and $dv = f'(t)\ dt$, we have $du = -se^{-st}\ dt$ and $v = f(t)$ [the integral of the derivative of a function is the function]. Therefore,

$$\mathcal{L}(f') = e^{-st}f(t)\big|_0^\infty + s \int_0^\infty e^{-st}f(t)\ dt$$

$$= 0 - f(0) + s\mathcal{L}(f).$$

It is noted that the integral in the second term on the right is the Laplace transform of $f(t)$ by definition. Therefore, the Laplace transform of the first derivative of a function is

$$\mathcal{L}(f') = s\mathcal{L}(f) - f(0). \tag{15-4}$$

Applying the same analysis, we may find the Laplace transform of the second derivative of a function. It is

$$\mathcal{L}(f'') = s^2\mathcal{L}(f) - sf(0) - f'(0). \tag{15-5}$$

Here it is necessary to integrate by parts twice to derive the result. The transforms of higher derivatives are found in a similar manner.

The usefulness of Eqs. (15-4) and (15-5) is that they allow us to express the transform of each derivative in terms of s and the transform of the function itself.

Example C. If $f(0) = 0$ and $f'(0) = 1$, express the transform of $f''(t) - 2f'(t)$ in terms of s and the transform of $f(t)$.

By the linearity property, Eq. (15-3), we have

$$
\begin{aligned}
\mathcal{L}[f''(t) - 2f'(t)] &= \mathcal{L}(f'') - 2\mathcal{L}(f') \\
&= [s^2\mathcal{L}(f) - s(0) - 1] - 2[s\mathcal{L}(f) - 0] \\
&= (s^2 - 2s)\mathcal{L}(f) - 1.
\end{aligned}
$$

If the Laplace transform of a function is known, it is then possible to find the function by finding the *inverse transform*

$$\mathcal{L}^{-1}(F) = f(t), \tag{15-6}$$

where $\mathcal{L}^{-1}$ denotes the inverse transform.

Example D. If $F(s) = s/(s^2 + a^2)$, from transform (5) of the table we see that

$$\mathcal{L}^{-1}(F) = \mathcal{L}^{-1}\left(\frac{s}{s^2 + a^2}\right) = \cos at$$

or

$$f(t) = \cos at.$$

Example E. If $(s^2 - 2s)\mathcal{L}(f) - 1 = 0$, then

$$\mathcal{L}(f) = \frac{1}{s^2 - 2s} \quad \text{or} \quad F(s) = \frac{1}{s(s - 2)}.$$

Thus,

$$\mathcal{L}^{-1}(F) = f(t) = -\tfrac{1}{2}(1 - e^{2t})$$

from transform (4) of the table.

Example F. If $F(s) = (s + 5)/(s^2 + 6s + 10)$, then

$$\mathcal{L}^{-1}(F) = \mathcal{L}^{-1}\left[\frac{s + 5}{s^2 + 6s + 10}\right].$$

It appears that this function does not fit any of the forms given. However,

$$s^2 + 6s + 10 = (s^2 + 6s + 9) + 1 = (s + 3)^2 + 1.$$

By writing $F(s)$ as

$$F(s) = \frac{(s + 3) + 2}{(s + 3)^2 + 1} = \frac{s + 3}{(s + 3)^2 + 1} + \frac{2}{(s + 3)^2 + 1},$$

we can find the inverse of each term. Therefore,

$$\mathcal{L}^{-1}(F) = e^{-3t}\cos t + 2e^{-3t}\sin t$$

or

$$f(t) = e^{-3t}(\cos t + 2\sin t).$$

Exercises

In Exercises 1 through 4, verify the indicated transforms given in the table.

1. Transform 1   2. Transform 3
3. Transform 6   4. Transform 11

In Exercises 5 through 10, find the transforms of the given functions by use of the table.

5. $f(t) = e^{3t}$ 6. $f(t) = 1 - \cos 2t$
7. $f(t) = t^3 e^{-2t}$ 8. $f(t) = 2e^{-3t}\sin 4t$
9. $f(t) = \cos 2t - \sin 2t$ 10. $f(t) = 2t\sin 3t + e^{-3t}\cos t$

In Exercises 11 through 14, express the transforms of the given expressions in terms of s and $\mathcal{L}(f)$.

11. $y'' + y', f(0) = 0, f'(0) = 0$
12. $y'' - 3y', f(0) = 2, f'(0) = -1$
13. $2y'' - y' + y, f(0) = 1, f'(0) = 0$
14. $y'' - 3y' + 2y, f(0) = -1, f'(0) = 2$

In Exercises 15 through 20, find the inverse transform of the given functions of s.

15. $F(s) = \dfrac{1}{s + 5}$ 16. $F(s) = \dfrac{3}{s^4 + 4s^2}$

17. $F(s) = \dfrac{1}{s^3 + 3s^2 + 3s + 1}$ 18. $F(s) = \dfrac{s^2 - 1}{s^4 + 2s^2 + 1}$

19. $F(s) = \dfrac{s + 2}{(s^2 + 9)^2}$ 20. $F(s) = \dfrac{s + 3}{s^2 + 4s + 13}$

15–4 Solving differential equations by use of Laplace transforms

We will now show how certain differential equations can be solved by the use of Laplace transforms. It must be remembered that these solutions are the *particular* solutions of the equations subject to the given conditions. The necessary operations were developed in the preceding section. The following examples illustrate the method.

Example A. Solve the differential equation $2y' - y = 0$ if $y(0) = 1$. (Note that we are using y to denote the function.)

Taking transforms of each term in the equation, we have

$$\mathcal{L}(2y') - \mathcal{L}(y) = \mathcal{L}(0), \qquad 2\mathcal{L}(y') - \mathcal{L}(y) = 0.$$

$\mathcal{L}(0) = 0$ by direct use of the definition of the transform. Now using Eq. (15–4), $\mathcal{L}(y') = s\mathcal{L}(y) - y(0)$, we have

$$2[s\mathcal{L}(y) - 1] - \mathcal{L}(y) = 0.$$

Solving for $\mathcal{L}(y)$ we obtain

$$2s\mathcal{L}(y) - \mathcal{L}(y) = 2, \qquad \mathcal{L}(y) = \frac{2}{2s - 1} = \frac{1}{s - 1/2}.$$

Finding the inverse transform of $F(s) = 1/(s - \frac{1}{2})$, we have

$$y = e^{t/2}.$$

The reader should check this solution with that obtained by methods developed in Chapter 13. Also it should be noted that the solution was essentially an algebraic one.

Example B. Solve the differential equation $y'' + 2y' + 2y = 0$, if $y(0) = 0$ and $y'(0) = 1$.

Using the same steps as outlined in Example A, we have the following solution:

$$\mathcal{L}(y'') + 2\mathcal{L}(y') + 2\mathcal{L}(y) = 0,$$

$$[s^2\mathcal{L}(y) - sy(0) - y'(0)] + 2[s\mathcal{L}(y) - y(0)] + 2\mathcal{L}(y) = 0,$$

$$s^2\mathcal{L}(y) - 1 + 2s\mathcal{L}(y) + 2\mathcal{L}(y) = 0,$$

$$(s^2 + 2s + 2)\mathcal{L}(y) = 1,$$

$$\mathcal{L}(y) = \frac{1}{s^2 + 2s + 2} = \frac{1}{(s + 1)^2 + 1},$$

$$y = e^{-t}\sin t.$$

Example C. Solve the differential equation $y'' + y = \cos t$ if $y(0) = 1$ and $y'(0) = 2$.

Taking transforms of each term in the equation, we have

$$\mathcal{L}(y'') + \mathcal{L}(y) = \mathcal{L}(\cos t).$$

The transform on the left is found by use of Eq. (15–5) and the transform on the right is found by direct use of transform (5) in the table. Therefore we have

$$[s^2\mathcal{L}(y) - s(1) - 2] + \mathcal{L}(y) = \frac{s}{s^2 + 1}.$$

Solving for $\mathcal{L}(y)$, we obtain

$$(s^2 + 1)\mathcal{L}(y) = \frac{s}{s^2 + 1} + s + 2,$$

$$\mathcal{L}(y) = \frac{s}{(s^2 + 1)^2} + \frac{s}{s^2 + 1} + \frac{2}{s^2 + 1}.$$

Finding the inverse-transform of each expression completes the solution:

$$y = \frac{t}{2} \sin t + \cos t + 2 \sin t.$$

Example D. An electric circuit contains a 1-henry inductor, a 10-ohm resistor and a battery whose voltage is 6 volts. Find the current as a function of the time, if the initial current is zero.

The differential equation for this circuit is

$$\frac{di}{dt} + 10i = 6.$$

Following the procedures outlined in the previous examples, the solution is found:

$$\mathcal{L}\left(\frac{di}{dt}\right) + 10\mathcal{L}(i) = \mathcal{L}(6), \qquad [s\mathcal{L}(i) - 0] + 10\mathcal{L}(i) = \frac{6}{s},$$

$$\mathcal{L}(i) = \frac{6}{s(s + 10)}, \qquad i = 0.6(1 - e^{-10t}).$$

Example E. A spring is stretched 1 ft by a weight of 16 lb (mass of $\frac{1}{2}$ slug). The medium resists the motion of the object with a force of $4v$, where v is the velocity. The differential equation describing the motion is

$$\frac{1}{2}\frac{d^2y}{dt^2} + 4\frac{dy}{dt} + 16y = 0.$$

Find y, the displacement of the object, as a function of the time if $y(0) = 1$ and $dy/dt = 0$ when $t = 0$.

Clearing fractions and denoting the derivatives by y'' and y', the differential equation becomes

$$y'' + 8y' + 32y = 0.$$

Following the procedure of solving this type of an equation by use of Laplace transforms, we have the following steps:

$$\mathcal{L}(y'') + 8\mathcal{L}(y') + 32\mathcal{L}(y) = 0,$$

$$[s^2\mathcal{L}(y) - s(1) - 0] + 8[s\mathcal{L}(y) - 1] + 32\mathcal{L}(y) = 0,$$

$$(s^2 + 8s + 32)\mathcal{L}(y) = s + 8,$$

$$\mathcal{L}(y) = \frac{s + 8}{(s + 4)^2 + 4^2} = \frac{s + 4}{(s + 4)^2 + 4^2} + \frac{4}{(s + 4)^2 + 4^2},$$

$$y = e^{-4t}\cos 4t + e^{-4t}\sin 4t,$$

$$= e^{-4t}(\cos 4t + \sin 4t).$$

Exercises

Solve the following differential equations by use of Laplace transforms, where the function is subject to the given conditions.

1. $y' + y = 0$, $y(0) = 1$

2. $y' - 2y = 0$, $y(0) = 2$

3. $2y' - 3y = 0$, $y(0) = -1$

4. $y' + 2y = 1$, $y(0) = 0$

5. $y' + 3y = e^{-3t}$, $y(0) = 1$

6. $y' + 2y = te^{-2t}$, $y(0) = 0$

7. $y'' + 4y = 0$, $y(0) = 0$, $y'(0) = 1$

8. $y'' - 4y = 0$, $y(0) = 2$, $y'(0) = 0$

9. $y'' + 2y' = 0$, $y(0) = 0$, $y'(0) = 2$

10. $y'' + 2y' + y = 0$, $y(0) = 0$, $y'(0) = -2$

11. $y'' - 4y' + 5y = 0$, $y(0) = 1$, $y'(0) = 2$

12. $4y'' + 4y' + y = 0$, $y(0) = 1$, $y'(0) = 0$

13. $y'' + y = 1$, $y(0) = 1$, $y'(0) = 1$

14. $y'' + 4y = 2t$, $y(0) = 0$, $y'(0) = 0$

15. $y'' + 2y' + y = e^{-t}$, $y(0) = 1$, $y'(0) = 2$

16. $y'' + 4y = \sin 2t$, $y(0) = 0$, $y'(0) = 0$

17. A constant force of 6 lb moves a 2-slug mass through a medium which resists the motion with a force equal to v, where v is the velocity. The differential equation relating the velocity and time is

$$2\frac{dv}{dt} = 6 - v.$$

Find v as a function of time if the object starts from rest.

18. A 100-ohm resistor and a 4×10^{-6}-farad capacitor make up an electric circuit. If the initial charge on the capacitor is 0.01 coul, find the charge on the capacitor as a function of time after the switch is closed.

19. A 10-henry inductor, a 4×10^{-5}-farad capacitor and a voltage supply whose voltage is given by $100 \sin 50t$ are connected in series in an electric circuit. Find the current as a function of time if the initial charge on the capacitor and the initial current are zero.

20. A spring is such that it is stretched 6 in. by an 8-lb (1/4-slug) weight. The spring is stretched 6 in. below the equilibrium position with the weight on it and is given a velocity of 4 ft/sec. If the spring is in a medium which resists the motion with a force equal to $4v$, find the displacement y as a function of time.

Miscellaneous exercises for Chapter 15

In Exercises 1 through 6 solve the given differential equations by the increment method for the specified values of x and Δx and for which the solution curve passes through the given point.

1. $y' = x^2 - y^2$, $0 \le x \le 0.5$, $\Delta x = 0.1$, $(0, 1)$

2. $y' = \dfrac{1}{1 + x + y}$, $0 \le x \le 1$, $\Delta x = 0.2$, $(0, 0)$

3. $y' = \sqrt{x + y}$, $0 \le x \le 2$, $\Delta x = 0.2$, $(0, 1)$

4. $y' = x^2 + \sin y$, $0 \le x \le 1$, $\Delta x = 0.1$, $(0, 1)$

5. $y' = \sin x + \tan y$, $0 \le x \le 0.7$, $\Delta x = 0.1$, $(0, 0.5)$

6. $y' = e^{2x} + \sin xy$, $0 \le x \le 1$, $\Delta x = 0.1$, $(0, 0)$

In Exercises 7 through 10 find the indicated approximation of the solution of each of the given differential equations for which the solution curve passes through the given point.

7. $y' = y + x^2$, y_3, $(0, 1)$

8. $y' = \cos x - y$, y_3, $(0, 1)$

9. $y' = 1 + x^2 y$, y_2, $(1, 1)$

10. $y' = y^2 - \sin x$, y_2, $(0, 2)$

In Exercises 11 through 18 solve the given differential equations by use of Laplace transforms where the function is subject to the given conditions.

11. $4y' - y = 0$, $y(0) = 1$

12. $2y' - y = 4$, $y(0) = 1$

13. $y' - 3y = e^t$, $y(0) = 0$

14. $y' + 2y = e^{-2t}$, $y(0) = 2$

15. $y'' + y = 0$, $y(0) = 0$, $y'(0) = -4$

16. $y'' + 4y' + 5y = 0$, $y(0) = 1$, $y'(0) = 1$

17. $y'' + 9y = 3t$, $y(0) = 0$, $y'(0) = -1$

18. $y'' + 4y' + 4y = 2e^{-2t}$, $y(0) = 0$, $y'(0) = 1$

19. Find the second approximation to the solution of the differential equation $y' = 1 + ye^{-x}$ if the solution curve passes through $(0, 1)$. Evaluate y_2 for $x = 0.5$.

20. Solve $y' = 1 + ye^{-x}$ by the increment method for $0 \leq x \leq 1$ using $\Delta x = 0.1$ if the solution curve passes through $(0, 1)$. Compare the value for $x = 0.5$ with that found in Exercise 19.

21. Repeat the instructions of Exercise 19 for $y' = 2x/(x^2 + e^y)$.

22. Repeat the instructions of Exercise 20 for the equation given in Exercise 21, and compare the results with those found in Exercise 21.

23. The differential equation relating current and time for a certain electric circuit is

$$2 \frac{di}{dt} + i = 12.$$

Solve this equation by use of Laplace transforms given that the initial current is zero. Evaluate the current for $t = 0.3$ sec.

24. Use the increment method to find the current for $t = 0.3$ sec for the equation of Exercise 23. Use $\Delta t = 0.05$ sec.

25. Find the third approximation for i as a function of t for the equation of Exercise 23. Evaluate i for $t = 0.3$ sec and compare this value with those found in Exercises 23 and 24.

26. An inductor of 0.5 henry, a resistor of 6 ohms and a capacitor of 2×10^{-4} farad are connected in series. If the initial charge on the capacitor is 0.01 coul, and the initial current is zero, find the charge on the capacitor as a function of time after the switch is closed. Use Laplace transforms.

27. A certain spring is such that an 8-lb weight (1/4-slug mass) stretches it 6 in. An external force of $\cos 8t$ is applied to the spring. Express the displacement y of the object as a function of time if the initial displacement and velocity are zero.

Appendix A | Study Aids

A-1 Introduction

The primary objective of this text is to give you, the student, an understanding of calculus and analytic geometry so that these topics may be understood and effectively used in your technology. Without an understanding of the basic methods, knowledge is usually short-lived. However, if you do have understanding, you will find your work more enjoyable and rewarding. This is true in any course you may take, be it in mathematics or any other field.

Mathematics is an indispensable tool in almost all scientific fields of study. Generally, in the introductory portions of allied courses, it suffices to have a grasp of elementary concepts in algebra, geometry, and trigonometry. However, as you have progressed in your field, the need for more mathematics undoubtedly has been apparent. This text is designed to develop some of these additional mathematical tools.

It is assumed that before you use this text you will have had a background which includes algebra and trigonometry. However, some of the essential topics from algebra and trigonometry have been reviewed in certain sections for your review and reference. You should utilize these sections so that you are sure that you know these topics well. You cannot derive full benefit from your mathematics course unless you devote the necessary amount of time to developing a sound understanding of the subject.

There is only one good way to develop the understanding and working knowledge necessary in any course, and that is to *work with it*. Many students consider mathematics difficult, and they will tell you that it is their lack of mathematical ability and the material itself which make it difficult. There is no doubt that certain topics in mathematics, especially in more advanced areas, require a certain aptitude if there is to be full comprehension. However, a large proportion of poor grades in elementary mathematics courses result from the fact that the student is not willing to put in the necessary time to develop the understanding. The student takes a quick glance through the material, tries a few problems, probably unsuccessfully to a large degree, and then decides that this is "impossible." A detailed reading of the text, a careful following of the illustrative examples, and the solving of problems would lead to more success, and therefore would make the work much more enjoyable and rewarding. No matter what text is used, no matter what methods are used in the course or what other variables may be introduced, if you do not put in an adequate amount of study time, you will not derive the proper results. More detailed suggestions for study are included in the following section.

If you consider these suggestions carefully, and follow good study habits, you should enjoy a successful learning experience in this as well as in other courses.

A–2 Suggestions for study

When you are studying the material presented in this text, the following suggestions may help you to derive full benefit from the time you devote to it.

(1) Before attempting to do the exercises, read through the material preceding them.

(2) Carefully follow through the illustrative examples, being certain that you know how to proceed from step to step. At this point you should have a good idea of the methods involved.

(3) Work through the exercises, spending a reasonable amount of time on each problem. If you cannot solve a certain problem in a reasonable amount of time, leave it and go to the next. Return to this problem later. If you find many problems difficult, you should reread the explanatory material and the examples, to determine what point or points you have not understood.

(4) When you have completed the exercises, or at least most of them, glance back through the explanatory material to be sure you have a good understanding of the methods and principles presented there.

(5) If you have gone through the first four steps and certain points still elude you, ask to have these points clarified in class. Do not be afraid to ask questions; only be sure that you have made a sincere effort before you ask them.

Some study habits which are useful not only here but in all of your other subjects are the following:

(1) Put in the required time to fully develop the material to yourself, being certain that you are making effective use of your time. A good place to study helps immeasurably.

(2) Learn the *methods and principles* being presented. Memorize as little as possible, for although there are certain basic facts which are more expediently learned by memorization, these should be kept to a minimum.

(3) Keep up with the material in all of your courses. Do not let yourself get so behind in your studies that it becomes difficult to make up the time. Usually the time is never really made up. Studying only before tests is a poor way of learning, and is usually rather ineffective.

(4) When you are taking examinations, always read each question carefully before attempting the solution. Solve those you find easiest first, and do not spend too much time on any one problem. Also, use all the time available for the examination. If you finish early, use the remainder of the time to check your work.

A-3 Problem analysis

Drill-type problems require a working knowledge of the methods presented. However, they do not require, in general, much analysis before being put in proper form for solution. Stated problems, on the other hand, do require proper interpretation before they can be put in a form for solution. The remainder of this section is devoted to some suggestions for solving stated problems.

We have to put stated problems in symbolic form before we attempt to solve them. It is this step which most students find difficult. Because such problems require the student to do more than merely go through a certain routine, they demand more analysis and thus appear more "difficult." There are several reasons for the student's difficulty, some of them being: (1) unsuccessful previous attempts at solving such problems, leading the student to believe that all stated problems are "impossible"; (2) failure to read the problem carefully; (3) a poorly organized approach to the solution; and (4) improper and incomplete interpretation of the statements given. These can be overcome only with the proper attitude and care.

There are numerous completely worked examples of stated problems (as well as many other problems which indicate a similar analysis) throughout this text, illustrating proper interpretations and approaches to these problems. Therefore, we shall not include specific examples here. However, we shall set forth the method of analysis of any stated problem. Such an analysis generally follows these steps:

(1) Read the problem carefully.
(2) Carefully identify known and unknown quantities.
(3) Draw a figure when appropriate (which is quite often the case).
(4) Write, in symbols, the relations given in the statements.
(5) Solve for the desired quantities.

If you follow this step-by-step method, and write out the solution neatly, you should find that stated problems lend themselves to solution more readily than you had previously found.

Appendix B
Formulas from Geometry

A = area, B = area of base, C = circumference, S = lateral area or surface area, V = volume.

1. *Triangle.* $A = \frac{1}{2}bh.$ (Fig. 1)

2. *Similar triangles.* $\dfrac{a'}{a} = \dfrac{b'}{b} = \dfrac{c'}{c}.$ (Fig. 2)

3. *Theorem of Pythagoras.* $c^2 = a^2 + b^2.$ (Fig. 3)

4. *Parallelogram.* $A = bh.$ (Fig. 4)

5. *Trapezoid.* $A = \frac{1}{2}(a + b)h.$ (Fig. 5)

6. *Circle.* $A = \pi r^2,\quad C = 2\pi r.$ (Fig. 6)

7. *Any cylinder or prism with parallel bases.* $V = Bh.$ (Fig. 7)

8. *Right circular cylinder.* $V = \pi r^2 h,\quad S = 2\pi rh.$ (Fig. 8)

9. *Any cone or pyramid.* $V = \frac{1}{3}Bh.$ Surface Area $= 2\pi rh$ (Fig. 9)

10. *Right circular cone.* $V = \frac{1}{3}\pi r^2 h,\quad S = \pi rs.$ (Fig. 10)

11. *Sphere.* $V = \frac{4}{3}\pi r^3,\quad A = 4\pi r^2.$ (Fig. 11)

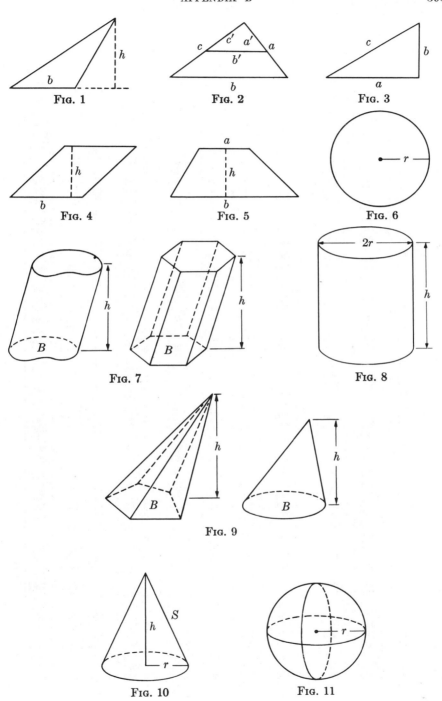

FIG. 1

FIG. 2

FIG. 3

FIG. 4

FIG. 5

FIG. 6

FIG. 7

FIG. 8

FIG. 9

FIG. 10

FIG. 11

Appendix C | Tables

Table 1

Powers and Roots

No.	Sq.	Sq. Root	Cube	Cube Root	No.	Sq.	Sq. Root	Cube	Cube Root
1	1	1.000	1	1.000	51	2,601	7.141	132,651	3.708
2	4	1.414	8	1.260	52	2,704	7.211	140,608	3.733
3	9	1.732	27	1.442	53	2,809	7.280	148,877	3.756
4	16	2.000	64	1.587	54	2,916	7.348	157,464	3.780
5	25	2.236	125	1.710	55	3,025	7.416	166,375	3.803
6	36	2.449	216	1.817	56	3,136	7.483	175,616	3.826
7	49	2.646	343	1.913	57	3,249	7.550	185,193	3.849
8	64	2.828	512	2.000	58	3,364	7.616	195,112	3.871
9	81	3.000	729	2.080	59	3,481	7.681	205,379	3.893
10	100	3.162	1,000	2.154	60	3,600	7.746	216,000	3.915
11	121	3.317	1,331	2.224	61	3,721	7.810	226,981	3.936
12	144	3.464	1,728	2.289	62	3,844	7.874	238,328	3.958
13	169	3.606	2,197	2.351	63	3,969	7.937	250,047	3.979
14	196	3.742	2,744	2.410	64	4,096	8.000	262,144	4.000
15	225	3.873	3,375	2.466	65	4,225	8.062	274,625	4.021
16	256	4.000	4,096	2.520	66	4,356	8.124	287,496	4.041
17	289	4.123	4,913	2.571	67	4,489	8.185	300,763	4.062
18	324	4.243	5,832	2.621	68	4,624	8.246	314,432	4.082
19	361	4.359	6,859	2.668	69	4,761	8.307	328,509	4.102
20	400	4.472	8,000	2.714	70	4,900	8.367	343,000	4.121
21	441	4.583	9,261	2.759	71	5,041	8.426	357,911	4.141
22	484	4.690	10,648	2.802	72	5,184	8.485	373,248	4.160
23	529	4.796	12,167	2.844	73	5,329	8.544	389,017	4.179
24	576	4.899	13,824	2.884	74	5,476	8.602	405,224	4.198
25	625	5.000	15,625	2.924	75	5,625	8.660	421,875	4.217
26	676	5.099	17,576	2.962	76	5,776	8.718	438,976	4.236
27	729	5.196	19,683	3.000	77	5,929	8.775	456,533	4.254
28	784	5.292	21,952	3.037	78	6,084	8.832	474,552	4.273
29	841	5.385	24,389	3.072	79	6,241	8.888	493,039	4.291
30	900	5.477	27,000	3.107	80	6,400	8.944	512,000	4.309
31	961	5.568	29,791	3.141	81	6,561	9.000	531,441	4.327
32	1,024	5.657	32,768	3.175	82	6,724	9.055	551,368	4.344
33	1,089	5.745	35,937	3.208	83	6,889	9.110	571,787	4.362
34	1,156	5.831	39,304	3.240	84	7,056	9.165	592,704	4.380
35	1,225	5.916	42,875	3.271	85	7,225	9.220	614,125	4.397
36	1,296	6.000	46,656	3.302	86	7,396	9.274	636,056	4.414
37	1,369	6.083	50,653	3.332	87	7,569	9.327	658,503	4.431
38	1,444	6.164	54,872	3.362	88	7,744	9.381	681,472	4.448
39	1,521	6.245	59,319	3.391	89	7,921	9.434	704,969	4.465
40	1,600	6.325	64,000	3.420	90	8,100	9.487	729,000	4.481
41	1,681	6.403	68,921	3.448	91	8,281	9.539	753,571	4.498
42	1,764	6.481	74,088	3.476	92	8,464	9.592	778,688	4.514
43	1,849	6.557	79,507	3.503	93	8,649	9.644	804,357	4.531
44	1,936	6.633	85,184	3.530	94	8,836	9.695	830,584	4.547
45	2,025	6.708	91,125	3.557	95	9,025	9.747	857,375	4.563
46	2,116	6.782	97,336	3.583	96	9,216	9.798	884,736	4.579
47	2,209	6.856	103,823	3.609	97	9,409	9.849	912,673	4.595
48	2,304	6.928	110,592	3.634	98	9,604	9.899	941,192	4.610
49	2,401	7.000	117,649	3.659	99	9,801	9.950	970,299	4.626
50	2,500	7.071	125,000	3.684	100	10,000	10.000	1,000,000	4.642

TABLE 2

NATURAL TRIGONOMETRIC FUNCTIONS

Angle					Angle				
Degree	Radian	Sine	Cosine	Tangent	Degree	Radian	Sine	Cosine	Tangent
0°	0.000	0.000	1.000	0.000					
1°	0.017	0.017	1.000	0.017	46°	0.803	0.719	0.695	1.036
2°	0.035	0.035	0.999	0.035	47°	0.820	0.731	0.682	1.072
3°	0.052	0.052	0.999	0.052	48°	0.838	0.743	0.669	1.111
4°	0.070	0.070	0.998	0.070	49°	0.855	0.755	0.656	1.150
5°	0.087	0.087	0.996	0.087	50°	0.873	0.766	0.643	1.192
6°	0.105	0.105	0.995	0.105	51°	0.890	0.777	0.629	1.235
7°	0.122	0.122	0.993	0.123	52°	0.908	0.788	0.616	1.280
8°	0.140	0.139	0.990	0.141	53°	0.925	0.799	0.602	1.327
9°	0.157	0.156	0.988	0.158	54°	0.942	0.809	0.588	1.376
10°	0.175	0.174	0.985	0.176	55°	0.960	0.819	0.574	1.428
11°	0.192	0.191	0.982	0.194	56°	0.977	0.829	0.559	1.483
12°	0.209	0.208	0.978	0.213	57°	0.995	0.839	0.545	1.540
13°	0.227	0.225	0.974	0.231	58°	1.012	0.848	0.530	1.600
14°	0.244	0.242	0.970	0.249	59°	1.030	0.857	0.515	1.664
15°	0.262	0.259	0.966	0.268	60°	1.047	0.866	0.500	1.732
16°	0.279	0.276	0.961	0.287	61°	1.065	0.875	0.485	1.804
17°	0.297	0.292	0.956	0.306	62°	1.082	0.883	0.469	1.881
18°	0.314	0.309	0.951	0.325	63°	1.100	0.891	0.454	1.963
19°	0.332	0.326	0.946	0.344	64°	1.117	0.899	0.438	2.050
20°	0.349	0.342	0.940	0.364	65°	1.134	0.906	0.423	2.145
21°	0.367	0.358	0.934	0.384	66°	1.152	0.914	0.407	2.246
22°	0.384	0.375	0.927	0.404	67°	1.169	0.921	0.391	2.356
23°	0.401	0.391	0.921	0.424	68°	1.187	0.927	0.375	2.475
24°	0.419	0.407	0.914	0.445	69°	1.204	0.934	0.358	2.605
25°	0.436	0.423	0.906	0.466	70°	1.222	0.940	0.342	2.748
26°	0.454	0.438	0.899	0.488	71°	1.239	0.946	0.326	2.904
27°	0.471	0.454	0.891	0.510	72°	1.257	0.951	0.309	3.078
28°	0.489	0.469	0.883	0.532	73°	1.274	0.956	0.292	3.271
29°	0.506	0.485	0.875	0.554	74°	1.292	0.961	0.276	3.487
30°	0.524	0.500	0.866	0.577	75°	1.309	0.966	0.259	3.732
31°	0.541	0.515	0.857	0.601	76°	1.326	0.970	0.242	4.011
32°	0.559	0.530	0.848	0.625	77°	1.344	0.974	0.225	4.332
33°	0.576	0.545	0.839	0.649	78°	1.361	0.978	0.208	4.705
34°	0.593	0.559	0.829	0.675	79°	1.379	0.982	0.191	5.145
35°	0.611	0.574	0.819	0.700	80°	1.396	0.985	0.174	5.671
36°	0.628	0.588	0.809	0.727	81°	1.414	0.988	0.156	6.314
37°	0.646	0.602	0.799	0.754	82°	1.431	0.990	0.139	7.115
38°	0.663	0.616	0.788	0.781	83°	1.449	0.993	0.122	8.144
39°	0.681	0.629	0.777	0.810	84°	1.466	0.995	0.105	9.514
40°	0.698	0.643	0.766	0.839	85°	1.484	0.996	0.087	11.43
41°	0.716	0.656	0.755	0.869	86°	1.501	0.998	0.070	14.30
42°	0.733	0.669	0.743	0.900	87°	1.518	0.999	0.052	19.08
43°	0.750	0.682	0.731	0.933	88°	1.536	0.999	0.035	28.64
44°	0.768	0.695	0.719	0.966	89°	1.553	1.000	0.017	57.29
45°	0.785	0.707	0.707	1.000	90°	1.571	1.000	0.000	

TABLE 3

FOUR-PLACE LOGARITHMS OF NUMBERS

N	0	1	2	3	4	5	6	7	8	9
10	0000	0043	0086	0128	0170	0212	0253	0294	0334	0374
11	0414	0453	0492	0531	0569	0607	0645	0682	0719	0755
12	0792	0828	0864	0899	0934	0969	1004	1038	1072	1106
13	1139	1173	1206	1239	1271	1303	1335	1367	1399	1430
14	1461	1492	1523	1553	1584	1614	1644	1673	1703	1732
15	1761	1790	1818	1847	1875	1903	1931	1959	1987	2014
16	2041	2068	2095	2122	2148	2175	2201	2227	2253	2279
17	2304	2330	2355	2380	2405	2430	2455	2480	2504	2529
18	2553	2577	2601	2625	2648	2672	2695	2718	2742	2765
19	2788	2810	2833	2856	2878	2900	2923	2945	2967	2989
20	3010	3032	3054	3075	3096	3118	3139	3160	3181	3201
21	3222	3243	3263	3284	3304	3324	3345	3365	3385	3404
22	3424	3444	3464	3483	3502	3522	3541	3560	3579	3598
23	3617	3636	3655	3674	3692	3711	3729	3747	3766	3784
24	3802	3820	3838	3856	3874	3892	3909	3927	3945	3962
25	3979	3997	4014	4031	4048	4065	4082	4099	4116	4133
26	4150	4166	4183	4200	4216	4232	4249	4265	4281	4298
27	4314	4330	4346	4362	4378	4393	4409	4425	4440	4456
28	4472	4487	4502	4518	4533	4548	4564	4579	4594	4609
29	4624	4639	4654	4669	4683	4698	4713	4728	4742	4757
30	4771	4786	4800	4814	4829	4843	4857	4871	4886	4900
31	4914	4928	4942	4955	4969	4983	4997	5011	5024	5038
32	5051	5065	5079	5092	5105	5119	5132	5145	5159	5172
33	5185	5198	5211	5224	5237	5250	5263	5276	5289	5302
34	5315	5328	5340	5353	5366	5378	5391	5403	5416	5428
35	5441	5453	5465	5478	5490	5502	5514	5527	5539	5551
36	5563	5575	5587	5599	5611	5623	5635	5647	5658	5670
37	5682	5694	5705	5717	5729	5740	5752	5763	5775	5786
38	5798	5809	5821	5832	5843	5855	5866	5877	5888	5899
39	5911	5922	5933	5944	5955	5966	5977	5988	5999	6010
40	6021	6031	6042	6053	6064	6075	6085	6096	6107	6117
41	6128	6138	6149	6160	6170	6180	6191	6201	6212	6222
42	6232	6243	6253	6263	6274	6284	6294	6304	6314	6325
43	6335	6345	6355	6365	6375	6385	6395	6405	6415	6425
44	6435	6444	6454	6464	6474	6484	6493	6503	6513	6522
45	6532	6542	6551	6561	6571	6580	6590	6599	6609	6618
46	6628	6637	6646	6656	6665	6675	6684	6693	6702	6712
47	6721	6730	6739	6749	6758	6767	6776	6785	6794	6803
48	6812	6821	6830	6839	6848	6857	6866	6875	6884	6893
49	6902	6911	6920	6928	6937	6946	6955	6964	6972	6981
50	6990	6998	7007	7016	7024	7033	7042	7050	7059	7067
51	7076	7084	7093	7101	7110	7118	7126	7135	7143	7152
52	7160	7168	7177	7185	7193	7202	7210	7218	7226	7235
53	7243	7251	7259	7267	7275	7284	7292	7300	7308	7316
54	7324	7332	7340	7348	7356	7364	7372	7380	7388	7396

TABLE 3—continued

N	0	1	2	3	4	5	6	7	8	9
55	7404	7412	7419	7427	7435	7443	7451	7459	7466	7474
56	7482	7490	7497	7505	7513	7520	7528	7536	7543	7551
57	7559	7566	7574	7582	7589	7597	7604	7612	7619	7627
58	7634	7642	7649	7657	7664	7672	7679	7686	7694	7701
59	7709	7716	7723	7731	7738	7745	7752	7760	7767	7774
60	7782	7789	7796	7803	7810	7818	7825	7832	7839	7846
61	7853	7860	7868	7875	7882	7889	7896	7903	7910	7917
62	7924	7931	7938	7945	7952	7959	7966	7973	7980	7987
63	7993	8000	8007	8014	8021	8028	8035	8041	8048	8055
64	8062	8069	8075	8082	8089	8096	8102	8109	8116	8122
65	8129	8136	8142	8149	8156	8162	8169	8176	8182	8189
66	8195	8202	8209	8215	8222	8228	8235	8241	8248	8254
67	8261	8267	8274	8280	8287	8293	8299	8306	8312	8319
68	8325	8331	8338	8344	8351	8357	8363	8370	8376	8382
69	8388	8395	8401	8407	8414	8420	8426	8432	8439	8445
70	8451	8457	8463	8470	8476	8482	8488	8494	8500	8506
71	8513	8519	8525	8531	8537	8543	8549	8555	8561	8567
72	8573	8579	8585	8591	8597	8603	8609	8615	8621	8627
73	8633	8639	8645	8651	8657	8663	8669	8675	8681	8686
74	8692	8698	8704	8710	8716	8722	8727	8733	8739	8745
75	8751	8756	8762	8768	8774	8779	8785	8791	8797	8802
76	8808	8814	8820	8825	8831	8837	8842	8848	8854	8859
77	8865	8871	8876	8882	8887	8893	8899	8904	8910	8915
78	8921	8927	8932	8938	8943	8949	8954	8960	8965	8971
79	8976	8982	8987	8993	8998	9004	9009	9015	9020	9025
80	9031	9036	9042	9047	9053	9058	9063	9069	9074	9079
81	9085	9090	9096	9101	9106	9112	9117	9122	9128	9133
82	9138	9143	9149	9154	9159	9165	9170	9175	9180	9186
83	9191	9196	9201	9206	9212	9217	9222	9227	9232	9238
84	9243	9248	9253	9258	9263	9269	9274	9279	9284	9289
85	9294	9299	9304	9309	9315	9320	9325	9330	9335	9340
86	9345	9350	9355	9360	9365	9370	9375	9380	9385	9390
87	9395	9400	9405	9410	9415	9420	9425	9430	9435	9440
88	9445	9450	9455	9460	9465	9469	9474	9479	9484	9489
89	9494	9499	9504	9509	9513	9518	9523	9528	9533	9538
90	9542	9547	9552	9557	9562	9566	9571	9576	9581	9586
91	9590	9595	9600	9605	9609	9614	9619	9624	9628	9633
92	9638	9643	9647	9652	9657	9661	9666	9671	9675	9680
93	9685	9689	9694	9699	9703	9708	9713	9717	9722	9727
94	9731	9736	9741	9745	9750	9754	9759	9763	9768	9773
95	9777	9782	9786	9791	9795	9800	9805	9809	9814	9818
96	9823	9827	9832	9836	9841	9845	9850	9854	9859	9863
97	9868	9872	9877	9881	9886	9890	9894	9899	9903	9908
98	9912	9917	9921	9926	9930	9934	9939	9943	9948	9952
99	9956	9961	9965	9969	9974	9978	9983	9987	9991	9996

Table 4

Natural Logarithms of Numbers

n	$\log_e n$	n	$\log_e n$	n	$\log_e n$
0.0	*	4.5	1.5041	9.0	2.1972
0.1	7.6974	4.6	1.5261	9.1	2.2083
0.2	8.3906	4.7	1.5476	9.2	2.2192
0.3	8.7960	4.8	1.5686	9.3	2.2300
0.4	9.0837	4.9	1.5892	9.4	2.2407
0.5	9.3069	5.0	1.6094	9.5	2.2513
0.6	9.4892	5.1	1.6292	9.6	2.2618
0.7	9.6433	5.2	1.6487	9.7	2.2721
0.8	9.7769	5.3	1.6677	9.8	2.2824
0.9	9.8946	5.4	1.6864	9.9	2.2925
1.0	0.0000	5.5	1.7047	10	2.3026
1.1	0.0953	5.6	1.7228	11	2.3979
1.2	0.1823	5.7	1.7405	12	2.4849
1.3	0.2624	5.8	1.7579	13	2.5649
1.4	0.3365	5.9	1.7750	14	2.6391
1.5	0.4055	6.0	1.7918	15	2.7081
1.6	0.4700	6.1	1.8083	16	2.7726
1.7	0.5306	6.2	1.8245	17	2.8332
1.8	0.5878	6.3	1.8405	18	2.8904
1.9	0.6419	6.4	1.8563	19	2.9444
2.0	0.6931	6.5	1.8718	20	2.9957
2.1	0.7419	6.6	1.8871	25	3.2189
2.2	0.7885	6.7	1.9021	30	3.4012
2.3	0.8329	6.8	1.9169	35	3.5553
2.4	0.8755	6.9	1.9315	40	3.6889
2.5	0.9163	7.0	1.9459	45	3.8067
2.6	0.9555	7.1	1.9601	50	3.9120
2.7	0.9933	7.2	1.9741	55	4.0073
2.8	1.0296	7.3	1.9879	60	4.0943
2.9	1.0647	7.4	2.0015	65	4.1744
3.0	1.0986	7.5	2.0149	70	4.2485
3.1	1.1314	7.6	2.0281	75	4.3175
3.2	1.1632	7.7	2.0412	80	4.3820
3.3	1.1939	7.8	2.0541	85	4.4427
3.4	1.2238	7.9	2.0669	90	4.4998
3.5	1.2528	8.0	2.0794	95	4.5539
3.6	1.2809	8.1	2.0919	100	4.6052
3.7	1.3083	8.2	2.1041		
3.8	1.3350	8.3	2.1163		
3.9	1.3610	8.4	2.1282		
4.0	1.3863	8.5	2.1401		
4.1	1.4110	8.6	2.1518		
4.2	1.4351	8.7	2.1633		
4.3	1.4586	8.8	2.1748		
4.4	1.4816	8.9	2.1861		

TABLE 5

EXPONENTIAL FUNCTIONS

x	e^x	e^{-x}	x	e^x	e^{-x}
0.00	1.0000	1.0000	2.5	12.182	0.0821
0.05	1.0513	0.9512	2.6	13.464	0.0743
0.10	1.1052	0.9048	2.7	14.880	0.0672
0.15	1.1618	0.8607	2.8	16.445	0.0608
0.20	1.2214	0.8187	2.9	18.174	0.0550
0.25	1.2840	0.7788	3.0	20.086	0.0498
0.30	1.3499	0.7408	3.1	22.198	0.0450
0.35	1.4191	0.7047	3.2	24.533	0.0408
0.40	1.4918	0.6703	3.3	27.113	0.0369
0.45	1.5683	0.6376	3.4	29.964	0.0334
0.50	1.6487	0.6065	3.5	33.115	0.0302
0.55	1.7333	0.5769	3.6	36.598	0.0273
0.60	1.8221	0.5488	3.7	40.447	0.0247
0.65	1.9155	0.5220	3.8	44.701	0.0224
0.70	2.0138	0.4966	3.9	49.402	0.0202
0.75	2.1170	0.4724	4.0	54.598	0.0183
0.80	2.2255	0.4493	4.1	60.340	0.0166
0.85	2.3396	0.4274	4.2	66.686	0.0150
0.90	2.4596	0.4066	4.3	73.700	0.0136
0.95	2.5857	0.3867	4.4	81.451	0.0123
1.0	2.7183	0.3679	4.5	90.017	0.0111
1.1	3.0042	0.3329	4.6	99.484	0.0101
1.2	3.3201	0.3012	4.7	109.95	0.0091
1.3	3.6693	0.2725	4.8	121.51	0.0082
1.4	4.0552	0.2466	4.9	134.29	0.0074
1.5	4.4817	0.2231	5	148.41	0.0067
1.6	4.9530	0.2019	6	403.43	0.0025
1.7	5.4739	0.1827	7	1096.6	0.0009
1.8	6.0496	0.1653	8	2981.0	0.0003
1.9	6.6859	0.1496	9	8103.1	0.0001
2.0	7.3891	0.1353	10	22026	0.00005
2.1	8.1662	0.1225			
2.2	9.0250	0.1108			
2.3	9.9742	0.1003			
2.4	11.023	0.0907			

TABLE 6

A Short Table of Integrals

The basic forms of Chapter 8 are not included. The constant of integration is omitted.

Forms containing $a + bu$ and $\sqrt{a + bu}$

1. $\displaystyle\int \frac{u\,du}{a + bu} = \frac{1}{b^2}\left[(a + bu) - a\ln(a + bu)\right]$

2. $\displaystyle\int \frac{du}{u(a + bu)} = -\frac{1}{a}\ln\frac{a + bu}{u}$

3. $\displaystyle\int \frac{u\,du}{(a + bu)^2} = \frac{1}{b^2}\left(\frac{a}{a + bu} + \ln(a + bu)\right)$

4. $\displaystyle\int \frac{du}{u(a + bu)^2} = \frac{1}{a(a + bu)} - \frac{1}{a^2}\ln\frac{a + bu}{u}$

5. $\displaystyle\int u\sqrt{a + bu}\,du = -\frac{2(2a - 3bu)(a + bu)^{3/2}}{15b^2}$

6. $\displaystyle\int \frac{u\,du}{\sqrt{a + bu}} = -\frac{2(2a - bu)\sqrt{a + bu}}{3b^2}$

7. $\displaystyle\int \frac{du}{u\sqrt{a + bu}} = \frac{1}{\sqrt{a}}\ln\left(\frac{\sqrt{a + bu} - \sqrt{a}}{\sqrt{a + bu} + \sqrt{a}}\right), \qquad a > 0$

8. $\displaystyle\int \frac{\sqrt{a + bu}}{u}\,du = 2\sqrt{a + bu} + a\int \frac{du}{u\sqrt{a + bu}}$

Forms containing $\sqrt{u^2 \pm a^2}$ and $\sqrt{a^2 - u^2}$

9. $\displaystyle\int \frac{du}{u^2 - a^2} = \frac{1}{2a}\ln\frac{u - a}{u + a}$

10. $\displaystyle\int \frac{du}{\sqrt{u^2 \pm a^2}} = \ln(u + \sqrt{u^2 \pm a^2})$

11. $\displaystyle\int \frac{du}{u\sqrt{u^2 + a^2}} = -\frac{1}{a}\ln\left(\frac{a + \sqrt{u^2 + a^2}}{u}\right)$

12. $\displaystyle\int \frac{du}{u\sqrt{u^2 - a^2}} = \frac{1}{a}\operatorname{Arcsec}\frac{u}{a}$

13. $\displaystyle\int \frac{du}{u\sqrt{a^2 - u^2}} = -\frac{1}{a}\ln\left(\frac{a + \sqrt{a^2 - u^2}}{u}\right)$

14. $\displaystyle\int \sqrt{u^2 \pm a^2}\,du = \frac{u}{2}\sqrt{u^2 \pm a^2} \pm \frac{a^2}{2}\ln(u + \sqrt{u^2 \pm a^2})$

(continued)

TABLE 6—continued

15. $\displaystyle\int \sqrt{a^2 - u^2}\, du = \frac{u}{2}\sqrt{a^2 - u^2} + \frac{a^2}{2}\operatorname{Arcsin}\frac{u}{a}$

16. $\displaystyle\int \frac{\sqrt{u^2 + a^2}}{u}\, du = \sqrt{u^2 + a^2} - a\ln\left(\frac{a + \sqrt{u^2 + a^2}}{u}\right)$

17. $\displaystyle\int \frac{\sqrt{u^2 - a^2}}{u}\, du = \sqrt{u^2 - a^2} - a\operatorname{Arcsec}\frac{u}{a}$

18. $\displaystyle\int \frac{\sqrt{a^2 - u^2}}{u}\, du = \sqrt{a^2 - u^2} - a\ln\left(\frac{a + \sqrt{a^2 - u^2}}{u}\right)$

19. $\displaystyle\int (u^2 \pm a^2)^{3/2}\, du$

$$= \frac{u}{4}(u^2 \pm a^2)^{3/2} \pm \frac{3a^2 u}{8}\sqrt{u^2 \pm a^2} + \frac{3a^4}{8}\ln(u + \sqrt{u^2 \pm a^2})$$

20. $\displaystyle\int (a^2 - u^2)^{3/2}\, du = \frac{u}{4}(a^2 - u^2)^{3/2} + \frac{3a^2 u}{8}\sqrt{a^2 - u^2} + \frac{3a^4}{8}\operatorname{Arcsin}\frac{u}{a}$

21. $\displaystyle\int \frac{(u^2 + a^2)^{3/2}}{u}\, du$

$$= \frac{1}{3}(u^2 + a^2)^{3/2} + a^2\sqrt{u^2 + a^2} - a^3\ln\left(\frac{a + \sqrt{u^2 + a^2}}{u}\right)$$

22. $\displaystyle\int \frac{(u^2 - a^2)^{3/2}}{u}\, du = \frac{1}{3}(u^2 - a^2)^{3/2} - a^2\sqrt{u^2 - a^2} + a^3\operatorname{Arcsec}\frac{u}{a}$

23. $\displaystyle\int \frac{(a^2 - u^2)^{3/2}}{u}\, du$

$$= \frac{1}{3}(a^2 - u^2)^{3/2} - a^2\sqrt{a^2 - u^2} + a^3\ln\left(\frac{a + \sqrt{a^2 - u^2}}{u}\right)$$

24. $\displaystyle\int \frac{du}{(u^2 \pm a^2)^{3/2}} = \pm\frac{u}{a^2\sqrt{u^2 \pm a^2}}$

25. $\displaystyle\int \frac{du}{(a^2 - u^2)^{3/2}} = \frac{u}{a^2\sqrt{a^2 - u^2}}$

26. $\displaystyle\int \frac{du}{u(u^2 + a^2)^{3/2}} = \frac{1}{a^2\sqrt{u^2 + a^2}} - \frac{1}{a^3}\ln\left(\frac{a + \sqrt{u^2 + a^2}}{u}\right)$

27. $\displaystyle\int \frac{du}{u(u^2 - a^2)^{3/2}} = -\frac{1}{a^2\sqrt{u^2 - a^2}} - \frac{1}{a^3}\operatorname{Arcsec}\frac{u}{a}$

28. $\displaystyle\int \frac{du}{u(a^2 - u^2)^{3/2}} = \frac{1}{a^2\sqrt{a^2 - u^2}} - \frac{1}{a^3}\ln\left(\frac{a + \sqrt{a^2 - u^2}}{u}\right)$

(continued)

TABLE 6—continued

Trigonometric forms

29. $\displaystyle \int \sin^2 u\, du = \frac{u}{2} - \frac{1}{2} \sin u \cos u$

30. $\displaystyle \int \sin^3 u\, du = -\cos u + \frac{1}{3} \cos^3 u$

31. $\displaystyle \int \sin^n u\, du = -\frac{1}{n} \sin^{n-1} u \cos u + \frac{n-1}{n} \int \sin^{n-2} u\, du$

32. $\displaystyle \int \cos^2 u\, du = \frac{u}{2} + \frac{1}{2} \sin u \cos u$

33. $\displaystyle \int \cos^3 u\, du = \sin u - \frac{1}{3} \sin^3 u$

34. $\displaystyle \int \cos^n u\, du = \frac{1}{n} \cos^{n-1} u \sin u + \frac{n-1}{n} \int \cos^{n-2} u\, du$

35. $\displaystyle \int \tan^n u\, du = \frac{\tan^{n-1} u}{n-1} - \int \tan^{n-2} u\, du$

36. $\displaystyle \int \cot^n u\, du = -\frac{\cot^{n-1} u}{n-1} - \int \cot^{n-2} u\, du$

37. $\displaystyle \int \sec^n u\, du = \frac{\sec^{n-2} u \tan u}{n-1} + \frac{n-2}{n-1} \int \sec^{n-2} u\, du$

38. $\displaystyle \int \csc^n u\, du = -\frac{\csc^{n-2} u \cot u}{n-1} + \frac{n-2}{n-1} \int \csc^{n-2} u\, du$

39. $\displaystyle \int \sin au \sin bu\, du = \frac{\sin (a-b)u}{2(a-b)} - \frac{\sin (a+b)u}{2(a+b)}$

40. $\displaystyle \int \sin au \cos bu\, du = -\frac{\cos (a-b)u}{2(a-b)} - \frac{\cos (a+b)u}{2(a+b)}$

41. $\displaystyle \int \cos au \cos bu\, du = \frac{\sin (a-b)u}{2(a-b)} + \frac{\sin (a+b)u}{2(a+b)}$

42. $\displaystyle \int \sin^m u \cos^n u\, du = \frac{\sin^{m+1} u \cos^{n-1} u}{m+n} + \frac{n-1}{m+n} \int \sin^m u \cos^{n-2} u\, du$

43. $\displaystyle \int \sin^m u \cos^n u\, du = -\frac{\sin^{m-1} u \cos^{n+1} u}{m+n} + \frac{m-1}{m+n} \int \sin^{m-2} u \cos^n u\, du$

(continued)

TABLE 6—continued

Other forms

44. $\displaystyle\int ue^{au}\,du = \frac{e^{au}(au-1)}{a^2}$

45. $\displaystyle\int u^2 e^{au}\,du = \frac{e^{au}}{a^3}\,(a^2u^2 - 2au + 2)$

46. $\displaystyle\int u^n \ln u\,du = u^{n+1}\left(\frac{\ln u}{n+1} - \frac{1}{(n+1)^2}\right)$

47. $\displaystyle\int u \sin u\,du = \sin u - u \cos u$

48. $\displaystyle\int u \cos u\,du = \cos u + u \sin u$

49. $\displaystyle\int e^{au} \sin bu\,du = \frac{e^{au}(a \sin bu - b \cos bu)}{a^2 + b^2}$

50. $\displaystyle\int e^{au} \cos bu\,du = \frac{e^{au}(a \cos bu + b \sin bu)}{a^2 + b^2}$

51. $\displaystyle\int \mathrm{Arcsin}\,u\,du = u\,\mathrm{Arcsin}\,u + \sqrt{1 - u^2}$

52. $\displaystyle\int \mathrm{Arctan}\,u\,du = u\,\mathrm{Arctan}\,u - \frac{1}{2}\ln(1 + u^2)$

Answers to odd-numbered exercises

[*Note:* "Answers" to curves indicate only the basic shape of the curve. No constant scale is used.]

SECTION 1–2

1. (a) rational, real   (b) irrational, real   (c) imaginary   (d) imaginary
(e) integer, rational, real   (f) irrational, real   (g) irrational, real
(h) rational, real

3. (a) <   (b) >   (c) >   (d) <   (e) >   (f) <

5.

7. On a line parallel to the y-axis, one unit to the right.

9. 0

11. To the right of the y-axis.

13. In quadrant II above a line parallel to the x-axis and one unit above.

15. I, III   17. 9/2   19.

SECTION 1–3

1.

3.

5.

7.

9.

11.

13.

15.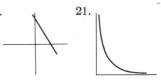

17. (a) No   (b) Yes   (c) Yes

19.

21.

23.

Steepness varies for (a), (b), and (c).

25.

405

SECTION 1–4

1. $2\sqrt{29}$ 3. 3   5. $\sqrt{85}$ 7. $\frac{5}{2}$ 9. Undefined   11. $-\frac{7}{6}$
13. $m_1 = m_2 = -2$ 15. -3 17. 20°   19. Two sides equal $2\sqrt{10}$
21. 10   23. All sides equal $\sqrt{29}$, slopes are $\frac{2}{5}$ and $-\frac{5}{2}$.

SECTION 1–5

1. $4x - y + 20 = 0$ 3. $x - y + 2 = 0$ 5. $x = -4$
7. $3x - 2y - 12 = 0$ 9. $x + 7y - 18 = 0$ 11. $x = -3$
13.

15. $y = \frac{5}{2}x + \frac{5}{2}$ 17. 8   19. $m_1 = 2,\ m_2 = -\frac{1}{2}$
21. $L = \frac{2}{3}F + 15$ 23. 800 cal   25.
27. $m = 0.3010$
29. $v = 40(0.613)^t$

SECTION 1–6

1. $x^2 + y^2 = 9$ 3. $x^2 + y^2 - 4x - 4y - 8 = 0$
5. $x^2 + y^2 - 4x - 2y - 3 = 0$
7. $x^2 + y^2 - 4x - 10y + 4 = 0$, $x^2 + y^2 + 4x + 10y + 4 = 0$
9. $x^2 + y^2 + 8x - 8y + 16 = 0$
11. $(1, 0)$ 13. $(-4, 5)$
     $r = 3$ $r = 7$

15. $(7, 0)$, $(-1, 0)$ 17. $3x^2 + 3y^2 + 4x + 8y - 20 = 0$, circle
19. $x^2 + y^2 = 0.48$ (Assume center of circle at origin of coordinate system.)
21. $x^2 + y^2 = 576$, $x^2 + y^2 + 36y + 315 = 0$ (in inches)

SECTION 1–7

1. $F(1, 0)$, $x = -1$ 3. $F(0, -1)$, $y = 1$ 5. $F(-4, 0)$, $x = 4$

7. $F(0, -\frac{7}{4})$, $y = \frac{7}{4}$ 9. $F(0, \frac{1}{4})$, $y = -\frac{1}{4}$ 11. $y^2 = -8x$
                                                         13. $x^2 = 4y$

15. $y^2 - 2y - 12x + 37 = 0$

17. $x^2 - 2x + 8y - 23 = 0$

19. $y = 4$

21.

23. $225y = -x^2$

SECTION 1–8

1. $V(2, 0), V(-2, 0)$
   $F(\sqrt{3}, 0), F(-\sqrt{3}, 0)$

3. $V(0, 6), V(0, -6)$
   $F(0, \sqrt{11}), F(0, -\sqrt{11})$

5. $V(12, 0), V(-12, 0)$
   $F(2\sqrt{35}, 0), F(-2\sqrt{35}, 0)$

7. $V(0, 4), V(0, -4)$
   $F(0, \sqrt{14}), F(0, -\sqrt{14})$

9. $V(\sqrt{3}, 0), V(-\sqrt{3}, 0)$
   $F(1, 0), F(-1, 0)$

11. $25x^2 + 16y^2 = 400$

13. $4x^2 + 13y^2 = 52$

15. $4x^2 + y^2 = 20$

17. $9x^2 + 5y^2 - 18x - 20y - 16 = 0$

19. $9x^2 + 25y^2 = 22{,}500$

21. $2.70x^2 + 2.76y^2 = 7.45 \times 10^7$

SECTION 1–9

1. $V(5, 0)$, $V(-5, 0)$
   $F(13, 0)$, $F(-13, 0)$

3. $V(0, \sqrt{2})$, $V(0, -\sqrt{2})$
   $F(0, 2)$, $F(0, -2)$

5. $V(0, 2)$, $V(0, -2)$
   $F(0, \sqrt{5})$, $F(0, -\sqrt{5})$

7. $V(2, 0)$, $V(-2, 0)$
   $F(\frac{2}{3}\sqrt{13}, 0)$, $F(-\frac{2}{3}\sqrt{13}, 0)$

9. $V(0, \sqrt{2})$, $V(0, -\sqrt{2})$
   $F(0, \sqrt{5})$, $F(0, -\sqrt{5})$

11. $9y^2 - 25x^2 = 900$

13. $3x^2 - y^2 = 3$

15.

17. $(0, 1)$, $(0, -1)$

19.   21.

      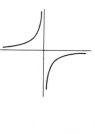

SECTION 1–10

1. Parabola, $(-1, 2)$

3. Hyperbola, $(1, 2)$

5. Ellipse, $(-1, 0)$

7. $y^2 - 6y - 16x - 7 = 0$
11. Ellipse, $(-3, 0)$

9. $9y^2 - 16x^2 + 72y + 32x - 16 = 0$
13. $x^2 + 4y - 12 = 0$
17. $A = 400w - w^2$

SECTION 1–11

1. Hyperbola   3. Parabola   5. Circle

7. Ellipse   9. Hyperbola   11. Hyperbola

MISCELLANEOUS EXERCISES FOR CHAPTER 1

1. $8x - y + 13 = 0$ 3. $y^2 = 12x$ 5. $144y^2 - 169x^2 = 24{,}336$

7. $x^2 + y^2 - 10x - 2y + 22 = 0$ 9. $2x^2 + y^2 = 9$ 11. $(0, -5), y = 5$

13. $V(2, 0), V(-2, 0)$ 15. $(2, -1)$
    $F(\frac{2}{5}\sqrt{35}, 0), F(-\frac{2}{5}\sqrt{35}, 0)$

17. $y = \frac{3}{5}x + \frac{6}{5}$ 19. $y + 3x + 10 = 0$

21.   23.   25.

27. $225y = 450x - x^2$ 29. No

31. $\dfrac{x^2}{8464} + \dfrac{y^2}{8462} = 1$

SECTION 2–1

1. $A = s^2$ 3. $A = \frac{1}{4}\pi d^2$ 5. $p = 4\sqrt{A}$ 7. $s = 120t - 16t^2$

9. $-5, -\frac{13}{4}$ 11. $15, 6a - 3$ 13. $3, 21$ 15. $-5t + 7, 25t + 42$

17. $\sqrt{x^2 + 3}$ 19. $\sqrt{x - 1}/(x^2 + 4)$ 21.   23.

25. $\sqrt{x^3 - 1}$ 27. $(3x + 4)/\sqrt{2x + 1}$

29. $1/(x^2 + 1)^{3/2}$ 31. $y \neq 1$

33. $C \geq 0$ (for physical reasons)

35. $0.006T^2 + 4.000T + 340$

37. $\dfrac{(4 + \pi)p^2 - 480p + 14400}{16\pi}$ 39. $p = 2\left(x + \dfrac{A}{x}\right)$

SECTION 2–2

1. $0, 1.71, 1.97, 2.03, 2.31, 6.00$ 3. 7 5. 1 7. -2 9. -4

11. 3 13. 0 15. 1.89×10^{-6} w   17. $34.8°C, 0°C$

SECTION 2–3

1. 4 3. -4 5. $m_{\tan} = 2x_1$

7. $m_{\tan} = -2x_1$ 9. $m_{\tan} = 2x_1 + 4$ 11. $m_{\tan} = -4x_1, -4, -8, -12$

SECTION 2–4

1. 3 3. $2x$ 5. $2x - 7$ 7. $3x^2 + 4$ 9. $(x^2 - 1)/x^2$

11. $-1/(x - 1)^2$ 13. $4x^3 + 2/x^2$ 15. $4x^3 + 3x^2 + 2x + 1$

17. $-3/2\sqrt{1 - 3x}$

SECTION 2–5

1. $-4t$ 3. $3t^2 - 6$ 5. $v_0 - at$ 7. $-g$ 9. $6t$

11. $2\pi r, 6\pi$ 13. 0.285 ohm/°C   15. $\dfrac{25}{(5 + R)^2}, \dfrac{25}{169}$

17. $-\dfrac{2 \times 10^6}{r^3}, -2 \times 10^3, -2$ 19. $4\pi r - \dfrac{200}{r^2}$

SECTION 2–6

1. $4x^3$ 3. $15x^2 - 1$ 5. $8x^7 - 28x^6 - 1$ 7. $x^2 + x$
9. 360 11. $30t^4 - 5$ 13. $120 - 32t$ 15. 107
17. $3\pi r^2$ 19. 6.0 volts/°C

SECTION 2–7

1. $4x + 9x^2$ 3. $-14x^6 + 30x^4 + 4x^3 - 18x^2 - 6x$

5. $\dfrac{-2x}{(x^2 + 1)^2}$ 7. $\dfrac{6x - 2x^2}{(3 - 2x)^2}$ 9. $\dfrac{9 - 60x^4}{(4x^5 - 3x - 4)^2}$

11. $\dfrac{8x^3 - 16x^2 + 8x + 1}{(x - 1)^2}$ 13. $-\frac{1}{16}$

15. $1, -1$ 17. 0.925 volts/sec   19. $\dfrac{E^2(R - r)}{(R + r)^3}$

SECTION 2–8

1. $10x(x^2 + 1)^4$ 3. $\dfrac{1}{2\sqrt{x}}$ 5. $-\dfrac{2}{x^3}$ 7. $\dfrac{5}{2} x\sqrt{x} + \dfrac{1}{x^2}$

9. $-\dfrac{6}{x^4} + \dfrac{1}{x^2}$ 11. $\dfrac{8x}{(1 - x^2)^5}$ 13. $\dfrac{-4x}{(1 - 8x^2)^{3/4}}$ 15. $\dfrac{x}{y} = \dfrac{\pm x}{\sqrt{x^2 - 1}}$

17. $\dfrac{2xy - y^2}{2xy - x^2}$ 19. 1 21. $x = \frac{1}{2}$ 23. $-4500/V^{5/2}, -0.045$ atm/cm³

25. $\dfrac{-kqx}{(x^2 + b^2)^{3/2}}$ 27. $\dfrac{-3kr}{[r^2 + (l/2)^2]^{5/2}}$

SECTION 2–9

1.   3.   5.

7. 9. 11.

-0.2 lb/sec

MISCELLANEOUS EXERCISES FOR CHAPTER 2

1. -4 3. $\frac{7}{3}$ 5. -2 7. $-4x$ 9. $-4/x^3$

11. $14x^6 - 6x$ 13. $-12(2 - 3x)^3$

15. $(x - 1)^2(x^2 - 2)(7x^2 - 4x - 6)$

17. $\dfrac{9x}{(5 - 2x^2)^{7/4}}$ 19. $\dfrac{2x - 6(2x - 3y)^2}{1 - 9(2x - 3y)^2}$

21. $C_2/2, 0$ 23. 0.04 volt   25. $-2k/r^3$

27. $\dfrac{a}{\sqrt{v_0^2 + 2as}}$ 29. $40V_2^{0.4}/V_1^{1.4}$ 31.

-0.05 atm/cm^3

33. $4x - x^3, 4 - 3x^2$

SECTION 3–1

1. $4x - y - 2 = 0$ 3. $2y + x - 2 = 0$ 5. $x + 4y - 21 = 0$

7. $8x - 4y - 7 = 0$ 9. $\sqrt{3}x + 8y - 7 = 0, 16x - 2\sqrt{3}y - 15\sqrt{3} = 0$

    11. $-\frac{1}{4}$ 13. $3x - 5y - 150 = 0$

15. $x - \sqrt{3}\,y + 4 = 0$

SECTION 3–2

1. $3.16, 341.5°$ 3. $0.479, 211.5°$ 5. $a = 0$

7. $0.442, 58.2°$ 9. $301, 86.2°$ 11. 1.105

13. 136 ft/sec, $28.1°$; 124 ft/sec, $345°$ 15. 32 ft/sec^2, $270°$ for both

17. 21.2 mi/min, $296.6°$

SECTION 3–3

1. 0.09 ohm/sec   3. 0.00402   5. 0.375 volt/sec   7. 100 ft^2/min
9. 10.5 ft/sec   11. −0.0375 atm/min   13. $45\sqrt{14}/14 = 12.0$ ft/sec
15. $\frac{25}{3}$ ft/sec

SECTION 3–4

1. Inc. $x > 1$; dec. $x < 1$
3. Inc. $-1 < x < 0, x > 1$; dec. $x < -1, 0 < x < 1$
5. Inc. $x < 0, 0 < x < 1$; dec. $x > 1$ 7. Min. $(1, -1)$
9. Min. $(-1, -1), (1, -1)$; max. $(0, 0)$ 11. Max. $(1, 1)$ 13. Conc. up all x
15. Conc. up $x < -\sqrt{3}/3, x > \sqrt{3}/3$; conc. down $-\sqrt{3}/3 < x < \sqrt{3}/3$;
    Infl. $(\pm\sqrt{3}/3, -5/9)$
17. Conc. up $0 < x < \frac{2}{3}$; conc. down $x < 0, x > \frac{2}{3}$; Infl. $(0, 0), (\frac{2}{3}, \frac{16}{27})$
19.   21.   23.

25.   27. $V = 4x^3 - 40x^2 + 96x$

SECTION 3–5

1.   3.   5.

7.   9.

SECTION 3–6

1. $8, 8$ 3. $5\sqrt{2}, 5\sqrt{2}$ 5. 108 ft^3 7. 12 9. $\frac{4}{3}$ in   11. 2 units

13. $0.58L$ 15. Width $= \dfrac{16\sqrt{3}}{3}$ in, depth $= \dfrac{16\sqrt{6}}{3}$ in

MISCELLANEOUS EXERCISES FOR CHAPTER 3

1. $5x - y + 1 = 0$ 3. $27x - 3y - 26 = 0$ 5. $48.0, 0.3°$

7. Int: $(0, 0)$, $(\pm 3\sqrt{3}, 0)$ 9. Int: $(0, 0)$ Asym: $x = -1, y = 1$
   Max: $(3, 54)$, Min: $(-3, -54)$
   Infl: $(0, 0)$

11. 9.7×10^3 cm/sec   13. $r = 1, \theta = 2$ 15. Width $= 1$ ft, depth $= \sqrt{3}$ ft

17. Int: $(1, 0)$
    Max: $(2, \frac{1}{4})$
    Infl: $(3, \frac{2}{9})$
    Asym: $P = 0$
    $V \geq 1$ (only meaningful values)

19. 13 mi/hr

SECTION 4–1

1. $(5x^4 + 1)\,dx$ 3. $8x(x^2 - 1)^3\,dx$ 5. $dx/(x + 1)^2$ 7. $-2\,dx/x^3$
9. $12.28, 12$ 11. -24 13. 32 in^2 15. 12.2 volts   17. 13.2 in^3
19. $dA/A = 2ds/s$

SECTION 4–2

1. x^3 3. $\frac{3}{2}x^4 + x$ 5. $\frac{1}{5}x^5 - \frac{1}{2}x^2$ 7. x^6 9. $\frac{2}{3}x^3 - \frac{1}{2}x^2$
11. $(x^2 - 1)^4$ 13. $\frac{2}{5}x^5 + x$ 15. $\frac{1}{40}(2x^4 + 1)^5$

SECTION 4–3

1. $x^2 + C$ 3. $\frac{2}{5}x^{5/2} + C$ 5. $\frac{3}{4}x^{4/3} + C$ 7. $\frac{1}{3}x^3 - \frac{1}{6}x^6 + C$
9. $\frac{2}{5}x^{5/2} - \frac{5}{3}x^3 + C$ 11. $\frac{2}{7}x^{7/2} - \frac{2}{5}x^{5/2} + C$ 13. $(x^2 - 1)^6/6 + C$
15. $(x^4 + 3)^5/5 + C$ 17. $(x^5 + 4)^8/40 + C$ 19. $\sqrt{6x^2 + 1}/6 + C$
21. $\sqrt{x^2 - 2x} + C$ 23. $y = 2x^3 + 2$ 25. $y = 5 - \frac{1}{18}(1 - x^3)^6$
27. $y = x^4 + 5$

SECTION 4–4

1. $\frac{7}{4}$ 3. 20   5. $\frac{61}{8}$ 7. $\frac{8}{3}$ 9. 27   11. 9

SECTION 4–5

1. 1   3. $\frac{26}{3}$ 5. $3\sqrt[3]{2}/2$ 7. $\frac{747}{20}$ 9. $\frac{4}{3}$ 11. 2   13. 49   15. $\frac{110}{3}$

SECTION 4–6

1.   3.   5.

7.   9. 6.8   11. 0.7   13.

15. 18.5

SECTION 4–7

1. $\frac{11}{2}$ 3. $\frac{49}{240}$ 5. 2.996   7. $\frac{21}{40}$ 9. 10.57   11. 31.70

MISCELLANEOUS EXERCISES FOR CHAPTER 4

1. $x^4 - \dfrac{x^2}{2} + C$ 3. 20/3   5. $\dfrac{1}{5(2 - 5x)} + C$

7. $-\dfrac{2}{7}(7 - 2x)^{7/4} + C$ 9. $\dfrac{9}{8}(3\sqrt[3]{3} - 1)$ 11. $\dfrac{3350}{3}$

13. $\dfrac{(1 - 4x)\,dx}{(1 - 3x)^{2/3}}$ 15. $y = 3x - \dfrac{x^3}{3} + \dfrac{17}{3}$

17. $A = 45$ 19. 1.01   21. 1.25

    23. 4.02 mm^3 25. $\dfrac{R\,dR}{R^2 + X^2}$

SECTION 5–1

1. 216 ft   3. $\frac{52}{3}$ ft/sec   5. 336 ft   7. 5.14 coul
9. 117 volts   11. $\theta = 2t^2$ 13. $\frac{110}{3}$ amps   15. K/x_1
17. $m = 1002 - 2\sqrt{t + 1}$, 2.51×10^5 min

SECTION 5–2

1. $\frac{1}{3}$ 3. 1   5. $\frac{1}{2}$ 7. $\frac{1}{2}$ 9. $\frac{7}{6}$ 11. $\frac{256}{5}$ 13. $\frac{1}{3}$ 15. 1
17. 18 joules   19. $\frac{128}{5}$ ft   21. 5.13×10^6 ergs   23. 3800 ft^2

SECTION 5–3

1. $\pi/3$ 3. $16\pi/15$ 5. $348\pi/5$ 7. $\pi/3$ 9. $8\pi/3$ 11. $1024\pi/5$
13. $8\pi/3$ 15. $\pi r^2 h/3$

SECTION 5–4

1. $(\frac{10}{3}, 0)$ 3. $(\frac{14}{15}, 0)$ 5. $(\frac{7}{22}, \frac{5}{22})$ 7. $(0, \frac{6}{5})$ 9. $(\frac{4}{3}, \frac{4}{3})$ 11. $(\frac{3}{5}, \frac{12}{35})$
13. $(\frac{2}{3}, 0)$ 15. $(\frac{9}{7}, 0)$ 17. $(2a/3, b/3)$ 19. $(3a/8, 0)$

SECTION 5–5

1. 128, 4   3. 214, 3.27   5. 64/15   7. $2\sqrt{6}/3$
9. $ma^2/6$ 11. $4\sqrt{7}/7$ 13. $8\sqrt{55}/11$ 15. $2\sqrt{3}/3$
17. $2\sqrt{10}/5$ 19. $m(r_2^2 + r_1^2)/2$

SECTION 5–6

1. 37.5 lb-in   3. 90 ft-lb   5. 2.4 n-m   7. 10,000 ft-lb
9. $\frac{8}{3}$ amps   11. 10   13. $\frac{14}{3}$ units

15. 11,700 lb   17. $\dfrac{15\pi}{4}$ sq. units

MISCELLANEOUS EXERCISES FOR CHAPTER 5

1. 160 ft/sec   3. 9.09 coul   5. $y = 20x + (x^3/120)$ 7. $\frac{2}{3}$
9. $48\pi/5$ 11. $(\frac{40}{21}, \frac{10}{3})$ 13. $\frac{8}{5}$ 15. 9 ft-lb
17. $\frac{2}{7}$ ohm   19. 172,000 lb   21. 81 ft/sec

SECTION 6–1

1. $\pi/12$ 3. $-\pi/3$ 5. 0.9397   7. -0.1763 9. 0.4536
11. $\pi/9, 8\pi/9$ 13. $13\pi/18, 31\pi/18$
15.   17.

19.   21.

23.　　　　　　　　25. 44.8 volts, −95.3 volts　　27.

SECTION 6–2

[*Note:* "Answers" to trigonometric identities are intermediate steps of suggested reductions of the left member.]

1. $\dfrac{\sin x}{\cos x} \cdot \csc x = \dfrac{1}{\cos x}$　　　3. $\sin x \left(\dfrac{\sin x}{\cos x}\right) + \cos x = \dfrac{\sin^2 x + \cos^2 x}{\cos x} = \dfrac{1}{\cos x}$

5. $(1 - \sin^2 x) - \sin^2 x$　　7. 9. Substitute proper expressions in left members and simplify.

11. $2 \sin x + \sin 2x = 2 \sin x + 2 \sin x \cos x = \dfrac{2 \sin x(1 + \cos x)(1 - \cos x)}{1 - \cos x}$

13. $\dfrac{1 - \cos \alpha}{2 \sin(\alpha/2)} = \dfrac{1 - \cos \alpha}{2\sqrt{(1 - \cos \alpha)/2}} = \sqrt{\dfrac{1 - \cos \alpha}{2}}$

15. $2A \sin \dfrac{2\pi t}{T} \cos \dfrac{2\pi x}{\lambda}$

17. $\cos \alpha = \dfrac{A}{C}$, $\sin \alpha = \dfrac{B}{C}$:

$$A \sin 2t + B \cos 2t = C \left(\dfrac{A}{C} \sin 2t + \dfrac{B}{C} \cos 2t\right)$$
$$= C \left(\cos \alpha \sin 2t + \sin \alpha \cos 2t\right)$$

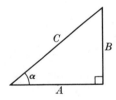

19. 19%

SECTION 6–3

1. $\cos (x + 2)$　　3. $8 \sin 4x \cos 4x$　　5. $-45 \cos^2 (5x + 2) \sin (5x + 2)$
7. $3x \cos 3x + \sin 3x$　　9. $(3x \cos 3x - \sin 3x)/x^2$
11. $3 \sin^2 x \cos x + 2 \sin 2x$　　13. $1 - 4 \sin^2 4x \cos 4x$　　17. 9.77 ft/sec

SECTION 6–4

1. $5 \sec^2 5x$

3. $\dfrac{3 \csc\sqrt{x} \cot\sqrt{x}}{2\sqrt{x}}$

5. $2(1 - x) \csc^2 (1 - x)^2$

7. $2 \tan 4x\sqrt{\sec 4x}$

9. $-\dfrac{\csc x(x \cot x + 1)}{x^2}$

11. $-\dfrac{\csc^2\sqrt{x - 2}}{2\sqrt{x - 2}}$

13. $\sec^2 x (\tan^2 x - 1)$

15. $4 \sec 4x (\tan^2 4x + \sec^2 4x)\, dx$

17. 140 ft/sec

SECTION 6–5

1. $\pi/3$ 3. $\pi/2$ 5. $-\pi/6$ 7. $-\pi/4$ 9. $\pi/4$ 11. $7\pi/10$

13. $\sqrt{3}/2$ 15. 1.00   17. $\frac{1}{3}$ Arcsec $(y-1)$

19. $\dfrac{x}{\sqrt{1-x^2}}$ 21. x 23. $2x\sqrt{1-x^2}$ 25. $\frac{1}{2}$ Arcsin $\dfrac{2E}{E_0}$

27. $t = \dfrac{1}{\omega}\left[\text{Arcsin }\dfrac{i}{I_m} - \alpha - \phi\right]$

SECTION 6–6

1. $\dfrac{2x}{\sqrt{1-x^4}}$ 3. $-\dfrac{1}{\sqrt{4-x^2}}$ 5. $\dfrac{1}{2\sqrt{x}(1+x)}$

7. $\dfrac{x}{\sqrt{1-x^2}} + \text{Arcsin } x$ 9. $2x \text{ Arccos } x - \dfrac{x^2}{\sqrt{1-x^2}}$

11. $-\dfrac{1}{x^2+1}$ 13. $\dfrac{-2(2x+1)^2}{(1+4x^2)^2}$ 15. $\dfrac{3 \text{ Arcsin}^2 x\, dx}{\sqrt{1-x^2}}$

17. Use same method as that used to derive Eq. (6–39).

19. Let $y = \text{Arccsc } u$; solve for u; take derivatives; substitute.

SECTION 6–7

1. $d \sin x/dx = \cos x$ and $d \cos x/dx = -\sin x$, and $\sin x = \cos x$ at points of intersection.   3. $1/(1+x^2)$ is always positive.

5. Dec., $x > 0$, $x < 0$;
   Infl. (0, 0)
   Asym., $x = \pi/2$, $x = -\pi/2$

7. $8\sqrt{2}\,x + 8y - 4\sqrt{2} - 5\pi\sqrt{2} = 0$

9. $-\dfrac{\sqrt{3}}{2}$ ft/sec, $-\dfrac{5}{2}$ ft/sec^2

11. 2π, 330°   13. 4, 240°

15. -0.0729 rad/sec   17. $\frac{4}{3}$ unit/sec

19. -0.0757 amp   21. 9 in^2

23. 14.05 ft

MISCELLANEOUS EXERCISES FOR CHAPTER 6

1. $-12 \sin (4x-1)$ 3. $\dfrac{-\sec^2\sqrt{3-x}}{2\sqrt{3-x}}$ 5. $(-2 \csc 4x)\sqrt{\csc 4x + \cot 4x}$

7. $\dfrac{9}{9+x^2}$ 9. Arccos x 11. $\dfrac{2y \sin 2x + \sin 2y}{\cos 2x - 2x \cos 2y}$

13. $-20 \sin 2t$ 15. $7.27x + y - 9.44 = 0$ 17. -0.831 units/sec

19. 377 ft/sec   21.   23. $5\sqrt{2} = 7.07$ in.

SECTION 7–1

1. $4 = \log_4 256$ 3. $16 = 8^{4/3}$ 5. $\frac{1}{3} = \log_8 2$ 7. $3 = 243^{1/5}$
9. $-2 = \log_{1/2} 4$ 11. 343   13. 0.2
15.   17. $\log_5 3$ 19. $-\frac{3}{2}\log_b x$ 21. 1.099

23. 1.921   25.

27. $-\dfrac{L}{R}\ln\left(\dfrac{E - iR}{E}\right)$

SECTION 7–2

1. $2\log_{10} e/x$ 3. $\dfrac{-3}{1 - 3x}$ 5. $1/2x$ 7. $1 + \ln x$ 9. $\dfrac{1}{x \ln x}$

11. $\dfrac{1}{x^2 + x}$ 13. $\dfrac{\cos \ln x}{x}$ 15. $\dfrac{x \sec^2 x + \tan x}{x \tan x}$

17. $\dfrac{x + 4}{x(x + 2)}$ 19. -1 21. $x^x (\ln x + 1)$

SECTION 7–3

1. $6e^{6x}$ 3. $e^{\sqrt{x}}/2\sqrt{x}$ 5. $e^x(x + 1)$ 7. $8x^3 e^{2x^4}$ 9. $2(e^{2x} + e^{-2x})$
11. $e^{-3x}(4 \cos 4x - 3 \sin 4x)$ 13. $12e^{6x} \cot 2e^{6x}$ 15. $8e^{-(2/x)}/x^2$
17. $e^{\sin x}(x \cos x + 1)$ 21. $dy/dx = e^a, y = e^a$

SECTION 7–4

1.   3.   5.

7.   9.

11. $y = x - 1$ 13. $2/\sqrt{e} = 1.21$ 15. $a = k^2 x$

17. $v = -e^{-0.5t}\,(1.4\cos 6t + 2.3\sin 6t), -2.02$

19. $d\left(\dfrac{T_2}{T_1}\right) = -\frac{1}{2}e^{k/\sin(\theta/2)}\csc\dfrac{\theta}{2}\cot\dfrac{\theta}{2}\,d\theta$

MISCELLANEOUS EXERCISES FOR CHAPTER 7

1. $\dfrac{6x}{x^2 + 1}$ 3. $2e^{2(x-3)}$ 5. $-2x\cot x^2$ 7. $\dfrac{2\cos x \ln(3 + \sin x)}{3 + \sin x}$

9. $e^{-x}\sec x\,(\tan x - 1)$ 11. $\dfrac{y(1 - 2x\ln y)}{x^2 - y}$ 13. $1.73x + 3.00y - 0.47 = 0$

15. -0.135 amp

17. -8 joules/min

19. 202 ft/sec

21. Derivative curve should be super-imposed on function curve.

23. 0.858 sq. units

25.

SECTION 8–1

1. $\dfrac{\sin^5 x}{5} + C$

3. $\dfrac{\tan^3 x}{3} + C$

5. $\dfrac{\sin^2 2x}{4} + C$, or $-\dfrac{\cos^2 2x}{4} + C$, or $-\dfrac{\cos 4x}{8} + C$

7. $\dfrac{[\ln(2x + 3)]^2}{4} + C$ 9. $\dfrac{-2(\cot x)^{3/2}}{3} + C$ 11. $\dfrac{[\text{Arctan }5x]^2}{10} + C$

13. $\dfrac{(1 + \sec^2 x)^5}{10} + C$ 15. $\dfrac{1}{6}$ 17. $\dfrac{1}{2}$ 19. $y = \dfrac{1}{3}(\ln x)^3 + 2$

SECTION 8–2

1. $\frac{1}{4}\ln|1 + 4x| + C$ 3. $-\frac{1}{6}\ln|4 - 3x^2| + C$ 5. $-\frac{1}{3}\ln|1 - x^3| + C$

7. $\frac{1}{4}\ln|4x + 2x^2| + C$ 9. $\frac{1}{4}\ln|1 + 4\sec x| + C$ 11. $\ln|\ln x| + C$

13. $\frac{1}{3}\ln\left(\frac{5}{4}\right) = 0.0744$ 15. $\frac{1}{3}\ln\left(\frac{7}{2}\right) = 0.418$ 17. $\pi\ln 2 = 2.18$

19. 0.549 coul   21. $v = 20(1 - e^{-t})$

SECTION 8–3

1. $\frac{1}{2}e^{2x+5} + C$ 3. $2e^{x/2} + C$ 5. $2e^{\sqrt{x}} + C$ 7. $\frac{1}{2}e^{2x^4} + C$

9. $\dfrac{2e^x - 3}{2e^{2x}} + C$ 11. $e^{\text{Arctan }x} + C$ 13. 0   15. $\pi(e^4 - e) = 163$

17. $\dfrac{e^8 - 1}{8} = 372$ 19. $V = \frac{1}{3}(980 - 800e^{-30t})$

SECTION 8–4

1. $\frac{1}{2} \sin 2x + C$ 3. $\frac{1}{2} \ln |\sec x^2 + \tan x^2| + C$ 5. $-\cot e^x + C$
7. $\cos (1/x) + C$ 9. $\frac{1}{4} \ln |\csc 4x - \cot 4x| + C$ 11. $\frac{1}{5} \sec 5x + C$
13. $\frac{1}{2} (\ln |\sin 2x| + \sin 2x) + C$
15. $\csc x - \cot x - \ln |\csc x - \cot x| + \ln |\sin x| + C$
17. $\pi\sqrt{3} = 5.44$ 19. $s = \frac{4}{3} \sin 3t$ 21. 0.742

SECTION 8–5

1. $\frac{1}{3} \sin^3 x + C$ 3. $\frac{1}{3} \sin^3 x - \frac{1}{5} \sin^5 x + C$ 5. $(x/2) + \frac{1}{8} \sin 4x + C$
7. $-\cos x + \frac{2}{3} \cos^3 x - \frac{1}{5} \cos^5 x + C$ 9. $(x/2) - \frac{1}{4} \sin 2x + C$
11. $\frac{1}{4} \sec^4 x + C$ 13. $\frac{1}{6} \tan^3 2x - \frac{1}{2} \tan 2x + x + C$
15. $\frac{1}{15} \sec^5 3x - \frac{1}{9} \sec^3 3x + C$ 17. $x - \frac{1}{2} \cos 2x + C$
19. $\frac{1}{4} \cot^4 x - \frac{1}{3} \cot^3 x + \frac{1}{2} \cot^2 x - \cot x + C$ 21. $1 + \frac{1}{2} \ln 2 = 1.347$
23. $\frac{1}{5} \tan^5 x + \frac{2}{3} \tan^3 x + \tan x + C$ 25. $\pi^2/2 = 4.935$ 27. $\frac{4}{3}$ 29. $\sqrt{2}$

SECTION 8–6

1. $\text{Arcsin } x + C$ 3. $\frac{1}{12} \text{Arctan } (3x/4) + C$ 5. $\frac{1}{3} \text{Arctan } 3x + C$

7. $\dfrac{\sqrt{35}}{35} \left(\text{Arctan} \dfrac{2\sqrt{35}}{7} - \text{Arctan} \dfrac{\sqrt{35}}{7} \right) = 0.057$ 9. $\dfrac{1}{2} \text{Arctan } 1 = 0.3927$

11. $\text{Arctan } (x + 1) + C$ 13. $\text{Arcsin } (x - 1) + C$
15. $2 \text{ Arcsin } (x/2) + \sqrt{4 - x^2} + C$ 17. $\text{Arctan } 2 = 1.11$

19. $\text{Arcsin } \dfrac{x}{A} = \sqrt{\dfrac{k}{m}} \, t + \text{Arcsin } \dfrac{x_0}{A}$ 21. 0.22

SECTION 8–7

1. $\cos x + x \sin x + C$ 3. $x \tan x + \ln |\cos x| + C$
5. $\text{Arctan } 1 - \frac{1}{2} \ln 2 = 0.438$ 7. $x \sec x - \ln |\sec x + \tan x| + C$
9. $(x/2) \sin 2x - \frac{1}{4}(2x^2 - 1) \cos 2x + C$
11. $\frac{1}{2}(e^{\pi/2} - 1) = 1.90$ 13. $1 - (3/e^2) = 0.594$ 15. $(\pi/2) - 1 = 0.571$
17. 0.43 19. $q = \frac{1}{5}[e^{-2t} (\sin t - 2 \cos t) + 2]$

SECTION 8–8

1. $-\dfrac{\sqrt{1 - x^2}}{x} - \text{Arcsin } x + C$ 3. $\ln |x + \sqrt{x^2 - 4}| + C$

5. $-\dfrac{\sqrt{x^2 + 9}}{9x} + C$ 7. $\dfrac{x}{4\sqrt{4 - x^2}} + C$ 9. $\dfrac{16 - 9\sqrt{3}}{24} = 0.017$

11. $\ln |\sqrt{x^2 + 2x + 2} + x + 1| + C$ 13. $\text{Arcsec } e^x + C$ 15. π

17. $\dfrac{ma^2}{4}$ 19. 2.75

SECTION 8–9

1. $\frac{3}{25}[2 + 5x - 2 \ln (2 + 5x)] + C$ 3. $-\frac{2}{27}(4 - 9x)(2 + 3x)^{3/2} + C$
5. $\frac{1}{2} x\sqrt{4 - x^2} + 2 \text{ Arcsin } (x/2) + C$ 7. $\frac{1}{2} \sin x - \frac{1}{10} \sin 5x + C$

9. $\sqrt{4x^2 - 9} - 3 \text{ Arcsec } (2x/3) + C$

11. $\frac{1}{20} \cos^4 4x \sin 4x + \frac{1}{5} \sin 4x - \frac{1}{15} \sin^3 4x + C$

13. $\frac{1}{2}x^2 \text{ Arctan } x^2 - \frac{1}{4} \ln(1 + x^4) + C$

15. $\dfrac{8\pi - 9\sqrt{3}}{4} = 2.386$

17. $-\ln\left(\dfrac{1 + \sqrt{4x^2 + 1}}{2x}\right) + C$

19. $-\ln\left(\dfrac{1 + \sqrt{1 - 4x^2}}{2x}\right) + C$

21. $\dfrac{1}{8} \cos 4x - \dfrac{1}{12} \cos 6x + C$

23. $\dfrac{1}{3}(\cos x^3 + x^3 \sin x^3) + C$

25. $\dfrac{x^2}{2\sqrt{1 - x^4}} + C$

27. $\dfrac{x^4}{4}\left(\ln x^2 - \dfrac{1}{2}\right) + C$

29. $-\dfrac{x^3}{3\sqrt{x^6 - 1}} + C$

31. $\frac{1}{4}[2\sqrt{5} + \ln(2 + \sqrt{5})] = 1.479$ 33. 333 lb   35. 1045

MISCELLANEOUS EXERCISES FOR CHAPTER 8

1. $-\frac{1}{2}e^{-2x} + C$ 3. $\ln(1 + \sin x) + C$ 5. 0

7. $\frac{1}{2} \ln 2 = 0.3466$ 9. $\frac{1}{12} \sec^4 3x + C$ 11. 1

13. $\frac{1}{2} \ln(2x + \sqrt{4x^2 - 9}) + C$ 15. $-\frac{1}{2}x\sqrt{9 - x^2} + \frac{9}{2} \text{ Arcsin } (x/3) + C$

17. $-\dfrac{1}{\ln 2x} + C$ 19. $\dfrac{x^2}{2} - 2x + 3 \ln(x + 2) + C$

21. $\Delta S = a \ln T + bT + (c/2)T^2 + C$

23. $v = 320(1 - e^{-t/10})$ 25. $y = \frac{1}{3} \tan^3 x + \tan x$

27. 11.0   29. (1.65, 0.22)

SECTION 9–1

1. $V = \pi r^2 h$ 3. $A = \frac{1}{2}bh$ 5. 24   7. -2 9. $2 - 3y + 4y^2$

11. $6xt + xt^2 + t^3$ 13. $2hx - 2kx - 2hy + h^2 - 2hk - 4h$

15. 18 volts   17. 1.48 atm   19. $\frac{20}{3}$ cm

21. $L = \dfrac{(1.28 \times 10^5)r^4}{l^2}$ 23. $y \le 1$ 25. $A = \frac{1}{4}ab$

27. $\dfrac{\pi h}{4}(4r^2 - h^2)$

SECTION 9–2

1.

3.

5.

7.

9.

11.

13.

15.

17.

19.

21.

23.

25.

SECTION 9–3

1. $\dfrac{\partial z}{\partial x} = 5 + 8xy, \dfrac{\partial z}{\partial y} = 4x^2$ 3. $\dfrac{\partial \varphi}{\partial r} = \dfrac{1 + 3rs}{\sqrt{1 + 2rs}}, \dfrac{\partial \varphi}{\partial s} = \dfrac{r^2}{\sqrt{1 + 2rs}}$

5. $\dfrac{\partial z}{\partial x} = 4(2x + y^3)(x^2 + xy^3)^3, \dfrac{\partial z}{\partial y} = 12xy^2(x^2 + xy^3)^3$

7. $\dfrac{\partial z}{\partial x} = y \cos xy, \dfrac{\partial z}{\partial y} = x \cos xy$ 9. $\dfrac{\partial y}{\partial r} = \dfrac{2r}{r^2 + s}, \dfrac{\partial y}{\partial s} = \dfrac{1}{r^2 + s}$

11. $\dfrac{\partial f}{\partial x} = e^x (\cos xy - y \sin xy) - 2e^{-2x} \tan y, \dfrac{\partial f}{\partial y} = -xe^x \sin xy + e^{-2x} \sec^2 y$

13. -8 15. $2e$ 17. $-4, -4$

19. $\left(\dfrac{R_2}{R_1 + R_2}\right)^2$

21. 1330 ohms

23. $\dfrac{k_2 + 2k_3FT}{L_0 + k_1F + k_2T + k_3FT^2}$ 25. $\dfrac{\partial f}{\partial T} = \dfrac{0.353}{L\sqrt{T}}$, 2.31×10^{-6} cycle/dyne

SECTION 9–4

1. $dz = (4x + 3)\,dx - 2y\,dy$

3. $dz = (y\cos xy + y\sin x)\,dx + (x\cos xy - \cos x)\,dy$

5. $dz = -\dfrac{2xy^2\,dx}{x^4 + y^2} + \left(\dfrac{yx^2}{x^4 + y^2} + \text{Arctan}\,\dfrac{y}{x^2}\right)dy$

7. Min $(1, 3, 6)$ 9. Min $(-1, 2, -1)$ 11. 9.6×10^4 rad/min^2
13. 1.3% 15. 4.1% 17. $40, 40, 40$ 19. 10 in, 10 in, 5 in
21. 28 ft^3/sec

SECTION 9–5

1. $\frac{1}{3}$ 3. $\frac{31}{10}$ 5. $\frac{1}{3}$

7. $\dfrac{\pi - 6}{12}$ 9. $\frac{74}{5}$ 11. $\frac{32}{3}$

13. 8π 15. $\frac{28}{3}$ 17. 18 19.

SECTION 9–6

1. $\left(\frac{2}{3}, \frac{2}{3}\right)$ 3. $\left(\frac{9}{8}, \frac{18}{5}\right)$ 5. $\frac{4}{3}, \frac{4}{3}$ 7. 1.34 9. $\left(\frac{3}{4}, \frac{7}{10}\right), 0.775$

11. $\left(\dfrac{a}{3}, \dfrac{b}{3}\right)$ 13. $\dfrac{mb^2}{3}$ 15. 0.577 units from side

MISCELLANEOUS EXERCISES FOR CHAPTER 9

1. $\dfrac{\partial z}{\partial x} = 15x^2y^2 - 2y^4$, $\dfrac{\partial z}{\partial y} = 10x^3y - 8xy^3$

3. $\dfrac{\partial z}{\partial x} = \dfrac{x}{\sqrt{x^2 - 3y^2}}$, $\dfrac{\partial z}{\partial y} = \dfrac{-3y}{\sqrt{x^2 - 3y^2}}$

5. $\dfrac{\partial z}{\partial x} = \dfrac{\partial z}{\partial y} = \dfrac{1}{2\sqrt{(x + y)(1 - x - y)}}$

7. $\dfrac{21}{2}$ 9. $\dfrac{e^2 - 3}{4}$ 11.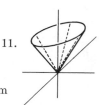

13. 0.113 15. $e^2x - y - e^2 + 1 = 0$
17. 1.47 19. 0.982 21. 1.25 cm

23. $(\frac{3}{2}, 3)$ 25. $\frac{292}{15}$ 27. $(\frac{14}{9}, \frac{8}{9})$

29. 1.82   31. -12 watts/min

SECTION 10–1

1.   3.   5.   7.   9.

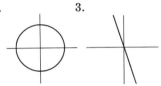

11. $(2, \pi/3)$ 13. $(1, 7\pi/6)$ 15. $(-4, -4\sqrt{3})$ 17. $(2.77, -1.15)$

19. $r = a$ 21. $r^2 = 4/(1 + 3\sin^2 \theta)$ 23. $r = \tan \theta \sec \theta$ 25. $x = 4$

27. $(x^2 + y^2)^2 = 16(x^2 - y^2)$ 29. $B_x = -k \sin \theta / r$, $B_y = k \cos \theta / r$

31. $r^2(1 - 3\cos^2 \theta) = 1$

SECTION 10–2

1.   3.   5.   7.   9

11.   13.   15.   17.

19.   21.   23.

$0 < \theta < 2\pi$
$0 < \theta$

SECTION 10–3

1. 9.49   3. 4.0 ft/sec   5. 8.25 ft/sec   7. 1.54 ft/sec

9. $\frac{1}{2}$ 11. π 13. 2

15. $\dfrac{\pi - 2}{2}$ 17. $v_r = 5$ ft/sec, $v_\theta = 5\sqrt{3}$ ft/sec   21. 4

MISCELLANEOUS EXERCISES FOR CHAPTER 10

1. $\theta = \text{Arctan } 2 = 1.11$ 3. $r^2 + 6r \sin \theta - 7 = 0$

5. $(x^2 + y^2)^3 = 16x^2y^2$ 7. $x^2 - 4y - 4 = 0$

9. 11. 13.

15.

17. $\frac{13}{4}$ 19. $\frac{9\pi}{2}$ 21. $r = k \tan \theta \sec \theta$

23. $v_r = \dfrac{2kx}{(x^2 + y^2)^2}$, $v_\theta = \dfrac{ky}{(x^2 + y^2)^2}$

25. $v_r = 0$, $v_\theta = 5 \text{ mi/sec}$

SECTION 11–1

1. 27   3. 14.5   5. 4.9   7.

0–9	10–19	20–29	30–39	40–49	50–59
0	2	4	3	1	1

9.

10–12	13–15	16–18	19–21	22–24
4	8	4	1	3

11. 13. 15.

17.   19. 4   21.   23. 3.435

SECTION 11–2

1. 10.6   3. 3.6   5. 0.05   7. 10.6   9. 3.85   11. 0.05
13. 70%   15. 64.5%

SECTION 11–3

1. $y = (1.0)x - 2.6$ 3. $y = -1.77x + 190$ 5. $V = -0.71i + 12.3$

7. $V = 0.41 \times 10^{-14} f - 1.90$

$f_0 = 4.6 \times 10^{14}$ 1/sec

$f_0 = 4.6 \times 10^{14}$ 1/sec

9. 0.985

11. -0.90

SECTION 11–4

1. $y = 1.96x^2 + 5.2$

3. $y = 10.9/x$

5. $y = 5.95t^2 + 0.55$

7. $y = 33.7(10^z) - 37.1$

9. $f = \dfrac{480}{\sqrt{L}} + 10$

MISCELLANEOUS EXERCISES FOR CHAPTER 11

1. 3.6

3. 0.8

5. 264 cp

7.

9. 0.93

11.

13. 0.012   15. $y = 0.0338x + 35.4$

17. $y = 488x^2$ 19. $y = (3.35 \times 10^4)/x$

SECTION 12–1

1. $1 + x + \dfrac{1}{2}x^2 + \cdots$

3. $1 - \dfrac{x^2}{2} + \dfrac{x^4}{24} - \cdots$

5. $1 + \dfrac{x}{2} - \dfrac{x^2}{8} + \cdots$

7. $1 - 8x^2 + \dfrac{32x^4}{3} - \cdots$

9. $1 + x + x^2 + \cdots$

11. $x - \dfrac{x^3}{3} + \cdots$ 　　　13. $-\dfrac{x^2}{2} - \dfrac{x^4}{12} - \cdots$ 　　15. $1 - \dfrac{x^4}{2} + \cdots$

17. (a), (c) functions are not defined at $x = 0$; (b) derivatives are not defined at $x = 0$.

SECTION 12–2

1. $1 - 8x^2 + \dfrac{32x^4}{3} - \dfrac{256x^6}{45} + \cdots$

3. $\left(x + \dfrac{\pi}{6}\right) - \dfrac{(x + \pi/6)^3}{6} + \dfrac{(x + \pi/6)^5}{120} - \dfrac{(x + \pi/6)^7}{5040} + \cdots$

5. $1 - 2x^6 + \dfrac{2x^{12}}{3} - \dfrac{4x^{18}}{45} + \cdots$

7. $x^2 - \dfrac{x^4}{2} + \dfrac{x^6}{3} - \dfrac{x^8}{4} + \cdots$

9. $2.63 + 1.44j$ 　　11. $6.08(\cos 9.5° + j\sin 9.5°)$

13. 0.3103 　　　　　　　　　　　15. 0.1901

17. $\dfrac{d}{dx}\left(x - \dfrac{x^3}{6} + \dfrac{x^5}{120} - \cdots\right) = 1 - \dfrac{x^2}{2} + \dfrac{x^4}{24} - \cdots$ 　　19. 0.003099

21. $1, \frac{1}{2}(-1 + j\sqrt{3}), -\frac{1}{2}(1 + j\sqrt{3})$ 　　23. 10 ohms

SECTION 12–3

1. 1.22 　　3. 0.09983 　　5. 2.718 　　7. 0.9986 　　9. 0.335
11. 0.8414 　　13. 1.0488 　　15. 1.032 　　17. 8×10^{-8}

19. $i = \dfrac{E}{L}\left(t - \dfrac{Rt^2}{2L}\right)$; small values of t 　　21. 66 ft

SECTION 12–4

1. 3.32 　　3. 2.049 　　5. 0.5150

7. $e^{-2}\left[1 - (x - 2) + \dfrac{(x - 2)^2}{2!} - \cdots\right]$

9. $\dfrac{1}{2}\left[\sqrt{3} + \left(x - \dfrac{\pi}{3}\right) - \dfrac{\sqrt{3}}{2!}\left(x - \dfrac{\pi}{3}\right)^2 - \cdots\right]$

11. $2 + \frac{1}{12}(x - 8) - \frac{1}{288}(x - 8)^2 + \cdots$

13. $1 + 2\left(x - \dfrac{\pi}{4}\right) + 2\left(x - \dfrac{\pi}{4}\right)^2 + \cdots$

15. 0.111 　　17. 2.02 　　19. 0.8746

SECTION 12–5

1. $f(x) = \dfrac{1}{2} - \dfrac{2}{\pi} \sin x - \dfrac{2}{3\pi} \sin 3x - \cdots$

3. $f(x) = \dfrac{3}{2} + \dfrac{2}{\pi} \sin x + \dfrac{2}{3\pi} \sin 3x + \cdots$

5. $f(x) = \dfrac{\pi}{4} - \dfrac{2}{\pi} \left(\cos x + \dfrac{1}{9} \cos 3x + \cdots \right) + \left(\sin x - \dfrac{1}{2} \sin 2x + \cdots \right)$

7. $f(x) = -\dfrac{1}{4} - \dfrac{1}{\pi} \cos x + \dfrac{1}{3\pi} \cos 3x - \cdots$

$\qquad + \dfrac{3}{\pi} \sin x - \dfrac{1}{\pi} \sin 2x + \dfrac{1}{\pi} \sin 3x - \cdots$

9. $f(x) = \dfrac{\pi}{2} - \dfrac{4}{\pi} \cos x - \dfrac{4}{9\pi} \cos 3x - \cdots$

11. $f(t) = \dfrac{2}{\pi} - \dfrac{4}{3\pi} \cos 2t - \dfrac{4}{15\pi} \cos 4t - \cdots$

MISCELLANEOUS EXERCISES FOR CHAPTER 12

1. $\dfrac{1}{2} - \dfrac{x}{4} + \dfrac{x^3}{48} - \cdots$

3. $2x^2 - \dfrac{4x^6}{3} + \dfrac{4x^{10}}{15} - \cdots$

5. $1 + \dfrac{x}{3} - \dfrac{x^2}{9} + \cdots$

7. $x + \dfrac{x^3}{6} + \dfrac{3x^5}{40} + \cdots$

9. 0.259   11. 0.82   13. 1.09   15. 0.9325

17. $f(x) = \dfrac{1}{2} + \dfrac{2}{\pi}\left(\cos x - \dfrac{1}{3}\cos 3x + \cdots\right)$ 19.

$y = 1 + x + \dfrac{x^2}{2}$

$y = x + 1$

$y = e^x$

$y = 1$

21. 0.00302   23. 1.25 mi

SECTION 13–1

[*Note:* "Answers" in this section are the unsimplified expressions obtained by substituting functions and derivatives.]

1. $1 = 1$ 3. $x(2cx) = 2(cx^2)$

5. $[e^{2x}(1 + 4c_1 + 4c_2 + 4x + 4c_2x + 2x^2)]$
$\qquad -4[e^{2x}(2c_1 + c_2 + x + 2c_2x + x^2)] + 4[e^{2x}(c_1 + c_2x + x^2/2)] = e^{2x}$

7. $x\left(-\dfrac{c_1}{x^2}\right) + \dfrac{c_1}{x} = 0$ 9. $x^2\left[-\dfrac{c^2}{(x - c)^2}\right] + \left[\dfrac{cx}{(x - c)}\right]^2 = 0$

11. $e^{-2x}(-8c_2 + 12 - 8x) + 4[e^{-2x}(4c_2 - 4 + 4x)]$
$\qquad\qquad + 4[e^{-2x}(-2c_2 + 1 - 2x)] = 0$

13. $(\cos x - \sin x + e^{-x}) + (\sin x + \cos x - e^{-x}) = 2\cos x$

15. $(e^{-x} + \frac{12}{5}\cos 2x + \frac{24}{5}\sin 2x) + (-e^{-x} + \frac{6}{5}\sin 2x - \frac{12}{5}\cos 2x) = 6\sin 2x$

SECTION 13–2

1. $x - 1/y = c$ 3. $\ln(x^3 + 5) + 3y = c$ 5. $e^x - e^{-y} = c$

7. $x^2 + 1 = x\ln y + cx$ 9. $y^2 + 4\,\text{Arcsin}\,x = c$

11. $(2/y^2) + \sqrt{1 + 4x^2} = c$ 13. $3\ln y + x^3 = 0$

15. $2\ln(1 - y) = 1 - 2\sin x$

SECTION 13–3

1. $2xy + x^2 = c$ 3. $x^3 - 2y = cx - 4$ 5. $\ln(y^2 - x^2) + 2x = c$

7. $x^2y - y = cx$ 9. $2\sqrt{x^2 + y^2} = x + c$ 11. $2x = 2xy^2 - 15y$

SECTION 13–4

1. $ye^x = x + c$ 3. $ye^x = \sin x + c$ 5. $2y = e^{4x}(x^2 + c)$
7. $y = 3 + ce^{-x}$ 9. $3y = x^4 - 6x^2 - 3 + cx$ 11. $y = e^{-x}$

SECTION 13–5

1. $y^2 = 2x^2 + 1$ 3. $y = 2e^x - x - 1$ 5. $3y^2 + x^2 = c$
7. $y = cx$ 9. $p = 15(\frac{2}{3})^{10^{-4}h}$ 11. $p = cv^k$
13. E/R 15. $q = q_0 e^{-t/RC}$ 17. 1.81 amp
19. 74.2 lb   21. 141 ft/sec

23. $v = 17.9 \left(\dfrac{1 + 0.833e^{-3.6t}}{1 - 0.833e^{-3.6t}} \right)$

MISCELLANEOUS EXERCISES FOR CHAPTER 13

1. $2 \ln (x^2 + 1) - (1/2y^2) = c$ 3. $ye^{2x} = x + c$
5. $2x^2 + 4xy + y^4 = c$ 7. $y = cx^3 - x^2$
9. $y = c(y + 2)e^{2x}$ 11. $y = \frac{1}{2}(c - x^2) \csc x$
13. $y = 2 \sin^2 x$ 15. $y = 2x - 1 - e^{-2x}$
17. $r = kt$ 19. 1600 cm/sec
21. $q = c_1 e^{-t/RC} + EC$ 23. $r = c \cos \theta$

SECTION 14–2

1. $y = c_1 e^{3x} + c_2 e^{-2x}$ 3. $y = c_1 e^{-x} + c_2 e^{-3x}$ 5. $y = c_1 + c_2 e^x$
7. $y = c_1 e^{x/3} + c_2 e^{-3x}$ 9. $y = c_1 e^{x/3} + c_2 e^{-x}$
11. $y = e^x(c_1 e^{\sqrt{2}x/2} + c_2 e^{-\sqrt{2}x/2})$ 13. $y = e^{3x/2}(c_1 e^{\sqrt{13}x/2} + c_2 e^{-\sqrt{13}x/2})$

15. $y = \frac{1}{5}(3e^{7x} + 7e^{-3x})$ 17. $y = \dfrac{e^3}{e^7 - 1} (e^{4x} - e^{-3x})$
19. $y = c_1 e^x + c_2 e^{-x} + c_3 e^{2x}$

SECTION 14–3

1. $y = (c_1 + c_2 x)e^x$ 3. $y = (c_1 + c_2 x)e^{3x}$ 5. $y = (c_1 + c_2 x)e^{3x/2}$
7. $y = c_1 + c_2 x$ 9. $y = c_1 \sin (x/2) + c_2 \cos (x/2)$
11. $y = (c_1 + c_2 x)e^{2x}$ 13. $y = c_1 \sin (\sqrt{2}x/5) + c_2 \cos (\sqrt{2}x/5)$
15. $y = c_1 e^{(-6+\sqrt{42})x/3} + c_2 e^{(-6-\sqrt{42})x/3}$ 17. $y = (4 - 14x)e^{4x}$

SECTION 14–4

1. $y = c_1 e^{2x} + c_2 e^{-x} - 2$ 3. $y = c_1 \sin x + c_2 \cos x + x^2 - 2$

5. $y = c_1 e^{-x} + c_2 e^{-3x} + \dfrac{e^x}{8} + \dfrac{2}{3}$ 7. $y = c_1 e^{5x} + c_2 e^{-4x} - \dfrac{e^{2x}}{18} - \dfrac{2}{5}$

9. $y = c_1 e^{2x} + c_2 e^{-2x} - \frac{1}{5} \sin x - \frac{2}{5} \cos x$
11. $y = c_1 \sin x + c_2 \cos x - \frac{1}{3} \sin 2x + 4$

13. $y = c_1 e^{-x} + c_2 e^{-4x} - \dfrac{7e^x}{100} + \dfrac{xe^x}{10} + 1$

15. $y = (c_1 + c_2 x)e^{-3x} + \dfrac{e^{2x}}{25} - e^{-2x}$ 17. $y = \dfrac{1}{6}(11e^{3x} + 5e^{-2x} + e^x - 5)$

19. $y = -\frac{2}{3}\sin x + \pi \cos x + x - \frac{1}{3}\sin 2x$

SECTION 14–5

1. $x = 4\cos 10t$ 3. 20   5. $y = \frac{1}{4}\cos 16t$

7. $y = \frac{1}{4}\cos 16t + \frac{8}{63}\sin 2t - \frac{1}{63}\sin 16t$ 9. $q = \frac{1}{100}(1 - \cos 316t)$

11. $e^{-10t}(c_1 \sin 99.5t + c_2 \cos 99.5t) - \frac{1}{2290}(2\cos 200t + 15\sin 200t)$

13. $\frac{20}{229}(2\sin 200t - 15\cos 200t)$

15. $-[(6.5 \times 10^{-4})\sin 400t + (8.5 \times 10^{-6})\cos 400\,t]$

MISCELLANEOUS EXERCISES FOR CHAPTER 14

1. $y = c_1 + c_2 e^{-x/2}$ 3. $y = (c_1 + c_2 x)e^{-x}$

5. $y = c_1 e^x + c_2 e^{-3x/2} - 2$ 7. $y = c_1 e^{2x/3} + c_2 e^{4x/3} + \frac{1}{2}x + \frac{25}{8}$

9. $y = e^{-x/2}(c_1 e^{\sqrt{5}x/2} + c_2 e^{-\sqrt{5}x/2}) + 2e^x$

11. $y = c_1 \sin 3x + c_2 \cos 3x + (\sin x)/8$ 13. $y = 2e^{-x/2}\sin(\sqrt{15}x/2)$

15. $y = \frac{1}{25}[16\sin x + 12\cos x - 3e^{-2x}(4 + 5x)]$

17. $y = (2 + 8t)e^{-4t}$, critically damped

19. $y = (10/3EI)[100x^3 - x^4 + xL^2(L - 100)]$ 21. $i = 0$

23. $\theta = \theta_0 \cos \omega t + \dfrac{\omega_0}{\omega}\sin \omega t;\ (\omega = \sqrt{2k/mr^2})$

SECTION 15–1

1.

x	0.0	0.2	0.4	0.6	0.8	1.0
y	1.00	1.20	1.44	1.72	2.04	2.40

$$y = \tfrac{1}{2}x^2 + x + 1$$

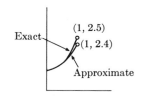

3.

x	0.0	0.1	0.2	0.3	0.4	0.5
y	0.0	0.10	0.22	0.36	0.53	0.73

$$y = xe^x$$

5.   7.   9.

5.

x	0.0	0.1	0.2	0.3	0.4	0.5	0.6	0.7	0.8	0.9	1.0
y	0.0	0.10	0.20	0.30	0.41	0.53	0.66	0.80	0.96	1.14	1.34

7.

x	0.0	0.2	0.4	0.6	0.8	1.0	1.2
y	0.0	0.20	0.41	0.64	0.93	1.35	2.12

9.

x	0.0	0.1	0.2	0.3	0.4	0.5	0.6	0.7	0.8	0.9	1.0
y	1.57	1.57	1.56	1.54	1.51	1.48	1.44	1.39	1.34	1.29	1.23

11. 1.21

13. $i_{\text{approx}} = 0.08$ amp

$i_{\text{exact}} = 0.09$ amp

SECTION 15–2

1. $y_2 = 1 + x + x^2 + \frac{1}{3}x^3$

$y = \dfrac{1}{1 - x}$

$y_2(0.1) = 1.1103$
$y(0.1) = 1.1111$

3. $y_3 = x^2 + \frac{1}{2}x^4 + \frac{1}{6}x^6$

$y = e^{x^2} - 1$

$y_3(1) = 1.67$
$y(1) = 1.72$

5. $y_3 = \frac{1}{2}x^2 + \frac{1}{20}x^5 + \frac{1}{160}x^8 + \frac{1}{4400}x^{11}$
7. $y_2 = \frac{3}{4} + x + \frac{1}{2}x^2 + \frac{1}{4}\cos 2x - \frac{1}{2}\sin 2x$
9. Maclaurin expansion: $y = 1 + x + x^2 + \frac{1}{3}x^3 + \frac{1}{12}x^4 + \cdots$
   Example A: $y_3 = 1 + x + x^2 + \frac{1}{3}x^3 + \frac{1}{24}x^4 + \cdots$
11. 0.58 ft/sec

SECTION 15–3

1. $F(s) = \displaystyle\int_0^\infty e^{-st}\, dt = -\frac{1}{s}e^{-st}\Big|_0^\infty = \frac{1}{s}$

3. $F(s) = \displaystyle\int_0^\infty e^{-st}\sin at\, dt = \frac{e^{-st}(-s\sin at - a\cos at)}{s^2 + a^2}\Big|_0^\infty = \frac{a}{s^2 + a^2}$

5. $\dfrac{1}{s - 3}$ 7. $\dfrac{6}{(s + 2)^4}$ 9. $\dfrac{s - 2}{s^2 + 4}$

11. $s^2 L(f) + s L(f)$ 13. $(2s^2 - s + 1)L(f) - 2s + 1$
15. e^{-5t} 17. $\frac{1}{2}t^2 e^{-t}$ 19. $\frac{1}{54}(9t \sin 3t + 2 \sin 3t - 6t \cos 3t)$

SECTION 15–4

1. $y = e^{-t}$ 3. $y = -e^{3t/2}$ 5. $y = (1 + t)e^{-3t}$
7. $y = \frac{1}{2}\sin 2t$ 9. $y = 1 - e^{-2t}$ 11. $y = e^{2t}\cos t$ 13. $y = 1 + \sin t$
15. $y = e^{-t}(\frac{1}{2}t^2 + 3t + 1)$ 17. $v = 6(1 - e^{-t/2})$ 19. $i = 5t \sin 50t$

MISCELLANEOUS EXERCISES FOR CHAPTER 15

1.

x	0	0.1	0.2	0.3	0.4	0.5
y	1.00	0.90	0.82	0.76	0.71	0.68

3.

x	0	0.2	0.4	0.6	0.8	1.0	1.2	1.4	1.6	1.8	2.0
y	1.00	1.20	1.44	1.71	2.01	2.35	2.72	3.12	3.55	4.00	4.48

5.

x	0.0	0.1	0.2	0.3	0.4	0.5	0.6	0.7
y	0.50	0.56	0.63	0.72	0.84	0.99	1.19	1.50

7. $y_3 = 1 + x + \frac{1}{2}x^2 + \frac{1}{2}x^3 + \frac{1}{12}x^4 + \frac{1}{60}x^5$

9. $y_2 = -\frac{7}{36} + x - \frac{1}{9}x^3 + \frac{1}{4}x^4 + \frac{1}{18}x^6$

11. $y = e^{t/4}$ 13. $y = \frac{1}{2}(e^{3t} - e^t)$ 15. $y = -4\sin t$

17. $y = \frac{1}{3}t - \frac{4}{9}\sin 3t$ 19. $y_2 = \frac{7}{2} + x - (3 + x)e^{-x} + \frac{1}{2}e^{-2x}$; $y_2(0.5) = 2.06$

21. $y_2 = \frac{1}{2}[\ln(2x^2 + e) + 1]$; $y_2(0.5) = 1.09$

23. $i = 12(1 - e^{-t/2})$; $i(0.3) = 1.68$ amps

25. $i_3 = 6t - \frac{3}{2}t^2 + \frac{1}{4}t^3$; $i(0.3) = 1.67$ amps

27. $y = \frac{1}{4}t \sin 8t$

Index